APPLICABLE MATHEMATICS

APPLICABLE MATHEMATICS

A COURSE FOR SCIENTISTS AND ENGINEERS

R. J. GOULT, R. F. HOSKINS, J. A. MILNER
and M. J. PRATT

Department of Mathematics, Cranfield Institute of Technology

MACMILLAN

First published 1973 by
THE MACMILLAN PRESS LTD
London and Basingstoke
Associated companies in New York Dublin
Melbourne Johannesburg and Madras

SBN 333 13235 1

Text set in 10/12 pt. IBM Press Roman, printed by photolithography,
and bound in Great Britain at The Pitman Press, Bath

CONTENTS

PREFACE

This book is primarily intended to serve the mathematical needs of students following introductory courses in engineering and the physical sciences, up to graduate level. The initial standard of knowledge assumed is that of 'A' level or O.N.C. mathematics, and the book is designed to provide an introduction to those branches of pure mathematics which have widespread applications in industry and research.

The typical student for whom this book is intended is likely to look upon mathematics mainly as a means to an end. We feel that it is nevertheless unfortunate if, as happens all too often, his mathematical armoury consists merely of a collection of unrelated techniques which he uses under appropriate (and possibly under inappropriate) circumstances. We have tried to avoid this situation by providing a background of mathematical analysis which will serve to unify the subject matter and to provide the reader with sufficient mathematical insight for his successful application of the methods described. This analytical material is contained in chapters 2, 3, 4 and 5 and, since the treatment it receives is rather more thorough than is customary in books for non-specialists, readers will undoubtedly find these chapters more difficult than the remainder of the book. However, a detailed knowledge of the entire content of the four analytical chapters is not a pre-requisite for reading those which follow; in particular, certain sections marked with an asterisk may be omitted on a first reading since their prime relevance is to more advanced topics. The analytical part of the book is also designed to provide a useful source of reference for students going on to post-graduate studies and applications involving more advanced mathematics. The remaining chapters cover number systems, polynomials and their applications, linear algebra, ordinary differential equations and vector algebra. These non-analytical chapters need not be read in numerical order; they all draw on material from the analytical section, but are otherwise largely self-contained.

Computers play an essential rôle in the solution of contemporary practical problems, and we have endeavoured to avoid the usual artificial division between numerical methods and the rest of mathematics by introducing related analytical and numerical techniques side by side. Notes and references are given at the end of chapters, pointing the way to more advanced studies along the same lines and indicating some possible applications. Many exercises are included, some routine, others developing the theory a stage further. For the most part, specific physical examples have been omitted, because students studying different disciplines do not all find the same physical examples relevant. Further, we feel that examples of this nature are best provided in the context of a student's specialist studies, since their physical aspects can sometimes distract attention from the underlying mathematics.

We thank Mrs. K. M. Thorogood for her competent typing of a difficult manuscript (some of it several times), and the publishers for their patience during the rather lengthy gestation period of this book.

R.J.G.
R.F.H.
J.A.M.
M.J.P.

1 NUMBERS AND NUMBER SYSTEMS

1.0 Introduction

Most applications of mathematics will at some stage involve calculations with numbers. These numbers may be integers, rational numbers, real numbers or complex numbers. The aim of this chapter is to give a semi-historical account of the various number systems together with a more detailed introduction to the properties of the complex-number system.

The development of electronic computers has removed much of the tedium from numerical calculations, but in order to use the computer efficiently it is necessary to have some knowledge of how it stores numbers and performs calculations within the various number systems. The application of this knowledge enables the computer to be programmed in a way which will minimise the inevitable errors. Accordingly a brief section on the computational aspects of real and complex arithmetic is included.

1.1 The development of number systems

1.1.1 The natural numbers

The *natural numbers*, 1, 2, 3, 4, etc. are the numbers we use to count with. Roughly speaking, a natural number is anything which may be used to answer a question which begins with the words 'How many?' (For this reason the number 0 is sometimes included among the natural numbers.) The sum $(a + b)$ and the product (ab) of two natural numbers are themselves both natural numbers; that is, the system of natural numbers is *closed* with respect to addition and multiplication. Further, these operations satisfy the following formal laws:

(1) Addition and multiplication are both *commutative* operations:

$$a + b = b + a \qquad \text{and} \qquad a \times b = b \times a$$

(2) Addition and multiplication are both *associative* operations:

$$(a + b) + c = a + (b + c) \qquad \text{and} \qquad (a \times b) \times c = a \times (b \times c)$$

(3) Addition and multiplication together satisfy a *distributive* law:

$$a \times (b + c) = (a \times b) + (a \times c)$$

On the other hand, the difference $(a - b)$ of two natural numbers is not always defined as a natural number. Hence, if we wish to ensure that every equation of the form

$$x + b = a$$

has a solution we will need to define an extended number system which includes the system of the natural numbers. This gives us the system of *integers.* In the same way we need a further enlargement if we wish to ensure that every equation of the form

$$xb = a$$

where $(b \neq 0)$ has a solution. This leads to the system of *rational* numbers or fractions.

1.1.2. The integers
The integers are obtained from the natural numbers by attaching to them the distinguishing labels, or *signs,* + and −, and by including the number 0:

$$\ldots -3, -2, -1, 0, +1, +2, +3, \ldots$$

So far as the number 0 is concerned we have only to state the following formal properties

  (i) for any integer x, $x + 0 = 0 + x = x$
  (ii) for any integer x, $x0 = 0x = 0$

The negative integer $(-n)$ is, by definition, that number x which satisfies the equation

$$x + (+n) = 0$$

The familiar sign laws of elementary algebra are a direct consequence of this definition and of the fact that addition and multiplication of integers are so defined as to preserve the commutative, associative and distributive laws. For example

$$(+1) + (-1) = 0 \qquad \text{(by definition of } -1\text{)}$$

and so $\qquad (+1) \times \{(+1) + (-1)\} = (+1) \times 0 = 0$

Thus, if the distributive law is to be valid, we must have

$$\{(+1) \times (+1)\} + \{(+1) \times (-1)\} = 0$$

and so $(+1) \times (-1)$ must be the number (-1) which satisfies the equation

$$x + (+1) = 0$$

Similarly we can show that for consistency we must have $(-1) \times (-1) = +1$. Equipped with these sign rules the integers form a system in which addition, multiplication, and subtraction are all always possible.

Strictly speaking there is a difference in significance between the natural number n (which is signless, and says no more than that a certain number n of objects is referred to) and the positive integer $+n$ (which carries additional information in virtue of the attached sign $+$). But so far as all arithmetic operations are concerned it makes no difference whether we interpret the numerals which appear as natural numbers or as positive integers; the positive integers and the natural numbers are *formally* indistinguishable. Accordingly we may identify the natural number n with the positive integer $+n$, and say that the integers (positive and negative) constitute an extension, or enlargement, of the natural-number system. Technically we say that the natural numbers may be *embedded* in the integers.

1.1.3 *The rational numbers*
If a and b are integers and $b \neq 0$ then the equation

$$xb = a$$

has, by definition, the *rational number* $x = a/b$ as its solution. If the integer a happens to be an exact multiple of the integer b, so that $a = nb$ for example, then the integer n may be formally identified with the rational number a/b; that is the integers may be embedded in the rational numbers, just as the natural numbers are embedded in the integers. Moreover addition and multiplication of rational numbers are defined so as to be compatible with this formal identification of the integer n with the rational number $n/1$, and also so as once again to preserve the commutative, associative and distributive laws. In view of the later definition of the so-called *complex numbers* it is instructive to note that the arithmetic of the rationals can be defined purely formally as a set of rules for manipulating certain ordered pairs of integers. Thus, if (p, q) denotes p/q, we have:

(i) *Equality.* $(p_1, q_1) = (p_2, q_2)$ if and only if $p_1 q_2 = p_2 q_1$ (This states, in effect, that for any integer $k \neq 0$, $(kp_1, kq_1) = (p_1, q_1)$.)

(ii) *Addition.* $(p_1, q_1) + (p_2, q_2) = (p_1 q_2 + p_2 q_1, q_1 q_2)$

(iii) *Multiplication.* $(p_1, q_1) \times (p_2, q_2) = (p_1 p_2, q_1 q_2)$

Then, simply using these definitions, we can show that the extension of the integers to the rational numbers yields a number system which is arithmetically complete in so far as the operations of multiplication and addition are concerned. Every linear equation of the form

$$ax + b = c$$

where a, b, and c are rational numbers and $a \neq 0$, will have a rational solution $x = (p, q)$ — or, in the more usual notation, $x = p/q$. However, we wish not only to be able to answer questions beginning with the words 'how many' but also those which begin with the words 'how much'; that is we wish not only to *count* discrete objects but also to *measure* continuous quantities (mass, time, temperature, etc.). Essentially this reduces to the basic problem of measuring *length*; it is necessary to be able to assign numbers (in some sense of the word) to the points of an ideal infinite line in such a way that every finite line segment has a definite length. The rational numbers do have one property which is essential for this purpose (and which, at first glance, might well be thought to be sufficient): given any rational numbers r_1 and r_2, however close they may be, we can always find infinitely many other rationals between them. For, if $r_1 = p_1/q_1$ and $r_2 = p_2/q_2$, Then

$$r_3 = (p_1q_2 + p_2q_1)/2q_1q_2 \equiv \tfrac{1}{2}(r_1 + r_2)$$

is a rational number which lies between r_1 and r_2. Similarly we can find r_4 between r_1 and r_3, and so on. This fact is usually expressed by saying that the rational numbers are *dense*. Even so, it turns out that denseness is not enough and that the rational-number system is inadequate for our purpose.

1.1.4 *The real numbers*
Consider the situation illustrated in figure 1.1 in which the rationals have been assigned to appropriate points of the line.

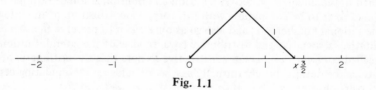

Fig. 1.1

If there were a rational number x corresponding to the point shown then we should be able to write $x = p/q$, where p and q are positive integers with no common factors. Moreover we must have

$$x^2 = p^2/q^2 = 2$$

or, equivalently, $$2q = p^2/q$$

But the L.H.S. of this equation is an integer whereas the R.H.S. is clearly a fraction, unless $q = 1$†. Since by inspection it is obvious that there is no integer p such that $p^2 = 2$, it follows that our assumption is false, that is that there exists no rational number x whose square is 2.

This argument readily generalises to give a theorem due to Gauss:

Theorem 1 (Gauss). A real, algebraical equation

$$x_1^n + a_1 x^{n-1} + a_2 x^{n-2} + \cdots + a_{n-1}x + a_n = 0$$

with integral coefficients, a_k, cannot have a rational but non-integral root.

Proof. If $x = p/q$, where p and q have no common factor, then, multiplying throughout by q^{n-1}

$$a_1 p^{n-1} + a_2 p^{n-2}q + \cdots + a_n q^{n-1} = -p^n/q$$

The L.H.S. of this equation is always an integer; the R.H.S. is integral only if $q = 1$.

Using this theorem it is easy to show, for example, that $\sqrt[3]{2}$ cannot be rational since it satisfies the equation $x^3 - 2 = 0$ and is clearly not an integer. Similarly, $\sqrt{2} + \sqrt{3}$ cannot be a rational number since it is a (non-integral) root of the equation $x^4 - 10x^2 + 1 = 0$.

These arguments show that there are gaps in the rational number system and that a further extension of the number concept is required. The technical process of defining numbers to fill these gaps is somewhat lengthy and we shall not attempt a rigorous discussion of the matter here. (See Note 1.) For most purposes it is enough to remark that the points of the line may be made to correspond to 'numbers' which can be expressed either as finite or as infinite (that is non-terminating) decimals. Even so, to appreciate the significance of this assertion it is necessary to have some understanding of what the representation of a number as a decimal entails.

1.1.5 *Decimal expansions*

In the case of a *finite* decimal, no real problem of interpretation is involved. To say that the fraction $\frac{1}{4}$ has the decimal expansion 0.25 is merely to express the fact that $\frac{1}{4} = \frac{2}{10} + \frac{5}{10^2}$.

---

† To prove that p^2/q must be a fraction we need only argue as follows: the greatest common divisor of p and q is 1, by hypothesis. Hence, the G.C.D. of p^2 and pq is p. Now, q is certainly a divisor of pq; if it were also a divisor of p^2 then we would either have $q = p$, or else q divides p.

On the other hand it is by no means a trivial matter to explain what is really meant by the statement that $\frac{1}{3}$ has the *infinite, recurring,* decimal expansion 0.3333 . . . If we write this statement in the form,

$$\frac{1}{3} = \frac{3}{10} + \frac{3}{10^2} + \frac{3}{10^3} + \cdots + \frac{3}{10^n} + \cdots \tag{1}$$

then the problem is seen to be precisely that of attaching a meaning to a sum which contains (apparently) infinitely many terms. In fact, no really satisfactory account of this point can be given without going into the theory of convergence of infinite sequences and series discussed in chapter 3. (It is salutary to note that the resolution of what appears to be a problem of elementary arithmetic actually depends on relatively advanced parts of mathematical analysis.) However, we can at least sketch the main issues involved. Intuitively it is clear that by taking as many decimal digits as required we can approximate the number $\frac{1}{3}$ as closely as we wish by *finite* decimal expansions, namely

$$0.3 = \frac{3}{10}, \quad 0.33 = \frac{3}{10} + \frac{3}{10^2}, \quad 0.333 = \frac{3}{10} + \frac{3}{10^2} + \frac{3}{10^3}, \quad \text{and so on}$$

We can make this more precise by appealing to a result from elementary algebra. Using the formula for the sum of a geometric progression we have

$$\frac{3}{10} + \frac{3}{10^2} + \frac{3}{10^3} + \cdots + \frac{3}{10^n} = \frac{3}{10} \left(\frac{1 - \dfrac{1}{10^n}}{1 - \dfrac{1}{10}} \right) = \frac{1}{3} - \frac{1}{3 \times 10^n}$$

The difference between the number $\frac{1}{3}$ and the finite decimal 0.333 . . . 3 is therefore $\frac{1}{3} \times 10^{-n}$, where n is the number of decimal digits. The statement that $\frac{1}{3}$ is the sum of the infinite series (1) (or the equivalent statement that $\frac{1}{3}$ has the infinite decimal expansion 0.3333 . . .) simply means that this difference can be made as small as we wish by taking n sufficiently large.

A simple generalisation of this argument shows that *every* non-terminating, recurring decimal must represent a rational number. Conversely it is the case that every rational number has either a finite or else an infinite recurring decimal expansion. To see this we need only consider the elementary problem of expressing a simple fraction, say $\frac{2}{7}$, as a decimal. The ordinary process of long division, from which the required decimal digits are obtained, can be laid out in the following way

$$\frac{3}{7} = \frac{1}{10}\left(\frac{30}{7}\right) = \frac{1}{10}\left\{4 + \frac{2}{7}\right\}$$

$$= \frac{4}{10} + \frac{1}{10^2}\left(\frac{20}{7}\right) = \frac{4}{10} + \frac{1}{10^2}\left\{2 + \frac{6}{7}\right\}$$

$$= \frac{4}{10} + \frac{2}{10^2} + \frac{1}{10^3}\left(\frac{60}{7}\right) = \frac{4}{10} + \frac{2}{10^2} + \frac{1}{10^3}\left\{8 + \frac{4}{7}\right\}$$

$$= \frac{4}{10} + \frac{2}{10^2} + \frac{8}{10^3} + \frac{1}{10^4}\left(\frac{40}{7}\right)$$

and so on. At each stage in the calculation which produces a new term in the decimal expansion, say $a_n/10^n$, we are left with a certain *remainder* term of the form $(1/10^n) \times (r/7)$. The number r can take one of the seven possible values 0, 1, 2, 3, 4, 5, 6. If at any stage we were to get $r = 0$ then the division process would terminate and we would be left with a *finite* decimal expansion. The only other possibility is that sooner or later the remainder digit r must repeat a value which it has previously assumed. In that event the intervening values of r will repeat in the same order of succession as before, and the decimal will be non-terminating and recurring. For example in the case of the fraction $\frac{3}{7}$ we find that the 6th stage of the division gives

$$\frac{3}{7} = \frac{4}{10} + \frac{2}{10^2} + \frac{8}{10^3} + \frac{5}{10^4} + \frac{7}{10^5} + \frac{1}{10^6}\left\{1 + \frac{3}{7}\right\}$$

that is $\qquad \frac{3}{7} = 0.428571428571\ldots$

The question of extending the concept of number beyond that of the rational numbers can now be re-stated in a slightly different context. We shall say that *every* infinite decimal, whether recurring or not, represents a certain number. If the decimal is recurring then the number concerned is said to be a *rational real number* (note that this includes all numbers which admit a finite decimal expansion; for example, we can always express 0.25 as 0.24999 . . .). If the infinite decimal expansion is non-recurring then the number is said to be an *irrational real number*. Thus, the symbol $\sqrt{2}$ denotes an irrational real number, with an infinite, non-recurring, decimal expansion, which can be approximated as closely as we please by rational real numbers such as 1.4, 1.41, 1.414, and so on. A rather simpler example of an irrational real number is afforded by

$$\frac{1}{10} + \frac{1}{10^3} + \frac{1}{10^6} + \frac{1}{10^{10}} + \frac{1}{10^{15}} + \cdots$$

that is a decimal expansion of the form 0.1010010001000010 . . . in which the number of 0's between successive 1's steadily increases. This number is irrational since its decimal expansion is quite clearly infinite and non-recurring. It can be approximated arbitrarily closely by rational real numbers (with finite decimal expansions) such as 0.1, 0.101, 0.101001, 0.1010010001, etc.

The real numbers may be assigned to the points of the line (as in figure 1.1) in a one-to-one manner; that is to each point there corresponds a unique real number and to each real number there corresponds a unique point of the line. The addition of the irrational real numbers to the rational numbers gives us a number system which is, so to speak, 'complete' in a geometric sense as well as in an arithmetic one. The real number system is, in fact, adequate for the measurement of magnitude.

In a sense which can be made quite precise the irrational real numbers are infinitely more numerous that the rationals. (See Note 2.) Roughly speaking, if from a segment of the line we were to remove all those points labelled with rational real numbers then the length of the remaining set of points would be the same as that of the original segment. If, on the other hand, we were to remove all the points corresponding to the irrational real numbers then the remaining set of points would have zero length. Nevertheless it is the rational numbers which, from a practical point of view, are of supreme importance since it is these (and these alone) which we can use in numerical computations. Hence it is a matter of crucial significance that the rational numbers are not merely dense (as remarked earlier) but are *dense in the real number system*; that is to say, given any irrational real number we can find rational real numbers which approximate to it as closely as we wish.

Exercises
1. Show that each of the following numbers is irrational
   (a) $\sqrt{3}$ (b) $\sqrt[3]{3}$. (c) $1 - \sqrt{2}$ (d) $\sqrt{3} + \sqrt{5}$.
   [Hint: use Gauss's theorem as in section 1.1.4.]
2. Give examples to show that the sum of two irrational numbers may be
   (a) irrational, or (b) rational.
3. Show that if the commutative, associative, and distributive laws are to be preserved in the system of signed integers, then

$$(-1) \times (-1) = +1$$

1.2 Complex numbers

1.2.1 *Definitions*

The complex-number system may be said to arise from a more purely technical need than any of the other systems. There is, for example, no real solution of the equation

$$x^2 + 1 = 0$$

and this must rank as a deficiency of the real-number system. More generally it would be desirable to say that every polynomial equation of the form

$$a_n x^n + a_{n-1} x^{n-1} + \cdots + a_1 x + a_0 = 0$$

should have precisely n roots. In practice, of course, such an equation could have any number of *real* roots up to, and including, n or possibly none at all. Hence we undertake one more enlargement of the number system and introduce the so-called *complex numbers*.

We define a complex number z to be an *ordered pair* (x, y) of real numbers and establish the arithmetic of such real number pairs by the following formal rules:

Equality. Two complex numbers $z_1 = (x_1, y_1)$ and $z_2 = (x_2, y_2)$ are said to be equal if and only if $x_1 = x_2$ and $y_1 = y_2$.

Addition. The sum, $z_1 + z_2$, of the complex numbers $z_1 = (x_1, y_1)$ and $z_2 = (x_2, y_2)$ is defined to be the complex number.

$$z_1 + z_2 = (x_1 + x_2, y_1 + y_2)$$

Multiplication. The product, $z_1 z_2$, of the complex numbers $z_1 = (x_1, y_1)$ and $z_2 = (x_2, y_2)$ is defined to be the complex number

$$z_1 z_2 = (x_1 x_2 - y_1 y_2, x_1 y_2 + x_2 y_1)$$

From these definitions it is a simple matter to deduce that complex numbers satisfy the commutative and associative laws for multiplication and addition and that the distributive law is also valid.

$$z_1 + z_2 = z_2 + z_1 \qquad \text{commutative laws} \qquad z_1 . z_2 = z_2 . z_1$$

$$(z_1 + z_2) + z_3 = z_1 + (z_2 + z_3) \qquad \text{associative laws} \qquad (z_1 z_2) z_3 = z_1 (z_2 z_3)$$

$$\text{distributive law: } z_1 (z_2 + z_3) = z_1 z_2 + z_1 z_3$$

Also the complex number $(0, 0)$ has the additive identity property that

$$z + (0, 0) = z \quad \text{for any } z$$

Similarly the complex number $(1, 0)$ has the multiplicative identity property

$$z(1, 0) = z \quad \text{for any } z$$

$-z$ is then defined to be the number for which $z + (-z) = (0, 0)$, and z^{-1} is defined to have the property $z^{-1} . z = (1, 0)$.

Having defined these inverse elements $-z$ (for any z) and z^{-1} (for any $z \neq (0, 0)$) subtraction and division can then be defined in terms of the basic operations of addition and multiplication:

$$z_1 - z_2 = z_1 + (-z_2) = (x_1, y_1) + (-x_2, -y_2) = (x_1 - x_2, y_1 - y_2)$$

$$z_1 \div z_2 = z_1 . z_2^{-1}$$

which expression will be further simplified in section 1.2.4.

This purely formal treatment is entirely adequate for our purposes and avoids any obligation to say what sort of entity a complex number really is. This is, indeed, no new problem. It may be conceded that we know, intuitively, just what a natural number is (although, when it comes to the point, it is extremely difficult to frame an acceptable definition). But, having granted this, it is still true that we never really go on to give explicit definitions of the integers, the rationals or the real numbers except in terms of the already given natural numbers. Thus, in the last resort, we are compelled to say merely that an integer is a signed natural number and that a rational number is an ordered pair (p, q), or p/q, of integers. Rational-number arithmetic is obtained by establishing a formal set of rules for combining such integer pairs, and in the same way complex-number arithmetic is defined in terms of manipulating real-number pairs. The complex arithmetic is simplified in practice by writing (x, y) in the form $x + iy$, and using the rules of ordinary arithmetic with the additional convention that i^2 is to be replaced by -1 whenever it occurs. The symbol i is a convenient shorthand for the complex number $(0, 1)$, or $0 + i1$, and allows us to give a conventional meaning to 'the square root of -1'. All that we mean by this last statement is that, using the formal multiplication rule given above, we get $(0, 1) \times (0, 1) = (-1, 0)$ and if we identify the real number -1 with the complex number $(-1, 0)$, then i is a solution of the equation

$$x^2 + 1 = 0$$

The identification of the real number α with the complex number $(\alpha, 0)$ is another example of embedding. The complex numbers form a system in which addition, subtraction, multiplication and division (except by zero) are always possible and in which any polynomial equation (with complex coefficients) of the nth order has precisely n complex roots. The subset of this class of entities which consists of complex numbers of the form $(\alpha, 0)$ constitutes a number system which is formally identical with the real number system. We need only remark in conclusion that the complex numbers can be put into a one—one correspondence with the points of the plane (just as the real numbers can be assigned to the points of a line); this yields the well known *Argand diagram* representation of the complex numbers.

Real and imaginary parts. Conventionally, for the complex number $z = x + iy$, x is called the *real part* of z and y is called the *imaginary part* of z. The definition of equality is then equivalent to the statement that two complex numbers are equal if and only if their real and imaginary parts are respectively equal.

A complex number of the form $x + i0$ is called real whereas one of the form $0 + iy$ is said to be wholly imaginary. This nomenclature is perhaps a little unfortunate. The existence of $i.1$ is no more in doubt than that of -1. The manner in which these quantities are interpreted depends upon the physical application. For an electrical engineer a current which is 90° out of phase with the input is represented by an imaginary number, but its existence is not thereby doubted.

1.2.2 *The Argand diagram*
We have seen that the real numbers can be represented geometrically by a line segment; in a similar way it is useful to construct a geometric representation of complex numbers. Since the complex numbers include the real numbers, the required geometric representation should include that of the real numbers. In the case of real numbers +1 is represented by a positive line segment of unit length and -1 is represented by the same line segment after rotation through 180°. All those complex numbers with zero imaginary part can be represented by a fixed horizontal line called the *real axis*.

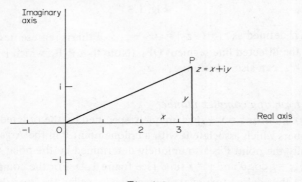

Fig. 1.2

For real numbers the result $(-1)^2 = +1$ corresponds to the fact that geometrically two rotations through $180°$ are equivalent to no rotation. This argument suggests that whereas -1 is obtained by rotating the unit line segment through $180°$, i, with $i^2 = -1$, could be obtained by a rotation through $90°$. In this way we obtain the 'imaginary axis' (containing all complex numbers of the form $0 + iy$) at an angle of $90°$ to the real axis (see figure 1.2).

The complex number $z = x + iy$ is then represented either by the point $P(x, y)$ on the diagram or by the directed line OP. This geometric representation of the complex numbers is called an *Argand diagram*; it is of necessity two-dimensional since a complex number z corresponds to an ordered pair (x, y) of real numbers.

Addition and subtraction on the Argand diagram (see figure 1.3). Suppose $z_1 = x_1 + iy_1$ is represented by the line OP_1 on the Argand diagram and $z_2 = x_2 + iy_2$ is represented by OP_2. Then $z_1 + z_2$ is given by the defining equation $z_1 + z_2 = (x_1 + x_2) + i(y_1 + y_2)$ and is represented on the Argand diagram by a line segment OP_3 obtainable by 'vector addition' of OP_1 and OP_2.

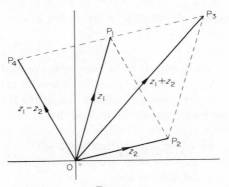

Fig. 1.3

$z_1 - z_2$ is defined as $z_1 + (-z_2) = -z_2 + z_1$ and this is represented on the same diagram by the directed line segment OP_4. (Note that P_2P_1, which is equal and parallel to OP_4, can also represent $z_1 - z_2$.)

1.2.3 *Polar form of a complex number*
The complex number $z = x + iy$ is uniquely specified by the ordered pair (x, y) of real numbers which associate it with a unique point P in the Argand diagram. Geometrically the point P is also uniquely determined by the polar coordinates (r, θ) where $x = r \cos \theta$ and $y = r \sin \theta$ (see figure 1.4). For the complex number $z = x + iy$ we thus define two related quantities; r, called the *modulus* of z,

denoted by $|z|$, and defined as $|z| = +\sqrt{(x^2 + y^2)}$; and θ, called the *argument,* or *amplitude* of z, and defined by the pair of equations

$$x = r \cos \theta, \qquad y = r \sin \theta$$

The argument of z is usually denoted by $\arg z$.

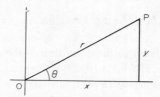

Fig. 1.4

r can be eliminated from these equations to give

$$\theta = \arg z = \tan^{-1} (y/x)$$

Notes. (i) Geometrically $r = |z|$ is the distance OP, and $\theta = \arg z$ is the angle between the positive half of the real axis and OP, measured in the counter-clockwise sense.

(ii) The equation $\theta = \tan^{-1} (y/x)$ is not by itself sufficient to define the argument of z. For example, $z_1 = 1 - i$ has argument $\dfrac{7\pi}{4}$ $\left(\text{or} -\dfrac{\pi}{4}\right)$, and $z_2 = -1 + i$ has argument $\dfrac{3\pi}{4}$ but, for both z_1 and z_2, $\tan^{-1}(y/x)$ gives $\tan^{-1} (-1)$. In practice the ambiguity over the value of $\tan^{-1} (y/x)$ is most easily resolved by using the signs of x and y to determine to which quadrant of the Argand diagram z belongs.

(iii) The argument, θ, of z is only defined up to an integral multiple of 2π. The unique value of θ which lies in the range $-\pi < \theta \leqslant \pi$ is called the *principal value* of the argument of z and, in most texts, is denoted by $\arg z$. The notation of $\arg z$ is usually reserved for an arbitrary value of the argument of z; thus, if $\arg z = \theta$ then $-\pi < \theta \leqslant \pi$ and for any integer n we can write

$$\arg z = \theta + 2n\pi$$

We have now obtained two distinct forms for expressing the complex number z. First there is the form $z = x + iy$ which could be called the *Cartesian form* and which lends itself naturally to the simplification of sums and differences of complex numbers. Secondly there is the *polar form* $z = r (\cos \theta + i \sin \theta)$, where $r = |z|$ and $\theta = \arg z$. As will be seen in section 1.2.5, this form is the simplest for multiplication and division of complex numbers.

1.2.4 *Conjugate complex numbers*

It can be shown (see chapter 6) that for a polynomial equation with real
coefficients any complex roots which occur will not appear singly but will be
obtained in simply related pairs.

For example,   the equation $z^2 + 1 = 0$ has roots $z = \pm i$,

$$\text{the equation } z^2 + z + 1 = 0 \text{ has roots } z = -\tfrac{1}{2} \pm \frac{i\sqrt{3}}{2}$$

The form of these pairs leads to the definition of the *complex conjugate, $\bar{z}$,* of a
given complex number z. If $z = x + iy$, $\bar{z}$ is defined as $\bar{z} = x - iy$. From this
definition the following properties are immediately obtained:

$$z + \bar{z} = 2x = 2 \text{ times real part of } z$$

$$z - \bar{z} = 2iy = 2i \text{ times imaginary part of } z$$

$$z\bar{z} = (x + iy)(x - iy) = x^2 + y^2 = |z|^2$$

On the Argand diagram $\bar{z}$ appears as the reflection of z in the real axis (see figure 1.5)

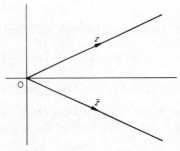

Fig. 1.5

For the polar form of z we have $z = (r \cos \theta + i \sin \theta)$. Hence,
$\bar{z} = r(\cos \theta - i \sin \theta) = r(\cos (-\theta) + i \sin (-\theta))$. Thus $|\bar{z}| = |z|$ and $\arg \bar{z} = - \arg z$.

Division of complex numbers. The property $z\bar{z} = |z|^2$ (a real quantity) is very
important. In particular it provides a method of simplifying the division of
complex numbers.

    Consider

$$\frac{z_1}{z_2} = \frac{x_1 + iy_1}{x_2 + iy_2}$$

Provided $z_2 \neq 0, \bar{z}_2$ will be non-zero, and numerator and denominator may be multiplied by this to give

$$\frac{z_1 z_2}{z_2 z_2} = \frac{(x_1 + iy_1)(x_2 - iy_2)}{x_2^2 + y_2^2}$$

$$= \frac{(x_1 x_2 + y_1 y_2)}{x_2^2 + y_2^2} + i\,\frac{y_1 x_2 - x_1 y_2}{x_2^2 + y_2^2}$$

This result confirms that division by z_2 is possible whenever $z_2 \neq 0$.

In particular we have

$$z^{-1} = \frac{1}{z} = \frac{\bar{z}}{|z|^2} = \frac{x - iy}{x^2 + y^2} \qquad (z \neq 0)$$

Example

$$\frac{3 - 2i}{4 + 3i} = \frac{(3 - 2i)(4 - 3i)}{4^2 + 3^2} = \frac{6}{25} - \frac{17}{25}\,i$$

[This process can be compared with the elementary arithmetic process of simplifying expressions involving surds:

$$\frac{2 + \sqrt{2}}{3 + \sqrt{2}} = \frac{(2 + \sqrt{2})(3 - \sqrt{2})}{(3 + \sqrt{2})(3 - \sqrt{2})} = \frac{4 + \sqrt{2}}{7}.]$$

1.2.5 *Multiplication and division in polar form*
Suppose

$$z_1 = r_1(\cos \theta_1 + i \sin \theta_1)$$

and $z_2 = r_2(\cos \theta_2 + i \sin \theta_2)$

From the definition of multiplication we obtain

$$z_1 z_2 = r_1 r_2(\cos \theta_1 \cos \theta_2 - \sin \theta_1 \sin \theta_2) + i r_1 r_2(\sin \theta_1 \cos \theta_2 + \cos \theta_1 \sin \theta_2)$$

$$= r_1 r_2 \{\cos (\theta_1 + \theta_2) + i \sin (\theta_1 + \theta_2)\}$$

Hence $z_1 z_2$ is a complex number of modulus $|z_1|.|z_2|$ and argument $\mathrm{Arg}\, z_1 + \mathrm{Arg}\, z_2$.

Provided $z_2 \neq 0$ we have also

$$\frac{z_1}{z_2} = \frac{z_1 \bar{z}_2}{|z_2|^2} = \frac{r_1}{r_2}\,(\cos \theta_1 + i \sin \theta_1)(\cos (-\theta_2) + i \sin (-\theta_2))$$

$$= \frac{r_1}{r_2}\,(\cos (\theta_1 - \theta_2) + i \sin (\theta_1 - \theta_2))$$

Thus z_1/z_2 is a complex number of modulus $|z_1|/|z_2|$ and argument $\arg z_1 - \arg z_2$. This is clearly an inversion of the two operations involved in calculating the polar form of the product $z_1 z_2$ (see figure 1.6).

On the Argand diagram $z_1 z_2$ corresponds to a line segment obtained from that representing z_1 by rotating it through θ_2 and multiplying its length by r_2; z_1/z_2 corresponds to a line segment obtained from that representing z_1 by rotating it through $-\theta_2$ and dividing its length by r_2.

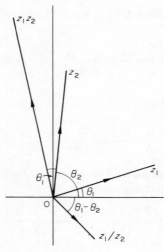

Fig. 1.6

Exercises

1. Simplify the following expressions, reducing each to the form $a + ib$:

   (a) $(3 + 4i)(2 - i)$,   (b) $\dfrac{2 + 3i}{1 - i}$,   (c) $\left\{ \dfrac{2}{1 + i} + \dfrac{3 + i}{1 - i} \right\}^2$,   (d) $\dfrac{i^5 + i^9 + i^{14}}{i^6 + i^{11} + i^{13}}$,

   (e) $\dfrac{(1 - i)(3 + 2i)(4 + i)}{(1 - i)^2}$

2. Find the modulus and the principal value of the argument of each of the following complex numbers:

   (a) $3 - 5i$,   (b) $\dfrac{1 - i}{1 + i}$,   (c) $\dfrac{1 + 2i}{1 - (1 - i)^2}$,   (d) $2 + 2\sqrt{(3)}i$

3. Show that $\dfrac{a + ib}{c + id}$ is real if and only if $ad = bc$.

4. Show that, for any complex number z, we have

$$\arg z + \arg \overline{z} = 2n\pi$$

where n is any positive or negative integer, or zero.

5. Show that the complex numbers $z_1 = 1 + 2i$, $z_2 = 4 - 2i$, and $z_3 = 1 - 6i$ form the vertices of an isosceles triangle in the Argand diagram.

1.2.6 *De Moivre's theorem*

Theorem 2. For any rational values of θ and n, $(\cos \theta + i \sin \theta)^n = \cos n\theta + i \sin n\theta$. (Using the polar form of a complex number this theorem provides a method of calculating powers and roots of a complex number z.)

Proof of theorem. The result is established in three separate stages corresponding to whether n is a positive integer, a negative integer, or a rational number.

(i) n a positive integer:
The proof in this case is by induction on n.
When $n = 1$ the result is trivially true since

$$(\cos \theta + i \sin \theta)^1 = \cos \theta + i \sin \theta$$

Suppose it is true for some value n. Then,

$$(\cos \theta + i \sin \theta)^{n+1} = (\cos \theta + i \sin \theta)^n .(\cos \theta + i \sin \theta)$$

$$= (\cos n\theta + i \sin n\theta)(\cos \theta + i \sin \theta), \text{ by induction hypothesis}$$

$$= \cos (n + 1)\theta + i \sin (n + 1)\theta, \text{ from polar form of product.}$$

Hence by induction the theorem is true for all positive integers n.

(ii) n is a negative integer:
Let $n = -p$ where p is a positive integer. Then

$$(\cos \theta + i \sin \theta)^n = (\cos \theta + i \sin \theta)^{-p}$$

$$= \frac{1}{(\cos \theta + i \sin \theta)^p}$$

$$= \frac{1}{(\cos p\theta + i \sin p\theta)} \quad \text{by (i)}$$

$$= \cos p\theta - i \sin p\theta$$

$$= \cos (-p\theta) + i \sin (-p\theta)$$

(iii) n is a rational number:

Let $n = p/q$ where p, q are integers, and $q > 0$. Then

$$\left(\cos\frac{p}{q}\theta + i\sin\frac{p}{q}\theta\right)^q = (\cos p\theta + i\sin p\theta), \text{ by (i) with } q \text{ replacing } n$$

$$= (\cos\theta + i\sin\theta)^p, \text{ by (i) or (ii) as appropriate}$$

Hence $$\left(\cos\frac{p}{q}\theta + i\sin\frac{p}{q}\theta\right)^q = (\cos\theta + i\sin\theta)^p$$

Taking the qth root of this equation establishes the fact that
$(\cos(p/q)\theta + i\sin(p/q)\theta)$ is one of the values of $(\cos\theta + i\sin\theta)^{p/q}$.

1.2.7 Applications of De Moivre's theorem

(a) *Trigonometric identities.* If n is a positive integer we have, by De Moivre's
theorem $\cos n\theta + i\sin n\theta = (\cos\theta + i\sin\theta)^n$.

If the right hand side of this equation is expanded then equating the real
and imaginary parts will give respectively expressions for $\cos n\theta$ and $\sin n\theta$ in
terms of powers of $\sin\theta$ and $\cos\theta$.

Example

$$\cos 3\theta + i\sin 3\theta = (\cos\theta + i\sin\theta)^3$$

$$= \cos^3\theta - 3\cos\theta\sin^2\theta + i(3\cos^2\theta\sin\theta - \sin^3\theta)$$

Equating separately the real and imaginary parts verifies the identities

$$\cos 3\theta = \cos^3\theta - 3\cos\theta\sin^2\theta = 4\cos^3\theta - 3\cos\theta$$

and $$\sin 3\theta = 3\cos^2\theta\sin\theta - \sin^3\theta = 3\sin\theta - 4\sin^3\theta$$

(b) *Roots of complex numbers.* To find $\sqrt[n]{z}$ where n is a positive integer and z is
a given complex number.

Suppose $$z = r(\cos\theta + i\sin\theta)$$

and $$\omega = \sqrt[n]{z} = p(\cos\phi + i\sin\phi)$$

Then $\omega^n = z$ and so by De Moivre's theorem

$$p^n(\cos n\phi + i\sin n\phi) = r(\cos\theta + i\sin\theta)$$

Since equal complex numbers must have the same modulus and argument we
have, on comparing moduli and arguments

$$p^n = r \quad \text{or} \quad p = \sqrt[n]{r} \quad (p \text{ must be real and positive})$$

and $\qquad n\phi = \text{Arg } z = \theta + 2m\pi \quad$ for some integer m.

This gives n essentially distinct values of ϕ:

$$\phi = \frac{\theta}{n}, \frac{\theta}{n} + \frac{2\pi}{n}, \dots, \frac{\theta}{n} + \frac{2(n-1)\pi}{n}$$

The final result is a set of n distinct nth roots of z:

$$\omega_1 = p\left(\cos\frac{\theta}{n} + i\sin\frac{\theta}{n}\right), \qquad \omega_2 = p\left[\cos\left(\frac{\theta}{n} + \frac{2\pi}{n}\right) + i\sin\left(\frac{\theta}{n} + \frac{2\pi}{n}\right)\right],$$

$$\dots, \omega_n = p\left\{\cos\left[\frac{\theta}{n} + \frac{2(n-1)\pi}{n}\right] + i\sin\left[\frac{\theta}{n} + \frac{2(n-1)\pi}{n}\right]\right\}; \qquad \text{where } p = \sqrt[n]{r}$$

An immediate consequence of this result is that every non-zero complex number will have precisely 2 square roots, 3 distinct cube roots, 4 fourth roots, etc. This should be contrasted with the corresponding situation for real numbers, where a non-zero real number will have 0 or 2 real square roots, 1 real cube root and 0 or 2 real fourth roots. These properties of the complex-number system can be deduced from the fundamental theorem of algebra (see chapter 6), which implies that the complex numbers form an algebraically closed system, every polynomial equation of degree n with complex coefficients having precisely n complex roots.

Example. Solve the equation $z^2 - 3z + 3 - i = 0$.
The usual formula for the roots of a quadratic equation may be used since the proof of this assumes only the validity of the elementary arithmetic operations. These operations remain valid when the coefficients are complex. z is thus given as

$$z = \frac{3 \pm \sqrt{(9 - 4(3 - i))}}{2}$$

$$= \tfrac{3}{2} \pm \tfrac{1}{2}\sqrt{(-3 + 4i)}.$$

To compute $\sqrt{(-3 + 4i)}$ we use the polar form:

$$-3 + 4i = 5(\cos\theta + i\sin\theta) \text{ where } \cos\theta = -3/5 \text{ and } \sin\theta = 4/5$$

One value of the root is given by $\sqrt{5}(\cos\theta/2 + i\sin\theta/2)$ where

$$\cos\frac{\theta}{2} = \sqrt{\left(\frac{1 + \cos\theta}{2}\right)} = \frac{\sqrt{2}}{5} \qquad \text{and} \qquad \sin\frac{\theta}{2} = \sqrt{\left(\frac{1 - \cos\theta}{2}\right)} = \frac{1}{\sqrt{5}}$$

The other value may be obtained from this by increasing the argument by π, or, more simply, by multiplying by -1. Thus, $z = \tfrac{3}{2} \pm \tfrac{1}{2}\sqrt{(-3 + 4i)} = \tfrac{3}{2} \pm \tfrac{1}{2}(1 + 2i)$, and the two roots are $z = 2 + i$ and $z = 1 - i$.

Clearly, the original quadratic could have been factorised to give:

$$(z - 2 - i)(z - 1 + i) = 0$$

but factorisation is usually much less straightforward than in the case of real coefficients and can rarely be done by inspection.

(c) *Complex roots of unity.* A particularly simple special case of $\sqrt[n]{z}$ occurs when $z = 1$. In this the modulus $r = 1$ and $\arg z = 0$. Using the above method we obtain n distinct roots of 1, all of unit modulus, and with arguments

$$0, \frac{2\pi}{n}, \frac{4\pi}{n}, \ldots, \frac{2(n - 1)\pi}{n}$$

The nth roots are thus

$$1, \cos\frac{2\pi}{n} + i \sin\frac{2\pi}{n}, \cos\frac{4\pi}{n} + i \sin\frac{4\pi}{n}, \ldots, \cos\left[\frac{2(n - 1)\pi}{n}\right] + i \sin\left[\frac{2(n - 1)\pi}{n}\right].$$

If $\omega = \cos\dfrac{2\pi}{n} + i \sin\dfrac{2\pi}{n}$ the above roots can be expressed as

$$1, \omega, \omega^2, \ldots, \omega^{n-1}$$

In particular, when $n = 3$, the complex cube roots of unity are

$$1, \quad \omega = \cos\frac{2\pi}{3} + i \sin\frac{2\pi}{3} = -\tfrac{1}{2} + i\frac{\sqrt{3}}{2}, \quad \omega^2 = \cos\frac{4\pi}{3} + i \sin\frac{4\pi}{3} = -\tfrac{1}{2} - i\frac{\sqrt{3}}{2}$$

On the Argand diagram these appear as in figure 1.7.

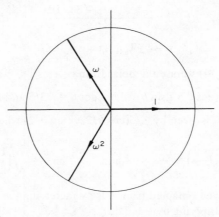

Fig. 1.7

More generally the complex nth roots of unity will be equally spaced on a unit circle, centre 0, in the Argand diagram, one of them lying on the positive real axis.

Each nth root of unity is a solution of the equation $z^n - 1 = 0$. This can be factorised to give $(z - 1)(z^{n-1} + z^{n-2} + \cdots + z + 1) = 0$. Eliminating the real positive root $z = 1$, each of the remaining complex nth roots of unity is a root of the equation

$$z^{n-1} + z^{n-2} + \cdots + z + 1 = 0$$

In particular ω and ω^2, the complex cube roots of unity, both satisfy the equation $z^2 + z + 1 = 0$.

Exercises
1. Use De Moivre's theorem to show that
   (a) $\cos 4\theta = 8 \sin^4 \theta - 8 \sin^2 \theta + 1$,
   (b) $\dfrac{\sin 4\theta}{4 \sin \theta} = 2 \cos^3 \theta - \cos \theta$.

2. Find (a) the square roots of i and of $-i$, (b) the square roots of $5 - 12i$, and (c) the cube roots of $-11 - 2i$.
3. Find the sixth roots of -1 and hence express $x^6 + 1$ as the product of real quadratic factors.
4. Find all the roots of the equation $(z - i)^3 + 8 = 0$, and indicate their positions on the Argand diagram.
5. Solve the equation $z^2 + (2 + i)z - 3 - i = 0$.
6. If ω is a complex cube root of 1, establish the following identities:
   (a) $a^3 - b^3 = (a - b)(a - \omega b)(a - \omega^2 b)$,
   (b) $a^3 + b^3 = (a + b)(a + \omega b)(a + \omega^2 b)$,
   (c) $a^2 + b^2 + c^2 - ab - ca - bc = (a + \omega b + \omega^2 c)(a + \omega^2 b + \omega c)$.

1.2.8 *Exponential functions – Euler's formula*
For real values of x the exponential function $\exp x$ may be defined as the sum of an infinite series

$$\exp x = 1 + x + \frac{x^2}{2!} + \frac{x^3}{3!} + \cdots + \frac{x^n}{n!} + \cdots$$

It can be shown that this series is convergent (see chapter 3) for all real values of x.

For the complex number z, the function $\exp z$ can still be defined in terms of the series

$$\exp z = 1 + z + \frac{z^2}{2!} + \frac{z^3}{3!} + \cdots + \frac{z^n}{n!} + \cdots \tag{1}$$

It can be shown that this series converges to a complex limit for all values of z so that, using this definition, exp z is well defined for all complex z.

In particular when $z = i\theta$ the series gives

$$\exp(i\theta) = 1 + i\theta - \frac{\theta^2}{2!} + i\frac{\theta^3}{3!} + \frac{\theta^4}{4!} + \cdots$$

Since the series is absolutely convergent (see section 3.4.2) it can be rearranged to give

$$\exp(i\theta) = 1 - \frac{\theta^2}{2!} + \frac{\theta^4}{4!} - \cdots + i\left(\theta - \frac{\theta^3}{3!} + \frac{\theta^5}{5!} - \cdots\right) \tag{2}$$

or exp $(i\theta) = \cos\theta + i\sin\theta$ (using the series definitions for $\cos\theta$ and $\sin\theta$).

By the properties of the polar form of the product of two complex numbers we have

$$\exp(i\theta).\exp(i\phi) = (\cos\theta + i\sin\theta).(\cos\phi + i\sin\phi)$$

$$= \cos(\theta + \phi) + i\sin(\theta + \phi) = \exp i(\theta + \phi)$$

Also, by De Moivre's theorem for rational n,

$$(\exp(i\theta))^n = (\cos\theta + i\sin\theta)^n = \cos n\theta + i\sin n\theta = \exp(in\theta)$$

These properties of exp $(i\theta)$ show that it satisfies the algebraic rules of indices and justify the use of conventional notation $e^{i\theta} = \exp(i\theta)$. (See Note 3.) Equation (2) can then be expressed as

$$e^{i\theta} = \cos\theta + i\sin\theta$$

a result known as *Euler's formula*.

Using this notation De Moivre's theorem can be written in the apparently trivial form $(e^{i\theta})^n = e^{in\theta}$, and the polar form of a complex number becomes $z = r(\cos\theta + i\sin\theta) = r\,e^{i\theta}$.

For any complex values of z_1 and z_2 we can prove by a direct multiplication of the defining power series (1) that exp $z_1.\exp z_2 = \exp(z_1 + z_2)$ thus providing a more general justification of the notation $e^z = \exp z$. (See section 3.7.1.)

To compute the numerical value of e^z for any particular z it is convenient to write z in the Cartesian form giving: $e^z = e^{x+iy} = e^x e^{iy} = e^x(\cos y + i\sin y)$. This shows that e^z is a complex number of modulus e^x and argument y.

Euler's formula can be used to relate the circular and hyperbolic functions. From Euler's formula we obtain

$$e^{i\theta} = \cos\theta + i\sin\theta$$

$$e^{-i\theta} = \cos\theta - i\sin\theta$$

Adding these equations gives

$$2 \cos \theta = e^{i\theta} + e^{-i\theta}$$

or, $$\cos \theta = \tfrac{1}{2}(e^{i\theta} + e^{-i\theta}) = \cosh i\theta \qquad (3)$$

Subtraction gives

$$2i \sin \theta = e^{i\theta} - e^{-i\theta}$$

or, $$i \sin \theta = \tfrac{1}{2}(e^{i\theta} - e^{-i\theta}) = \sinh i\theta \qquad (4)$$

Equations (3) and (4) provide a justification for *Osborn's rule* (a means of obtaining identities between hyperbolic functions from corresponding trigonometric identities): In any identity connecting the circular functions, replace every circular function by the corresponding hyperbolic function and change the sign of every product, or implied product, of two sines.

1.2.9 *Worked examples*

1. The complex variables z and w are related by the equation $w = (2z + i)/(3 + z)$. Find in terms of x and y the real and imaginary parts of w. Hence find the locus of the point P representing z on the Argand diagram if
(a) w is real,
(b) w is purely imaginary.

Solution. If $z = x + iy$, let $w = u + iv$.

Then $$u + iv = \frac{2(x + iy) + i}{3 + x + iy} = \frac{(2x + i(2y + 1))(3 + x - iy)}{(3 + x)^2 + y^2}$$

Equating real and imaginary parts gives

$$u = \frac{2x^2 + 2y^2 + 6x + y}{(3 + x)^2 + y^2}, \qquad v = \frac{x + 6y + 3}{(3 + x)^2 + y^2}$$

(a) When w is real, $v = 0$
Thus $x + 6y + 3 = 0$.
Locus of P is thus a straight line of slope $-\tfrac{1}{6}$ passing through the point $-\tfrac{1}{2}i$ on the Argand diagram.

(b) When w is purely imaginary, $u = 0$.
Thus $$2x^2 + 2y^2 + 6x + y = 0$$
that is $$(x + \tfrac{3}{2})^2 + (y + \tfrac{1}{4})^2 = \tfrac{37}{16}$$
Locus of P is thus a circle of centre $-\tfrac{3}{2} - \tfrac{1}{4}i$ and radius $\sqrt{(37)}/4$.

2. The point P_0, representing the complex number z, moves anti-clockwise round the unit circle $|z| = 1$ in the Argand diagram, starting from the point $z = 1$. Find the locus of the point P which represents each of the following complex numbers in turn

(a) $3z^2$

(b) $\dfrac{1}{z}$

(c) $2z + \dfrac{1}{z}$

Solution. The locus of point P_0 is given in parametric form by the equations

$x_0 = \cos \theta$ and $y_0 = \sin \theta$, $\qquad 0 \leqslant \theta < 2\pi$, where $z = x_0 + iy_0$ (see figure 1.8)

(a)   If P has coordinates (u, v) then

$$u + iv = 3z^2 = 3(\cos \theta + i \sin \theta)^2$$
$$= 3 \cos 2\theta + i\, 3 \sin 2\theta$$

Hence the parametric equations of P are

$$u = 3 \cos 2\theta, v = 3 \sin 2\theta, 0 \leqslant \theta < 2\pi$$

θ can be eliminated from these equations to give $u^2 + v^2 = 9$, but note that whilst P_0 describes the unit circle once only in an anti-clockwise direction (θ increasing from 0 to 2π), P will describe a circle of radius 3 twice (2θ increasing from 0 to 4π).

(b)   If P has coordinates (u, v) then

$$u + iv = \frac{1}{z} = \frac{1}{\cos \theta + i \sin \theta} = \cos \theta - i \sin \theta$$

The parametric equations of P are thus

$$u = \cos \theta = \cos (-\theta) \quad \text{and} \quad v = -\sin \theta = \sin (-\theta) \cdot$$

In this case P also describes the unit circle but in a clockwise sense starting from $z = 1$ (θ decreasing from 0 to -2π).

(c)   If P has coordinates (u, v) then

$$u + iv = 2z + \frac{1}{z} = 2(\cos \theta + i \sin \theta) + \frac{1}{\cos \theta + i \sin \theta}$$

This gives parametric equations

$$u = 3 \cos \theta \quad \text{and} \quad v = \sin \theta$$

θ can be eliminated from these equations to give the equation of the ellipse $(u^2/3^2) + (v^2/1^2) = 1$.

As P_0 describes the unit circle in an anti-clockwise sense starting from $z = 1$, P will trace out the above ellipse in an anti-clockwise sense starting from $z = 3$.

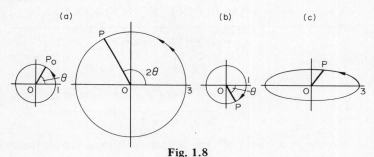

Fig. 1.8

3. Find the sum to $n + 1$ terms of the series

$$1 + \frac{1}{3} \cos \theta + \frac{1}{9} \cos 2\theta + \cdots + \frac{1}{3^n} \cos n\theta$$

By letting $n \to \infty$ deduce the sum to infinity of this series.

Solution

Let
$$C_n = 1 + \frac{1}{3} \cos \theta + \frac{1}{9} \cos 2\theta + \cdots + \frac{1}{3^n} \cos n\theta$$

and
$$S_n = \frac{1}{3} \sin \theta + \frac{1}{9} \sin 2\theta + \cdots + \frac{1}{3^n} \sin n\theta$$

Then
$$C_n + i S_n = 1 + \frac{1}{3} (\cos \theta + i \sin \theta) + \frac{1}{9} (\cos 2\theta + i \sin 2\theta) + \cdots$$
$$+ \frac{1}{3^n} (\cos n\theta + i \sin n\theta)$$

If Z denotes $\cos \theta + i \sin \theta$ then, by De Moivre's theorem

$$C_n + i S_n = 1 + \frac{1}{3} Z + \frac{1}{9} Z^2 + \cdots + \frac{1}{3^n} Z^n$$

This is a geometric progression with common ratio $Z/3$.
Hence

$$C_n + i S_n = \frac{1 - (Z/3)^{n+1}}{1 - Z/3} = \frac{3 - \frac{1}{3^n}\{\cos(n+1)\theta + i \sin(n+1)\theta\}}{3 - \cos\theta - i \sin\theta}$$

C_n is thus given as the real part of this expression

$$C_n = \frac{3(3 - \cos\theta) - \frac{1}{3^n}[\cos(n+1)\theta](3 - \cos\theta) - \sin\theta . \sin(n+1)\theta}{(3 - \cos\theta)^2 + \sin^2\theta}$$

Simplifying this gives

$$C_n = \frac{9 - 3\cos\theta - \frac{1}{3^n}\{3\cos(n+1)\theta - \cos n\theta\}}{10 - 6\cos\theta}$$

In the limit as $n \to \infty$ we have $1/3^n \to 0$. Thus the sum to infinity of the series is

$$C = \frac{9 - 3\cos\theta}{10 - 6\cos\theta}$$

Exercises

1. If the real part of $(z + 4)/(2z + i)$ is equal to $\frac{1}{2}$, prove that the point z lies on a certain straight line in the Argand diagram.

2. The points representing z_1 and z_2 on the Argand diagram form, together with the origin, the vertices of an equilateral triangle. Show that,

$$z_1^2 - z_1 z_2 + z_2^2 = 0$$

3. The point z describes an anti-clockwise unit circle, centre the origin, on the Argand diagram. Find the loci of the points representing

    (a) $2z^3$, (b) $z + \frac{1}{z}$, (c) $1 + z$, (d) $\frac{1}{z^2}$

4. Find the values of p if the complex number $(1 + i)/(2 + ip) + (2 + 3i)/(3 + i)$ lies on a line making an angle $\pi/4$ with the positive real axis.

5. Find the sum of the series

    $$\cos^2\theta + 2\cos^2\theta \cos 2\theta + 4\cos^3\theta \cos 3\theta + \cdots + 2^{n-1}\cos^n\theta \cos n\theta.$$

6. If z_1 and z_2 are any complex numbers, prove that $|z_1| \sim |z_2| \leqslant |z_1 + z_2| \leqslant |z_1| + |z_2|$, where $a \sim b$ denotes the absolute value of the magnitude of the difference between a and b. Under what circumstances will equality hold? Give an

interpretation of these results in terms of the Argand diagram. *Note:* the inequality $|z_1 + z_2| \leqslant |z_1| + |z_2|$ is known as the 'triangle inequality'.

1.3 Computing with numbers

1.3.1 *Integer computation*

The usual form of expression when performing integer calculations by hand is *decimal notation,* in which there are 10 digits 0, 1, 2, 3, . . ., 9. The prevalence of this notation is closely related to the fact that man has ten fingers. The computer, being an electronic device, does not have fingers, and the preferred form for integer computation is *binary notation.* Here there are only 2 digits, 1 or 0, corresponding to the presence or absence of an electric pulse. In binary notation the successive digits represent $2^n, 2^{n-1}, \ldots, 2^2, 2^1, 2^0 = 1$. For example the binary

$$101011 = 1 \times 2^5 + 1 \times 2^3 + 1 \times 2 + 1$$

represents the same integer as does the decimal 43. This example shows that the number of digits in a binary expression will nearly always exceed the number of digits in the corresponding decimal; with most computers there is a restriction (the word length of the machine) on the number of binary digits which can be stored in one location as one number.

When performing arithmetic operations with integers the computer stores them in binary notation and performs the calculations in this form. Multiplication is particularly simple since it involves nothing more than addition together with a translation of digits. The results obtained by the computer using integer arithmetic will always be absolutely precise subject to the requirement that at no stage of the calculation is the capacity of the machine exceeded. For example a typical computer with 24 bit (or binary digit) word length could store and calculate with integers in the range $-8,388,607$ to $+8,338,607$, the first bit being used to represent a $+$ or $-$ sign and the remaining 23 bits to represent any natural number up to $2^{23} - 1$. If at any stage of the calculation this range is exceeded the machine will 'overflow' and an error will result.

Apart from overflow the only other source of error when performing integer arithmetic occurs in the process of division. If the division is exact the correct answer is of course produced, but if it is not exact the computer will completely ignore the remainder. This can lead to false answers when performing compound calculations even when the final answer should be an integer. For example $6 \times 4 \div 3 = 8$, but a computer asked to calculate in integer arithmetic $6 \times (4/3)$ will produce the answer 6 although producing an answer 8 for $(6 \times 4)/3$.

1.3.2 *Real-number computation*

Unlike integers, real numbers cannot generally be stored exactly in the computer, because of the limitations of a binary notation with a finite number of digits. This is true both for irrational and for rational numbers since, unless the rational is one whose denominator is of the form 2^n, it will have no exact finite expression in binary notation. For example $\frac{1}{5}$ is 0.2 in decimal notation but becomes the repeating binary 0.001100110011 . . ., where the successive digits after the point correspond to $\frac{1}{2}, \frac{1}{4}, \frac{1}{8}, \ldots, 2^{-n}$. Whereas there are infinitely many real numbers, the computer is only able to deal with a finite number of approximations to these numbers. In certain types of calculations the errors in these approximations can lead to substantial errors in the final answer. To see how to minimise these errors it is necessary to consider in rather more detail just how real numbers are handled by the computer.

Floating-point numbers. Most computers store real numbers in so-called 'floating-point' form. This form allows them to handle numbers over a very wide range but at the cost of a slight loss in accuracy. In floating-point form the number is expressed as $a \times 2^b$ where a (the argument) is a binary fraction of the form ±0.1 . . . and b is a binary integer exponent. The number of bits available for storing a and b will vary from machine to machine. In a typical computer using 2 words of 24 bits for storing floating-point numbers, 39 bits might be devoted to storing the argument and sign, and 9 to storing the exponent. In this case the computer could store real numbers in the range -2^{256} to $+2^{256}$ with an accuracy of 37 significant binary digits. In decimal terms this is a range of approximately -10^{76} to 10^{76} with an accuracy of about 11 significant figures. A different computer with a shorter word length would either have to restrict the range of possible numbers, or reduce the accuracy, or both. An additional facility available with some computers is 'double precision' numbers. In this an extra word is devoted to storing the argument of the real number resulting in a considerable increase in the accuracy of the approximation; as a penalty for this added accuracy the computer requires more memory space for storing the numbers and more time to perform the calculations.

Errors in floating-point arithmetic. It is important to realise that the fact that a computer can store approximations to real numbers in floating point form with an accuracy of, say, 11 significant figures does not mean that the answer finally produced at the end of the calculation will have the same degree of accuracy. To illustrate the way in which errors are propagated we will consider the results obtained when performing a few simple calculations on a simple computer with a 16 bit word length. Suppose 11 bits of this word correspond to the argument and 5 to the exponent. In theory this computer is able to handle real numbers in the range -2^{16} to 2^{16} with an accuracy of 10 binary digits. In decimal terms this corresponds to approximately -10^5 to 10^5 with an accuracy of 3 significant figures.

Example 1. Addition of small numbers to a larger number.
Suppose we attempt to start with 64 and add 0.2 to this 100 times. The exact answer is, of course, 84. Now consider the calculation as performed by our simple computer:

$64 = 2^6$ is stored as $+0.1 \times 2^7$ (the argument being given here in binary form)

0.2 becomes in binary notation 0.001100110011 . . . and is stored as $+.1100110011 \times 2^{-2}$.

Before performing the addition these must be converted to a form in which both numbers have the same exponent. Effectively this gives:

$$+1000000.000$$

and $+$ 0.0011001100

In performing the first addition the computer is only able to store a sign and ten digits and consequently the result is 1000000.001 (assuming that the computer simply truncates). The equivalent rounding off will occur on each subsequent addition, the final answer produced in binary form being 1001100.100. Expressed as a decimal this is 76.5 rather than the expected answer of 84.0. The final answer is thus only accurate to one significant figure and contains an error of about 10 per cent.

In this case the error could have been almost completely avoided if the calculation had been performed in a different order, first adding 0.2 to itself 100 times and finally adding this answer to 64; this procedure would have avoided the basic cause of the error which was the addition of a small number to a large one.

Example 2. Subtraction of two numbers of similar size.
Suppose we attempt: $73.2 - 73.0$, with the simple computer.

73.2 in binary form is: 1001001.00110011 . . . but as only 10 digits can be stored this is rounded to 1001001.001 by the computer. Clearly the subtraction will give the answer 0.001 or, in decimal form, 0.125.

In this case we have an absolute error of 0.075 which is small when compared with the original numbers but which represents no less than $37\frac{1}{2}$ per cent of the correct answer. This kind of error is less easily eliminated than that of the previous calculation. It can be minimised by using double precision arithmetic or it may be possible to re-organise the calculation and so avoid this subtraction; this is illustrated in the following example.

Example 3. Solution of a quadratic equation, $ax^2 + bx + c = 0$.
Suppose the problem is to solve $8x^2 - 1601x + 200 = 0$. The exact roots are
200 and $\frac{1}{8}$.

The most obvious solution method is to use the formulae

$$x_1 = \frac{1601 + \sqrt{[(1601)^2 - 6400]}}{16}$$

and
$$x_2 = \frac{1601 - \sqrt{[(1601)^2 - 6400]}}{16}$$

The exact value of $\sqrt{[(1601)^2 - 6400]}$ is 1599, but our simple computer with
10 binary digit accuracy will store both this number and 1601 as equivalent to
1600. Hence the answers it would produce are: $x_1 = 200, x_2 = 0$.

The first of these is of course accurate to 3 significant figures; the second
(since it involved the subtraction of two nearly equal numbers) is very inaccurate.
An alternative procedure to avoid this source of inaccuracy is: first calculate x_1
as before; then use the 'product of roots' property of a quadratic equation

$$x_1 x_2 = \frac{c}{a} = \frac{200}{8} = 25$$

From this $x_2 = 25/x_1 = 25/200$ can be calculated with the same degree of
accuracy as x_1.

1.3.3 *Complex-number computations*

A normal digital computer is designed to perform real number computations
rather than complex-number computations. The FORTRAN language does in
fact make provision for storing and calculating with complex numbers but the
ALGOL language does not. When complex numbers are used their real and
imaginary parts can be stored as an ordered pair of real numbers, and subroutines
written to perform the operations of addition, subtraction, multiplication and
division of these ordered pairs. These subroutines will incorporate the definitions
given in section 1.2 (which involve nothing more than arithmetic operations with
real numbers). Whether this complex arithmetic is organised automatically by
the compiler (as in FORTRAN), or by subroutines as described above, the
essential processes will be the same. This means that to perform a computation
with complex numbers will require more computer storage space and considerably
more time than to perform the corresponding calculation with real numbers. If it
is possible to re-organise a problem so as to avoid the use of complex numbers
this will generally result in a worthwhile increase in efficiency.

Exercises

1. Express 0.1 in binary notation.

   It is required to use a computer to calculate the squares of numbers between 1.0 and 2.0 at intervals of 0.1. The program for this uses the following procedure:

   (1) Start with $x = 0.9$
   (2) Add 0.1 to x
   (3) Calculate x^2
   (4) Print x^2
   (5) Stop if $x = 2.0$ otherwise return to (2)

   The computer fails to stop after performing the required 10 calculations. Why?

2. The simple 16 bit computer described in section 1.3.2 is used to compute

   (a) 16.0×16.1
   (b) $16.0 + 16.1$
   (c) $16.1 - 16.0$
   (d) $\dfrac{128.1}{16.1 - 16.0}$

   Find the error in each computation and express this as a percentage of the correct answer.

3. It is required to calculate

   $$S = 128 + 64 + 16 + 8 + 4 + 2 + 1 + \tfrac{1}{2} + \tfrac{3}{4} + \tfrac{3}{16} + \tfrac{3}{64}$$

   How should this computation be arranged in order to minimise the error produced? If the calculation is performed by the 16 bit computer of section 1.3.2 determine the error produced when S is calculated (a) directly, (b) in the most accurate way.

NOTES ON CHAPTER 1

1. Definition of the real numbers

There are, essentially, two ways of obtaining a formal definition of the real numbers. We may take the definition of $\sqrt{2}$ as a typical example. First note that since there is no rational solution of the equation $x^2 = 2$ we can divide the rational numbers into two mutually exclusive classes as follows

   L: the class of all rational numbers r such that $r^2 < 2$,

   R: the class of all rational numbers r such that $r^2 > 2$.

This classification of the rational numbers is associated with the particular real number $\sqrt{2}$ in a unique manner, and therefore may be said, in a sense, to *define* that number. In general any such division of the rational numbers into a 'left-hand' class, L, and a 'right-hand' class, R (which does not overlap) is called a *Dedekind section* of the rationals; each section defines a specific real number.

Alternatively we might use rational approximations to $\sqrt{2}$ as a means of defining it. Take, for example, the following two sequences of rationals

$$1, 1.4, 1.41, 1.414, \ldots \qquad \text{and} \qquad 2, 1.5, 1.42, 1.415, \text{etc.}$$

The first sequence approaches $\sqrt{2}$ from below while the second approaches it from above; the number $\sqrt{2}$ itself is specified with increasing accuracy by the sequence of inequalities

$$1 < \sqrt{2} < 2, \quad 1.4 < \sqrt{2} < 1.5, \quad 1.41 < \sqrt{2} < 1.42, \quad \text{and so on.}$$

This gives rise to the general idea of defining a real number by means of a 'nest' of rational intervals; that is to say, a sequence of intervals $a_n \leqslant x \leqslant b_n$ (with rational end-points a_n and b_n) such that each one contains the next in order, and the length $(b_n - a_n)$ becomes arbitrarily small as n increases. A detailed account of the theory of the real numbers and their arithmetic, treated from this point of view, is to be found in R. Courant: *Differential and Integral Calculus,* Vol. II, Blackie. The Dedekind section approach is used in G. H. Hardy: *A Course of Pure Mathematics,* C.U.P.

2. Countability of the rational numbers

Let A and B denote two collections, or *sets,* of any objects whatsoever. A is said to be *equivalent* to B if it is possible to set up a correspondence between the members of the two sets in such a way that, to each object belonging to A there corresponds one and only one object belonging to B, and to each object belonging to B there corresponds one and only one object belonging to A. (Such a correspondence is said to be *one-one.*) It is clear that where finite sets are concerned two sets are equivalent if and only if they each contain the same number of objects. We carry over to infinite sets the inference that 'equivalence' means, in effect, 'having the same number of members'.

The set of all positive integers typifies the smallest kind of infinite set, and any collection of objects which is equivalent to it is said to be *countably,* or *denumerably,* infinite. An infinite set which is not countably infinite is said to be *uncountably infinite*; the members of such a set may be said to be infinitely more numerous than the positive integers.

Now consider the set of all positive rational numbers arranged in accordance with the following rule: p/q precedes m/n if either (i) $p + q < m + n$, or

(ii) $p + q = m + n$ and $p < m$. (p/q and m/n being positive fractions expressed in their lowest terms.) This arrangement makes it clear that the positive rationals constitute a set which is countably infinite:

$$\tfrac{1}{1}, \tfrac{1}{2}, \tfrac{2}{1}, \tfrac{1}{3}, \tfrac{3}{1}, \tfrac{1}{4}, \tfrac{2}{3}, \tfrac{3}{2}, \tfrac{4}{1}, \tfrac{1}{5}, \ldots$$

In contrast, the assumption that the set of all positive real numbers (rational and irrational) can be put into one-one correspondence with the set of all positive integers leads to a contradiction. Since the rationals on their own constitute a countably infinite set we are led to the conclusion that the irrational numbers are actually infinitely more numerous than the rationals.

These considerations stem from a well-developed theory of infinite sets. Most modern texts on analysis contain an account of the essential features of the theory; for the reader who wishes to pursue the matter in more detail there is a comprehensive and reasonably accessible treatment to be found in E. Kamke: *The Theory of Sets,* Dover Publications (distributed in the UK by Constable & Co.).

3. The number e

A detailed discussion of the exponential function, $\exp x$, is given in section 3.7.1. From the initial definition of the function as a power series

$$\exp x = 1 + x + \frac{x^2}{2!} + \frac{x^3}{3!} + \cdots + \frac{x^n}{n!} + \cdots$$

we obtain the number e as the value of that function when $x = 1$

$$e = 1 + 1 + \frac{1}{2!} + \frac{1}{3!} + \cdots + \frac{1}{n!} + \cdots$$

The addition theorem for the exponential function then allows us to show that, for any positive integer n,

$$\exp n = e^n$$

It is easy to deduce that the same result holds if n is replaced by any rational number, $r = p/q$. However, note that while $\exp x$ is defined even when x is irrational, this is not the case for e^x. In fact we can only interpret an expression like $e^{\sqrt 2}$ if we use the relation

$$\exp \sqrt 2 \equiv e^{\sqrt 2}$$

in the sense of a *definition*.

The number e, like $\sqrt 2$, is irrational; its decimal expansion is infinite and non-recurring. However, there is a further classification of the irrational numbers themselves which should be noted here. An *algebraic number* is defined to be any real number which satisfies a polynomial equation of the form

$$a_n x^n + a_{n-1} x^{n-1} + \cdots + a_1 x + a_0 = 0$$

where the coefficients a_k are rational. Clearly, $\sqrt{2}$ is algebraic. The number e, on the other hand, is not a root of any polynomial equation with rational coefficients and is, accordingly, said to be *transcendental*. The transcendental numbers form a set which is uncountably infinite, whereas the algebraic numbers are only countably infinite. In spite of this the transcendental numbers e and π are the only ones which turn up with any frequency in mathematical analysis.

Miscellaneous exercises

1. If $0.3 < a < 0.5$ and $0.1 < b < 0.2$, show that

   (a) $2 < \dfrac{1}{a - b} < 10$ and   (b) $\dfrac{1}{2} < \dfrac{(a+b)^2}{a^2 + b^2} < 5$

2. Show that the error in representing $\dfrac{1357246}{3579468}$ by $\dfrac{13}{35}$ is less than 0.04.

3. If $0 < x < 1$ show that $(1 - \tfrac{1}{2}x - \tfrac{1}{2}x^2)^2 < 1 - x < (1 - \tfrac{1}{2}x)^2$. Hence show that, if $0 < b < a$, the error in taking $a - b^2/(2a)$ as an approximation to $\sqrt{(a^2 - b^2)}$ is positive and less than $b^4/(2a^3)$.

4. If $0 < \beta < \alpha$ show that the error in taking $\tfrac{1}{2}(\alpha + \beta) - \dfrac{(\alpha - \beta)^2}{4(\alpha + \beta)}$ as an approximation to $\sqrt{(\alpha\beta)}$ is positive and less than $\dfrac{(\alpha - \beta)^4}{4(\alpha + \beta)^3}$.

5. Let $a_1, a_2, \ldots, a_n$ be positive numbers which are less than 1. If $s_n = a_1 + a_2 + \cdots + a_n$, prove that

   $$1 - s_n < (1 - a_1)(1 - a_2) \cdots (1 - a_n) < \frac{1}{1 + s_n}$$

   and, if $s_n < 1$,

   $$1 + s_n < (1 + a_1)(1 + a_2) \cdots (1 + a_n) < \frac{1}{1 - s_n}$$

6. Show that, if A, B, C, are real and $A > 0$, then $Ax^2 + 2Bx + C \geqslant 0$ for all real values of x if, and only if, $B^2 - AC \leqslant 0$. Apply this result to the expression

   $$(a_1 x + b_1)^2 + (a_2 x + b_2)^2 + \cdots + (a_n x + b_n)^2$$

and derive the *Cauchy-Schwarz inequality*

$$\left\{ \sum_{i=1}^{n} (a_i b_i) \right\}^2 \leqslant \left\{ \sum_{i=1}^{n} a_i^2 \right\} \left\{ \sum_{i=1}^{n} b_i^2 \right\}$$

7. If $a_1, a_2, \ldots, a_n$ and $b_1, b_2, \ldots, b_n$ are any real numbers obtain the *Minkowski inequality*

$$\left(\sum_{i=1}^{n} (a_i + b_i)^2 \right)^{\frac{1}{2}} \leqslant \left(\sum_{i=1}^{n} a_i^2 \right)^{\frac{1}{2}} + \left(\sum_{i=1}^{n} b_i^2 \right)^{\frac{1}{2}}$$

[Hint: use the fact that $(a_i + b_i)^2 = (a_i + b_i)a_i + (a_i + b_i)b_i$.]

8. Establish whether the following numbers are rational or irrational:

(a) $1 + \sqrt{2} + \sqrt{3}$,   (b) $\sqrt{(7 + \sqrt{7})}$,   (c) $\dfrac{\sqrt{3} + \sqrt{2}}{\sqrt{3} - \sqrt{2}}$,   (d) $\sqrt[3]{3} + \sqrt[3]{2}$.

9. If z_1, z_2, z_3, are any complex numbers such that

$$z_1^2 + z_2^2 + z_3^2 = z_1 z_2 + z_2 z_3 + z_3 z_1$$

show that $|z_2 - z_3| = |z_3 - z_1| = |z_1 - z_2|$

10. Show that for any complex numbers z_1 and z_2 we have

$$|z_1 + z_2|^2 + |z_1 - z_2|^2 = 2|z_1|^2 + 2|z_2|^2$$

Deduce that

$$|\alpha + \sqrt{(\alpha^2 - \beta^2)}| + |\alpha - \sqrt{(\alpha^2 - \beta^2)}| = |\alpha + \beta| + |\alpha - \beta|$$

(where α and β are, in general, complex).

11. If z_1 and z_2 are the roots of the equation $\alpha z^2 + 2\beta z + \gamma = 0$ prove that

$$|z_1| + |z_2| = \frac{1}{|\alpha|} \left\{ |-\beta + \sqrt{(\alpha\gamma)}| + |-\beta - \sqrt{(\alpha\gamma)}| \right\}.$$

12. Show that $|z_1| + |z_2| + \cdots + |z_n| = |z_1 + z_2 + \cdots + z_n|$ if and only if $\arg z_1 = \arg z_2 = \ldots = \arg z_n$.

13. Show that for any pair of complex numbers, z_1 and z_2, we have $(\bar{z}_1 \bar{z}_2) = \bar{z}_1 . \bar{z}_2$. Deduce that $(\bar{z}^n) = (\bar{z})^n$. Hence prove that if z_0 is a complex root of the real polynomial equation

$$a_0 + a_1 x + a_2 x^2 + \cdots + a_n x^n = 0$$

then so also is $\bar{z}_0$.

14. If $z = e^{i\theta}$ show that $\cos \theta$ and $\sin \theta$ may be expressed in terms of z and z^{-1}; More generally, show that $\cos n\theta$ and $\sin n\theta$ may be expressed in terms of z^n and z^{-n}. Hence obtain the result

$$\sin^4 \theta = \tfrac{1}{8}(\cos 4\theta - 4 \cos 2\theta + 3)$$

and use this to evaluate
$$\int_0^{\pi/4} \sin^4 \theta \, d\theta.$$

15. ω is called a *primitive* nth root of 1 if $\omega^n = 1$ and $\omega^m \neq 1$ for each integer m in the range $0 < m < n$ (for example, i is a primitive 4th root of $1; -1$ is a 4th root of 1 but not a primitive 4th root). Show that there are 4 primitive 5th roots of 1 and determine the number of primitive 6th roots of 1. If ω is any primitive nth root of 1 prove that $\{\omega, \omega^2, \omega^3, \ldots, \omega^{n-1}, 1\}$ is a complete set of nth roots of 1.

16. Let a be any fixed complex number and r any fixed positive real number. Find the locus of the point z in the complex plane which satisfies the equation

$$z\bar{z} - a\bar{z} - a\bar{z} = r^2 - |a|^2$$

17. Find the regions of the complex plane for which

$$\left| \frac{z-a}{z+\bar{a}} \right| < 1, \quad = 1, \quad \text{or} \quad > 1$$

where a is a fixed complex number whose real part is positive.

18. Find the equation of the circle described in the complex plane on the join of the points a, b as diameter.

19. Find the equation of the circle through the points $1, i, 1 + i$, and determine its centre and radius.

20. (i) Prove that an equation for a line passing through fixed points z_1 and z_2 is given by $\arg \{(z - z_1)/(z_2 - z_1)\} = 0$.

    (ii) Prove that an equation for a circle passing through fixed points z_1, z_2, and z_3 is given by

$$\left(\frac{z - z_1}{z - z_2}\right) \Big/ \left(\frac{z_3 - z_1}{z_3 - z_2}\right) = \left(\frac{\bar{z} - \bar{z}_1}{\bar{z} - \bar{z}_2}\right) \Big/ \left(\frac{\bar{z}_3 - \bar{z}_1}{\bar{z}_3 - \bar{z}_2}\right)$$

21. If P, Q, R, S are any four points in the complex plane, prove that

$$\text{PS} \cdot \text{QR} \leqslant \text{QS} \cdot \text{RP} + \text{RS} \cdot \text{PQ}$$

22. If ω is a complex cube root of 1 show that

$$(x - u - v)(x - u\omega - v\omega^2)(x - u\omega^2 - v\omega) = x^3 - 3uvx - u^3 - v^3$$

Use this result to solve each of the following equations

(a) $x^3 - 3x - 2 = 0$

(b) $x^6 - 12x^2 - 16 = 0$

2 FUNCTIONS OF A SINGLE REAL VARIABLE

2.1 Limits and continuity

2.1.1 *Functions of a single real variable*

If to each real number x in a certain specified range there corresponds a well-defined number y, then y is said to be a *real-valued function of the real variable x* over that range, and we write $y = f(x)$. The range of values of x for which $f(x)$ is defined is called the *domain of definition* of the function.

Usually we are interested in cases when $f(x)$ is defined for *every* real number x, or else when $f(x)$ is defined for all x in a certain finite interval. In the first place we write

$$y = f(x) \qquad \text{for } -\infty < x < +\infty$$

In the second it is necessary to distinguish between *open* and *closed* intervals†

$$y = f(x) \qquad \text{for } a < x < b \qquad \qquad \text{(open interval)}$$

$$y = f(x) \qquad \text{for } a \leqslant x \leqslant b \qquad \qquad \text{(closed interval)}$$

Sometimes (but not always) a function is defined by a *formula* valid for every x within the domain of definition. On the other hand, it often happens that the formula becomes meaningless for certain values of x. Then it is necessary to complete the definition of the function by assigning specific values to y where necessary.

Example. Consider the following three formulae:

$$f_1(x) = \frac{\sin x}{x} \qquad f_2(x) = \frac{1}{2} \left\{ 1 + \frac{x}{|x|} \right\} \qquad f_3(x) = \sin \frac{1}{x}$$

In each case we have an explicit rule for finding the value of the function

---

† It is sometimes convenient to adopt the following notation:
For the open interval $a < x < b$ we write (a, b);
For the closed interval $a \leqslant x \leqslant b$ we write $[a, b]$.

concerned when the variable x is given any non-zero value. When $x = 0$, however, each of the formulae becomes meaningless. To obtain functions defined
over the whole real axis we would have to specify separately the values $f_1(0)$,
$f_2(0)$, and $f_3(0)$.

2.1.2 Intuitive idea of continuity

At an elementary level a function is usually thought of in terms of a graph, and
concepts such as continuity are assessed on a visual and intuitive basis. Graphs of
the functions $f_1(x)$, $f_2(x)$, and $f_3(x)$ defined in the above example are shown in
figure 2.1. In the case of $f_1(x)$ it is clear that we need to assign the value 1 to the
function when $x = 0$, if we wish to obtain a function which is continuous in the
intuitive sense. This is because if we evaluate the formula $(\sin x)/x$ for smaller and
smaller values of x (both positive and negative) the results obtained approach
more and more closely to unity:

$$1 > f_1(x) > 0.99 \qquad \text{for all } x \text{ in the range } 0.245 > |x| > 0$$

$$1 > f_1(x) > 0.999 \qquad \text{for all } x \text{ in the range } 0.077 > |x| > 0$$

$$1 > f_1(x) > 0.9999 \qquad \text{for all } x \text{ in the range } 0.024 > |x| > 0$$

and so on.

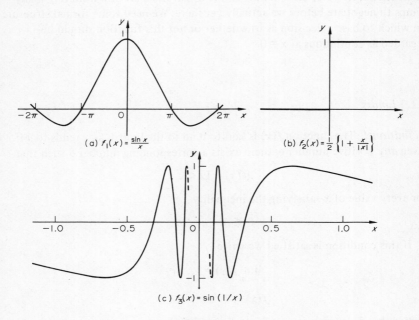

(a) $f_1(x) = \dfrac{\sin x}{x}$ (b) $f_2(x) = \dfrac{1}{2}\left\{1 + \dfrac{x}{|x|}\right\}$

(c) $f_3(x) = \sin(1/x)$

Fig. 2.1

For $f_2(x)$ there is an abrupt jump in the graph at the point $x = 0$ and it is plain that the value assigned to $f_2(0)$ can in no way alter this fact. If we confine ourselves to positive values of x then the value 1 suggests itself as the obvious choice to preserve 'continuity' of the graph at the origin; if we consider only negative values then, equally obviously, we would wish to assign the value 0 to $f_2(x)$ when $x = 0$.

With $f_3(x)$ we are in an even worse case. It is not possible to draw the graph in the neighbourhood of $x = 0$, and no choice of $f_3(0)$ will produce a smooth curve there even if we restrict ourselves wholly to positive values or wholly to negative values of x. In general, when it is not possible to draw the graph of a function then it becomes less easy to decide whether or not it is continuous and if so in what sense. An extreme example is afforded by the following:

Let $f(x) = x$ for all rational values of x, and

$f(x) = 0$ for all irrational values of x

We shall probably decide fairly readily that, at every point other than the origin, $f(x)$ is discontinuous, but we shall be less certain about its behaviour at $x = 0$. Certainly the function gets smaller and smaller with its argument, but, nevertheless, however close we are to the origin there are still infinitely many jumps to negotiate before we actually get there. We need some formal structure on which to base a decision as to whether or not this function should be regarded as continuous at $x = 0$.

2.1.3 *Limits*

Definition 1. The function $f(x)$ is said to tend to the limit L as x tends to a if given *any* positive number ϵ, there exists a corresponding number δ such that

$$|f(x) - L| < \epsilon$$

for every value of x satisfying the inequality

$$0 < |x - a| < \delta$$

If this condition is satisfied we write

$$\lim_{x \to a} f(x) = L, \text{ or}$$

$$f(x) \to L \text{ as } x \to a$$

Notice that δ depends upon ϵ (as well as upon a).

With this formal definition of limit it is easy to confirm that the function defined by

$$f(x) = x \text{ for all rational values of } x,$$

$$f(x) = 0 \text{ for all irrational values of } x,$$

does tend to zero as x tends to zero. In fact, if ϵ is any positive number then for every value of x such that $|x| < \epsilon$ we have

$$|f(x) - 0| = |f(x)| \leqslant |x| < \epsilon$$

It is likewise true that, in the strict sense of the definition given above, we have $\lim_{x \to 0} \dfrac{\sin x}{x} = 1$. In fact a strict proof of this limit depends upon defining $\sin x$ as a power series in x and upon certain properties of power series which will be considered in the next chapter. We may, however, make the result plausible by the following geometric argument. In figure 2.2, OAC is a segment of a circle centre O and radius a, and OAB and OAD are right-angled triangles.

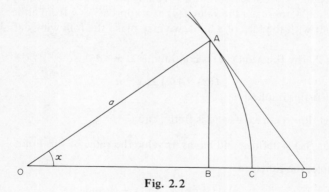

Fig. 2.2

Clearly $\qquad$ Area OAB $<$ Area OAC $<$ Area OAD

That is $\qquad \dfrac{1}{2} a^2 \cos x \sin x < \dfrac{x}{2\pi} \pi a^2 < \dfrac{1}{2} a^2 \tan x$

Dividing throughout by $a^2/2 \sin x$ we obtain

$$\cos x < \frac{x}{\sin x} < \frac{1}{\cos x}$$

that is $\qquad\qquad \cos x < \dfrac{\sin x}{x} < \dfrac{1}{\cos x}$

As $x \to 0$, $\cos x$ and $1/\cos x$ both tend to unity (each is a ratio of quantities which tend to a as $x \to 0$), and since $(\sin x)/x$ is sandwiched between these values it also tends to unity.

Exercise

1. Use the definition of a limit to prove each of the following results:

(i) $\lim\limits_{x \to a} A = A$, for any constant A;

(ii) $\lim\limits_{x \to a} x = a$;

(iii) $\lim\limits_{x \to 1} x(x - 2) = -1$;

(iv) $\lim\limits_{x \to -1} \dfrac{x + 1}{x^2 + 2} = 0$;

(v) $\lim\limits_{\theta \to \alpha} \cos \theta = \cos \alpha$;

(vi) $\lim\limits_{y \to 2} \sqrt{y} = \sqrt{2}$ [Hint: note that $(\sqrt{y} - \sqrt{2})(\sqrt{y} + \sqrt{2}) = y - 2$];

(vii) if $\lim\limits_{x \to a} f(x) = L$ then $\lim\limits_{x \to a} kf(x) = kL$, for any constant k.

2.1.4 *Continuity*

For a function, $f(x)$, to be continuous at some point, say at $x = a$, we require that $f(x)$ should approach the value $f(a)$ as x approaches a from either side. Having dealt with the idea of a limit, we may make the following definition.

Definition 2. The function $f(x)$ is continuous at $x = a$ if

$$f(x) \to f(a) \text{ as } x \to a$$

Note that this implies,

(i) that $\lim\limits_{x \to a} f(x)$ exists and is finite, and

(ii) that $f(a)$ is defined and has as its value the value of this limit.

For example, the function

$$f_1(x) = (\sin x)/x \text{ for } x \neq 0, \text{ and}$$

$$f_1(0) = 1$$

is continuous for all values of x, including $x = 0$.

If we write the definition of a limit directly into the definition of continuity we have the following:

The function, $f(x)$, is continuous at $x = a$ if given any positive ϵ there exists δ such that

$$|f(x) - f(a)| < \epsilon \text{ for all } x \text{ satisfying } |x - a| < \delta$$

Note that we do not have to write $0 < |x - a| < \delta$, thus excluding $x = a$, since clearly the inequality is satisfied there.

2.1.5 *Discontinuous functions*

A function $f(x)$ is said to be *discontinuous* at $x = a$ if either $\lim\limits_{x \to a} f(x)$ does not exist, or if it exists but has a value different from $f(a)$. The second of these cases is rather trivial since the function can be made continuous simply by redefining $f(a)$. (For this reason such a discontinuity is usually described as a *removable* discontinuity.)

Example. If $f(x) = (\sin x)/x$ for $x \neq 0$, and $f(0) = 0$, then $f(x)$ has a removable discontinuity at $x = 0$.

We now consider situations in which $\lim\limits_{x \to a} f(x)$ does not exist. Note first that any point x to *the right of* a can be expressed as

$$x = a + \delta$$

where δ is positive. As δ tends to zero the point $(a + \delta)$ approaches a from the right; if the corresponding values $f(a + \delta)$ tend to a limit then this limit is called the *right-hand limit* of $f(x)$ as x tends to a, and is usually written as $f(a+)$

Definition 3. We say that $f(x)$ tends to L as x tends to a from the right, if, given any strictly positive number ϵ, there exists a corresponding number δ such that

$$|f(x) - \text{L}| < \epsilon$$

for every value of x satisfying the inequality $a < x < a + \delta$.

We write
$$\lim_{x \to a+} f(x) = \text{L}$$

or
$$f(x) \to \text{L} \text{ as } x \to a+$$

If, in addition, this limit is equal to the value, $f(a)$, which the function actually assumes at a, then $f(x)$ is said to be *continuous from the right* at a.

Similarly, any point *to the left* of a can be expressed as

$$x = a - \delta$$

where δ is positive. The limit, if it exists, of $f(a - \delta)$ as δ tends to zero is called the *left-hand limit* of $f(x)$ as x tends to a, and is usually written as $f(a-)$. If this limit does exist and is equal to $f(a)$ then $f(x)$ is said to be *continuous from the left* at a. Clearly $f(x)$ is continuous at a if and only if it is both continuous from the right and continuous from the left there.

Definition 4. If $\lim\limits_{x \to a+} f(x)$ and $\lim\limits_{x \to a-} f(x)$ both exist, but are unequal, then

$f(x)$ is said to have a 'simple discontinuity', or 'jump discontinuity', at $x = a$.
The quantity

$$\left\{ \lim_{x \to a+} f(x) - \lim_{x \to a-} f(x) \right\}$$

is called the value of the jump (or 'saltus') at $x = a$.

Example. If $f_2(x) = \dfrac{1}{2} \left\{ 1 + \dfrac{x}{|x|} \right\}$ for $x \neq 0$ then $f_2(x)$ has a simple discontinuity
at the origin. We have

$$\lim_{x \to 0+} f_2(x) = 1 \quad \text{and} \quad \lim_{x \to 0-} f_2(x) = 0$$

so that the saltus of $f_2(x)$ at $x = 0$ is 1. If we set $f_2(0) = 1$ then we obtain a
function continuous from the right at the origin; if we set $f_2(0) = 0$ then the
result is a function continuous from the left there.

The function defined by $f_3(x) = \sin(1/x)$ for $x \neq 0$ has a discontinuity at the
origin of an altogether more drastic nature. Neither the right-hand limit nor the
left-hand limit of $f_3(x)$ as x tends to 0 is well defined. Hence, the function
cannot be continuous from the right nor from the left. It is said to have a
discontinuity of the *second* kind at $x = 0$.

2.2 Properties of continuous functions

2.2.1 *Theorem 1*
If, as $x \to a$, $f(x) \to L_1$ and $g(x) \to L_2$, then

   (i) $f(x) + g(x) \to L_1 + L_2$,

  (ii) $f(x) - g(x) \to L_1 - L_2$,

 (iii) $f(x) \times g(x) \to L_1 \times L_2$, and

 (iv) $f(x)/g(x) \to L_1/L_2$ provided $L_2 \neq 0$.

The four proofs are similar, although those for (iii) and (iv) are somewhat
more complicated than those for (i) and (ii). We shall prove proposition (i) as a
specimen.

Given $\epsilon > 0$, we wish to find δ such that $|[f(x) + g(x)] - (L_1 + L_2)| < \epsilon$ for
all $|x - a| < \delta$. Since $f(x) \to L_1$ and $g(x) \to L_2$ we know that we can make both
$|f(x) - L_1|$ and $|g(x) - L_2|$ as small as we please. Hence we arrange that $f(x)$ and
$g(x)$ occur only in these combinations. We have

$$|[f(x) + g(x)] - (L_1 + L_2)| = |[f(x) - L_1] + [g(x) - L_2]|$$

$$\leqslant |f(x) - L_1| + |g(x) - L_2|$$

Since $f(x) \to L_1$ as $x \to a$, and $\frac{1}{2}\epsilon$ is positive there exists δ_1 such that

$$|f(x) - L_1| < \tfrac{1}{2}\epsilon \text{ for } 0 < |x - a| < \delta_1$$

Similarly there exists δ_2 such that

$$|f(x) - L_2| < \tfrac{1}{2}\epsilon \text{ for } 0 < |x - a| < \delta_2$$

Now if we let δ represent the smaller of the two numbers δ_1 and δ_2, then for all x satisfying $0 < |x - a| < \delta$ both the previous restrictions on x are satisfied and hence the inequalities on $f(x)$ and $g(x)$ hold. It follows that

$$|f(x) - L_1| + |g(x) - L_2| < \epsilon$$

As an immediate consequence of this theorem we have the following result:

The sum, difference, and product of two continuous functions are themselves continuous. The quotient of two continuous functions is continuous at every point at which the denominator does not vanish.

2.2.2 *Continuity in an interval*

Up to now we have considered continuity as a *local* property of a function. In fact it is often more important to deal with the entire domain of definition. Accordingly we extend the definition of continuity as follows:

Definition 5. A function $f(x)$ is said to be continuous in the *open* interval, $a < x < b$, if it is continuous at each point in that interval. If, in addition, it is continuous from the right at a and from the left at b then it is said to be continuous on the *closed* interval $a \leqslant x \leqslant b$.

Now suppose that $f(x)$ is continuous on $a \leqslant x \leqslant b$ and that its functional values $y = f(x)$ lie in the interval $\alpha \leqslant y \leqslant \beta$. If $g(y)$ is some continuous function of y on this interval then we would expect that the function $g[f(x)]$ is continuous in x on $a \leqslant x \leqslant b$. That this is, in fact, the case is a simple consequence of the following theorem:

Theorem 2. If
$$f(x) \to b \text{ as } x \to a \text{ and}$$
$$g(y) \to L \text{ as } y \to b, \text{ then}$$
$$g[f(x)] \to L \text{ as } x \to a.$$

Proof. Given $\epsilon > 0$ there exists δ_1 such that

$$|g[f(x)] - L| < \epsilon \text{ for all } |f(x) - b| < \delta_1$$

since $g \to$ L as its argument tends to b. But since also $f(x) \to b$ as $x \to a$ and $\delta_1 > 0$, there exists δ_2 such that

$$|f(x) - b| < \delta_1 \quad \text{for all} \ \ 0 < |x - a| < \delta_2$$

Hence, for all $0 < |x - a| < \delta_2$,

$$|g[f(x)] - L| < \epsilon, \text{ and hence}$$

$$g[f(x)] \to \text{L as } x \to a$$

Exercises

1. State for which values of its argument each of the following functions is continuous:

   (i) $f(x) = \cos(1/x)$;   (ii) $f(x) = x \sin(1/x)$ for $x \neq 0$, $f(0) = 1$;

   (iii) $f(x) = x \cos(1/x)$ for $x \neq 0$, $f(0) = 0$;

   (iv) $f(x) = (x - \pi) \cot(x - \pi)$ for $x \neq n\pi$, $f(n\pi) = 1$, for all integers n;

   (v) $f(x) = 3 - |x|$;   (vi) $f(x) = \sqrt{x}$;

   (vii) $f(x) = \sqrt{x}$ for $x \geqslant 0$, and $f(x) = \sin x$ for $x < 0$.

2. (i) If $f(x)$ is continuous at $x = a$ and if $f(a) < 0$, show that there is an interval, centred on a, throughout which $f(x) < 0$.

   (ii) Given that $f(x)$ is continuous at $x = a$ and is such that for any $\delta > 0$ there exists at least one value of x such that $|f(x)| < \delta$ and $|x - a| < \delta$, show that $f(a) = 0$.

*2.2.3 *The bounds of a continuous function*

For functions in general (whether continuous or not) the following definitions apply:

   (i) If, for some finite number M we have $f(x) \leqslant M$ for all x in a certain range then $f(x)$ is said to be *bounded above* over that range. The *smallest* number M such that $f(x) \leqslant M$ for all such x is said to be the *least upper bound* of $f(x)$ in that range. We write

$$M = \text{l.u.b.} \ f(x) \qquad \text{or} \qquad M = \text{sup.} \ f(x)$$

   (ii) If, for some finite number m we have $f(x) \geqslant m$ for all x in a certain range then $f(x)$ is said to be *bounded below* over that range. The *largest* number m such that $f(x) \geqslant m$ for all such x is said to be the *greatest lower bound* of $f(x)$ in that range. We write

$$m = \text{g.l.b.} \ f(x) \qquad \text{or} \qquad m = \text{inf.} \ f(x)$$

It is sometimes convenient to specify directly the range of values of x over which the bounds are taken. Thus we may write,

$$M = \underset{a \leqslant x \leqslant b}{\text{l.u.b.}} f(x) \quad \text{or} \quad m = \underset{a \leqslant x \leqslant b}{\text{inf.}} f(x)$$

(iii) A function $f(x)$ which is both bounded above and bounded below over a given range is said to be a *bounded* function in that range. This means that we can always find a finite positive number K such that

$$|f(x)| \leqslant K$$

for all values of x concerned.

Then for *continuous* functions defined on *closed* intervals the following very important results hold:

Theorem 3. If $f(x)$ is defined and continuous for all x in a finite, closed, interval, $a \leqslant x \leqslant b$, then $f(x)$ is necessarily bounded in that interval.

Theorem 4. Let $f(x)$ be defined and continuous on a finite, closed, interval $a \leqslant x \leqslant b$, and let m and M denote respectively its greater lower bound and its least upper bound on that interval. Then,

(a)   there exist numbers x_1 and x_2 in $a \leqslant x \leqslant b$ such that

$$f(x_1) = m \text{ and } f(x_2) = M$$

(b)   if c is any number lying between m and M then there is at least one value of x in $a < x < b$ for which $f(x) = c$

Briefly we may say that a function which is continuous in a *closed* interval attains a maximum value and a minimum value, and all values in between. Although to prove what we say would demand a more fundamental analysis of the real-number system than we can encompass in this book, the results are at least very plausible geometrically. For a full discussion of these and allied points the reader is referred to G. H. Hardy: *A Course of Pure Mathematics*, C.U.P.

Examples
1. The function $f(x) = 1/x$ is continuous on the *open* interval $0 < x < 1$ and is bounded below there; for we have $1/x > 1$ throughout the interval. But there is no number M which is such that $1/x \leqslant M$ for all x in $0 < x < 1$. The function is said to be *unbounded* in the neighbourhood of the origin. This example shows that 'closed' is necessary in theorem 3.

2. If $f(x) = e^{-x} \sin(1/x)$ for $0 < x \leqslant b$, and $f(0) = 0$, then $f(x)$ is bounded in $0 \leqslant x \leqslant b$, and its least upper bound is unity. But nowhere is the function equal to unity in this interval. That is, there is no x_2 such that

$$0 \leqslant x_2 \leqslant b, \text{ and } f(x) \leqslant f(x_2) \text{ for all } 0 \leqslant x \leqslant b$$

The function is, of course, discontinuous at one end of the interval (figure 2.3).

3. Suppose that $f(x)$ is defined by

$$f(x) = 1 \qquad \text{for } x \leqslant 0$$
$$f(x) = x \qquad \text{for } 0 < x < 1$$
$$f(x) = 0 \qquad \text{for } x \geqslant 1 \quad \text{(figure 2.4)}$$

Then $f(x)$ is bounded on the closed interval $0 \leqslant x \leqslant 1$, has a maximum value 1, a minimum value 0, and assumes every value between 0 and 1 on this interval. Nevertheless it is not continuous there (that is the intermediate value property is *not* sufficient for continuity).

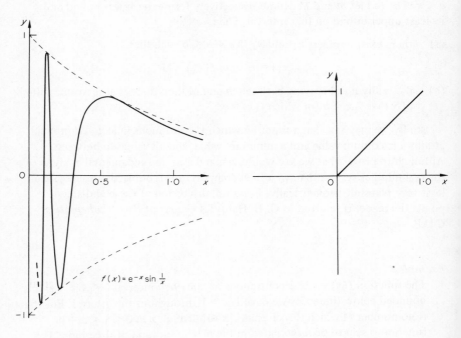

$$f(x) = e^{-x} \sin \frac{1}{x}$$

Fig. 2.3   Fig. 2.4

*2.2.4 *Uniform continuity*

Definition 6. A function $f(x)$ is said to be *uniformly* continuous on the interval $a \leqslant x \leqslant b$ when the following criterion is satisfied: given any positive number ϵ there exists a corresponding positive number δ such that
$$|f(x_1) - f(x_2)| < \epsilon$$
for *any* pair of points x_1, x_2, in the interval $a \leqslant x \leqslant b$ whose distance apart, $|x_1 - x_2|$, is less than δ.

Clearly, if $f(x)$ is uniformly continuous on $a \leqslant x \leqslant b$ then it is certainly continuous on that interval in the ordinary sense, that is continuous at each point of $a \leqslant x \leqslant b$. What is not so obvious is that every function continuous on a *closed* interval is necessarily uniformly continuous there — indeed, the proof is far from trivial, and we shall not attempt it here. The important thing to notice is that the fact that the interval is a closed one is, once again, of crucial importance.

Consider, for example, the function $f(x) = e^{-x} \sin (1/x)$. (See figure 2.3) This is continuous in the open interval $0 < x < 1$, but no choice of value for $f(0)$ can make it continuous in the closed interval $0 \leqslant x \leqslant 1$. Note also that we have
$$\sin\frac{1}{x} = +1 \text{ when } x = \frac{2}{5\pi}, \frac{2}{9\pi}, \frac{2}{13\pi}, \dots$$
$$\sin\frac{1}{x} = -1 \text{ when } x = \frac{2}{3\pi}, \frac{2}{7\pi}, \frac{2}{11\pi}, \dots$$
It follows at once that given any number $\delta > 0$, however small, we can always find points x_1, x_2, in $0 < x < 1$ such that
$$|x_1 - x_2| < \delta \text{ but } |f(x_1) - f(x_2)| = e^{-x_1} + e^{-x_2} > 2/e$$
Thus although $f(x)$ is continuous on the open interval $0 < x < 1$ the condition for uniform continuity is not fulfilled there.

Exercises
1. Using the fact that $\lim_{x \to 0} \dfrac{\sin x}{x} = 1$, establish the following results:

(a) $\lim_{x \to 0} \dfrac{\tan x}{x} = 1$, (b) $\lim_{x \to 0} \dfrac{1 - \cos x}{x} = 0$, (c) $\lim_{x \to 0} \dfrac{1 - \cos x}{x^2} = \dfrac{1}{2}$.

2. Sketch the graphs of the following functions in the neighbourhood of the origin. Where possible complete the definition at $x = 0$ to give a continuous function there.

(a) $x \sin \dfrac{1}{x}$ (b) $x^2 \sin \dfrac{1}{x}$

(c) $(1 - \cos x)/x^3$ (d) $\sinh x/|x|$

2.3 Differentiation

Figure 2.5 represents the graph of a function $f(x)$, of which we wish to consider the differential coefficient at the point P, where $x = a$.

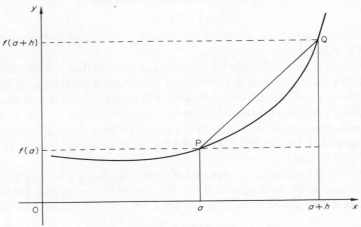

Fig. 2.5

The differential coefficient is the limit of the slope of the chord PQ as Q approaches the fixed point, P. That is, it is the limit of $[f(a + h) - f(a)]/h$ as h tends to zero. Note that the point Q is not restricted to lying to the right of P, but may approach P in any manner as long as it remains on the curve. That is to say, h may tend to zero through positive and negative values. With our precise definition of limiting processes available we may dispense with the graph and make the following definition.

2.3.1 *Definition 7*

If $\lim\limits_{h \to 0} [f(x_0 + h) - f(x_0)]/h$ exists, the function $f(x)$ is said to be 'differentiable' at $x = x_0$. The value of the limit is then called the *differentiation. coefficient'* or '(first) derivative' of $f(x)$ at $x = x_0$ and is denoted by

$$f'(x_0), \text{ or } \frac{\mathrm{d}f(x_0)}{\mathrm{d}x}, \text{ or } \left(\frac{\mathrm{d}f}{\mathrm{d}x}\right)_{x = x_0}$$

The operation of calculating the derivative is called differentiation. Note that the function

$$g(h) = \frac{1}{h} [f(x_0 + h) - f(x_0)]$$

is not defined for $h = 0$, but it is in any case not required, since only $\lim_{h \to 0} g(h)$ is needed.

If there is a second variable, y, dependent on x, so that

$$y = f(x)$$

then $\mathrm{d}y/\mathrm{d}x$ means $f'(x)$, usually with the implication that this exists for some relevant range of values of x. Note that $\mathrm{d}y/\mathrm{d}x$ does not mean $\mathrm{d}y$ divided by $\mathrm{d}x$, but should be read rather as $(\mathrm{d}/\mathrm{d}x)\,y$, that is, as the operation of differentiation with respect to x (denoted by $\mathrm{d}/\mathrm{d}x$) acting upon y.

2.3.2 Some examples of differentiation from first principles

(i) If $f(x) = \sin x$, then

$$\frac{1}{h} [f(x_0 + h) - f(x_0)] = \frac{1}{h} [\sin(x_0 + h) - \sin x_0]$$

$$= \frac{1}{h} 2 \cos\left(x_0 + \frac{1}{2}h\right) \sin\left(\frac{1}{2}h\right)$$

$$= \left[\sin\left(\frac{1}{2}h\right) \Big/ \left(\frac{1}{2}h\right)\right] \cos\left(x_0 + \frac{1}{2}h\right)$$

$$\to 1 \times \cos x_0 \text{ as } h \to 0$$

That is, $f'(x_0)$ exists and is equal to $\cos x_0$. No special value was assumed for x_0, and it follows that $f(x)$ is differentiable for all values of x. We may write

$$f'(x) = \frac{\mathrm{d}}{\mathrm{d}x} (\sin x) = \cos x$$

(ii) We consider whether or not the function defined by

$$f(x) = x^2 \qquad \text{for all rational values of } x, \text{ and}$$

$$f(x) = 0 \qquad \text{for all irrational values of } x$$

is differentiable at the origin. We have

$$g(h) = \frac{1}{h} [f(0 + h) - f(0)] = \begin{cases} h \text{ for all rational values of } h \\ 0 \text{ for all irrational values of } h \end{cases}$$

The function $g(h)$ tends to zero as h tends to zero, and therefore the differential coefficient of $f(x)$ exists at $x = 0$ and $f'(0) = 0$.

(iii) Let $f(x) = x^n$, where n is a positive integer.

Then
$$g(h) = \frac{1}{h} [f(x + h) - f(x)] = \frac{1}{h} [(x + h)^n - x^n]$$

$$= nx^{n-1} + \frac{n(n-1)}{2} hx^{n-2} + \cdots + h^{n-1}$$

$$\rightarrow nx^{n-1} \text{ as } h \rightarrow 0$$

Hence, $f(x)$ is differentiable for all values of x, and

$$f'(x) = nx^{n-1}$$

Exercises
1. Find from first principles the first derivatives of each of the following functions:

   (i) A (any constant);   (ii) $1/x$;   (iii) $\sqrt{x}$;

   (iv) $\cos x$;   (v) $(x - 2)/x^2$.

2. Show that the functions defined below are not differentiable at $x = 0$;

   (i) $f(x) = \begin{cases} x \text{ for all rational values of } x, \\ 0 \text{ for all irrational values of } x. \end{cases}$

   (ii) $g(x) = |x|$

   Are these functions differentiable for other values of x?

3. If $f(x) = x^2 \sin (1/x)$ for $x \neq 0$, and $f(0) = 0$, find $f'(0)$.

2.3.3 *Theorem 5*
Continuity is a prerequisite for differentiability. That is: if $f(x)$ is differentiable at $x = x_0$, then it is also continuous at that point.

Proof. If $f(x)$ is differentiable at $x = x_0$ then

$$\lim_{h \to 0} \frac{1}{h} [f(x_0 + h) - f(x_0)] = f'(x_0), \text{ a finite number}$$

Noting the identity

$$f(x_0 + h) = h \times \frac{1}{h} [f(x_0 + h) - f(x_0)] + f(x_0), \text{ we have}$$

$$\lim_{h \to 0} f(x_0 + h) = 0 \times f'(0) + f(x_0) = f(x_0)$$

Therefore, $f(x)$ is continuous at $x = x_0$. (The reader is invited to prove from first principles that if $\lim_{h \to 0} f(a + h)$ exists then so does $\lim_{x \to a} f(x)$, and that the limits are equal.)

The converse of the theorem is not true. For example, the functions in example (i) of 2.3.2 are both continuous at $x = 0$ although they are not differentiable there.

2.3.4 *Theorem 6*

The following rules may be proved from the definition of differentiation and the rules of combination of limits.

If $f(x)$ and $g(x)$ are differentiable at $x = x_0$, then so are the functions

$$f(x) + g(x), \qquad f(x) - g(x), \qquad f(x) \times g(x) \qquad \text{and} \qquad f(x)/g(x)$$

and their differential coefficients are respectively:

$$f'(x_0) + g'(x_0), \ f'(x_0) - g'(x_0), \ f(x_0)g'(x_0) + f'(x_0)g(x_0) \ \text{and}$$

$$[g(x_0)f'(x_0) - g'(x_0)f(x_0)] / [g(x_0)]^2$$

We assume in the last case that $g(x_0)$ is not zero.

Proof. We shall prove the proposition for

$$\phi(x) = f(x)/g(x), \qquad g(x_0) \neq 0$$

and leave the other cases as exercises for the reader.

$$\frac{1}{h} [\phi(x_0 + h) - \phi(x_0)] = \frac{1}{h} \left[\frac{f(x_0 + h)}{g(x_0 + h)} - \frac{f(x_0)}{g(x_0)} \right]$$

$$= \frac{g(x_0) [f(x_0 + h) - f(x_0)] - f(x_0) [g(x_0 + h) - g(x_0)]}{hg(x_0)g(x_0 + h)}$$

$$\to \frac{g(x_0)f'(x_0) - f(x_0)g'(x_0)}{g(x_0) \times g(x_0)} \text{ as } h \to 0$$

and hence

$$\phi'(x_0) = \lim_{h \to 0} \frac{1}{h} [\phi(x_0 + h) - \phi(x_0)] = \frac{g(x_0)f'(x_0) - f(x_0)g'(x_0)}{[g(x_0)]^2}$$

2.3.5 *Theorem 7* (The derivative of a function of a function.)

Let $y = g(z)$ and $z = f(x)$ so that $y = y(x) = g[f(x)]$. If $f(x)$ is differentiable at $x = x_0$, and $g(z)$ is differentiable at $z = f(x_0)$, then dy/dx exists at $x = x_0$ and is equal to $g'[f(x_0)] f'(x_0)$.

Proof

$$\frac{1}{h}\{y(x_0 + h) - y(x_0)\} = \frac{1}{h}\{g[f(x_0 + h)] - g[f(x_0)]\}$$

$$= \frac{g[f(x_0 + h)] - g[f(x_0)]}{f(x_0 + h) - f(x_0)} \times \frac{f(x_0 + h) - f(x_0)}{h}$$

$f(x)$ is continuous at $x = x_0$, since it is differentiable there, and hence

$$\delta = [f(x_0 + h) - f(x_0)] \rightarrow 0 \quad \text{as} \quad h \rightarrow 0$$

Consequently

$$\frac{g[f(x_0 + h)] - g[f(x_0)]}{f(x_0 + h) - f(x_0)} = \frac{g[f(x_0) + \delta] - g[f(x_0)]}{\delta} \rightarrow g'[f(x_0)]$$

as $h \rightarrow 0$.

Also

$$\frac{1}{h}[f(x_0 + h) - f(x_0)] \rightarrow f'(x_0)$$

Therefore $\left(\dfrac{dy}{dx}\right)_{x = x_0} = \lim_{h \to 0} \dfrac{1}{h}[y(x_0 + h) - y(x_0)] = g'[f(x_0)]f'(x_0)$

Exercises

1. Write down the differential coefficients of the following functions:

   (i) $\sin x / (\cos x)^2$ (ii) $(\tan x)/x$

   (iii) $(1 + x + 2x^2)(1 + 3x^3 + x^4)$ (iv) $(\cos x + 2 \sin x)^{10}$

   (v) $(x + \sin x)/(1 + \cos x)$.

2. Show by induction that the nth derivatives of $\sin x$ and e^{ax} are respectively:

$$\sin(x + n\pi/2) \quad \text{and} \quad a^n e^{ax}$$

2.3.6 Numerical approximations to derivatives

We have seen that sometimes we cannot evaluate a formula $f(x)$ at a particular point $x = x_0$, but that by identifying $f(x_0)$ with $\lim_{x \to x_0} f(x)$ we may approximate the required quantity as closely as we please by evaluating $f(x)$ for x sufficiently close to x_0. A differential coefficient is defined as the limit of a certain function, and clearly we may approximate it numerically by evaluating this function. That is, we may approximate $f'(x_0)$ arbitrarily closely by evaluating

$$\frac{1}{h}[f(x_0 + h) - f(x_0)]$$

for sufficiently small h. For example, if we require the differential coefficient of sin x at, say, $x = 0.5$ radians, we may evaluate

$$g(h) = \frac{1}{h} [\sin (0.5 + h) - \sin (0.5)]$$

The following table shows the value of $g(h)$ for a range of diminishing values of h, taken from four-figure mathematical tables.

h	1.0	0.5	0.2	0.1	0.05	0.02	0.01
$g(h)$	0.5181	0.7242	0.824	0.852	0.866	0.875	0.88

The differential coefficient of sin x is, of course, cos x, and the same table gives the value of cos (0.5) as 0.8776. Initially $g(h)$ becomes closer to the true value as h decreases, but we may note the effect of rounding error as h becomes even smaller. The last entry in the table, $g(0.01)$, has only two significant figures left after the subtraction of sin (0.5) from sin (0.51), and although it is correct to two significant figures it is further away from the four-figure value of cos (0.5) than is the tabulated value of $g(0.02)$. The value of $g(0.001)$ would be calculated as 0.9, which is further away still although it is correct to the one significant figure that remains. In forming an estimate of a derivative of a function represented by experimental data, the random experimental error or 'noise' will have an effect similar to that of the rounding error in the above example, becoming more and more important as the sampling interval decreases. The effect may be lessened by smoothing the data before differentiating. (See chapter 6.)

2.3.7 *Higher derivatives*

If a function $f(x)$ is differentiable in some neighbourhood of a point $x = x_0$; that is to say, for some range of values of x

$$x_0 - d < x < x_0 + d$$

then we may consider differentiating the function $f'(x)$ at $x = x_0$. If $f'(x)$ is differentiable at $x = x_0$ then $f(x)$ is said to be twice differentiable at that point, and the derivative of $f'(x)$ is called the 'second derivative' or $f(x)$ and written

$$f''(x_0) \quad \text{or} \quad \frac{d^2 f(x_0)}{dx^2} \quad \text{or} \quad \left(\frac{d^2 f}{dx^2} \right)_{x = x_0}$$

Note that the existence of $f''(x_0)$ requires the existence of

$$\lim_{h \to 0} \frac{1}{h} [f'(x_0 + h) - f'(x_0)]$$

which means that $f'(x_0 + h)$ must exist for some range of values of h about $h = 0$. Hence the requirement that $f'(x)$ exists in some neighbourhood of x_0.

Higher derivatives are defined similarly; so that, for example, the differential coefficient of $f''(x)$ is the third differential coefficient of $f(x)$ and is written

$$f'''(x) \quad \text{or} \quad \frac{\mathrm{d}^3 f}{\mathrm{d}x^3}$$

After the third derivative the superscript dashes are usually not employed, being replaced by Roman numerals or letters in brackets. For example

$$f^{(vi)}(x) \quad \text{and} \quad f^{(m)}(x)$$

denote the sixth and the mth derivatives respectively.

2.4 Other limiting processes

Before continuing in the next section with the main development of the analysis of functions, we shall discuss certain limiting processes which are used for the first time in that section.

2.4.1 *Unbounded functions*
We need at some stage to formalise the idea of a function becoming indefinitely large as its argument approaches some value, and to provide a convenient notation to express the idea. Being more precise, we might say that the function becomes indefinitely large if it can be made greater than any given number — however large that number may be chosen — and this leads directly to the following definition.

Definition 8. A function $f(x)$, is said to tend to infinity as x tends to a if, given any number C, however large and positive it may be, there exists a corresponding number δ such that

$$f(x) > C$$

for every value of x satisfying

$$0 < |x - a| < \delta$$

We write

$$f(x) \to \infty \quad \text{as} \quad x \to a$$

If we compare this with the definition of a limit in paragraph 2.1.3, we see that it is the same except that the condition

$$|f(x) - L| < \epsilon \qquad [f(x) \text{ arbitrarily close to L}]$$

has been replaced by the condition

$$f(x) > C \qquad [f(x) \text{ arbitrarily large}]$$

As before, x may take values greater than a and values less than a; thus it is necessary that the inequality is satisfied for some range of values of x about the value of a.

The definition of $f(x) \to -\infty$ as $x \to a$ ($f(x)$ tends to minus infinity as x tends to a) is similar, except that the inequality $f(x) > C$ is replaced by the inequality $f(x) < -C$.

As an example we may consider the function

$$f(x) = \frac{1}{|x|} \quad \text{for all } x \neq 0$$

Then $\qquad f(x) > 100 \qquad$ for $0 < |x| < 0.01$,

$\qquad\qquad\quad f(x) > 10\,000 \qquad$ for $0 < |x| < 0.0001$, and in general

$\qquad\qquad\quad f(x) > C \qquad\quad$ for $0 < |x - 0| < \dfrac{1}{|C|}$

Hence, $\qquad f(x) \to \infty \quad$ as $\quad x \to 0$

On the other hand, although the function $f(x) = \dfrac{1}{x}$ is not bounded near $x = 0$

we can neither say $f(x) \to +\infty$ nor $f(x) \to -\infty$ as $x \to 0$. Given any $C > 0$

$$f(x) < C \quad \text{for all } x < 0$$

and hence there is no neighbourhood of zero throughout which $f(x) > C$. Consequently $f(x)$ does not tend to infinity as $x \to 0$. Similarly

$$f(x) > -C \quad \text{for all } x > 0$$

and so $f(x)$ does not tend to minus infinity.

2.4.2 *Arithmetic expressions involving unbounded functions*
The limiting behaviour of a simple arithmetic expression containing unbounded functions is not always simply related to the behaviour of the individual functions. For example, let $f(x) = x^2$. Then

(i) if $g(x) = \dfrac{1}{|x|}$, $\quad f(x)g(x) \to 0$ as $x \to 0$,

(ii) if $g(x) = \dfrac{1}{x^2}$, $\quad f(x)g(x) \to 1$ as $x \to 0$, and

(iii) if $g(x) = \dfrac{1}{|x|^3}$, $\quad f(x)g(x) \to \infty$ as $x \to 0$,

  although in each case $g(x) \to \infty$ and $f(x) \to 0$ as $x \to 0$.

Similar examples, not involving unbounded functions, can arise in considering the limit of $f(x)/g(x)$ when both $f(x)$ and $g(x)$ tend to zero, and this case is included here for convenience.

Cases such as this, when the limiting behaviour cannot be deduced solely from the limiting behaviour of the component functions are called 'indeterminate forms'. The following table shows some of the more important indeterminate forms, together with the result of those combinations which are determinate.

We suppose that $f \rightarrow f_L$ and $g \rightarrow g_L$.

f_L	g_L	$f + g$	$f - g$	$f \times g$	f/g
Finite ($\neq 0$)	0	f_L	f_L	0	$\lvert f/g \rvert \rightarrow \infty$
	$+\infty$	$+\infty$	$-\infty$	$\pm\infty$	0
	$-\infty$	$-\infty$	$+\infty$	$\pm\infty$	0
0	0	0	0	0	Indeterminate
	$+\infty$	$+\infty$	$-\infty$	Indeterminate	0
	$-\infty$	$-\infty$	$+\infty$	Indeterminate	0
∞	0	∞	∞	Indeterminate	$\lvert f/g \rvert \rightarrow \infty$
	$+\infty$	∞	Indeterminate	∞	Indeterminate
	$-\infty$	Indeterminate	∞	$-\infty$	Indeterminate
$-\infty$	0	$-\infty$	$-\infty$	Indeterminate	$\lvert f/g \rvert \rightarrow \infty$
	$+\infty$	Indeterminate	$-\infty$	$-\infty$	Indeterminate
	$-\infty$	$-\infty$	Indeterminate	$+\infty$	Indeterminate

For the evaluation of the indeterminate forms in this table, see section 2.7.

In the other cases quoted, the results are straightforward to prove. For example, suppose that $f(x) \rightarrow +\infty$ and $g(x) \rightarrow 0$ as x tends to a. Then, given any positive number C, however large, we can find a number $\delta > 0$ such that, if $\lvert x - a \rvert < \delta$, then

$$f(x) > 1$$

and

$$\lvert g(x) \rvert < \frac{1}{C}$$

Hence $$\frac{\lvert f(x) \rvert}{\lvert g(x) \rvert} > C \quad \text{for all } x \text{ such that } \lvert x - a \rvert < \delta$$

and so $$\frac{\lvert f(x) \rvert}{\lvert g(x) \rvert} \rightarrow \infty \quad \text{as } x \rightarrow a$$

2.4.3 *Limits as* $x \to \pm\infty$

We are frequently concerned with the behaviour of a physical quantity as the independent variable becomes very large, rather than as it approaches some particular finite value, and we extend our definition of a limit to cover this by replacing in definitions 1 and 8 the condition 'x arbitrarily close to a' by 'x indefinitely large'. This gives us the following definitions of the behaviour of a function as its argument tends to plus or minus infinity.

Definitions 9

(i) $f(x)$ tends to the limit L as x tends to infinity if, given any positive number ϵ, there exists a corresponding number X such that

$$|f(x) - \mathrm{L}| < \epsilon$$

for all x satisfying the inequality $x > \mathrm{X}$.

We write

$$\lim_{x \to \infty} f(x) = \mathrm{L} \text{ or } f(x) \to \mathrm{L} \text{ as } x \to \infty$$

(ii) $f(x)$ tends to infinity (or minus infinity) as x tends to infinity if, given any number C, there exists a corresponding number X such that

$$f(x) > \mathrm{C} \quad (\text{or } f(x) < -\mathrm{C})$$

for all x satisfying the inequality $x > \mathrm{X}$.

We write $f(x) \to \infty$ (or $-\infty$) as $x \to \infty$.

(iii) If the inequality $x > \mathrm{X}$ is replaced by $x < -\mathrm{X}$ in (i) and (ii) we have respectively definitions for $\lim_{x \to -\infty} f(x) = \mathrm{L}$ as $x \to -\infty$ and for

$$f(x) \to \pm\infty \quad \text{as } x \to -\infty$$

Again the rules of combination of limits still hold if either $x \to +\infty$ throughout or $x \to -\infty$ throughout.

Instead of examining the behaviour of $f(x)$ as $x \to \infty$ (or $-\infty$) it is often more convenient to introduce a new variable

$$y = \frac{1}{x}$$

and to consider the behaviour of $f(1/y)$ as $y \to 0$. Note, however, that it then becomes necessary to distinguish between y approaching 0 through *positive* values ($y \to 0+$), and y approaching 0 through *negative* values ($y \to 0-$).

It is a simple matter to show that

$$f(x) \to L \text{ as } x \to \infty \text{ if and only if } f\left(\frac{1}{y}\right) \to L \text{ as } y \to 0+, \text{ and}$$

$$f(x) \to L \text{ as } x \to -\infty \text{ if and only if } f\left(\frac{1}{y}\right) \to L \text{ as } y \to 0-$$

It follows that if $f\left(\dfrac{1}{y}\right) \to L$ as $y \to 0$, then

$$f(x) \to L \text{ as } x \to \infty \text{ and } f(x) \to L \text{ as } x \to -\infty$$

The same considerations apply if L is replaced by $+\infty$ or by $-\infty$.

Example. If $f(x)$ is a rational function, say

$$f(x) = \frac{a_n x^n + a_{n-1} x^{n-1} + \cdots + a_0}{b_m x^m + b_{m-1} x^{m-1} + \cdots + b_0}$$

Then

$$f\left(\frac{1}{y}\right) = \frac{y^m}{y^n} \frac{a_n + a_{n-1}y + a_{n-2}y^2 + \cdots + a_0 y^n}{b_m + b_{m-1}y + \cdots + b_0 y^m}$$

As $y \to 0+$, $y^{m-n} \to 0$ if $m > n$, $y \to 1$ if $m = n$,   and $y \to \infty$ if $m < n$.

Hence: for $m > n$, $f(x) \to 0$ as $x \to \infty$

for $m = n$, $f(x) \to a_n/b_m$ as $x \to \infty$

for $m < n$, $f(x) \to \infty$ as $x \to \infty$

Exercises

1. Discuss the behaviour of the following functions as $x \to 0$ and as $x \to \infty$:

(i) $\sin(1/x)$;   (ii) $1/\sin x$;   (iii) $\log x$;   (iv) $x\,e^x$

2. Use the definition of 'tends to infinity' to obtain the following results:

(i) $1/x \to 0$ as $x \to \infty$;

(ii) $1/|x| \to \infty$ as $x \to 0$;

(iii) $e^{-x} \to 0$ as $x \to \infty$;

(iv) $|\log x| \to \infty$ as $x \to 0+$.

2.5 Rolle's theorem and its applications

We shall concern ourselves next with *Taylor's theorem,* maxima and minima of functions, and *L'Hôpital's rule* for the evaluation of limits; all of these depend upon *Rolle's theorem.*

Ultimately Taylor's theorem leads to the idea, very important from the theoretical point of view, of treating functions as power series. (See chapter 3.) More immediately it can be regarded as providing a justification for one of the fundamental tools of numerical analysis — the approximation of a function by a polynomial.

Having proved Rolle's theorem, we first derive the special case of Taylor's theorem with $n = 1$ (called the *first mean value theorem*) and then develop the general case. A discussion of maxima and minima of a function is closely allied to Rolle's theorem itself, but its full treatment depends upon Taylor's theorem. L'Hôpital's rule is the most important means available for evaluating the limit of a function when the result is not a straightforward consequence of the application of the rules of combination of limits.

2.5.1 *Theorem 8 (Rolle's theorem)*
Let $f(x)$ be a function defined in the range $a \leqslant x \leqslant b$ with the following properties:

(i) $f(x)$ is differentiable in the open interval $a < x < b$,

(ii) $f(x)$ is continuous in the closed interval $a \leqslant x \leqslant b$, and

(iii) $f(a) = f(b)$.

Then there is some value of x in the open interval at which the derivative of the function is zero. That is

$$f'(\xi) = 0 \text{ for some } \xi \text{ such that } a < \xi < b$$

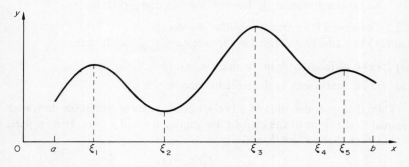

Fig. 2.6

For the function sketched in figure 2.6, the theorem is satisfied with ξ taking any of the values ξ_1, ξ_2, ξ_3, ξ_4 or ξ_5.

Proof. There are three cases to consider.

(i) $f(x)$ is a constant for $a \leqslant x \leqslant b$. Then $f'(\xi) = 0$ for all $a < \xi < b$ and the theorem is trivial.

(ii) There is some point in the interval at which $f(x)$ is greater than the value at the end points. Then (using section 2.2.3 and the continuity of $f(x)$) there exists a number, ξ, satisfying $a < \xi < b$ and such that

$$f(x) \leqslant f(\xi) \text{ for all } a \leqslant x \leqslant b$$

Note that ξ is not an end point since $f(\xi)$ is, by hypothesis, strictly greater than $f(a)$ and $f(b)$. It follows that $f(x)$ is differentiable at $x = \xi$, and we shall show that its derivative is zero there. For $b - \xi > h > 0$, $[f(\xi + h) - f(\xi)] \leqslant 0$ and therefore

$$\lim_{h \to 0+} \frac{1}{h} [f(\xi + h) - f(\xi)] \leqslant 0$$

For $a - \xi < h < 0$, $[f(\xi + h) - f(\xi)]/h \geqslant 0$ and therefore

$$\lim_{h \to 0-} \frac{1}{h} [f(\xi + h) - f(\xi)] \geqslant 0$$

But since $f'(\xi)$ exists, these one-sided limits are equal, and consequently zero. That is $f'(\xi) = 0$.

(iii) If neither (i) nor (ii) is true, then there is some point in the interval at which $f(x)$ is less than the value at the end points. There is, then, some ξ such that $a < \xi < b$, and

$$f(x) \geqslant f(\xi) \text{ for all } a \leqslant x \leqslant b$$

An argument similar to that in (ii) shows that $f'(\xi) = 0$.

2.5.2 Theorem 9 (the first mean value theorem)

Let $f(x)$ be a function defined in the range $a \leqslant x \leqslant b$ such that

(i) $f(x)$ is differentiable in the open interval $a < x < b$, and

(ii) $f(x)$ is continuous in the closed interval $a \leqslant x \leqslant b$.

Then there is some value of x in the open interval at which the derivative is equal to the slope of the straight line joining the end points. That is, there is some ξ such that $a < \xi < b$, and

$$f'(\xi) \equiv \frac{f(b) - f(a)}{b - a}$$

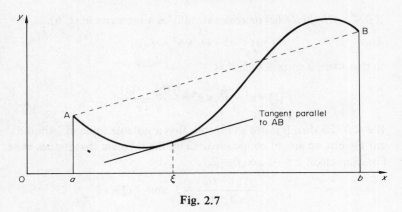

Fig. 2.7

Figure 2.7 makes the theorem plausible, and may suggest how it may be proved from Rolle's theorem. If we consider the difference between the function $f(x)$ and the expression for the straight line we have a function which is zero at both ends of the interval, and to which we may apply Rolle's theorem. Let

$$h(x) = f(x) - \frac{(x-a)}{(b-a)} [f(b) - f(a)] - f(a)$$

Clearly $h(x)$ is differentiable for $a < x < b$, and continuous for $a \leqslant x \leqslant b$. Also $h(a) = h(b) = 0$.

Hence, there exists ξ such that $a < \xi < b$ and $h'(\xi) = 0$.

But $\qquad h'(x) = f'(x) - \dfrac{f(b) - f(a)}{b - a}$, therefore $f'(\xi) = \dfrac{f(b) - f(a)}{b - a}$

The theorem is not much concerned with the value of ξ, but only that it should exist somewhere in the interval. Nevertheless, we can illustrate the theorem with one or two functions for which ξ can readily be found explicitly.

(i) Let $f(x) = \sin x$, $a = 0$ and $b = \pi/2$.

   Then $\qquad \dfrac{f(b) - f(a)}{b - a} = \dfrac{2}{\pi} \simeq 0.6366.$

   Also $f'(x) = \cos x$ and $\cos x = 0.6366$ when $x \simeq 0.8808$. This value of x lies in the range $0 < x < \pi/2$.

(ii) Let $f(x) = x^3$.

   Then $\dfrac{f(b) - f(a)}{b - a} = \dfrac{b^3 - a^3}{b - a} = a^2 + ab + b^2$, and $f'(x) = 3x^2$

If $0 < a < b$ then $f'(x)$ increases steadily as x increases in (a, b).

Also
$$f'(a) < a^2 + ab + b^2 < f'(b)$$

so that there is some ξ such that

$$f'(\xi) = a^2 + ab + b^2 = \frac{f(b) - f(a)}{b - a}$$

If $a < 0 < b$ then it is not so obvious that a suitable value of ξ should exist — but we are, of course, assured by the theorem that it does exist. For example, if $a = -1$ and $b = 2$.

$$\frac{f(b) - f(a)}{b - a} = 3 \quad \text{and} \quad f'(1) = 3$$

If x_1 and x_2 are points such that $a \leqslant x_1 < x_2 \leqslant b$, then the conditions of the theorem are satisfied for the interval $[x_1, x_2]$ and we have

$$\frac{f(x_2) - f(x_1)}{x_2 - x_1} = f'(\xi), \text{ or}$$

$$f(x_2) = f(x_1) + (x_2 - x_1)f'(\xi)$$

Note, however, that all we can say about ξ is that $x_1 < \xi < x_2$: it is not in general a constant in (a, b) and depends on x_1 and x_2.

An immediate consequence is that if $f'(x)$ is zero throughout (a, b) then $f(x)$ is a constant throughout the interval. (The reader should write out the proof of this in detail.) It follows then that if $f'(x) = g'(x)$ for all $a \leqslant x \leqslant b$ then $f(x)$ and $g(x)$ differ only by a constant in that interval. This forms the basis for the concept of an indefinite integral. (See chapter 5.)

2.5.3 Taylor's theorem

If a function is a polynomial in x of degree n, then it may equally well be expressed as a polynomial in $(x - a)$ — where a is any number — so that

$$f(x) = p_0 + p_1(x - a) + \cdots + p_n(x - a)^n$$

Substituting $x = a$ in the expressions for $f(x), f'(x), \ldots$, and so on gives expressions for p_0 to p_n: $p_0 = f(a)$, $p_1 = f'(a)$, $\ldots$, $p_n = f^{(n)}(a)/n!$ so that for any polynomial, and any a

$$f(x) = f(a) + f'(a)(x - a) + \frac{1}{2} f''(a)(x - a)^2 + \cdots + \frac{1}{n!} f^{(n)}(a)(x - a)^n$$

Provided $f(x)$ is differentiable at least n times, the right-hand side of this expression is defined whether or not $f(x)$ is a polynomial, and it provides an obvious choice for a polynomial approximation to the function. If $f(x)$ is not a polynomial the question is not exact, and we are concerned here with the discrepancy between this polynomial approximation and the function itself. Concentrating upon a particular point, say $x = b$, we write

$$f(b) = f(a) + (b - a)f'(a) + \cdots + \frac{1}{n!} (b - a)^n f^{(n)}(a) + R$$

and examine the remainder term R. Taylor's theorem relates the remainder to the $(n + 1)$th derivative of the function. We first define the function

$$R(x) = f(b) - f(x) - (b - x)f'(x) - \cdots - \frac{1}{n!} (b - x)^n f^{(n)}(x)$$

and try to find an expression for the value of

$$R(a) = R$$

The most common form of the remainder term (Lagrange's form) is obtained by constructing the function

$$h(x) = R(x) - \frac{(b - x)^{n + 1}}{(b - a)^{n + 1}} R(a)$$

and applying Rolle's theorem in the interval $a \leqslant x \leqslant b$. This leads to the expression

$$R(a) = \frac{1}{(n + 1)!} f^{(n + 1)}(\xi)(b - a)^{n + 1}$$

for some ξ in the range $a < \xi < b$, and gives the following theorem:

Theorem 10 (Taylor's theorem). If $f(x)$ is differentiable n times in the interval $a \leqslant x \leqslant b$, and if $f^{(n)}(x)$ is

(i) differentiable in $a < x < b$, and

(ii) continuous in $a \leqslant x \leqslant b$,

then there exists ξ in the interval $a < \xi < b$ such that

$$f(b) = f(a) + (b - a)f'(a) + \frac{1}{2} (b - a)^2 f''(a) + \cdots + \frac{1}{n!} (b - a)^n f^{(n)}(a) +$$
$$+ \frac{1}{(n + 1)!} (b - a)^{n + 1} f^{(n + 1)}(\xi) \ \dagger$$

† An alternative form for the remainder term (Cauchy's form) is obtained by applying the first mean value theorem directly to the function $R(x)$ in the interval $a \leqslant x \leqslant b$. This leads to

$$R = \frac{1}{n!} f^{(n + 1)}(\xi) (b - a)(b - \xi)^n$$

which is sometimes more useful than Lagrange's form.

The point b was not a special point in any way, and we may treat it as a variable in this expression. Using the more common symbol x to stand for a variable, we write

$$f(x) = f(a) + (x-a)f'(a) + \frac{1}{2}(x-a)^2 f''(a) + \cdots + \frac{1}{n!}(x-a)^n f^{(n)}(a) +$$
$$+ \frac{1}{(n+1)!}(x-a)^{n+1} f^{(n+1)}(\xi)$$

Notice that the right-hand side of this equation is not a polynomial since all we know about ξ is that it lies between (strictly) a and x, and that it, and hence also the coefficient of x^{n+1}, varies as x varies.

It is convenient sometimes to take as the independent variable the deviation from the base point a. That is, to put h equal to $(x-a)$ and write:

$$f(a+h) = f(a) + hf'(a) + \frac{1}{2}h^2 f''(a) + \cdots + \frac{1}{n!}h^n f^{(n)}(a) +$$
$$+ \frac{1}{(n+1)!}h^{n+1} f^{(n+1)}(\xi)$$

We may illustrate the theorem by considering the expansion about $x = 0$ of the function $f(x) = (1+x)^{-1}$.

Then $$f^{(n)}(x) = (-1)^n n!(1+x)^{-(n+1)}$$

With $x > -1$ and ξ between 0 and x

$$(1+x)^{-1} = 1 - x + x^2 - \cdots + (-1)^n x^n + (-1)^{n+1} x^{n+1}/(1+\xi)^{n+2}$$

In this case we can find an explicit expression for ξ. Multiplying both sides by $(1+x)$

$$1 = 1 + (-1)^n x^n + (-1)^{n+1}(1+x)x^{n+1}/(1+\xi)^{n+2}, \text{ so that}$$
$$\xi = (1+x)^{1/(n+2)} - 1$$

2.5.4 Numerical approximations

The most obvious use of Taylor's theorem is to extrapolate, or predict, the value of a function. If, for example, the position, velocity and acceleration of a point on a line are given, at time $t = 0$, by

$$x = x_0, \quad \dot{x} = v_0 \quad \text{and} \quad \ddot{x} = a_0$$

and if acceleration is known to be constant, then the position at a general time t is

$$x(t) = x_0 + v_0 t + \frac{1}{2}a_0 t^2$$

Clearly this may be obtained readily by successive integrations, but if the acceleration is not constant we may still write — *for each particular value of t*

$$x(t) = x_0 + v_0 t + \frac{1}{2} a_0 t^2 + \frac{1}{6} \dddot{x}(\xi) t^3$$

and if $\dddot{x}$ is known always to be small, then the quadratic expression may be accepted as a sufficiently good approximation for sufficiently small t.

We have emphasised above that the expression is not a cubic function of t, since ξ varies with t and hence $\dddot{x}(\xi)$ is not a constant. The expression, however, may justify the quadratic approximation and — if a bound is known for the third derivative — provide a value for the error involved. Taylor's theorem provides a starting point for polynomial approximations in general. Note, however, that if a polynomial is fitted to a function in some way other than by using the values of derivatives at a single point, then the error involved may exceed the error term given by Taylor's theorem.

Exercises

1. Write out the first five terms, and the general form of the remainder term, of the Taylor expansion about $x = 1$ for each of the following:

   (i) $\sin \pi x$;　　(ii) e^x;　　(iii) $\log x$

2. Use Taylor's theorem to calculate the following correct to 3 decimal places:

   (i) $\sqrt[5]{33}$　(Note that $\sqrt[5]{32} = 2$);

   (ii) $e^{0.2}$　(Use the fact that $e < 3$);

   (iii) $\cos 1.51$　(Assume that $\pi = 3.1416$);

   (iv) $\log 1.2$

3. Use Taylor's theorem to show that if $f''(x)$ exists and is continuous in some neighbourhood of a, then

$$\lim_{h \to 0} \frac{f(a+h) - 2 f(a) + f(a-h)}{h^2} = f''(a)$$

2.6 Maxima and minima

We say that a function $f(x)$ has a local maximum at $x = x_0$ if there is some neighbourhood of x_0 within which the greatest value of $f(x)$ is $f(x_0)$. That is: there exists some δ such that

$$f(x_0) > f(x) \quad \text{for all } x \text{ satisfying } x_0 - \delta < x < x_0 + \delta \text{ and } x \neq x_0$$

If we replace '$f(x_0) > f(x)$' by '$f(x_0) < f(x)$' we have the definition of a local minimum.

A local maximum is not necessarily the overall greatest value of a function, nor is a local minimum necessarily the smallest. Nevertheless, the word 'local' is usually dropped, and reference made only to maxima and minima.

The function sketched in figure 8 has maxima at x_2 and x_4 and minima at x_1 and x_3. There are, of course, values of $f(x)$ greater than the maxima, and values less than the minima.

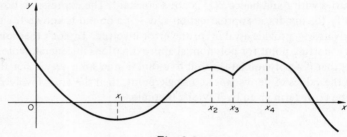

Fig. 2.8

It is well known that maxima and minima may be found by equating the first derivative to zero, but we shall have to consider whether or not this always gives a maximum or a minimum and if so which, as well as noting that there may be such values which cannot be found this way. Taking the second point first, it is obvious that there may be points, such as x_3 in figure 2.8, at which the function has a maximum or minimum, but does not have a derivative. It is necessary, then, to examine separately any point at which the function is not differentiable. Elsewhere we may make use of the following theorem:

If $f(x)$ is differentiable at x_0 and has a local maximum or minimum there, then

$$f'(x_0) = 0$$

The proof has already given as part of the proof of Rolle's theorem. Briefly, if $f(x_0)$ is a maximum then

$$\text{for } h > 0, \frac{1}{h}[f(x_0 + h) - f(x_0)] < 0, \text{ but}$$

$$\text{for } h < 0, \frac{1}{h}[f(x_0 + h) - f(x_0)] > 0$$

Hence, $$f'(x_0) = \lim_{h \to 0} \frac{1}{h}[f(x_0 + h) - f(x_0)] = 0$$

Similarly for a minimum.

It is clear, however, that not all points at which a derivative is zero provide either a maximum or minimum. For example, if

$$f(x) = x^3 \quad \text{then}$$

$$f'(0) = 0, \quad \text{but}$$

$$f(x) > 0 \quad \text{for } x > 0 \quad \text{and} \quad f(x) < 0 \quad \text{for } x < 0$$

so that $f(x)$ has neither a maximum nor a minimum at $x = 0$. A point at which $f'(x) = 0$ is called a stationary value of $f(x)$. If it is neither a maximum nor a minimum it is a *point of inflection*. (Note that in general a point of inflection is a point at which the first derivative has a local maximum or a local minimum but is not necessarily zero.)

To distinguish maxima, minima and points of inflection we may examine higher derivatives of the function, assuming they exist. For example, if $f'(x_0)$ is zero, but $f''(x_0)$ is not, we have

if $f''(x_0) < 0$, then $f(x)$ has a maximum at $x = x_0$, but

if $f''(x_0) > 0$, then $f(x)$ has a minimum at $x = x_0$.

However, $f''(x_0)$, and possibly higher derivatives, may also be zero, and in general we have to examine the first non-zero derivative.

Let the first $(n-1)$ derivatives of $f(x)$ all be zero at $x = x_0$, and let $f^{(n)}(x)$ be continuous at $x = x_0$ and non-zero there.

The continuity condition assures that $f^{(n)}(x)$ exists and has the same sign as $f^{(n)}(x_0)$ in some neighbourhood of x_0. Applying Taylor's theorem, we have, for sufficiently small h

$$f(x_0 + h) = f(x_0) + hf'(x_0) + \cdots + \frac{1}{(n-1)!} h^{n-1} f^{(n-1)}(x_0) +$$

$$+ \frac{1}{n!} h^n f^{(n)}(x_0 + \xi)$$

Therefore $\qquad f(x_0) - f(x_0 + h) = -\frac{1}{n!} h^n f^{(n)}(x_0 + \xi)$

where $f^{(n)}(x_0 + \xi)$ has the same sign as $f^{(n)}(x_0)$.

If n is even, h^n is positive for both positive and negative values of h, but if n is odd, then h^n changes sign as h changes sign. Hence:

(i) If n is even and $f^{(n)}(x_0) > 0$, then $f(x)$ has a minimum at $x = x_0$,

(ii) if n is even and $f^{(n)}(x_0) < 0$, then $f(x)$ has a maximum at $x = x_0$,

(iii) if n is odd, then $f(x)$ has a point of inflexion whatever the sign of $f^{(n)}(x_0)$.

Example   If $f(x) = x^N$, $N \geqslant 2$,

$$f^{(n)}(x) = \frac{N!}{(N-n)!} x^{N-n}, \quad n \leqslant N,$$

$$f^{(n)}(0) = 0 \quad \text{for} \quad n < N,$$

$$f^{(N)}(0) = 1$$

Hence,   if N is odd $f(x)$ has a point of inflexion at $x = 0$.

If N is even $f(x)$ has a minimum at $x = 0$.

Exercises

1. Find the stationary points of

    (i) $f(x) = e^{x\sqrt{3}} \cos x$;   (ii) $f(x) = x^4 e^{-2x^2}$;

    (iii) $f(x) = \dfrac{x}{(x^2 + a^2)^5}$;   (iv) $f(x) = 4 \sin x + \cos 2x$.

    State in each case whether the stationary point concerned is a maximum, a minimum, or a point of inflexion.

2. If $f(x)$ has a local maximum at $x = x_0$ and is continuous there, show that provided $f(x_0) \neq 0$, the function

    $$g(x) = \frac{1}{f(x)}$$

    has a local minimum at $x = x_0$.

2.7 Indeterminate forms and L'Hôpital's rule

We now consider the problem of evaluating $\lim\limits_{x \to x_0} [f(x)/g(x)]$ in the case when $\lim\limits_{x \to x_0} f(x) = \lim\limits_{x \to x_0} g(x) = 0$. This is the most frequently encountered of the indeterminant forms introduced in section 2.4.2, and the limit, if it exists, may be determined by using what is known as l'Hôpital's rule. It will later be shown how this rule may be employed in finding limits of other types of indeterminate forms.

2.7.1 *l'Hôpital's rule*

We shall first derive a restricted form of l'Hôpital's rule which is often useful and which is an immediate consequence of the mean-value theorem (section 2.5.2).

Suppose that $f(x)$ and $g(x)$ are defined and have continuous derivatives on some interval containing the point x_0, and that $f(x_0) = g(x_0) = 0$, while

$g'(x_0) \neq 0$. Then if $x_0 + h$ is any other point in the interval the mean-value theorem gives

$$\frac{f(x_0 + h)}{g(x_0 + h)} = \frac{f(x_0) + hf'(x_0 + \theta h)}{g(x_0) + hg'(x_0 + \phi h)} = \frac{f'(x_0 + \theta h)}{g'(x_0 + \phi h)}$$

where θ and ϕ both lie between 0 and 1, and $|h|$ is assumed small enough to ensure that $g'(x)$ is nowhere zero in the interval $[x_0, x_0 + h]$. It then follows that

$$\lim_{x \to x_0} \frac{f(x)}{g(x)} = \lim_{h \to 0} \frac{f(x_0 + h)}{g(x_0 + h)} = \lim_{h \to 0} \frac{f'(x_0 + \theta h)}{g'(x_0 + \phi h)} = \frac{f'(x_0)}{g'(x_0)}$$

Example. Let $f(x) = e^{2x} - 1$ and $g(x) = 3x$. These functions are continuously differentiable for all x, and $f(0) = g(0) = 0$. Since $f'(x) = 2e^{2x}$ and $g'(x) = 3$, the above rule gives the result

$$\lim_{x \to 0} \frac{e^{2x} - 1}{3x} = \frac{f'(0)}{g'(0)} = \frac{2}{3}$$

It should be noted that this rule is only valid for $g'(x_0) \neq 0$. It is not difficult to see that, if $g'(x_0) = 0$, $\lim_{x \to x_0} [f(x)/g(x)]$ does not exist if $f'(x_0) \neq 0$. On the other hand, if both $f'(x_0)$ and $g'(x_0)$ are zero we may be able to find the required limit by using a generalisation of the foregoing result which depends upon Taylor's theorem (section 2.5.3) in its general form.

If $f(x)$ and $g(x)$ possess continuous derivatives up to at least the nth order on some interval containing the point x_0, and if $x_0 + h$ is any other point in the interval, we may write

$$\frac{f(x_0 + h)}{g(x_0 + h)} = \frac{f(x_0) + hf'(x_0) + \frac{1}{2!} h^2 f''(x_0) + \cdots + \frac{1}{n!} h^n f^{(n)}(x_0 + \theta_n h)}{g(x_0) + hg'(x_0) + \frac{1}{2!} h^2 g''(x_0) + \cdots + \frac{1}{n!} h^n g^{(n)}(x_0 + \phi_n h)}$$

where θ_n and ϕ_n lie between 0 and 1. If also

$$f(x_0) = f'(x_0) = \cdots = f^{(n-1)}(x_0) = 0$$

and

$$g(x_0) = g'(x_0) = \cdots = g^{(n-1)}(x_0) = 0$$

while $g^{(n)}(x_0) \neq 0$, then it follows that

$$\lim_{x \to x_0} \frac{f(x)}{g(x)} = \lim_{x \to 0} \frac{f(x_0 + h)}{g(x_0 + h)} = \lim_{h \to 0} \frac{f^{(n)}(x_0 + \theta_n h)}{g^{(n)}(x_0 + \phi_n h)} = \frac{f^{(n)}(x_0)}{g^{(n)}(x_0)}$$

Example. Let $f(x) = \tan x - x$ and $g(x) = x - \sin x$, so that $f(0) = g(0) = 0$. Now

(i) $f'(x) = \sec^2 x - 1$ and $g'(x) = 1 - \cos x$, whence $f'(0) = g'(0) = 0$ and the
      earlier rule does not apply;

(ii) $f''(x) = 2 \sec^2 x \tan x$ and $g''(x) = \sin x$, whence $f''(0) = g''(0)$ and the
      generalised rule with $n = 2$ does not apply;

(iii) $f'''(x) = 4 \sec^2 x \tan^2 x + 2 \sec^4 x$ and $g'''(x) = \cos x$, whence $g'''(0) \neq 0$.
      We can therefore apply the generalised rule with $n = 3$ to get

$$\lim_{x \to 0} \left\{ \frac{\tan x - x}{x - \sin x} \right\} = \frac{f'''(0)}{g'''(0)} = \frac{2}{1} = 2$$

A stronger and more useful form of l'Hôpital's rule than we have so far derived may be stated as follows:

If, as $x \to x_0$, $f(x) \to 0$ and $g(x) \to 0$, then $\lim_{x \to x_0} \dfrac{f(x)}{g(x)} = \lim_{x \to x_0} \dfrac{f'(x)}{g'(x)}$, provided the latter limit exists.

The following notes apply:

(i)   The earlier condition that $f(x_0) = g(x_0) = 0$ has now become
      $\lim_{x \to x_0} f(x) = \lim_{x \to x_0} g(x) = 0$, so that the rule allows us to deal with cases
      for which $f(x_0)$ and $g(x_0)$ are not defined.

(ii) The previous restriction that $g'(x_0) \neq 0$ has now been removed. If, therefore,
      both $\lim_{x \to x_0} f(x)$ and $\lim_{x \to x_0} g(x)$ are zero, the right-hand side of the above
      relation is another indeterminate form, and the rule may be applied
      repeatedly until the required limit (if it exists) is found.

(iii) The proof of this stronger form of l'Hôpital's rule will be omitted, since it
      is not particularly enlightening to the non-mathematician.

Example. Consider once again $\lim_{x \to 0} \left\{ \dfrac{\tan x - x}{x - \sin x} \right\}$. The strong form of l'Hôpital's
rule gives

$$\lim_{x \to 0} \left\{ \frac{\tan x - x}{x - \sin x} \right\} = \lim_{x \to 0} \left\{ \frac{\sec^2 x - 1}{1 - \cos x} \right\} = \lim_{x \to 0} \sec^2 x (1 + \cos x) = 2$$

Note that a single differentiation is now all that is needed, whereas previously it was necessary to differentiate three times because both $g'(0)$ and $g''(0)$ turned out to be zero.

2.7.2 *Other indeterminate forms*

L'Hôpital's rule provides a convenient means of finding limits of indeterminate forms of '0/0' type. The three other kinds of indeterminate form mentioned in section 2.4.2 were

(i) $f(x)/g(x) \to \infty/\infty$ as $x \to x_0$,

(ii) $f(x)g(x) \to 0 \times \infty$ as $x \to x_0$, and

(iii) $f(x) - g(x) \to \infty - \infty$ as $x \to x_0$.

The second of these may be expressed as a 0/0 form by writing it as $f(x)/[1/g(x)]$, while the third is expressible in terms of an ∞/∞ form if it is written as $f(x)[1 - g(x)/f(x)]$. The ∞/∞ form itself may be written as $[1/g(x)]/[1/f(x)]$, when l'Hôpital's rule becomes applicable, though the following result (quoted without proof) allows it to be dealt with more directly:

If $\qquad \lim\limits_{x \to x_0} f(x) = \lim\limits_{x \to x_0} g(x) = \infty$, then $\lim\limits_{x \to x_0} \dfrac{f(x)}{g(x)} = \lim\limits_{x \to x_0} \dfrac{f'(x)}{g'(x)}$,

provided the latter limit exists.

Examples

1. To find the limit of $x^2 e^{-x}$ as $x \to \infty$.

$$x^2 e^{-x} = x^2/e^x \to \infty/\infty$$

Differentiating numerator and denominator of this expression gives

$$2x/e^x \to \infty/\infty$$

Differentiating again: $\qquad 2/e^x \to 0$ as $x \to \infty$

Hence $\qquad 2x/e^x \to 0$ and $x^2/e^x \to 0$ as $x \to \infty$

In fact, by differentiating sufficiently many times we can show that

$$x^\lambda e^{-x} \to 0 \text{ as } x \to \infty$$

however large λ may be.

2. $\qquad\qquad (\log x)/x^\lambda \to \infty/\infty$ if $\lambda > 0$

$$(1/x)/(\lambda x^{\lambda - 1}) = 1/(\lambda x^\lambda) \to 0 \text{ as } x \to \infty$$

$$\therefore \ \log x/x^\lambda \to 0$$

From this result and the result of example (1) we have (for any fixed $\lambda > 0$) that, for sufficiently large x,

$$\log x/x^\lambda < 1, \text{ and } x^\lambda e^{-x} < 1, \text{ and hence}$$

$$\log x < x^\lambda < e^x$$

Exercises

1. Evaluate each of the following limits:

   (i) $\lim\limits_{x \to 1} \left(\dfrac{1 + \cos \pi x}{x^2 - 2x + 1} \right)$

   (ii) $\lim\limits_{x \to 0} \dfrac{1 - \cos 5x}{2^x - 3^x}$

   (iii) $\lim\limits_{x \to 0} \left\{ \dfrac{\log (\sec x) - \sin^2 x}{x \tan x} \right\}$

   (iv) $\lim\limits_{x \to 0} \left\{ \dfrac{1}{x} - \dfrac{1}{\sin x} \right\}$

   (v) $\lim\limits_{x \to \pi/2} \dfrac{\tan x}{\tan 3x}$

   (vi) $\lim\limits_{x \to r\pi} \left\{ (x - r\pi) \operatorname{cosec} x \right\}$

2. Given that $f''(x)$ is continuous at $x = 0$, find

$$\lim\limits_{x \to 0} \frac{2f(x) - 3f(2x) + f(4x)}{x^2}$$

   in terms of $f''(0)$.

3. Show that $\lim\limits_{x \to 0} \dfrac{x^2 \sin 1/x}{\sin x} = 0$, but that l'Hôpital's rule cannot be used here.

2.9 Inverse functions

2.9.1

If $y = ax + b$, where $a \neq 0$, then y is defined as a function of x over the whole range $-\infty < y < +\infty$. However, the relationship which then subsists between x and y could equally well be expressed by writing the above formula in the following equivalent form

$$x = \frac{1}{a} y - \frac{b}{a}$$

This now expresses x explicitly in terms of y; given any specific value of y in the range $-\infty < y < +\infty$ we can compute a corresponding value for x which is uniquely defined by the formula.

In general, when a functional relationship between x and y is expressed in terms of a formula, $y = f(x)$, which defines y as a function of x, it may or may not be possible to replace it by an equivalent form, $x = \phi(y)$, which defines x as a function of y. When this can be done, as in the case of the linear function discussed above, the functions $y = f(x)$ and $x = \phi(y)$ are said to be *inverse functions*. The geometrical meaning is fairly obvious: if $y = f(x)$ is represented as a curve in the (x, y) plane with respect to rectangular axes O_x, O_y in the usual way, then $x = \phi(y)$ is represented by the curve obtained when the axes are interchanged. (See figure 2.9.) This transformation corresponds to first rotating the coordinate axes, together with the curve $y = f(x)$, through a right angle and then reflecting the graph with respect to the x-axis. Equivalently, the graph of $x = \phi(y)$ can be obtained by simply reflecting the graph of $y = f(x)$ about the line bisecting the angle between the positive x-axis and the positive y-axis.

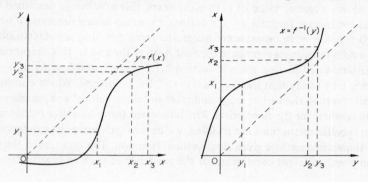

Fig. 2.9

The geometrical interpretation emphasises the point that the existence of a function inverse to a given function, $y = f(x)$, is not automatically assured. If the function is such that a line, $y = k$, drawn parallel to the x-axis intersects the curve $y = f(x)$ at more than one point then the functional value $y = k$ must correspond to more than one value of x, that is at the point $y = k$ at least there can be no equation of the form $x = \phi(y)$ which defines x *uniquely* in terms of y. As a simple example of this consider the situation shown in figure 2.10 with respect to the function $y = x^2$.

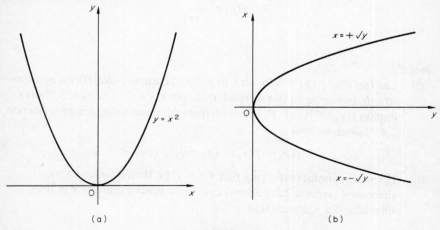

Fig. 2.10

Any line $y = k$, where $k > 0$, drawn parallel to the x-axis in figure 2.10a cuts the curve $y = x^2$ in two distinct points. Interchange of the x- and y-axes gives rise to the curve shown in figure 2.10b; to each positive value of y there corresponds not one but two values of x, and there is no value of x whatsoever which corresponds to any negative value of y. In older texts, this situation is described by saying that the inverse formula $x = \sqrt{y}$ defines x as a *two-valued function* of y over the range $0 < y < +\infty$. In more recent usage, the term 'function' is understood to imply single-valuedness (compare the first note at the end of this chapter and the definition of function given in section 2.1.1 above); in this sense, it is perfectly true to say that the function $y = x^2$ has no inverse. Where convenient we shall revert to the earlier usage and refer to 'many-valued' and 'single-valued' functions wherever the need arises. The important thing to notice is that unless certain specific restrictions are fulfilled, we cannot guarantee the existence of a *single-valued* inverse to a given single-valued function. The theorem in the next section gives sufficient conditions for the existence of such an inverse.

2.9.2 *Theorem*

Let $y = f(x)$ be a function defined and continuous on the interval $a \leqslant x \leqslant b$ and differentiable on the interval $a < x < b$. Then if $f'(x) > 0$ for all x in $a < x < b$ there exists a (single-valued) function, $x = \phi(y)$, such that

(i) x is defined for all y such that $f(a) < y < f(b)$,

(ii) $\phi(y)$ is a differentiable function of y throughout the interval $f(a) < y < f(b)$ and its differential coefficient is given by

$$\phi'(y) = \frac{1}{f'(x)}$$

Proof

(i)   The fact that $f'(x) > 0$ for all x in $a < x < b$ implies that $f(x)$ is *monotone strictly increasing* in this interval; that is to say $a < x_1 < x_2 < b$ always implies $f(x_1) < f(x_2)$. This follows from the mean-value theorem (section 2.5.2) since we have

$$f(x_2) - f(x_1) = (x_2 - x_1)f'(\xi) > 0$$

(ii)   If y is any number satisfying $f(a) < y < f(b)$, then it follows from theorem 4 (section 2.2.3 above) that there exists a number x in the interval $a < x < b$ such that

$$f(x) = y$$

Moreover, the monotonicity established in (i) shows that this value of x must be unique, i.e. we have shown the existence of a one-valued function $\phi(y)$ on $f(a) < y < f(b)$.

(iii) If $f(a) < y < f(b)$ then for all sufficiently small values of $|\delta|$ we have $f(a) < y + \delta < f(b)$ also.

Moreover, given y and δ we can find corresponding points x_0 and x such that $y = f(x_0)$ and $y + \delta = f(x)$, and it follows that

$$\frac{\phi(y + \delta) - \phi(y)}{\delta} = \frac{x - x_0}{f(x) - f(x_0)}$$

But, for some ξ between x and x_0, we have $f(x) - f(x_0) = (x - x_0) f'(\xi)$, where $f'(\xi) \neq 0$.

Now, as $\delta \to 0$ so $x \to x_0$ and therefore $\xi \to x_0$ also. Hence, we get

$$\phi'(y) = \lim_{\delta \to 0} \frac{\phi(y + \delta) - \phi(y)}{\delta}$$

$$= \lim_{\xi \to x_0} \frac{1}{f'(\xi)} = \frac{1}{f'(x_0)}$$

Note: The result holds good if we replace the condition $f'(x) > 0$ in $a < x < b$ by $f'(x) < 0$; the only change in the proof is the trivial one resulting from the fact that then $f(x)$ is monotone strictly *decreasing*. In either case, the relation between the derivatives of a function and its inverse can be alternatively expressed as follows

$$\frac{dx}{dy} \cdot \frac{dy}{dx} = 1$$

2.9.3 *Branches*

We have already remarked on the fact that even so simple a function as $y = x^2$ may not possess a single-valued inverse. The formula $x \sqrt{y}$ is two-valued; we can remove the ambiguity of this notation by clearly distinguishing between positive and negative square roots and writing

$$x_1 = + \sqrt{y} \qquad \text{and} \qquad x_2 = - \sqrt{y}$$

Now, the formula $x_1 = + \sqrt{y}$ defines a function which is single-valued and differentiable for all $y > 0$. Moreover, this function and the function defined by

$$y = x^2 \qquad \text{where} \qquad x > 0$$

are clearly inverse functions.

Similarly, the function $x_2 = -\sqrt{y}$ is single-valued and differentiable for all $y > 0$. This time we must take the function defined by

$$y = x^2 \qquad \text{where} \qquad x < 0$$

in order to obtain a pair of inverse functions.

Thus, by splitting the domain of definition of the function $y = x^2$ into two parts, say $(-\infty < x < 0)$ and $(0 \leqslant x < +\infty)$, we could consider the function as the combination of two components, each of which possesses a single-valued inverse. The two functions $x_1 = +\sqrt{y}$ and $x_2 = -\sqrt{y}$ are called the *branches* of the two-valued function $x = \sqrt{y}$. This device is frequently useful in connection with a number of the standard elementary functions for which no single-valued inverses exist. For a discussion of the more important cases which arise in elementary analysis, the reader is referred to section 3.7 of the following chapter.

NOTES ON CHAPTER 2

1. Functions (section 2.1)

Let E and F be sets, or collections, of any elements whatsoever. If there is a rule, or law of correspondence, which assigns to each member of E a unique member of F then the correspondence is said to define a *function, f*, which maps E into F. The set E, on which *f* is defined, is called the *domain* of the function; the set of all the functional values corresponding to the elements of the domain (which will be, in general, a subset of F) is called the *range* of the function. If b in F corresponds to a in E then we write

$$b = f(a)$$

According to this (quite general) definition the term 'function' automatically implies single-valuedness, and the older phrase 'single-valued function' is redundant. However, as remarked in section 2.9.1, it is often convenient to revert to earlier usage and to speak of 'many-valued functions', whenever the need arises. In the particular situation in which to each element b of F there corresponds one and only one element a of E for which $b = f(a)$, it is clear that the correspondence also defines a function (in the strict sense) whose domain is F and whose range is E. It is this function which is properly referred to as the *inverse function, f^{-1}*, of *f*.

Usually both domain and range are numbers, or sets of numbers. For example, a rule which associates a real number with each point in some region of three-dimensional space is a function whose domain is a certain set of number triples (a point P in three-dimensional space being specified by some ordered triple,

(x, y, z), of real numbers). However, it is worth noting here that in modern texts of advanced mathematical analysis, the term 'function' is frequently used in a much broader sense.

2. Neighbourhoods and limits

The distance between two points on the line (or, in 'one-dimensional space') is given by the absolute value of the difference, $|x - y|$, between the real numbers x and y which correspond to those points. In two dimensions, the natural definition of the distance between $x = (x_1, x_2)$ and $y = (y_1, y_2)$ is

$$+ \sqrt{[(x_1 - y_1)^2 + (x_2 - y_2)^2]}$$

Other definitions of 'distance' are possible and, on occasion, useful. In some situations, for example, it is convenient to define the distance between $x = (x_1, x_2)$ and $y = (y_1, y_2)$ as

$$\max [|x_1 - y_1|, |x_2 - y_2|]$$

Once a satisfactory definition of distance has been agreed upon it is possible to make precise the idea of a 'neighbourhood' of a point. Broadly speaking, a neighbourhood of a point a in a given space is understood to be the set of all points x which are near to a. In the plane a neighbourhood of a given point $a = (a_1, a_2)$ would normally be specified as the set of all points $x = (x_1, x_2)$ such that

$$\sqrt{[(a_1 - x_1)^2 + (a_2 - x_2)^2]} < \epsilon$$

where ϵ is some given positive number. Alternatively, we might define neighbourhood in terms of the other concept of distance given above:

$$\max [|a_1 - x_1|, |a_2 - x_2|] < \epsilon$$

The sense in which the term neighbourhood is being used is of fundamental importance in connection with the concepts of limit and of convergence. To say that the function $f(x)$ approaches a limit L as x tends to a is to say that, for all values of x 'sufficiently close' to a, the corresponding numbers $f(x)$ will be 'sufficiently close' to L. In terms of neighbourhoods: $f(x) \to$ L as $x \to a$ if and only if, given any neighbourhood of L (denoted by N(L), say) there is a corresponding neighbourhood of a (denoted by N(a)) such that $f(x)$ belongs to N(L) whenever x belongs to N(a).

Just as the term function can itself be used in more general senses than the familiar, elementary one so also can the ideas of limit, convergence, and continuity be generalised. As briefly indicated above, the concept of neighbourhood is of basic importance in this connection.

Miscellaneous exercises

1. Find dy/dx where

    (i) $y = \arccos \sqrt{(x-1)/(x+1)}$,

    (ii) $y = \dfrac{1}{2} \log \left[(1 + \sin x)/(1 - \sin x) \right]$,

    (iii) $y = e^{-x} \log (1 - 2x^3)$,

    (iv) $x^3 + y^3 = 3y^2$,

    (v) $x^3 + xy^2 + y^3 = 8$,

    (vi) $y = \left(1 + \dfrac{1}{x} \right)^x$ $\{$Hint: $[f(x)]^x = e^{x \log [f(x)]}\}$

2. Show from first principles:

    (i) that if $g(0) = g'(0) = 0$, $f(x) = xg(x)/|x|$, and $f(x)$ is continuous at $x = 0$, then $f'(0)$ exists and is equal to zero,

    (ii) that the function $g(x) = \sqrt{|x|}$ is not differentiable at $x = 0$, but that if $f(x)$ is any function which is differentiable at $x = 0$ then so is the function

$$F(x) = g(x) \left[f(x) - f(0) \right]$$

    (iii) that if $f(x) = e^{-1/x^2}$ for $x \neq 0$, and if $f(0)$ is defined so that the function is continuous at $x = 0$, then it is differentiable at $x = 0$ and has a minimum there.

3. Discuss the behaviour of the following functions as x tends to zero:

    (i) $\dfrac{\sin x}{|x|}$,   (ii) $(1 - e^x)/\sqrt{x}$,

    (iii) 2^x,   (iv) $(1 - e^x)/(1 - \cos x)$,

    (v) $(1/2)^{(1/x)}$ (vi) $[\log (\sec x) - \sin^2 x]/[x \tan x]$

4. Show that

$$\lim_{x \to \infty} x \tan^{-1} \left\{ \frac{x(b-a)}{x^2 + ab} \right\} = b - a$$

5. If $f(x) \to \infty$ and $g(x) \to \infty$ as $x \to x_0$, in such a way that $f(x)/g(x)$ tends to a finite limit L, show that

$$\lim_{x \to x_0} \left\{ \frac{f(x) + a}{g(x) + b} \right\} = L$$

where a and b are any constants.

6. Given that $\qquad$ $f(x) \to L$ as $x \to 0+,$ and

$\qquad\qquad\qquad g(y) \to \infty$ as $y \to a,$

show from first principles that $f[1/g(y)] \to L$ as $y \to a.$

7. For each of the following functions, find all the stationary points and distinguish between maxima, minima and points of inflexion.

(i) x^x

(ii) $x^{(1/x)}$

(iii) $\dfrac{(x+a)(x+b)}{(x-a)(x-b)}$ where $a > 0$ and $b > 0,$

(iv) $2 \sin^2 x - 3(1 + \cos x)^2,$

(v) $3x^4 - 4x^3 - 18x^2 + 36x + 24 \log (1 + x^2) - 48 \tan^{-1} x.$

(In (i) and (ii) the domain of definition is confined to strictly positive values of $x.$)

3 SEQUENCES AND SERIES

3.1 Sequences and limits

3.1.1 *Finite and infinite sequences*

A real sequence, (A_n), is a set of real numbers

$$A_1, A_2, A_3, \ldots, A_n, \ldots$$

in a definite order. The individual numbers A_n (which need not necessarily be all different) are called the *terms* of the sequence.

A finite sequence is one which has only a finite number of terms and which, therefore, has a last term, A_N, as well as a first term, A_1. In principle, at least, we can always specify a particular finite sequence by naming or displaying each of its terms. An infinite sequence, on the other hand, has infinitely many terms and therefore has no last term. It is obviously impossible to write down all the terms in such a case, and a particular infinite sequence can be defined only by giving some specific rule or formula for calculating the *general* term A_n.

In what follows our main concern will be with infinite sequences, and we shall take the term 'sequence' to mean 'infinite sequence', unless the contrary is explicitly stated.

3.1.2 *Limits and convergence*

If the terms, A_n, of an infinite sequence become arbitrarily small in absolute magnitude as n increases then the sequence is said to *converge to zero*. More precisely:

Definition 1. The sequence (A_n) is said to converge to the limit 0 if, given any positive number ϵ (however small), we can always find a corresponding integer N such that

$$|a_n| < \epsilon \qquad \text{for all } n > N$$

The crux of Definition 1 is that it gives meaning and precision to the somewhat vague phrase 'arbitrarily small' used in the preceding remark. Consider, for example, the behaviour as n increases of the sequence

$$\frac{1}{6}, \frac{1}{10}, \frac{1}{14}, \ldots, \frac{1}{4n+2}, \ldots$$

Intuitively it is clear that by taking sufficiently large values of n we can make the general term $1/(4n+2)$ as small as we please in absolute value. In the sense of Definition 1 this fact can be expressed *quantitatively*.

For, the inequality

$$|A_n| = \frac{1}{4n+2} < \epsilon$$

will hold provided that $4n + 2 > 1/\epsilon$

that is if $n > \dfrac{1}{4\epsilon} - \dfrac{1}{2}$

Substituting specific values for ϵ in this formula it follows that

$$|A_n| < 0.1 \quad \text{for all } n > 2,$$

$$|A_n| < 0.01 \quad \text{for all } n > 24,$$

$$|A_n| < 0.001 \text{ for all } n > 249,$$

and so on.

   More generally, a sequence (A_n) is said to *converge to the finite number A as its limit* if and only if the difference between A and the terms A_n of the sequence become arbitrarily small in absolute value as n increases:

Definition 2. A sequence (A_n) is said to converge to a limit A if, given any positive number ϵ (however small) we can always find an integer N (which will generally depend on ϵ) such that

$$|A_n - A| < \epsilon \qquad \text{for all } n > N$$

This definition says, in effect, that the sequence (A_n) converges to A if and only if the sequence $(A_n - A)$ converges to 0. With the usual notation

$$\lim_{n \to \infty} A_n = A \qquad \text{if and only if} \qquad \lim_{n \to \infty} (A_n - A) = 0$$

Example 1. The sequence

$$\frac{1}{3}, \frac{2}{5}, \frac{3}{7}, \frac{4}{9}, \ldots, \frac{n}{2n+1}, \ldots$$

has the general term

$$A_n = \frac{n}{2n+1} = \frac{1}{2} - \frac{1}{4n+2}$$

Since we have shown above that

$$\lim_{n \to \infty} \frac{1}{4n+2} = 0,$$

it follows at once that

$$\lim_{n \to \infty} \frac{n}{2n+1} = \frac{1}{2}$$

3.1.3 *Non-convergent sequences*

A sequence may fail to be convergent in a number of quite different ways. The simplest and most clear-cut situations are those in which the general term, A_n, becomes arbitrarily large in absolute value as n increases:

An infinite sequence (A_n) is said to *diverge to* $+\infty$ if, given any positive number M (however large), we can always find a corresponding integer N such that,

$$A_n > M, \qquad \text{for all } n > N$$

(Note that although it is strictly an abuse of notation it is often convenient to write

$$\lim_{n \to \infty} A_n = + \infty$$

For this reason we sometimes refer to a sequence converging to a *finite* limit A although, in the proper sense of Definition 2 the word 'finite' is redundant here.)

Instead of framing a dual definition for the case when A_n is very large and negative we need only say that:

An infinite sequence (A_n) is said to *diverge to* $-\infty$ if and only if the sequence $(-A_n)$ diverges to $+\infty$.

Example 1. $1, 4, 9, 16, \ldots, n^2, \ldots$ Diverges to $+\infty$.

Example 2. $3, 1, -1, -3, \ldots, 5 - 2n, \ldots$ Diverges to $-\infty$.

Example 3. $1, -1, 1, -1, \ldots, (-1)^{n+1}, \ldots$

This sequence does not converge to any finite number as its limit; neither does it diverge to $+\infty$ nor to $-\infty$. It is said to *oscillate finitely*.

3.1.4 *Limits of sequences and of functions*

Given any sequence (A_n) let $f(x)$ be the function defined by

$$f(x) = A_n \qquad \text{for} \qquad (n-1) < x \leqslant n$$

If, for example, $A_n = 1/n$ for $n = 1, 2, \ldots$, then $f(x)$ would be the function whose graph is sketched in figure 3.1.

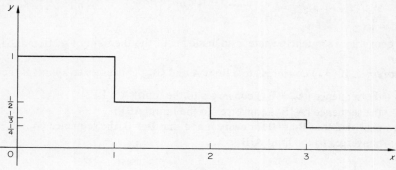

Fig. 3.1

It is clear that if the sequence (A_n) converges to a limit L as n goes to infinity then the function $f(x)$ tends to the limit L as x goes to infinity. Now let $f(x)$ denote *any* function which is defined for all $x > 0$ and let (A_n) be the sequence formed by putting

$$A_n = f(n)$$

It is almost immediately obvious that if $f(x)$ tends to L as $x \to \infty$ then the sequence (A_n) must converge to L. In fact we can prove without difficulty the more general proposition which follows:

Theorem 1. If $x_n \to x_0$ as $n \to \infty$ and if $f(x) \to$ L as $x \to x_0$, then the sequence $A_n = f(x_n)$ tends to L as $n \to \infty$.

Proof. Since $f(x) \to$ L as $x \to x_0$ it follows that given any $\epsilon > 0$ there exists a corresponding $\delta > 0$ such that

$$|f(x) - \text{L}| < \epsilon \quad \text{for all } x \text{ satisfying } |x - x_0| < \delta$$

But, since $x_n \to x_0$ as $n \to \infty$, we can find an integer N such that

$$|x_n - x_0| < \delta \qquad \text{for all} \qquad n \geqslant \text{N}$$

Thus, $|f(x_n) - \text{L}| < \epsilon$ for all $n \geqslant \text{N}$

and so
$$\lim_{n \to \infty} f(x_n) = \text{L}$$

Example. Let $f(x) = (\sin x)/x$ and $s_n = 1/n$. Since

$$\lim_{x \to 0} \frac{\sin x}{x} = 1 \qquad \text{and} \qquad \lim_{n \to \infty} \frac{1}{n} = 0,$$

we have
$$\lim_{n \to \infty} n \sin \frac{1}{n} = 1$$

For convergent sequences there is an analogue of the theorem of section 2.2.1:

Theorem 2. If (A_n) converges to a limit A and (B_n) converges to a limit B then

(i)   the sequence $(A_n + B_n)$ converges to the limit $(A + B)$,
(ii) the sequence $(A_n B_n)$ converges to the limit (AB),
(iii) provided that $B_n \neq 0$ for every n and that $B \neq 0$, the sequence (A_n/B_n) converges to the limit A/B.

Exercises

1. Find the least positive integer N such that for all $n > N$ we have

$$\left| \frac{5n + 9}{2n + 1} - \frac{5}{2} \right| < \epsilon$$

   where (a) $\epsilon = 0.01$, (b) $\epsilon = 0.001$, (c) $\epsilon = 0.0001$.

2. Use the definition of limit to show that

   (a) $\displaystyle \lim_{n \to \infty} \frac{5 - n}{3n + 7} = -\frac{1}{3}$, (b) $\displaystyle \lim_{n \to \infty} \frac{\sin n}{n} = 0$.

3. Evaluate each of the following limits, using any theorems on limits which may apply:

   (a) $\displaystyle \lim_{n \to \infty} \frac{n^5 + 3n + 1}{n^6 + 7n^2 + 2}$, (b) $\displaystyle \lim_{n \to \infty} \frac{6n^3 + 17n + 1}{n^3 + 2n^2 + 4}$, (c) $\displaystyle \lim_{n \to \infty} \frac{(n + 3)}{(n + 1)(n + 2)}$,

   (d) $\displaystyle \lim_{n \to \infty} \sqrt[3]{\left\{ \frac{(3 - \sqrt{n})(\sqrt{n} + 2)}{8n - 4} \right\}}$, (e) $\displaystyle \lim_{n \to \infty} \frac{\sqrt{(3n^2 - 5n + 4)}}{2n - 7}$,

   (f) $\displaystyle \lim_{n \to \infty} \frac{7.10^n - 5.10^{2n}}{2.10^{n-1} + 3.10^{2n-1}}$, (g) $\displaystyle \lim_{n \to \infty} \left\{ \sqrt{(n^2 + n)} - n \right\}$.

   [Hint: in (g) use the fact that $\left\{ \sqrt{(n^2 + n)} - n \right\} \left\{ \sqrt{(n^2 + n)} + n \right\} = n$.]

3.2 The general principle of convergence

3.2.1 *Bounded sequences*

A sequence (A_n) is said to be *bounded above* if we can find some finite number M such that $A_n \leqslant M$ for every term A_n; any number M which has this property is called an *upper bound* of the sequence. The *smallest* number M such that $A_n \leqslant M$ for every term A_n is called the *least upper bound* of the sequence. (Compare the definition of least upper bound of a function in section 2.2.3.) We write

$$M = \text{l.u.b.} (A_n) \qquad \text{or.} \qquad M = \sup (A_n)$$

Dually, (A_n) is said to be *bounded below* if we can find some finite number m such that $A_n \geqslant m$ for every term A_n; the largest such number m is called the *greatest lower bound* of the sequence and we write

$$m = \text{g.l.b.} (A_n) \qquad \text{or} \qquad m = \inf (A_n)$$

A sequence (A_n) which is both bounded above and bounded below is said to be *bounded.* It is obvious that every convergent sequence is necessarily bounded. On the other hand boundedness is not generally enough to ensure convergence. (See Note 1.)

Example. Consider the sequence

$$\frac{1}{2}, +\frac{1}{2}, -\frac{1}{4}, +\frac{3}{4}, -\frac{1}{8}, +\frac{7}{8}, \cdots \text{ (figure 3.2)}$$

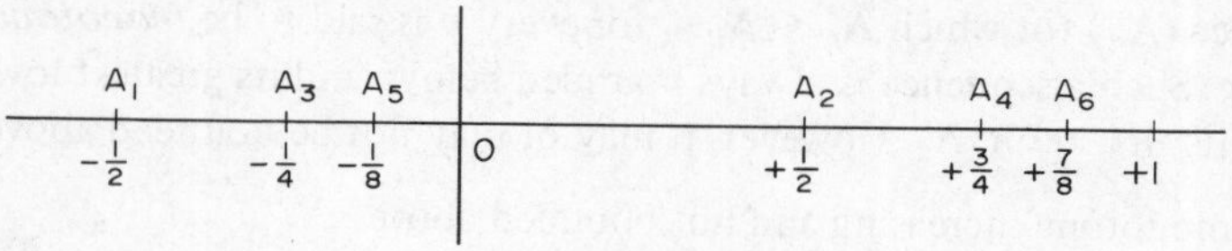

Fig. 3.2

The sequence is bounded since $-\frac{1}{2} \leqslant A_n < 1$ for all n, but there is no limiting value to which it converges as $n \to \infty$.

*3.2.2 *The Cauchy criterion*

We now state a very general criterion (known as the *Cauchy criterion,* or as the *general principle of convergence*) for the convergence of an infinite sequence:

Theorem 3. A sequence (A_n) is convergent if and only if, given any positive number ϵ (however small) we can find a corresponding positive integer N such that for all $n \geqslant N$ and all $m \geqslant N$ we have

$$|A_n - A_m| < \epsilon$$

The 'necessity' part of this theorem is easily proved. For, if (A_n) converges to a limit A then, given $\epsilon > 0$, we can always find N such that

$$|A - A_n| < \epsilon/2 \qquad \text{for all } n \geqslant N$$

Then, if $n \geqslant N$ and $m \geqslant N$ we have

$$|A_n - A_m| \leqslant |A - A_n| + |A - A_m| < \frac{\epsilon}{2} + \frac{\epsilon}{2} = \epsilon$$

To prove sufficiency is more difficult. If the condition is fulfilled then, in particular, we have

$$|A_n - A_N| < \epsilon \qquad \text{for all } n \geqslant N$$

that is $\qquad A_N - \epsilon < A_n < A_N + \epsilon \qquad \text{for all } n \geqslant N$

This shows that, as n increases, the numbers A_n are packed into a smaller and smaller section of the line. It is intuitively obvious that there must in fact be a specific point about which the A_n are clustering. But to prove the existence of such a limiting value would need a much deeper investigation of the structure of the real number system. Roughly speaking, if the criterion were fulfilled but no number A existed such that (A_n) converged to A as its limit, then there would be a 'gap' in the real number system. The system of real numbers is explicitly constructed to ensure that no such gaps exist. (See also Note 1 of chapter 1.)

3.2.3 *Monotone sequences*

A sequence (A_n) for which $A_n \leqslant A_{n+1}$ for every n is said to be *monotone increasing*. Such a sequence is always bounded below, and its greatest lower bound is its first term, A_1. However, it may or may not be bounded above:

(i) (A_n) monotone increasing and not bounded above.

Since the sequence is not bounded above it follows that given any positive number M (however large) we can always find some positive integer N such that $A_N \geqslant M$. Further, since the sequence is monotone increasing, we must have

$$A_n \geqslant A_N \geqslant M \qquad \text{for all } n \geqslant N$$

(ii) (A_n) monotone increasing and bounded above.

Let (A_n) have least upper bound M. If, for some value N of n, we have $A_N = M$ then since the sequence is monotone increasing it follows that $A_n = M$ for all $n \geqslant N$ and so the sequence (A_n) converges to M as its limit. Otherwise we have a sequence with no largest term. In this case let B be *any* number less than M. Then we may write

$$B = M - \epsilon \qquad \text{where} \qquad \epsilon > 0$$

B cannot be an upper bound of the sequence (since M itself is the *least* upper bound) and so, for some positive integer N

$$B = M - \epsilon < A_N < M$$

Again, since the sequence is monotone increasing, this must mean that

$$M - \epsilon < A_n < M \qquad \text{for all } n \geqslant N$$

Since B is any number less than M this inequality will be true for any given positive number ϵ, however small. In other words, the sequence (A_n) converges to M as its limit.

These results can be summarised in the following Theorem — one of the key results in the study of sequences:

Theorem 4. If (A_n) is a monotone increasing sequence then either

   (i) (A_n) is not bounded above, and diverges to $+\infty$,
or (ii) (A_n) is bounded above, and converges to its least upper bound as its limit.

Dually, for monotone decreasing sequences we have,

Theorem 4a. If (A_n) is a monotone decreasing sequence then either

   (i) (A_n) is not bounded below, and diverges to $-\infty$,
or (ii) (A_n) is bounded below, and converges to its greatest lower bound as its limit.

Briefly we may remark that so far as *monotone* sequences are concerned boundedness is sufficient to ensure convergence.

Example. Let $A_n = 1 - 1/2^n$ for $n = 1, 2, 3, \ldots$. Since $2^n < 2^{n+1}$ we have $1/2^n > 1/2^{n+1}$ and so $A_n < A_{n+1} < 1$ for every n. The sequence is thus monotone increasing and bounded above; its least upper bound is 1. Given $\epsilon > 0$ we can find N such that $2^N > 1/\epsilon$. Then, for $n \geqslant N$ we have

$$1 - \epsilon < 1 - 1/2^n < 1$$

and so (A_n) converges to the limit 1.

3.3 Some special limits

To establish the results of this section we shall need some basic inequalities. If h is any positive real number and n any positive integer then the binomial theorem for a positive integral index gives us

$$(1 + h)^n = 1 + nh + \frac{n(n-1)}{2!} h^2 + \frac{n(n-1)(n-2)}{3!} h^3 + \cdots + h^n$$

Hence, for $n > 1$, $(1 + h)^n > 1 + nh$

For $n > 2$, $(1 + h)^n > \dfrac{n(n-1)}{2!} h^2$

and, similarly for $n > 3$, $(1 + h)^n > \dfrac{n(n-1)(n-2)}{3!} h^3$

In general, for $n > k$, $(1 + h)^n > \dfrac{n(n-1)(n-2) \cdots (n-k+1)}{k!} h^k$

3.3.1 *The function $n^\alpha x^n$*. (α and x real)

The behaviour as n goes to infinity of the function x^n, where x is any given real number, presents no real difficulty. The graphs of the first few of these functions (for positive values of x) are sketched in figure 3.3, and the general behaviour can be summarised as follows:

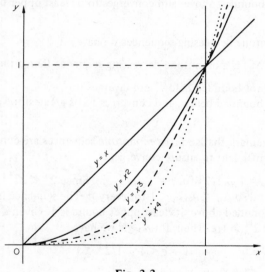

Fig. 3.3

(i)   for any value of x such that $|x| < 1$ we have

$$\lim_{n \to \infty} x^n = 0.$$

(ii)   If $x = 1$ then $x^n = 1$ for all n and so $\lim_{n \to \infty} x^n = 1$; if $x = -1$ then x^n oscillates finitely between the values $+1$ and -1.

(iii) If $x > 1$ then x^n diverges to $+\infty$; if $x < -1$ then x^n oscillates infinitely.

The situation is more complicated in the case of $n^\alpha x^n$. In particular if $|x| < 1$ and $\alpha > 0$, then as n increases so n^α becomes arbitrarily large while $|x^n|$ becomes arbitrarily small; it is by no means obvious what will happen to the product $n^\alpha x^n$. The difficulties are clearly shown by a specific example. In the table below we give a few numerical values for the case when $x = \frac{1}{2}$, $\alpha = 4$.

	1	2	3	4	5	10	20	30
n^4	1	16	81	256	625	10 000	160 000	810 000
2^n	2	4	8	16	32	1 024	1 048 576	~1 x 10⁹
$n^4/2^n$	0.5	4	10.125	16	19.531	9.768	0.153	~0.0008

The last entries do indicate that eventually $(\frac{1}{2})^n$ approaches zero 'faster' then n^4 goes to infinity. But the earlier results do not show any sign of the eventual trend at all. Accordingly we examine the general case when $|x| < 1$ in some detail.

To find the limit, $\quad \lim_{n \to \infty} n^\alpha x^n, \quad$ *when* $|x| < 1$.

(i) If $x = 0$ the result is trivial since then $n^\alpha x^n = 0$ for all n.

If $x \neq 0$ then we can write $|x| = 1/(1 + h)$, where $h > 0$.

Suppose first that α is a positive integer, say $\alpha = k$. Then for $n > k + 1$ we have, using the general inequality given at the beginning of this section,

$$|n^k x^n| = \frac{n^k}{(1 + h)^n} < \frac{n^k}{\frac{n(n - 1)(n - 2) \ldots (n - k)}{(k + 1)!} h^{k+1}}$$

$$= \frac{(k + 1)!}{h^{k+1}} \cdot \frac{1}{(1 - 1/n)(1 - 2/n) \ldots (1 - k/n)} \cdot \frac{1}{n}$$

and it follows at once that $\lim_{n \to \infty} n^k x^n = 0$

If α is positive but not an integer then let k denote the next largest integer (that is, if $[\alpha]$ is the integral part of α then we write $k = 1 + [\alpha]$). Then

$$|n^\alpha x^n| < n^k |x|^n$$

Finally, if $|x| < 1$ and $\alpha < 0$ then we have

$$n^\alpha |x|^n < |x|^n$$

Combining these results we can say that

$$\lim_{n \to \infty} n^\alpha x^n = 0$$

for any real value of α and any real x such that $|x| < 1$.

(ii) If $|x| > 1$ then we can write $x = 1/y$, where $|y| < 1$. By what has already been proved we can draw the following conclusions

if $x > 1$ then $n^\alpha x^n$ diverges to $+\infty$;

if $x < -1$ then $n^\alpha x^n$ oscillates infinitely. (To be specific, it will tend to $+\infty$ if n goes to infinity through *even* values, and to $-\infty$ if n goes to infinity through *odd* values.)

3.3.2 *To evaluate (i)* $\lim\limits_{n\to\infty} \sqrt[n]{a}$, *i) (ii)* $\lim\limits_{n\to\infty} \sqrt[n]{n}$

(i) Consider the sequence (A_n) whose nth term is $10^{1/n}$. The sequence is clearly monotone decreasing and is bounded below by 1. The values shown in the table below suggest that 1 is actually the greatest lower bound (and therefore the limit) of the sequence.

n	1	2	3	4	5	10	100
$\sqrt[n]{10}$	10	3.162	2.154	1.778	1.585	1.259	1.024
h_n	9	2.162	1.154	0.778	0.585	0.259	0.024

To confirm this, note first that since $10^{1/n} > 1$ for every n, we can write $10^{1/n} = 1 + h_n$, where $h_n > 0$. The values of h_n for a few values of n are also shown in the table, and our object is to show that h_n decreases to 0 as n goes to infinity.

Now, if $\qquad\qquad 10^{1/n} = 1 + h_n$

then $\qquad\qquad\qquad 10 = (1 + h_n)^n > 1 + nh_n$

Hence $\qquad\qquad nh_n < 9 \qquad$ or, $\qquad h_n < 9/n$

Thus $\qquad\qquad \lim\limits_{n\to\infty} h_n = 0 \qquad$ and so $\qquad \lim\limits_{n\to\infty} \sqrt[n]{10} = 1$

The same argument clearly applies to $a^{1/n}$, where a is any number > 1. If $a = 1$, then $1^{1/n} = 1$ for all n and the result is trivial. Finally, let a be any number such that $0 < a < 1$. Then $a = 1/b$, where $b > 1$, and so

$$\lim_{n\to\infty} \sqrt[n]{a} = \lim_{n\to\infty} n\sqrt{\frac{1}{b}} = \lim_{n\to\infty} \frac{1}{\sqrt[n]{b}} = 1$$

Thus, for any positive number a we have the result

$$\lim_{n\to\infty} \sqrt[n]{a} = 1$$

(ii) The behaviour of the sequence $(\sqrt[n]{n})$ is not quite so simple but the limit can be obtained by the same sort of attack. For all $n > 1$ we must have $n^{1/n} > 1$ and so we can write

$$n^{1/n} = (1 + h_n) \qquad \text{where} \qquad h_n > 0$$

Hence
$$n = (1 + h_n)^n > \frac{n(n-1)}{2} h_n^2, \qquad \text{(for } n > 2)$$

so that
$$h_n^2 < \frac{2}{n-1}$$

Thus
$$\lim_{n \to \infty} h_n = 0 \qquad \text{and so} \qquad \lim_{n \to \infty} \sqrt[n]{n} = 1$$

3.3.3 *The number* e

Let $A_n = (1 + 1/n)^n$. Then it can be shown that the sequence (A_n) is monotone increasing and bounded above, and hence that it converges to a definite limit. This limit is the *number* e, the base of Napierian logarithms; its approximate value is $2.7182818\ldots$. The properties of this number, and its significance in analysis, arise more naturally in connection with the exponential function (section 3.7.1). For the moment it is enough to draw attention to the existence of the limit itself and to note the forms in which it may occur:

$$e = \lim_{n \to \infty} \left(1 + \frac{1}{n}\right)^n = \lim_{n \to \infty} \left(\frac{n+1}{n}\right)^n = \lim_{n \to \infty} \left(\frac{n}{n-1}\right)^n$$

Exercises

1. Evaluate each of the following limits:

   (a) $\lim_{n \to \infty} \dfrac{n^{10}}{10^n}$, (b) $\lim_{n \to \infty} \dfrac{10^n}{n!}$, (c) $\lim_{n \to \infty} \dfrac{n!}{n^n}$, (d) $\lim_{n \to \infty} \sqrt[n]{n^2}$, (e) $\lim_{n \to \infty} (2^n + 3^n)^{1/n}$

2. Show that each of the following sequences converges to the limit 2:

   (a) $\sqrt{2}, \sqrt{2\sqrt{2}}, \sqrt{2\sqrt{2\sqrt{2}}}, \ldots$, (b) $\sqrt{2}, \sqrt{2 + \sqrt{2}}, \sqrt{2 + \sqrt{2 + \sqrt{2}}}, \ldots$

3. A sequence of positive terms $A_1, A_2, \ldots, A_n, \ldots$ satisfies the relation

$$A_{n+1} = \frac{3(1 + A_n)}{3 + A_n}$$

Show that the sequence is monotone decreasing if $A_1 > \sqrt{3}$ and monotone increasing if $A_1 < \sqrt{3}$. Find $\lim_{n \to \infty} A_n$.

$$\left[\text{Hint: use the fact that } A_{n+1} - A_n = \frac{3(1 + A_n)}{3 + A_n} = \frac{3 - A_n^2}{3 + A_n}.\right]$$

4. (a) Criticise the following argument:

$$\left(1 + \frac{1}{n}\right) \to 1 \text{ as } n \to \infty, \text{ and } \lim_{n\to\infty} 1^n = 1$$

Hence $$\lim_{n\to\infty} \left(1 + \frac{1}{n}\right)^n = 1$$

(b) Show that $$2\tfrac{1}{2} \leqslant \lim_{n\to\infty} \left(1 + \frac{1}{n}\right)^n \leqslant 2\tfrac{3}{4}$$

$$\left[\text{Hint: expand } (1 + 1/n)^n \text{ by the binomial theorem and use the fact that}\right.$$

$$\left.\frac{1}{3.4.5\ldots n} < \frac{1}{3^{n-2}}.\right]$$

3.4 Infinite series

3.4.1 *Convergence of a series*
Consider any infinite sequence of real numbers,

$$a_1, a_2, a_3, \ldots, a_k, \ldots$$

and for each positive integer n form the nth *partial sum*, A_n

$$A_n = a_1 + a_2 + \cdots + a_n \equiv \sum_{k=1}^{n} a_k$$

Then, if the sequence (A_n) converges to a finite limit A as n goes to infinity, this

number A is said to be the *sum of the infinite series* $\sum_{k=1}^{\infty} a_k$, and the series is

said to converge to A.

The Cauchy criterion for convergence of the sequence (A_n) immediately gives us a necessary and sufficient condition for the infinite series to converge:

Theorem 5. The infinite series $\sum_{k=1}^{\infty} a_k$ converges if and only if the number

$$|A_m - A_n| \equiv |a_{n+1} + a_{n+2} + \cdots + a_m|$$

can be made arbitrarily small by choosing n sufficiently large (m then being *any* number larger than n).

In particular, taking $m = n + 1$ shows that a *necessary* condition for convergence

of the series $\sum\limits_{k=1}^{\infty} a_k$ is that

$$\lim_{k \to \infty} |a_k| = 0$$

If the Cauchy criterion is not fulfilled then the sequence (A_n) of the partial sums does not tend to a finite limit, and the series is said to be *divergent*. If (A_n) tends to $+\infty$, or to $-\infty$, as n goes to infinity then the infinite series is said to be *properly divergent*. Note that if all the terms a_k of the series are *positive* then the sequence of partial sums must be monotone increasing. Hence either it tends to a finite limit A or else diverges to $+\infty$. A series of positive terms is therefore either convergent, or else properly divergent.

Example. (discussion of the geometric series). For a fixed real number x, let $a_n = x^{n-1}$. The resulting infinite series is called a *geometric series*:

$$1 + x + x^2 + x^3 + \cdots + x^{n-1} + \cdots$$

We have
$$A_n = 1 + x + x^2 + \cdots + x^{n-1},$$

and so
$$xA_n = x + x^2 + \cdots + x^{n-1} + x^n$$
$$= (1 + x + x^2 + \cdots + x^{n-1}) - 1 + x^n$$
$$= A_n - 1 + x_n$$

Hence
$$A_n = \frac{1 - x^n}{1 - x} = \frac{1}{1 - x} - \frac{x^n}{1 - x}.$$

and the fact that we can obtain a closed formula like this for the sum of the first n terms allows a direct investigation to be made of the convergence (or non-convergence) of the infinite geometric series.

The term $x^n/(1 - x)$ tends to zero as n goes to infinity if and only if $|x| < 1$.

Thus,
$$\sum_{k=1}^{\infty} x^{k-1} \equiv \lim_{n \to \infty} A_n = \frac{1}{1 - x}, \qquad |x| < 1$$

In particular, for $x = \frac{1}{2}$ we get for the nth partial sum

$$1 + \frac{1}{2} + \frac{1}{4} + \cdots + \frac{1}{2^{n-1}} = 2 - \frac{1}{2^{n-1}}$$

and so the infinite series $\sum\limits_{n=1}^{\infty} \dfrac{1}{2^{n-1}}$ converges to the sum 2. The Cauchy criterion suggests a way of obtaining an estimate of the maximum error involved if only finitely many terms of the series are taken. We have

$$|A_m - A_n| = \frac{1}{2^n} + \frac{1}{2^{n+1}} + \cdots + \frac{1}{2^{m-1}}$$

$$= \frac{1}{2^n} \left\{ 1 + \frac{1}{2} + \cdots + \frac{1}{2^{m-n-1}} \right\} < \frac{1}{2^n} \cdot 2 = \frac{1}{2^{n-1}}$$

Hence, if we sum just the first n terms of the series we know that the remaining terms can never contribute more than $1/2^{n-1}$ to the sum, no matter how many of them are taken.

For $x = 1$ the series becomes $1 + 1 + 1 + \cdots$, and diverges properly to $+\infty$; the same is true for any $x > 1$ since then we have $x^{n-1} > 1$ for all $n > 1$. If $x = -1$ the series becomes $1 - 1 + 1 - 1 + \cdots$ and for the partial sums we get $A_n = 1$ (n odd) and $A_n = 0$ (n even). The series is *finitely oscillating*. Finally, for $x < -1$, A_n becomes arbitrarily large in absolute magnitude as n increases, but alternates in sign. The series is *infinitely oscillating*.

3.4.2 *Absolute and conditional convergence*

The convergence (or non-convergence) of a series will in no way be affected by the presence or absence of any *finite* number of terms. (In the case of a convergent series the removal or addition of finitely many terms will at most alter the value of the sum of the series; it cannot have any bearing on the *existence* of the sum.) Hence we may say of a series all of whose terms are positive, except possibly for a finite number, that it is either convergent or else properly divergent. In the same way a series with only finitely many positive terms must either be convergent or else properly divergent (to $-\infty$). There remains the case when there are both infinitely many positive terms, say p_ν, and infinitely many negative terms, say $-q_\nu$. The sum of the first n terms can then be written in the form

$$A_n \equiv \sum_{k=1}^{n} a_k = \sum_{\nu=1}^{n_1} p_\nu - \sum_{\nu=1}^{n_2} q_\nu, \quad \text{where } n = n_1 + n_2$$

Since there are infinitely many terms of each sign we know that both n_1 and n_2 must go to infinity as n goes to infinity. We shall write

$$P = \lim_{n_1 \to \infty} \sum_{1}^{n_1} p_\nu \quad \text{and} \quad Q = \lim_{n_2 \to \infty} \sum_{1}^{n_2} q_\nu$$

The following four cases may be distinguished:

(i) *P and Q both finite*

$$\lim_{n\to\infty} \sum_{k=1}^{n} a_k = P - Q \qquad \sum_{k=1}^{\infty} a_k \text{ is convergent}$$

$$\lim_{n\to\infty} \sum_{k=1}^{n} |a_k| = P + Q \qquad \sum_{k=1}^{\infty} |a_k| \text{ is convergent}$$

(ii) $P = +\infty$, Q *finite*

The series $\sum_{1}^{\infty} a_k$ is properly divergent to $+\infty$.

The series $\sum_{1}^{\infty} |a_k|$ is properly divergent to $+\infty$.

(iii) P *finite*, $Q = +\infty$

The series $\sum_{1}^{\infty} a_k$ is properly divergent to $-\infty$.

The series $\sum_{1}^{\infty} |a_k|$ is properly divergent to $+\infty$.

(iv) $P = +\infty$, $Q = -\infty$

This time we can only say that the series $\sum_{1}^{\infty} |a_k|$ is properly divergent to $+\infty$. The series $\sum_{1}^{\infty} a_k$ itself may diverge or it may converge.

Note that the only case in which the series of the absolute values of the terms, $\sum_{1}^{\infty} |a_k|$, is convergent is the first one. In these circumstances the series $\sum_{1}^{\infty} a_k$ is said to be *absolutely convergent*. Strictly, to say that a series $\sum_{1}^{\infty} a_k$ is absolutely convergent is to assert something about another series, namely $\sum_{1}^{\infty} |a_k|$. However, the above analysis shows that the convergence of $\sum_{1}^{\infty} |a_k|$ necessarily implies the convergence of $\sum\limits_{1}^{\infty} a_k$; that is, an *absolutely convergent series is convergent*.

Example. If $a_n = (-1)^{n-1} \dfrac{1}{2^{n-1}}$ then we have the convergent geometric series

$$\sum_{1}^{\infty} a_n = 1 - \tfrac{1}{2} + \tfrac{1}{4} - \tfrac{1}{8} + \cdots = \frac{1}{1-(-\tfrac{1}{2})} = \tfrac{2}{3}.$$

Here we have

$$\sum_{1}^{\infty} p_\nu = 1 + \tfrac{1}{4} + \tfrac{1}{16} + \cdots = \frac{1}{1 - \tfrac{1}{4}} = \tfrac{4}{3}$$

and

$$\sum_{1}^{\infty} q_\nu = \tfrac{1}{2} + \tfrac{1}{8} + \tfrac{1}{32} + \cdots = \frac{\tfrac{1}{2}}{1 - \tfrac{1}{4}} = \tfrac{2}{3}$$

Thus

$$\sum_{1}^{\infty} a_n = \sum_{1}^{\infty} p_\nu - \sum_{1}^{\infty} q_\nu = \tfrac{4}{3} - \tfrac{2}{3} = \tfrac{2}{3}$$

Also

$$\sum_{1}^{\infty} |a_n| = 1 + \tfrac{1}{2} + \tfrac{1}{4} + \tfrac{1}{8} + \cdots = \frac{1}{1 - \tfrac{1}{2}} = 2$$

so that

$$\sum_{1}^{\infty} |a_n| = \sum_{1}^{\infty} p_\nu + \sum_{1}^{\infty} q_\nu = \tfrac{4}{3} + \tfrac{2}{3} = 2$$

$\sum\limits_{1}^{\infty} (-1)^{n-1} \dfrac{1}{2^{n-1}}$ is therefore an absolutely convergent series. (Case (i).)

It is easy to construct divergent series corresponding to Cases (ii), (iii) and (iv) respectively. However the most interesting situation occurs when the positive and negative terms each separately constitute divergent series, but the series as a whole converges. Convergence in these circumstances is said to be *conditional*. In the next section we examine a particular type of series in which conditional convergence can be demonstrated in a reasonably simple manner.

3.4.3 *Alternating series*
Consider any series of the form

$$b_1 - b_2 + b_3 - b_4 + b_5 - \cdots$$

where all the numbers b_n are positive, $b_{n+1} \leqslant b_n$ for all n, and $\lim\limits_{n \to \infty} b_n = 0$.

Then
$$A_1 = b_1$$
$$A_3 = b_1 - b_2 + b_3 = b_1 - (b_2 - b_3) \leqslant A_1$$
$$A_5 = b_1 - b_2 + b_3 - b_4 + b_5$$
$$= b_1 - (b_2 - b_3) - (b_4 - b_5) \leqslant A_3 \quad \text{and so on,}$$

that is
$$A_1 \geqslant A_3 \geqslant A_5 \geqslant \cdots$$

Similarly
$$A_2 = b_1 - b_2$$
$$A_4 = b_1 - b_2 + b_3 - b_4 = (b_1 - b_2) + (b_3 - b_4) \geqslant A_2$$
$$A_6 = b_1 - b_2 + b_3 - b_4 + b_5 - b_6$$
$$= (b_1 - b_2) + (b_3 - b_4) + (b_5 - b_6) \geqslant A_4$$

that is
$$A_2 \leqslant A_4 \leqslant A_6 \leqslant \cdots$$

Moreover
$$A_{2n+1} = A_{2n} + b_{2n+1}, \quad \text{where } b_{2n+1} > 0$$

and so
$$A_2 \leqslant A_{2n} \leqslant A_{2n+1} \leqslant A_1 \quad \text{for all } n.$$

Hence, the odd partial sums $A_1, A_3, A_5, \ldots$, form a monotone decreasing sequence which is bounded below by A_2 and so must converge to some finite limit L_1 (where $L_1 \geqslant A_2$). Also, the even partial sums $A_2, A_4, A_6, \ldots$, form a monotone increasing sequence which is bounded above by A_1 and so must converge to a limit L_2 (where $L_2 \leqslant A_1$).

But since
$$A_{2n+1} - A_{2n} = b_{2n+1}$$

where $\lim\limits_{n \to \infty} b_{2n+1} = 0$, we must have
$$L_1 = L_2$$

that is, any series of this nature must necessarily converge, its sum L lying between A_1 and A_2:
$$b_1 - b_2 \leqslant L \leqslant b_1$$

It is worth noting that this gives us the first example of a *test* for convergence (that is, a way of establishing the convergence of a series without necessarily being able to find out its sum). Formally the test may be stated as follows:

Theorem 6 (*Leibnitz's convergence test*). If the terms of a series $\sum\limits_{1}^{\infty} a_n$ alternate in sign, and if the absolute values $|a_n|$ of the terms decrease *monotonically* to zero as n goes to infinity, then the series converges.

Note that, using this test, we could have deduced the convergence of the series $1 - \frac{1}{2} + \frac{1}{4} - \frac{1}{8} + \cdots$ without directly computing its sum. However, the test would have given us no information at all about the series $1 + \frac{1}{2} + \frac{1}{4} + \frac{1}{8} + \cdots$. Hence we would not have been able to infer the *absolute* convergence of the series $1 - \frac{1}{2} + \frac{1}{4} - \frac{1}{8} + \cdots$. This is typical of the limitations of Leibnitz's test; it is very easy to apply but, clearly, it will only be of use in rather special circumstances and the information which it gives will be limited even then.

Now consider the series, $1 - \frac{1}{2} + \frac{1}{3} - \frac{1}{4} + \frac{1}{5} - \cdots$.

Here, since $1/n > 1/(n + 1)$ for all n, and $\lim\limits_{n \to \infty} 1/n = 0$, Leibnitz's test applies and we can conclude that there is a certain number L, where $\frac{1}{2} \leqslant L \leqslant 1$, such that

$$L = 1 - \frac{1}{2} + \frac{1}{3} - \frac{1}{4} + \frac{1}{5} - \cdots$$

On the other hand it is not difficult to show that the series of absolute values of the terms

$$1 + \frac{1}{2} + \frac{1}{3} + \frac{1}{4} + \frac{1}{5} + \cdots$$

is properly divergent. To see this we need only examine the following sequence of partial sums

$$A_2 = 1 + \frac{1}{2} = \frac{3}{2}$$
$$A_4 = 1 + \frac{1}{2} + \frac{1}{3} + \frac{1}{4} > 1 + \frac{1}{2} + \frac{1}{4} + \frac{1}{4} = 2$$
$$A_8 = 1 + \frac{1}{2} + \frac{1}{3} + \frac{1}{4} + \frac{1}{5} + \frac{1}{6} + \frac{1}{7} + \frac{1}{8}$$
$$> 1 + \frac{1}{2} + \frac{1}{4} + \frac{1}{4} + \frac{1}{8} + \frac{1}{8} + \frac{1}{8} + \frac{1}{8} = \frac{5}{2}$$

and in general,
$$A_{(2^n)} > \frac{n + 2}{2}$$

In effect this means that given any positive integer N (however large), we have only to take the first 2^{2N+1} terms of the series $\sum\limits_{1}^{\infty} \frac{1}{n}$ to obtain a sum which exceeds N. It follows that this series must be properly divergent to $+\infty$ and, therefore, that the series

$$1 - \frac{1}{2} + \frac{1}{3} - \frac{1}{4} + \frac{1}{5} - \cdots$$

is *conditionally convergent*.

Note: As a corollary to Theorem 5 it was remarked that a *necessary* condition for the convergence of an infinite series, $\sum\limits_{1}^{\infty} a_n$, was that $\lim\limits_{n\to\infty} a_n = 0$. The series $\sum\limits_{1}^{\infty} \dfrac{1}{n}$ shows that this is certainly not a *sufficient* condition for convergence.

3.4.4 *Manipulation of convergent series*

For series which are convergent (absolutely or conditionally) the following results are easily established:

(i)   If $\sum\limits_{1}^{\infty} a_n = A$ then $\sum\limits_{1}^{\infty} c \cdot a_n = cA$, for any constant c.

(ii) If $\sum\limits_{1}^{\infty} a_n = A$ and $\sum\limits_{1}^{\infty} b_n = B$, then, $\sum\limits_{1}^{\infty} (a_n + b_n) = A + B$.

(iii) If $\sum\limits_{1}^{\infty} a_n = A$ and $\sum\limits_{1}^{\infty} b_n$ denotes any series obtained from the original

series by grouping the terms in brackets in any manner but leaving the

order of the terms unchanged, then, $\sum\limits_{1}^{\infty} b_n = A$.

The only one of these which may need comment is (iii). To confirm the given statement, suppose that the series $\sum\limits_{1}^{\infty} b_n$ is defined as follows:

$$b_1 = a_1 + a_2 + \cdots + a_{n_1}; \quad b_2 = a_{n_1 + 1} + a_{n_1 + 1} + \cdots + a_{n_2}; \text{ and so on,}$$

Then,
$$\sum_{r=1}^{v} b_v \equiv \sum_{k=1}^{nv} a_k = A_{(nv)}$$

As v tends to infinity so also does n_v; hence

$$\lim_{v\to\infty} B_v = \lim_{nv\to\infty} A_{(nv)} = A$$

In contrast it is worth remarking that brackets may not generally be removed with impunity when the series contains terms of different sign. The series

$$(1 - 1) + (1 - 1) + (1 - 1) + \cdots$$

for example, has every term equal to 0 and therefore converges to 0. But the series obtained by removing the brackets is the finitely oscillating series

$$1 - 1 + 1 - 1 + 1 - \cdots$$

(iv)　Let $\sum_1^\infty a_n$ be a series of *positive* terms, and let $\sum_1^\infty b_n$ be any series whose terms are those of the original series taken in a different order. If $\sum_1^\infty a_n$ converges to a limit A then $\sum_1^\infty b_n$ also converges to A; if $\sum_1^\infty a_n$ is properly divergent then so also is $\sum_1^\infty b_n$.

For, let $b_1 = a_{m_1}$, $b_2 = a_{m_2}$, $b_3 = a_{m_3}$, etc.:

Then
$$B_n = \sum_{v=1}^n a_{m_v} \leqslant A_p \tag{1}$$

where p is the largest of the integers $m_1, m_2, \ldots, m_n$.

In the same way we can show that there is an integer q such that

$$A_n \leqslant B_q \tag{2}$$

From (1), if $\sum_1^\infty a_n = A$ then $\lim\limits_{n\to\infty} B_n \leqslant A$.

From (2), on the other hand, $\lim\limits_{q\to\infty} B_q \geqslant A$;

therefore
$$\sum_{b=1}^\infty b_n = A$$

Finally, if $\sum_1^\infty a_n$ is properly divergent then (2) shows that $\lim\limits_{q\to\infty} B_q = +\infty$, so that $\sum_1^\infty b_n$ is also properly divergent.

Corollary. For an absolutely convergent series we can re-arrange the terms at will without affecting the convergence or altering the sum.

(This follows from the fact that an absolutely convergent series can be expressed as the difference of two convergent series of positive terms.)

Example. That the result of the above corollary does *not* hold for conditionally convergent series can be seen from the following example

If
$$L = 1 - \tfrac{1}{2} + \tfrac{1}{3} - \tfrac{1}{4} + \tfrac{1}{5} - \tfrac{1}{6} + \tfrac{1}{7} - \tfrac{1}{8} + \ldots,$$

then
$$\tfrac{1}{2}L = \quad \tfrac{1}{2} \quad -\tfrac{1}{4} \quad +\tfrac{1}{6} \quad -\tfrac{1}{8} + \ldots,$$

and so, adding
$$\frac{3L}{2} = 1 \quad +\tfrac{1}{3} - \tfrac{1}{2} + \tfrac{1}{5} \quad +\tfrac{1}{7} - \tfrac{1}{4} + \ldots, \quad$$

which will be recognised as a simple re-arrangement of the terms of the original series.

Exercises

1. By finding their sums to n terms show that each of the following series is convergent:

   (a) $1 + 3x + 5x^2 + 7x^3 + \cdots, \qquad |x| < 1.$

   (b) $\dfrac{1}{1.2} + \dfrac{1}{2.3} + \dfrac{1}{3.4} + \dfrac{1}{4.5} + \cdots,$ \qquad (c) $\dfrac{1}{1.2.3} + \dfrac{1}{2.3.4} + \dfrac{1}{3.4.5} + \cdots,$

   (d) $\displaystyle\sum_{n=1}^{\infty} \frac{n}{(n+1)!},$ \qquad (e) $\displaystyle\sum_{n=1}^{\infty} \frac{1}{4n^2 - 1}.$

2. Which of the following series is convergent? In convergent cases establish whether the convergence is absolute or conditional.

   (a) $1 - \tfrac{3}{2} + \tfrac{5}{4} - \tfrac{7}{8} + \tfrac{9}{16} - \cdots$

   (b) $2 - \tfrac{3}{4} + \tfrac{4}{9} - \tfrac{5}{16} + \tfrac{6}{25} - \cdots$

   (c) $\tfrac{1}{6} - \tfrac{2}{11} + \tfrac{3}{16} - \tfrac{4}{21} + \tfrac{5}{26} - \cdots.$

3.5. Convergence tests for infinite series

3.5.1 *The comparison tests*

When an explicit formula for the nth partial sum, A_n, can be obtained (as in the geometric series) the convergence or divergence of the series $\displaystyle\sum_{1}^{\infty} a_n$ can usually be established directly. Otherwise it is necessary to investigate the convergence of the series by other means. Many of the most useful and important convergence tests apply essentially to series with *positive* terms; they can, therefore, be used to investigate the *absolute* convergence of a general series. Into this category fall those tests which derive from the very general and very important *comparison tests:*

Theorem 7 (comparison tests). Let $\sum\limits_{1}^{\infty} a_n$ and $\sum\limits_{1}^{\infty} b_n$ be series of *positive* terms.

(i) If $\sum\limits_{1}^{\infty} b_n$ is known to be *convergent* and if there exists a positive number k such that $a_n < kb_n$ for all n, then the series $\sum\limits_{1}^{\infty} a_n$ is also convergent.

(ii) If $\sum\limits_{1}^{\infty} b_n$ is known to be *divergent* and if there exists a positive number k' such that $a_n > k'b_n$ for all n, then the series $\sum\limits_{1}^{\infty} a_n$ is also divergent.

Proof. (i) $\sum\limits_{r=n+1}^{m} a_r < k \sum\limits_{r=n+1}^{m} b_r.$

Since $\sum\limits_{1}^{\infty} b_n$ converges we can make the R.H.S. of this inequality as small as we please by choosing n large enough. The result then follows from the Cauchy criterion.

(ii) If $a_n > k'b_n$ for all n, then $A_n > k'B_n$. Since B_n goes to infinity with n and $k' > 0$ it follows that A_n goes to infinity also.

Remarks.

1. The presence or absence of any finite number of terms can in no way affect the convergence or divergence of a series. Hence we can always replace 'for all n' in Theorem 7 by 'for all n greater than some fixed positive integer N'. Similar remarks apply to the other tests in this section which are derived from the comparison tests.

2. A slight modification allows us to apply a form of the comparison test directly to cases in which *one* of the two series involved has both positive and negative terms:

Modified comparison test. If $\sum_{1}^{\infty} a_n$ is any series and $\sum_{1}^{\infty} b_n$ is a series of *positive* terms, and if the ratio a_n/b_n tends to a non-zero limit, L, (which may be negative) as n goes to infinity, then either $\sum_{1}^{\infty} a_n$ and $\sum_{1}^{\infty} b_n$ both converge or they both diverge.

3. The comparison tests are most frequently used in conjunction with certain standard 'test series' whose behaviour is already known. The use of the geometric series in this context, for example, gives rise to the familiar 'ratio' and 'root' tests discussed below.

3.5.2 *The test series* $\sum_{n=1}^{\infty} \dfrac{1}{n^p}$

It has already been shown in section 3.4.3 that the series

$$1 + \frac{1}{2} + \frac{1}{3} + \frac{1}{4} + \cdots + \frac{1}{n} + \cdots$$

diverges to $+\infty$. If p is any number such that $p < 1$ then it is certainly the case that $1/n^p > 1/n$ for every n. By the comparison test it follows that the series $\sum_{n=1}^{\infty} \dfrac{1}{n^p}$ is divergent whenever $p < 1$. Now consider the series $\sum_{n=1}^{\infty} \dfrac{1}{n^p}$ when $p > 1$. A suitable grouping of terms allows us to compare this series with a *convergent* geometric series:

$$1 + \frac{1}{2^p} + \frac{1}{3^p} + \frac{1}{4^p} + \frac{1}{5^p} + \frac{1}{6^p} + \frac{1}{7^p} + \cdots$$
$$< 1 + \frac{1}{2^p} + \frac{1}{2^p} + \frac{1}{4^p} + \frac{1}{4^p} + \frac{1}{4^p} + \frac{1}{4^p} + \cdots$$
$$= 1 + \frac{2}{2^p} + \frac{4}{4^p} + \cdots = 1 + \frac{1}{2^{p-1}} + \frac{1}{2^{2(p-1)}} + \cdots$$

which is a geometric series whose common ratio $1/2^{p-1}$ is less than 1. Summarising, we have the important result:

The series $\dfrac{1}{1^p} + \dfrac{1}{2^p} + \dfrac{1}{3^p} + \cdots + \dfrac{1}{n^p} + \cdots$ is convergent if $p > 1$ and divergent if $p \leqslant 1$.

This fact can be used to investigate the convergence of a wide class of series — in particular those in which $|a_n|$ is a rational function of n. The use of $\sum_{n=1}^{\infty} \dfrac{1}{n^p}$ as a test series is sometimes formalised as the so-called 'p-test':

If we can find a number p such that $\lim\limits_{n\to\infty} n^p |a_n| = A$, then

(i) $\sum\limits_{n=1}^{\infty} |a_n|$ converges if $p > 1$ and A is finite,

(ii) $\sum\limits_{n=1}^{\infty} |a_n|$ diverges if $p \leqslant 1$ and $A > 0$ (possibly infinite).

In practice the comparison with an appropriate test series of the form $\sum\limits_{n=1}^{\infty} \dfrac{1}{n^p}$ can be done very rapidly by inspection. If, for example, we have $|a_n| = \dfrac{5n^3 + 3}{2n^7 + 3n^2 + 4}$ then we need only note that for 'large' n the term $|a_n|$ behaves like $5/2n^4$. This is equivalent to carrying out the above 'p-test' and observing that a finite limit is obtained when $p = 4$. The series $\sum\limits_{n=1}^{\infty} (-1)^n \dfrac{5n^3 + 3}{2n^7 + 3n^2 + 4}$ is therefore absolutely convergent. Similarly, the fact that $\dfrac{n + 11}{n^2 + 6n + 4}$ behaves like $\dfrac{1}{n}$ for large n enables us to conclude at once that the series $\sum\limits_{n=1}^{\infty} \dfrac{n + 11}{n^2 + 6n + 4}$ diverges.

3.5.3 The ratio test and the root test

The most immediately useful forms of the comparison tests are obtained when we use the geometric series as a test series:

Ratio test (d'Alembert). Let $\sum\limits_{1}^{\infty} a_n$ be a series of positive terms.

(i) If $a_n/a_{n-1} < k < 1$ for all n, the series is convergent.

(ii) If $a_n/a_{n-1} \geqslant 1$ for all n, the series is divergent.

In particular, if the ratio a_n/a_{n-1} tends to a definite limit as n goes to infinity, say $\lim\limits_{n\to\infty} a_n/a_{n-1} = L$, then the series converges if $L < 1$ and diverges if $L > 1$.

Proof. (i) If $a_n/a_{n-1} < k < 1$ for every n then

$$a_n = \left\{ \frac{a_n}{a_{n-1}} \cdot \frac{a_{n-1}}{a_{n-2}} \cdots \frac{a_3}{a_2} \cdot \frac{a_2}{a_1} \right\} a_1 < a_1 . k^{n-1}$$

Since $k < 1$ the series $\displaystyle\sum_{n=1}^{\infty} a_1 k^{n-1}$ is a convergent geometric series.

Hence, by the comparison test, the series $\displaystyle\sum_{n=1}^{\infty} a_n$ is also convergent.

(ii) If $a_n/a_{n-1} \geqslant 1$ for all n then

$$a_n \geqslant a_{n-1} \geqslant a_{n-2} \geqslant \cdots \geqslant a_1$$

so that $a_1 + a_2 + \cdots + a_n \geqslant na_1$ which tends to ∞ with n.

Example. If $a_n = (n + 1)/2^n(n + 2)$, then

$$\frac{a_n}{a_{n-1}} = \frac{n + 1}{2^n(n + 2)} \cdot \frac{2^{n-1}(n + 1)}{n} = \frac{1}{2} \frac{n^2 + 2n + 1}{n^2 + 2n}$$

Thus $\displaystyle\lim_{n\to\infty} \frac{a_n}{a_{n-1}} = \frac{1}{2} < 1$, and so the series $\displaystyle\sum_{n-1}^{\infty} a_n$ converges.

Remark. If $\displaystyle\lim_{n\to\infty} \frac{a_n}{a_{n-1}} = 1$ then, in general, further investigation is called for. A glance at the proof of the ratio test shows that if the ratio a_n/a_{n-1} approaches 1 *from above,* then we may indeed conclude that the series $\displaystyle\sum_{1}^{\infty} a_n$ diverges. In all other cases, however, the ratio test fails when $\displaystyle\lim_{n\to\infty} a_n/a_{n-1} = 1$. For example,

$$1 + \frac{1}{2} + \frac{1}{3} + \frac{1}{4} + \ldots; \qquad \lim_{n\to\infty} \frac{a_n}{a_{n-1}} = \lim_{n\to\infty} \frac{n - 1}{n} = 1$$

$$1 + \frac{1}{2^2} + \frac{1}{3^2} + \frac{1}{4^2} + \ldots; \qquad \lim_{n\to\infty} \frac{a_n}{a_{n-1}} = \lim_{n\to\infty} \frac{(n - 1)^2}{n^2} = 1$$

We know, however, that the first series is divergent and the second convergent.

Root test (Cauchy). Let $\displaystyle\sum_{n=1}^{\infty} a_n$ be a series of positive terms.

(i) If $\sqrt[n]{a_n} < k < 1$ for all n, the series is convergent.

(ii) If $\sqrt[n]{a_n} \geqslant 1$ for infinitely many values of n, the series is divergent.

In particular, if $a_n^{1/n}$ tends to a limit L, then $\displaystyle\sum_{n=1}^{\infty} a_n$ converges when $L < 1$ and diverges when $L > 1$.

Proof. (i) If $\sqrt[n]{a_n} < k < 1$ for all n then $a_n < k^n$ and the geometric series $\displaystyle\sum_{1}^{\infty} k^n$ is convergent. Hence $\displaystyle\sum_{1}^{\infty} a_n$ also converges.

(ii) If $\sqrt[n]{a_n} \geqslant 1$ for infinitely many values of n then $a_n \geqslant 1$ for infinitely many values of n and so we cannot have $\displaystyle\lim_{n \to \infty} a_n = 0$. Hence, $\displaystyle\sum_{1}^{\infty} a_n$ diverges.

It can be shown that if the ratio a_n/a_{n-1} tends to a definite limit L as n goes to infinity then $\sqrt[n]{a_n}$ tends to the limit L also. That the root test is actually more general than the ratio test can be seen from the following example.

Example. $2(\frac{3}{4}) + (\frac{3}{4})^2 + 2(\frac{3}{4})^3 + \cdots + (\frac{3}{4})^{2m} + 2(\frac{3}{4})^{2m+1} + \cdots$

If n is even, then $a_n = (\frac{3}{4})^n$ and $a_{n-1} = 2(\frac{3}{4})^{n-1}$. Hence

$$\frac{a_n}{a_{n-1}} = (\tfrac{3}{4})^n / 2(\tfrac{3}{4})^{n-1} = \tfrac{3}{8}; \quad \sqrt[n]{a_n} = \tfrac{3}{4}$$

If n is odd, then $a_n = 2(\frac{3}{4})^n$ and $a_{n-1} = (\frac{3}{4})^{n-1}$. Hence

$$\frac{a_n}{a_{n-1}} = 2(\tfrac{3}{4})^n / (\tfrac{3}{4})^{n-1} = \tfrac{3}{2}; \quad \sqrt[n]{a_n} = \tfrac{3}{4} \sqrt[n]{2}$$

Thus, the ratio a_n/a_{n-1} oscillates between $\frac{3}{8}$ and $\frac{3}{2}$ and the ratio test cannot be applied. On the other hand, since $\displaystyle\lim_{n \to \infty} \sqrt[n]{2} = 1$, it follows that $\sqrt[n]{a_n}$ tends to the number $\frac{3}{4}$ as its limit as n goes to infinity. Hence the series is convergent by the root test.

Remark. If $\displaystyle\lim_{n \to \infty} \frac{a_n}{a_{n-1}} = 1$ then $\displaystyle\lim_{n \to \infty} \sqrt[n]{a_n} = 1$ also, and the ratio and root tests both fail. There are more delicate tests available for situations like this and, as an illustration, we quote one of the most useful:

Raabe's test. Let $\sum\limits_{n=1}^{\infty} a_n$ be a series of positive terms and suppose that

$$\lim_{n\to\infty} n\left(\frac{a_{n-1}}{a_n} - 1\right) = L$$

Then $\sum\limits_{n=1}^{\infty} a_n$ converges or diverges according as $L > 1$ or as $L < 1$.

As an example of of the use of Raabe's test consider the series

$$\sum_{n=1}^{\infty} \frac{1.3.5\,\cdots\,(2n-1)}{2.4.6\,\cdots\,(2n)} \cdot \frac{1}{n}$$

Here $\quad \dfrac{a_n}{a_{n-1}} = \dfrac{(2n-1)(n-1)}{(2n)n} \quad$ and so $\quad \lim\limits_{n\to\infty} \dfrac{a_n}{a_{n-1}} = 1$

Thus the ratio test (and hence also the root test) is inconclusive.

However, $\quad n\left(\dfrac{a_{n-1}}{a_n} - 1\right) = n\left(\dfrac{2n^2 - 2n^2 + 3n - 1}{(2n-1)(n-1)}\right) = \dfrac{3n^2 - n}{(2n-1)(n-1)}$

so that $\lim\limits_{n\to\infty} n\left(\dfrac{a_{n-1}}{a_n} - 1\right) = \frac{3}{2}$ and the series converges, by Raabe's test. (See Note 3.)

Exercises

1. Use either the ratio test or the root test to investigate the convergence of each of the following series:

(a) $\sum\limits_{n=1}^{\infty} \dfrac{n}{2^n}$, (b) $\sum\limits_{n=1}^{\infty} \dfrac{2^{3n}}{3^{2n}}$, (c) $\sum\limits_{n=1}^{\infty} \dfrac{3^n}{n^3}$, (d) $\sum\limits_{n=1}^{\infty} \dfrac{(2n)!}{(n!)(n!)}$,

(e) $\sum\limits_{n=1}^{\infty} \dfrac{n!}{n^n}$, (f) $\sum\limits_{n=1}^{\infty} \left(\dfrac{2n+3}{3n+2}\right)^n$, (g) $\sum\limits_{n=1}^{\infty} \dfrac{2^n + 3^n}{5^n}$.

2. Use the '*p*-test' to investigate the convergence of each of the following series:

(a) $\sum\limits_{n=1}^{\infty} \dfrac{1}{n^2 + n + 1}$, (b) $\sum\limits_{n=1}^{\infty} \dfrac{n}{4n^2 - 3}$; (c) $\sum\limits_{n=1}^{\infty} \dfrac{n + \sqrt{n}}{2n^3 - 1}$, (d) $\sum\limits_{n=1}^{\infty} \dfrac{3n}{\sqrt{(2n^3 + 1)}}$.

3. Show that the ratio test fails for the series,

$$\left(\frac{1}{3}\right)^2 + \left(\frac{1 \cdot 4}{3 \cdot 6}\right)^2 + \left(\frac{1 \cdot 4 \cdot 7}{3 \cdot 6 \cdot 9}\right)^2 + \cdots$$

but that convergence can be established using Raabe's test.

3.6 Power series

3.6.1 *Taylor series*
Suppose that the conditions for Taylor's theorem (section 2.5.3) apply to a function $f(x)$ over some interval (which may be finite or infinite). Let a be a fixed point in that interval and let x denote any other point in that interval. Then Taylor's theorem states that

$$f(x) = f(a) + (x - a)f'(a) + \frac{(x - a)^2}{2!} f''(a) + \cdots + \frac{(x - a)^n}{n!} f^{(n)}(a) + \mathrm{R}_n(x)$$

where $\mathrm{R}_n(x)$ denotes the remainder term (in either the Lagrange or the Cauchy form). Suppose now that

(i) $f(x)$ is actually *infinitely differentiable* over the interval concerned (that is, that $f^{(n)}(x)$ exists for each positive integral value of n).

(ii) for each x in the interval concerned we have $\lim\limits_{n \to \infty} \mathrm{R}_n(x) = 0$.

Then we can allow n to tend to infinity in Taylor's theorem and obtain an infinite series expansion for $f(x)$, called the *Taylor series* for $f(a)$ about the point $x = a$:

$$f(x) = f(a) + (x - a)f'(a) + \frac{(x - a)^2}{2!} f''(a) + \cdots + \frac{(x - a)^n}{n!} f^{(n)}(a) + \cdots$$

In the particular case when $a = 0$ we get

$$f(x) = f(0) + xf'(0) + \frac{x^2}{2!} f''(0) + \cdots + \frac{x^n}{n!} f^{(n)}(0) + \cdots$$

This is most often referred to as the *Maclaurin expansion* of $f(x)$, or the *Maclaurin series* for $f(x)$.

As an example we shall consider the function $f(x) = (1 + x)^\alpha$, where $x > -1$ and α is any given real number (rational or irrational). The successive derivatives of $f(x)$ are as follows

$f'(x) = \alpha(1 + x)^{\alpha - 1}$ so that $f'(0) = \alpha$

$f''(x) = \alpha(\alpha - 1)(1 + x)^{\alpha - 2}$ so that $f''(0) = \alpha(\alpha - 1)$

$f^{(k)}(x) = \alpha(\alpha - 1) \cdots (\alpha - k + 1)(1 + x)^{\alpha - k};$ $f^{(k)}(0) = \alpha(\alpha - 1) \cdots (\alpha - k + 1)$

Applying Taylor's theorem then gives

$$(1 + x)^\alpha = 1 + \alpha x + \frac{\alpha(\alpha - 1)}{2!} x^2 + \cdots + \frac{\alpha(\alpha - 1)(\alpha - 2) \cdots (\alpha - n + 1)}{n!} x^n + R_n(x)$$

For $x > 0$ we can write the remainder in the Lagrange form as

$$R_n(x) = \frac{x^{n+1}}{(n + 1)!} \alpha(\alpha - 1) \cdots (\alpha - n) \frac{(1 + \theta x)^\alpha}{(1 + x)^{n+1}} \qquad \text{where } 0 < \theta < 1.$$

If p denotes the smallest integer such that $|\alpha| \leqslant p$ then we have

$$|R_n(x)| \leqslant \left| \frac{\alpha(\alpha - 1)(\alpha - 2) \cdots (\alpha - n)}{(n + 1)!} \right| x^{n+1} (1 + x)^\alpha$$

$$\leqslant 2^p \frac{p(p + 1)(p + 2) \cdots (p + n)}{(n + 1)!} x^{n+1} = \frac{2^p}{(n + 1)!} \frac{(p + n)!}{(p - 1)!} x^{n+1}$$

$$= 2^p \frac{(n + 2)(n + 3) \cdots (n + p)}{(p - 1)!} x^{n+1} \leqslant \frac{2^p}{(p - 1)!} (n + p)^{p-1} x^{n+1}$$

For any value of x such that $0 < x < 1$ this shows that $\lim_{n \to \infty} R_n(x) = 0$.

On the other hand, for the range $-1 < x < 0$ we need to write the remainder in the Cauchy form (see 2.5.3, footnote)

$$R_n(x) = \frac{x^{n+1}}{n!} (1 - \theta)^n \alpha(\alpha - 1)(\alpha - 2) \cdots (\alpha - n) \frac{(1 + \theta x)^{n-1}}{(1 + \theta x)^n}$$

Then

$$|R_n(x)| \leqslant \frac{(1 - \theta)^n}{(1 - \theta |x|)^n} |x|^{n+1} \left| \frac{\alpha(\alpha - 1) \cdots (\alpha - n)}{n!} \right| |(1 + \theta x)^{\alpha - 1}|$$

Since $|x| < 1$ we must have $|(1 + \theta x)^{\alpha - 1}| \leqslant A$, where A is some finite number independent of n; again, since $0 < \theta < 1$ it must be the case that $(1 - \theta)/(1 - \theta |x|) < 1$. Hence, if p has the same significance as before

$$|R_n(x)| \leqslant A |x|^{n+1} \frac{p(p + 1)(p + 2) \cdots (p + n)}{n!} = \frac{A |x|^{n+1}}{(p - 1)!} \frac{(p + n)!}{n!}$$

$$= \frac{A |x|^{n+1}}{(p - 1)!} (n + 1)(n + 2) \cdots (n + p) \leqslant \frac{A |x|^{n+1}}{(p - 1)!} (n + p)^p$$

Once again it follows that $\lim_{n \to \infty} R_n(x) = 0$.

Thus we have shown that for any value of x such that $|x| < 1$ the function $(1 + x)^\alpha$ can be expanded as the following series

$$(1 + x)^\alpha = 1 + \alpha x + \frac{\alpha(\alpha - 1)}{2!} x^2 + \cdots + \frac{\alpha(\alpha - 1) \cdots (\alpha - n + 1)}{n!} x^n + \cdots$$

(This series is known as the *binomial series*. If α is a positive integer then the series terminates and reduces to the ordinary binomial expansion; clearly, there is no restriction on x in this case. For any other, non-zero, value of α we obtain an infinite series and the expansion is valid for the finite range $-1 < x < +1$.)

In general the calculation of the Taylor coefficients $f^{(n)}(a)/n!$ can be a complicated and tedious business; moreover it is often very difficult to discuss the behaviour of the remainder term. As will appear in the following sections there are other ways of developing infinite series expansions of functions. The Taylor expansion of a function $f(x)$ about a point $x = a$ is a series of a rather special kind, namely a series in ascending powers of $(x - a)$. Accordingly it is of particular importance to study the general properties of series of this type; without loss of generality we may assume that $a = 0$ in what follows.

3.6.2 *Interval of convergence*
A *power series* is any series of the form

$$\sum_{n=0}^{\infty} a_n x^n \equiv a_0 + a_1 x + a_2 x^2 + \cdots + a_n x^n + \cdots$$

In general we would expect such a series to converge for some values of the real variable x and to diverge for others. Suppose that it does converge (either absolutely or conditionally) for some particular value, say for $x = x_1$. Then it must be the case that $|a_n x_1^n| \to 0$ as $n \to \infty$, and hence that there exists some positive number k such that

$$|a_n x_1^n| < k \qquad \text{for every } n.$$

Now for any x such that $|x| < |x_1|$ we have

$$|a_n x^n| = |a_n x_1^n| \cdot \left| \frac{x}{x_1} \right|^n < k \left| \frac{x}{x_1} \right|^n$$

so that each term of the series $\sum_{n=0}^{\infty} |a_n x^n|$ is less than the corresponding term of the convergent series

$$k + k \left| \frac{x}{x_1} \right| + k \left| \frac{x}{x_1} \right|^2 + \cdots$$

Thus, $\sum_{n=0}^{\infty} a_n x^n$ is absolutely convergent for all x such that $|x| < |x_1|$.

Suppose on the other hand that the power series diverges for some value of

x, say for $x = x_2$. If the series were convergent for any value of x such that $|x| > |x_2|$ then, by what has been proved above, it would necessarily also con-

verge for $x = x_2$. Hence it must be true that $\displaystyle\sum_{n=0}^{\infty} a_n x^n$ diverges for every value

of x such that $|x| > |x_2|$.

These results together imply that, given any power series $\displaystyle\sum_{n=0}^{\infty} a_n x^n$, there

will be just three possibilities:

(i) the series converges when $x = 0$ and diverges for all other values of x,
(ii) the series converges for every value of x,
(iii) there exists a finite positive number, R, such that the series converges
    absolutely for every value of x such that $|x| < R$ and diverges for every
    value of x such that $|x| > R$.

The number R in case (iii) is called the *radius of convergence* of the power
series and the interval $-R < x < +R$ is called the *interval of convergence*. In
case (i) we say that the series has *zero* radius of convergence, and that the
'interval' of convergence reduces to the single point $x = 0$; in case (ii) we say
that the series has an *infinite* radius of convergence and that the interval of
convergence becomes the entire x-axis.

3.6.3 *Calculation of radius of convergence*

Suppose that, in the case of a particular power series $\displaystyle\sum_{n=0}^{\infty} a_n x^n$, the ratio

$|a_{n+1}/a_n|$ tends to a definite limit, L, as n goes to infinity. Applying the ratio

test to the series of positive terms $\displaystyle\sum_{n=0}^{\infty} |a_n| \cdot |x|^n$, we have

$$\lim_{n \to \infty} \frac{|a_{n+1}| \cdot |x|^{n+1}}{|a_n| \cdot |x|^n} = \lim_{n \to \infty} |x| \cdot \left|\frac{a_{n+1}}{a_n}\right| = L|x|$$

The series $\displaystyle\sum_{n=0}^{\infty} a_n x^n$ is therefore absolutely convergent for all values of x such

that $L|x| < 1$, that is for all x such that

$$|x| < 1/L$$

It follows that the radius of convergence, R, is given by

$$R = \frac{1}{L} = 1/\lim_{n \to \infty} \left| \frac{a_{n+1}}{a_n} \right|$$

A similar argument, using the root test, shows that, provided the limit concerned exists, we have $R = 1/\lim_{n \to \infty} \sqrt[n]{|a_n|}$.

In most cases of practical interest it turns out that $\lim_{n \to \infty} \sqrt[n]{|a_n|}$ does exist (or else that $\sqrt[n]{|a_n|}$ diverges to $+\infty$), and we shall assume that this is so in all that follows. Note that the root test (and the ratio test) will leave the question of convergence undecided when $|x| = 1/L$. The behaviour of a power series at the points $x = \pm R$ (the end-points of its interval of convergence) cannot be decided on general grounds, and must be investigated separately in individual cases.

*3.6.4 *Manipulations with power series*

If $\displaystyle\sum_{n=0}^{\infty} a_n x^n$ has a radius of convergence R then it converges for all x such that $x < R$ and hence represents a well defined function in that range. We may write

$$\alpha(x) \equiv \sum_{n=0}^{\infty} a_n x^n \quad \text{for } -R < x < +R$$

Suppose now that $\beta(x) \equiv \displaystyle\sum_{n=0}^{\infty} b_n x^n$ is another function of x defined by a power series which has the same radius of convergence, R, as $\alpha(x)$. It follows readily enough that if x is any point in the common interval of convergence, $-R < x < +R$ then

$$\sum_{n=0}^{\infty} (a_n + b_n)x^n = \alpha(x) + \beta(x)$$

It is also the case that

$$\sum_{n=0}^{\infty} [a_0 b_n + a_1 b_{n-1} + a_2 b_{n-2} + \ldots + a_{n-1} b_1 + a_n b_0] x^n = \alpha(x)\, \beta(x)$$

but this result is rather more troublesome to establish. Essentially the proof consists of three stages. First, by expanding the product

$$\left(\sum_{k=0}^{n} a_k x^k\right)\left(\sum_{k=0}^{n} b_k x^k\right),$$ we can show that the series

$$a_0 b_0 + [a_0 b_1 x + a_1 b_1 x^2 + a_1 b_0 x] + [a_0 b_2 x^2 + a_1 b_2 x^3 + a_2 b_2 x^4 + a_2 b_1 x^3 + a_2 b_0 x^2] + \ldots$$

converges to the sum $\alpha(x)\beta(x)$. Next, by applying the same arguments to the

product $\left(\sum_{k=0}^{n} |a_k| . |x|^k\right)\left(\sum_{k=0}^{n} |b_k| . |x|^k\right),$ we can show that the series

$$|a_0 b_0| + \left[|a_0 b_1||x| + |a_1 b_1||x|^2 + |a_1 b_0||x|\right] + \cdots$$

converges and therefore that

$$a_0 b_0 + a_0 b_1 x + a_1 b_1 x^2 + a_1 b_0 x + a_0 b_2 x^2 + a_1 b_2 x^3 + \cdots$$

is actually an *absolutely* convergent series. It is this fact which allows us to re-arrange and re-group the terms to give the final result.

Example. The importance of the above result on the multiplication of power series can be seen from its application to the exponential series. The function $\epsilon(x)$ is defined for all real x as the power series

$$\epsilon(x) = 1 + x + x^2/2! + x^3/3! + \cdots + x^n/n! + \cdots.$$

Hence,

$$\epsilon(ax) . \epsilon(bx) \equiv \left\{1 + ax + \frac{a^2}{2!} x^2 + \frac{a^3}{3!} x^3 + \cdots\right\}\left\{1 + bx + \frac{b^2}{2!} x^2 + \frac{b^3}{3!} x^3 + \cdots\right\}$$

$$= 1 + (a + b)x + \left(\frac{a^2}{2!} + ab + \frac{b^2}{2!}\right)x^2 + \left(\frac{a^3}{3!} + \frac{a^2 b}{2!} + \frac{ab^2}{2!} + \frac{b^3}{3!}\right)x^3 + \cdots$$

$$= 1 + (a + b)x + \frac{1}{2!}(a + b)^2 x^2 + \frac{1}{3!}(a + b)^3 x^3 + \cdots = \quad [(a + b)x]$$

The final property of a power series which we shall consider here concerns the *differentiability* of the sum function within the interval of convergence. If

$$\alpha(x) = \sum_{n=0}^{\infty} a_n x^n$$ has radius of convergence R, let $\phi(x)$ denote the series obtained

from $\alpha(x)$ by formally differentiating $\sum_{n=0}^{\infty} a_n x^n$ term by term. That is to say

$$\phi(x) \equiv \sum_{n=1}^{\infty} n a_n x^{n-1}$$

Note first that $\lim\limits_{n\to\infty} \sqrt[n]{(n|a_n|)} = \lim\limits_{n\to\infty} \sqrt[n]{n} \cdot \sqrt[n]{|a_n|} = 1/R$, since $\lim\limits_{n\to\infty} \sqrt[n]{n} = 1$. Thus, the power series which defines $\phi(x)$ has the same interval of convergence as that which defines $\alpha(x)$. Moreover, if x and $x + h$ are points within the common interv of convergence of these two series then it can be shown that the quantity

$$\left| \frac{\alpha(x+h) - \alpha(x)}{h} - \phi(x) \right| = \left| \sum_{n=0}^{\infty} a_n \left\{ \frac{(x+h)^n - x^n}{h} - nx^{n-1} \right\} \right|$$

can be made arbitrarily small by making $|h|$ sufficiently small. (The proof of this is straightforward in principle but somewhat complicated in detail and will not be discussed here.) That is to say, $\phi(x)$ is the derivative of $\alpha(x)$:

$$\alpha(x) = a_0 + a_1x + a_2x^2 + \cdots + a_nx^n + \cdots \quad , \ |x| < R$$

$$\alpha'(x) = \quad a_1 + 2a_2x + \cdots + na_nx^{n-1} + \cdots, \ |x| < R$$

The same argument applied to the power series $\alpha'(x)$ gives

$$\alpha''(x) = 2a_2 + 3a_3x + \cdots + n(n-1)a_nx^{n-2} + \cdots, \ |x| < R$$

and so on. It follows that the power series $\sum\limits_{n=0}^{\infty} a_nx^n$ can be differentiated term-by-term as often as we wish at any point x within the interval of convergenc and that the sum-function $\alpha(x)$ is an *infinitely differentiable* function throughout that interval.

Since for any positive integer k we have

$$\alpha^{(k)}(x) = \sum_{n=k}^{\infty} n(n-1) \cdots (n-k+1)a_nx^{n-k}$$

we can obtain the following explicit representation for the coefficients a_n

$$a_k = \frac{\alpha^{(k)}(0)}{k!}$$

In other words the following theorem holds:

Theorem 8. Every power series $\sum\limits_{n=0}^{\infty} a_nx^n$ is the Maclaurin series of its sum function $\alpha(x)$:

$$\alpha(x) = \alpha(0) + x\,\alpha'(0) + \frac{x^2}{2!}\alpha''(0) + \cdots + \frac{x^n}{n!}\alpha^{(n)}(0) + \cdots$$

Exercises

1. Find the radius of convergence of each of the following power series:

(a) $\displaystyle\sum_{n=1}^{\infty} \frac{n!}{(2n)!} x^{n-1}$,   (b) $\displaystyle\sum_{n=1}^{\infty} \frac{(n!)^2}{(2n)!} x^{n-1}$,   (c) $\displaystyle\sum_{n=0}^{\infty} \frac{x^n}{\sqrt{n}}$,

(d) $\displaystyle\sum_{n=1}^{\infty} (n!) x^{n-1}$,   (e) $\displaystyle\sum_{n=0}^{\infty} \left(\frac{n+1}{n+2}\right)^n x^n$.

2. Expand each of the following functions in power series, stating in each case the region in which the expansion is valid:

(a) $\dfrac{1}{(1-x)^2}$,   (b) $\dfrac{1}{2-x^2}$,   (c) $\dfrac{1+x}{1-x}$,   (d) $\dfrac{1}{(2-x^2)^2}$.

3.7 Special functions and series

Theorem 3.8 provides the necessary link between the theory of infinite series and the general theory of functions of a real variable discussed in chapter 2. We conclude with a treatment of the exponential function and of the more important of the transcendental functions associated with it. Apart from the intrinsic importance of the subject-matter, this provides a useful illustration of the value and significance of infinite series in real variable theory.

3.7.1 *The exponential function*

The ratio test shows that the exponential series, $1 + x + x^2/2! + x^3/3! + \cdots$, has infinite radius of convergence; hence its sum-function $\epsilon(x)$ is defined as a differentiable function for all x. Differentiating term by term

$$\epsilon'(x) = 1 + x + \frac{x^2}{2!} + \frac{x^3}{3!} + \cdots = \epsilon(x)$$

and it is clear that $\epsilon(0) = 1$. Thus $\epsilon(x)$ satisfies the differential equation

$$\frac{dy}{dx} = y$$

subject to the condition $y = 0$ when $x = 1$.

Next, by direct multiplication of the power series concerned we can show, as in section 3.6.3, that

$$\epsilon[(a+b)x] = \epsilon(ax) \cdot \epsilon(bx)$$

Setting $x = 1$ we obtain the so-called *addition theorem* for $\epsilon(x)$

$$\epsilon(a + b) = \epsilon(a) . \epsilon(b)$$

This addition theorem and the fact that $\epsilon(x)$ is its own derivative are the two most fundamental and characteristic properties of the exponential function. From them we can establish all the familiar features of this function and give a comprehensive account of its behaviour:

(i) Putting $a = x$ and $b = -x$ in the addition theorem, we obtain

$$\epsilon(x) . \epsilon(-x) = \epsilon(0) = 1$$

which shows that
$$\epsilon(-x) = 1/\epsilon x)$$

and also that there can be no value of x such that $\epsilon(x) = 0$.

It is clear from the definition of $\epsilon(x)$ as the sum-function of the exponential series that if $0 < x_1 < x_2$ then $\epsilon(x_1) < \epsilon(x_2)$. Since $\epsilon(-x) = 1/\epsilon(x)$ it follows that $\epsilon(-x_2) < \epsilon(-x_1)$; that is, $\epsilon(x)$ is a strictly monotone increasing function for all x.

Now let n be any positive integer. Then for any $x > 0$

$$\frac{\epsilon(x)}{x^n} = \frac{1}{x^n} \left\{ 1 + x + \frac{x^2}{2!} + \cdots + \frac{x^{n+1}}{(n+1)!} + \cdots \right\} > \frac{x}{(n+1)!}$$

Hence $\lim_{x \to \infty} \epsilon(x)/x^n = +\infty$, and so the function $\epsilon(x)$ increases more rapidly than any power of x. In particular, $\lim_{x \to \infty} \epsilon(x) = +\infty$ and, since $\epsilon(-x) = 1/\epsilon(x)$, it follows that $\lim_{x \to -\infty} \epsilon(x) = 0$.

(ii) For $x = 1$ the exponential series becomes

$$\epsilon(1) = 1 + 1 + 1/2! + 1/3! + \cdots + 1/n! + \cdots$$

and this number, as is customary, we denote by the symbol e. If m is any positive integer then, using the addition theorem

$$\epsilon(m) = \epsilon(m - 1) . \epsilon(1) = \epsilon(m - 2) . \{\epsilon(1)\}^2 = \cdots$$
$$= \{\epsilon(1)\}^m \equiv e^m$$

Now let r be any positive rational number and suppose that $r = m/n$ where m and n are positive integers. Then

$$\{\epsilon(r)\}^n = \epsilon(nr) = \epsilon(m) = e^m$$

and so
$$\epsilon(r) = e^{m/n} \equiv e^r, \quad \text{for any positive rational } r.$$

If r is a negative rational, say $r = -s$, then we have

$$\epsilon(-s) = 1/\epsilon(s) = e^{-s}$$

Accordingly we adopt the usual notation and write $\epsilon(x) \equiv e^x$; when x is irrational this now serves as the *definition* of the power e^x.

(iii) Write $E_n = 1 + 1 + \dfrac{1}{2!} + \dfrac{1}{3!} + \cdots + \dfrac{1}{n!}$, and $A_n = \left(1 + \dfrac{1}{n}\right)^n$.

Expanding by the binomial theorem we find that

$$A_n = 1 + n \cdot \frac{1}{n} + \frac{n(n-1)}{2!}\frac{1}{n^2} + \cdots \frac{n(n-1)\cdots(n-n+1)}{n!} \cdot \frac{1}{n^n}$$

$$= 1 + 1 + \frac{1}{2!}\left(1 - \frac{1}{n}\right) + \cdots + \frac{1}{n!}\left(1 - \frac{1}{n}\right)\left(1 - \frac{2}{n}\right)\cdots\left(1 - \frac{n-1}{n}\right)$$

Clearly, $A_n < 1 + 1 + \dfrac{1}{2!} + \dfrac{1}{3!} + \cdots + \dfrac{1}{n!} = E_n$, for every n,

and so

$$\lim_{n\to\infty} A_n \leqslant \lim_{n\to\infty} E_n = e$$

On the other hand, if $m > n$ then

$$A_m > 1 + \frac{1}{2!}\left(1 - \frac{1}{m}\right) + \cdots + \frac{1}{n!}\left(1 - \frac{1}{m}\right)\left(1 - \frac{2}{m}\right)\cdots\left(1 - \frac{n-1}{m}\right)$$

Hence, keeping n fixed and allowing m to tend to infinity

$$\lim_{m\to\infty} A_m \geqslant 1 + 1 + \frac{1}{2!} + \cdots + \frac{1}{n!} = E_n$$

and it follows that

$$\lim_{n\to\infty}\left(1 + \frac{1}{n}\right)^n = \lim_{n\to\infty} E_n = e$$

This limit is an important one and in some texts is taken as the definition of the number e. For the numerical computation of e, however, we would expect to use E_n rather than A_n as an approximation. Note that

$$e - E_n = \frac{1}{(n+1)!} + \frac{1}{(n+2)!} + \frac{1}{(n+3)!} + \cdots$$

$$= \frac{1}{(n+1)!}\left\{1 + \frac{1}{n+2} + \frac{1}{(n+2)(n+3)} + \cdots\right\}$$

$$< \frac{1}{(n+1)!}\left\{1 + \frac{1}{n+1} + \frac{1}{(n+1)^2} + \cdots\right\} = \frac{1}{(n+1)!} \cdot \frac{n+1}{n} = \frac{1}{n(n!)}$$

that is, the error in taking E_n as an approximation to e can never exceed $\dfrac{1}{n(n!)}$.

3.7.2 *The logarithmic function*

The logarithmic function is the inverse of the exponential function. If $x = e^y$ then, as y ranges from $-\infty$ through 0 to $+\infty$, so e^y increases steadily and continuously from 0 through 1 to $+\infty$. Hence, for each *positive* value of x there will be one and only one value for y; this value will be positive or negative according as $x > 1$ or as $x < 1$, and we write $y = \log x$. Using the results of section 2.9 on inverse functions it follows that

$$\frac{dy}{dx} = 1 \bigg/ \frac{dx}{dy} = e^{-y} = \frac{1}{x}$$

The characteristic properties of the logarithmic function are simple consequences of its definition as the inverse of the exponential function. The verification of the entries in the following table is left as an exercise.

Properties of exponential and logarithmic functions (*see figure 3.4*)

(i) $e^x > 0$ for all x ; $\log x$ defined for all $x > 0$

(ii) $\dfrac{d}{dx} e^x = e^x$; $\dfrac{d}{dx} \log x = \dfrac{1}{x}$

(iii) $e^{x+y} = e^x \cdot e^y$; $\log(xy) = \log x + \log y$

(iv) $e^0 = 1$; $\log 1 = 0$

(v) $\lim\limits_{x \to \infty} \left\{ \dfrac{e^x}{x^n} \right\} = +\infty$; $\lim\limits_{x \to \infty} \left\{ \dfrac{\log x}{x^n} \right\} = 0$

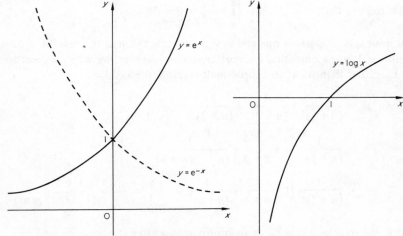

Fig. 3.4 Exponential and logarithmic functions

The point $x = 0$ is a singularity of the logarithmic function since $\log x$ tends to $-\infty$ as x approaches 0. However, the function $\log(1 + x)$ is well behaved in the neighbourhood of $x = 0$ and we can obtain the following Maclaurin expansion:

$$\log(1 + x) = x - \frac{x^2}{2} + \frac{x^3}{3} - \frac{x^4}{4} + \cdots, \qquad -1 < x \leqslant +1$$

The ratio test shows that the series converges absolutely for $|x| < 1$; when $x = 1$ we obtain the conditionally convergent series studied in section 3.4.3, giving the important special result

$$\log 2 = 1 - \tfrac{1}{2} + \tfrac{1}{3} - \tfrac{1}{4} + \tfrac{1}{5} - \cdots$$

Writing $-x$ for x in the series for $\log(1 + x)$ we get

$$\log(1 - x) = -x - \frac{x^2}{2} - \frac{x^3}{3} - \frac{x^4}{4} - \cdots, \qquad -1 \leqslant x < +1$$

so that, combining the two series

$$\log \frac{1 + x}{1 - x} = 2\left\{ x + \frac{x^3}{3} + \frac{x^5}{5} + \cdots \right\}, \qquad -1 < x < +1$$

3.7.3 *Hyperbolic functions*

The hyperbolic functions, $\cosh x$ and $\sinh x$, may be defined as linear combinations of real exponentials or else directly as the sum-functions of the appropriate power series:

$$\cosh x \equiv \tfrac{1}{2}(e^x + e^{-x}) = 1 + \frac{x^2}{2!} + \frac{x^2}{4!} + \frac{x^6}{6!} + \cdots, \qquad \text{for all } x$$

$$\sinh x \equiv \tfrac{1}{2}(e^x - e^{-x}) = x + \frac{x^3}{3!} + \frac{x^5}{5!} + \frac{x^7}{7!} + \cdots, \qquad \text{for all } x$$

It follows at once from the definitions that

$$\cosh x + \sinh x = e^x, \qquad \cosh x - \sinh x = e^{-x}$$

$$\cosh^2 x - \sinh^2 x = 1$$

$$\frac{d}{dx} \cosh x = \sinh x \qquad \text{and} \qquad \frac{d}{dx} \sinh x = \cosh x$$

Now let $x = \sinh y = \tfrac{1}{2}(e^y - e^{-y})$ so that

$$e^{2y} - 2xe^y - 1 = 0$$

that is

$$e^y = x \pm \sqrt{(x^2 + 1)}$$

If $y = \sinh^{-1} x$ is to be real then e^y must be positive. Hence the inverse function $\sinh^{-1} x$ is defined as the *single-valued* function,

$$y = \log\{x + \sqrt{(x^2 + 1)}\}$$

Again, $dx/dy = \cosh y = \sqrt{(x^2 + 1)}$, and since $\cosh y$ is essentially positive there is no ambiguity of sign and we can write (see figure 3.5)

$$\frac{d}{dx} \sinh^{-1} x = \frac{1}{\sqrt{(1 + x^2)}}$$

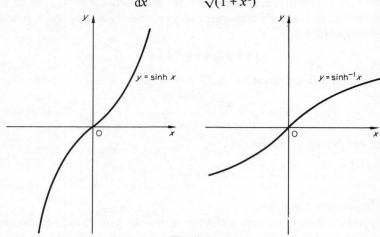

Fig. 3.5

In contrast, if $x = \cosh y = \frac{1}{2}(e^y + e^{-y})$ then a similar argument gives

$$e^y = x \pm \sqrt{(x^2 - 1)}$$

This time for any given value of x greater than unity there are two values of y and for these dy/dx has opposite signs (see figure 3.6)

$$y = \log\{x \pm \sqrt{(x^2 - 1)}\} \qquad \text{and} \qquad \frac{d}{dx} \cosh^{-1} x = \pm \frac{1}{\sqrt{(x^2 - 1)}}$$

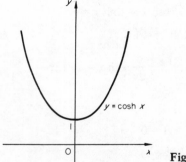
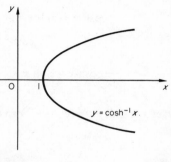

Fig. 3.6

3.7.4 *The circular functions*

(i) At an elementary level the functions $\sin x$, $\cos x$, etc. are defined as trigonometric functions of the angle x (measured in radians). Various trigonometric identities, and familiar results such as

$$\frac{d}{dx} \sin x = \cos x, \qquad \frac{d}{dx} \cos x = -\sin x, \text{ etc.}$$

are then derived by judicious appeals to geometric intuition. Using such results we eventually arrive at the following Maclaurin expansions, valid for all real x

$$\sin x = x - \frac{x^3}{3!} + \frac{x^5}{5!} + \frac{x^7}{7!} + \cdots$$

$$\cos x = 1 - \frac{x^2}{2!} + \frac{x^4}{4!} + \frac{x^6}{6!} + \cdots$$

A rigorous treatment of the functions $\sin x$ and $\cos x$ may be developed by using the above power series as *definitions* of the functions concerned. Such a procedure is possible just because each of these series is absolutely convergent for every real value of x.

However, as already remarked in section 1.2.8, the series expansions of $\sin x$ and $\cos x$ lead formally to expressions of these functions in terms of complex exponentials

$$\cos x = \frac{1}{2}\{e^{ix} + e^{-ix}\}, \qquad \sin x = \frac{1}{2i}\{e^{ix} - e^{-ix}\}$$

$$e^{ix} = \cos x + i \sin x, \qquad e^{-ix} = \cos x - i \sin x$$

To justify fully the steps taken here would lead us outside the scope of this book, but we can at least sketch the principal concepts and processes involved:

A series $\sum\limits_{n=0}^{\infty} (a_n + ib_n)$ of complex terms is defined to be convergent to the

(complex) sum A + iB if and only if the real series $\sum\limits_{n=0}^{\infty} a_n$ and $\sum\limits_{n=0}^{\infty} b_n$ converge,

in the usual sense, to the sums A and B respectively. It is said to be absolutely

convergent if and only if the real series $\sum\limits_{n=0}^{\infty} |a_n + ib_n| \equiv \sum\limits_{n=0}^{\infty} \sqrt{(a_n^2 + b_n^2)}$ is

convergent. We can show that, as for real series, absolute convergence implies convergence, and that the terms of an absolutely convergent series may be re-arranged and re-grouped at will. Then, with these facts established, it is a straightforward matter to show that the series obtained by replacing x by ix in the exponential series converges (absolutely) to the sum $\cos x + i \sin x$.

(ii) *Inverse functions.* The functions $\cos^{-1} x$ is defined only for $|x| \leqslant 1$ and is infinitely many valued. We usually take $\cos^{-1} x$ to mean the angle between 0 and π whose cosine is x; then $d(\cos^{-1}x)/dx = -1/\sqrt{(1 - x^2)}$ (see figure 3.7)

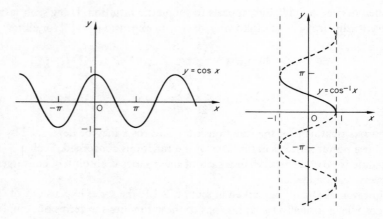

Fig. 3.7

The function $\sin^{-1} x$ is defined only for $|x| \leqslant 1$ and is infinitely many valued. We usually take $\sin^{-1} x$ to mean the angle between $-\pi/2$ and $\pi/2$ whose sine is x; then $d(\sin^{-1}x)/dx = +1/\sqrt{(1 - x^2)}$ (see figure 3.8).

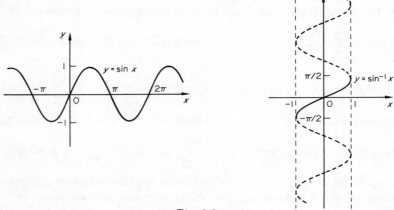

Fig. 3.8

The function $\tan x$ is defined by the relation

$$y = \tan x = \frac{\sin x}{\cos x} = \frac{1}{i}\frac{e^{ix} - e^{-ix}}{e^{ix} + e^{-ix}}$$

and is a function with singularities at the points $\pm n\pi/2$; its derivative is given by

$$\frac{d}{dx}\tan x = \frac{1}{\cos^2 x} \equiv \sec^2 x$$

Note that although $\tan^{-1} x$ is infinitely many-valued, its derivative is the *single-valued* function (see figure 3.9)

$$\frac{dy}{dx} = \frac{1}{1 + x^2}$$

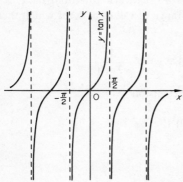

Fig. 3.9

Exercises

1. Using the definitions of $\sinh x$ and $\cosh x$ given in section 3.7.3, establish the following formulae:

    (a) $\cosh^2 x + \sinh^2 y = \sinh^2 x + \cosh^2 y = \cosh(x + y)\cosh(x - y)$.
    (b) $\cosh^2 x - \cosh^2 y = \sinh^2 x - \sinh^2 y = \sinh(x + y)\sinh(x - y)$.
    (c) $\sinh x + \sinh y = 2\sinh\tfrac{1}{2}(x + y)\cosh\tfrac{1}{2}(x - y)$.
    (d) $\sinh x - \sinh y = 2\cosh\tfrac{1}{2}(x + y)\sinh\tfrac{1}{2}(x - y)$.
    (e) $\cosh x + \cosh y = 2\cosh\tfrac{1}{2}(x + y)\cosh\tfrac{1}{2}(x - y)$.
    (f) $\cosh x - \cosh y = 2\sinh\tfrac{1}{2}(x + y)\sinh\tfrac{1}{2}(x - y)$.

2. The hyperbolic functions $\tanh x$, $\coth x$, $\operatorname{cosech} x$ and $\operatorname{sech} x$ are defined as follows:

$$\tanh x = \frac{\sinh x}{\cosh x}, \quad \coth x = \frac{\cosh x}{\sinh x}, \quad \operatorname{cosech} x = \frac{1}{\sinh x}, \quad \operatorname{sech} x = \frac{1}{\cosh x}.$$

Show that

(a) $\quad \sinh 2x = \dfrac{2 \tanh x}{1 - \tanh^2 x}, \quad \cosh 2x = \dfrac{1 + \tanh^2 x}{1 - \tanh^2 x} \; ;$

(b) $\quad \tanh \dfrac{x}{2} = \dfrac{\sinh x}{\cosh x + 1} = \dfrac{\cosh x - 1}{\sinh x} = \sqrt{\left(\dfrac{\cosh x - 1}{\cosh x + 1} \right)};$

(c) $\quad \dfrac{\mathrm{d}}{\mathrm{d}x} \tanh x = \operatorname{sech}^2 x, \quad \dfrac{\mathrm{d}}{\mathrm{d}x} \coth x = -\operatorname{cosech}^2 x,$

$\quad \dfrac{\mathrm{d}}{\mathrm{d}x} \operatorname{sech} x = -\dfrac{\sinh x}{\cosh^2 x}, \quad \dfrac{\mathrm{d}}{\mathrm{d}x} \operatorname{cosech} x = -\dfrac{\cosh x}{\sinh^2 x}.$

(d) Obtain explicit logarithmic formulae for the inverse functions $\tanh^{-1} x$ and $\coth^{-1} x$, stating in each case the range of values of x for which these functions are defined. Confirm that

$$\frac{\mathrm{d}}{\mathrm{d}x} \tanh^{-1} x = \frac{1}{1 - x^2} \quad \text{and} \quad \frac{\mathrm{d}}{\mathrm{d}x} \coth^{-1} x = -\frac{1}{x^2 - 1}$$

3. By direct application of the Maclaurin expansion

$$f(x) = f(0) + x \, f'(0) + \frac{x^2}{2!} f''(0) + \frac{x^3}{3!} f'''(0) + \cdots,$$

show that

(a) $\quad \cos^2 x = 1 - x^2 + \dfrac{2^3 x^4}{4!} - \dfrac{2^5 x^6}{6!} + \cdots$

(b) $\quad \cosh x \cos x = 1 - \dfrac{2^2 x^4}{4!} + \dfrac{2^4 x^8}{8!} - \dfrac{2^6 x^{12}}{12!} + \cdots$

(c) $\quad e^x \sin x = x + x^2 + \dfrac{2x^3}{3!} - \dfrac{2^2 x^5}{5!} - \dfrac{2^3 x^6}{6!} - \dfrac{2^3 x^7}{7!} + \cdots$

4. Confirm the results of Ex. 1 above by multiplying together the known expansions for $\cos x$, $\cosh x$, $\sin x$, and e^x, as appropriate.

5. The function $\sec x$ is even, that is $\sec(-x) = \sec x$; hence its Maclaurin expansion must take the form

$$\sec x = a_0 + a_2 x^2 + a_4 x^4 + a_6 x^6 + \cdots$$

By using the series for $\cos x$, and the relation $\sec x \cos x = 1$, determine the coefficients a_0, a_2, a_4, a_6.

Devise a similar technique to show that

$$\tan x = x + \frac{x^3}{3} + \frac{2x^5}{15} + \frac{17x^7}{315} + \cdots$$

6. If $y = a_0 + a_1 x + a_2 x^2 + a_3 x^3 + \cdots$, is a solution of the differential equation

$$(1 - x^2)\frac{d^2 y}{dx^2} - x\frac{dy}{dx} = 0, \text{ show that}$$

$$(n + 2)(n + 1)a_{n+2} - n^2 a_n = 0, \quad \text{for } n \geqslant 1.$$

Hence derive the result

$$\sin^{-1} x = x + \frac{x^3}{6} + \frac{3}{40}x^5 + \frac{15}{336}x^7 + \cdots, \quad |x| < 1$$

NOTES ON CHAPTER 3

1. Sequences and subsequences

Let (A_n) be any sequence of real numbers. By a *subsequence* of (A_n) we mean any sequence obtained by selecting terms from (A_n), in the same relative order as they occur in that sequence. The terms selected may be denoted by $A_{n_1}, A_{n_2}, A_{n_3}, \ldots$, where (n_k) is a certain monotone increasing sequence of positive integers. (For example, taking $n_k = 2k - 1$ gives the subsequence of (A_n) which consists of all the odd-numbered terms: $A_1, A_3, A_5, \ldots$.) If (A_{n_k}) is a subsequence which happens to be a convergent sequence then its limit is said to be a *subsequential* limit of the original sequence (A_n). For a sequence which is unbounded it may happen that no infinite subsequence is convergent; the set of all its subsequential limits would then be empty. But for bounded sequences, whether convergent or not, the following crucial result can be proved:

Theorem. Every bounded infinite sequence (A_n) contains an infinite subsequence which is convergent.

The set of all subsequential limits of a bounded sequence is, therefore, not empty. It is necessarily a bounded set and hence, by the fundamental property of the real number system, has a greatest lower bound, α, and a least upper bound β. These numbers can be characterised explicitly as follows:

The number α is called the *lower limit* of the sequence (A_n); given any positive number ϵ, however small, infinitely many terms of the sequence will be less than $\alpha + \epsilon$ but only finitely many terms will be less than $\alpha - \epsilon$. We write

$$\alpha = \varliminf_{n \to \infty} A_n \qquad \text{or} \qquad \alpha = \liminf_{n \to \infty} A_n$$

The number β is called the *upper limit* of the sequence (A_n); given any positive number ϵ, however small, infinitely many terms of the sequence will be greater than $\beta - \epsilon$ but only finitely many terms will be greater than $\beta + \epsilon$. We write

$$\beta = \varlimsup_{n \to \infty} A_n \qquad \text{or} \qquad \beta = \limsup_{n \to \infty} A_n$$

If $\alpha = \beta$ then the sequence (A_n) converges to this common value as its limit; if $\alpha < \beta$ then the sequence does not converge. Equivalently we have the result: a bounded sequence (A_n) converges to a limit A if and only if every infinite subsequence (A_{n_k}) of (A_n) also converges to the same limit A.

2. Iterative processes

In the text we have been primarily concerned with sequences of partial sums of series. But this is by no means the only way (or even the most important way) in which sequences arise. In a typical iterative procedure we hope to generate a sequence of successive approximations to a desired solution, and it is clearly important to know whether or not such a sequence converges. Consider, for example, the following situation:

Let $f(x)$ be a differentiable function defined on the interval $0 \leqslant x \leqslant 1$ and suppose that throughout this interval we have

$$|f'(x)| \leqslant k < 1$$

This means that if x and y are any two points in $[0, 1]$ then

$$|f(x) - f(y)| \leqslant k|x - y|$$

Now choose x_1 arbitrarily in $[0, 1]$ and generate a sequence (x_n) by iteration:

$$x_{n+1} = f(x_n)$$

Then

$$|x_{n+p} - x_n| \leqslant k|x_{n+p-1} - x_{n-1}| \leqslant \cdots \leqslant k^{n-1}|x_{p+1} - x_1|$$

$$\leqslant k^{n-1}(|x_2 - x_1| + |x_3 - x_2| + \cdots + |x_{p+1} - x_p|)$$

$$\leqslant k^{n-1}|x_2 - x_1|(1 + k + k^2 + \cdots + k^{p-1}) \leqslant \frac{k^{n-1}}{1-k}|x_2 - x_1|$$

Since $k < 1$ it follows that $|x_{n+p} - x_n|$ tends to 0 as n goes to infinity and therefore that there exists some point x in $[0, 1]$ such that $x = \lim_{n \to \infty} x_n$. By the continuity of $f(x)$ we have

$$f(x) = f\left\{\lim_{n \to \infty} x_n\right\} = \lim_{n \to \infty} f(x_n) = \lim_{n \to \infty} x_{n+1} = x$$

Thus we have shown the existence of a solution to the equation

$$f(x) = x \qquad (0 \leqslant x \leqslant 1)$$

and also that the iterative process defined above will actually converge to this solution. (See Exercise 3 of section 3.3, and Nos. 3, 4, 5, of the Miscellaneous Exercises of this chapter.) The principle employed in the above argument generalises to apply to situations involving iterative solutions of systems of linear algebraic equations, certain types of differential equation, and important types of integral equation. In a general context it is known as the *Principle of the contraction mapping*.

3. Convergence tests

In testing series for absolute convergence the ratio and root tests are the most frequently employed. A glance at the proofs of these tests, given in section 3.5.3, makes it clear that we do not actually need the existence of the limits

$$\lim_{n \to \infty} \left| \frac{a_{n+1}}{a_n} \right| \text{ and } \lim_{n \to \infty} \sqrt[n]{|a_n|}$$ in order to apply the tests. Using the concepts of upper and lower limit introduced in Note 1 above we can state the tests in the following form:

The series $\sum_{n=1}^{\infty} a_n$ of positive terms will be convergent if $\lim_{n \to \infty} \sup a_{n+1}/a_n < 1$
and properly divergent if $\lim_{n \to \infty} \inf a_{n+1}/a_n > 1$.

Again: the series will converge if $\lim_{n \to \infty} \sup \sqrt[n]{a_n} < 1$ and will be properly divergent if $\lim_{n \to \infty} \sup \sqrt[n]{a_n} > 1$.

The more delicate tests mentioned in the text (such as Raabe's test) which may apply when the ratio and root tests fail, stem from a general test due to *Kummer* which we quote without proof:

If $a_n > 0$, $b_n > 0$ and $\sum_{n=1}^{\infty} b_n$ is properly divergent, let

$$\lim_{n \to \infty} \left\{ \frac{1}{b_n} \frac{a_n}{a_{n+1}} - \frac{1}{b_{n+1}} \right\} = \kappa$$

Then $\sum_{n=1}^{\infty} a_n$ converges or diverges according as $\kappa > 0$ or $\kappa < 0$.

More detailed information on convergence tests (and on infinite sequences and series in general) will be found in standard texts on analysis such as:

D. B. Scott and H. R. Tims: *Mathematical Analysis. An Introduction,* C.U.P. A useful reference text in this connection is:

J. M. Hyslop: *Infinite Series,* University Mathematical Texts (Oliver and Boyd).

On the subject of contraction mappings, and more general work on convergence, the reader should consult one of the many books now appearing on *functional analysis.* Of these the most readily approachable is probably,

A. M. Kolmogorov and S. V. Fomin: *Elements of the Theory of Functions and Functional Analysis,* Vol. I, Graylock Press.

Miscellaneous Exercises

1. Evaluate each of the following limits:

   (a) $\lim\limits_{n\to\infty} \left(\dfrac{2n-1}{4n+5}\right)^7$ (b) $\lim\limits_{n\to\infty} \sqrt{(2n+1)}\left\{\sqrt{(n+1)} - \sqrt{n}\right\}$

   (c) $\lim\limits_{n\to\infty} \dfrac{a^n + n}{a^{n-1} + 3n}$, where a is any fixed real number.

2. Show that

   (a) $\lim\limits_{n\to\infty} \left\{\dfrac{1}{n^2} + \dfrac{1}{(n+1)^2} + \cdots + \dfrac{1}{(2n)^2}\right\} = 0$

   (b) $\lim\limits_{n\to\infty} \left\{\dfrac{1}{\sqrt{n}} + \dfrac{1}{\sqrt{(n+1)}} + \cdots + \dfrac{1}{\sqrt{(2n)}}\right\} = \infty$

3. An infinite sequence (A_n) is defined as follows

   $$A_1 = 1; \quad A_{n+1} = +\sqrt{(7 + 2A_n)}, \quad n \geqslant 1$$

   Show that the sequence converges and find its limit.

4. If $\kappa > 0$, and A is chosen positive, show that the sequence (A_n) which satisfies the relation

   $$A_{n+1} = \sqrt{(\kappa + A_n)}$$

   is monotone increasing or monotone decreasing according as A_1 is less than or greater than the positive root of the equation.

   $$x^2 - x - \kappa = 0$$

   Show that, in either case, the sequence converges to this root as its limit.

5. If $\kappa > 0$, and A_1 is chosen positive, show that the sequence (A_n) which satisfies the relation

$$A_{n+1} = \frac{\kappa}{1 + A_n}$$

converges to the positive root of the equation

$$x^2 + x - \kappa = 0$$

but that the sequence is not monotone.

6. Find the sum of the first n terms of each of the following series and hence find their sums to infinity:

(a) $\dfrac{1}{2.5.8} + \dfrac{1}{5.8.11} + \dfrac{1}{8.11.14} + \cdots$,

(b) $\dfrac{1}{1.2.3} + \dfrac{3}{2.3.4} + \dfrac{5}{3.4.5} + \cdots$,

(c) $\dfrac{1}{1.5} + \dfrac{1}{3.7} + \dfrac{1}{5.9} + \cdots$,

(d) $\dfrac{3}{1.2.4} + \dfrac{4}{2.3.5} + \dfrac{5}{3.4.6} + \cdots$,

7. Test each of the following series for convergence:

(a) $\displaystyle\sum_{n=1}^{\infty} \frac{5n+3}{5n^3 + 3n^2 + 1}$ (b) $\displaystyle\sum_{n=1}^{\infty} \frac{10^{2n}}{(2n-1)!}$ (c) $\displaystyle\sum_{n=1}^{\infty} \frac{3^n . n!}{n^n}$

(d) $\displaystyle\sum_{n=1}^{\infty} \frac{1}{\sqrt{\{n(n+1)\}}}$ (e) $\displaystyle\sum_{n=1}^{\infty} \left(\frac{n}{n+1}\right)^{n^2}$ (f) $\displaystyle\sum_{n=1}^{\infty} \{\sqrt{(n+1)} - \sqrt{n}\}$

(g) $\displaystyle\sum_{n=1}^{\infty} \frac{(n!)^n}{n^{n^2}}$ (h) $\displaystyle\sum_{n=1}^{\infty} \frac{n+2}{n^2\sqrt{(n+3)}}$ (j) $\displaystyle\sum_{n=1}^{\infty} \frac{\sin n^3}{n^2}$

8. Find the radius of convergence of each of the following power series:

(a) $\displaystyle\sum_{n=1}^{\infty} \frac{2^n}{n^5 + 1} x^n$ (b) $\displaystyle\sum_{n=1}^{\infty} \frac{3^{2n+1}}{(n+1)!} x^n$

(c) $\displaystyle\sum_{n=1}^{\infty} \frac{2^n . (n!)}{n^n} x^{n-1}$ (d) $\displaystyle\sum_{n=1}^{\infty} \frac{(n!)^3}{(3n)!} x^{n-1}$ (e) $\displaystyle\sum_{n=1}^{\infty} \frac{x^n}{1 + 1/n}$

9. Show that, for any positive integer n, the following inequality holds

$$\frac{1}{n+1} < \int_n^{n+1} \frac{dx}{x} < \frac{1}{n}$$

Hence show that, $\lim_{n\to\infty} \left(1 + \frac{1}{2} + \frac{1}{3} + \cdots + \frac{1}{n} - \log n\right) = \gamma$, where γ is a certain number lying between 0 and 1. (This number is usually called 'Euler's constant', and is approximately equal to 0.5772157.)

10. The result of the preceding exercise can be expressed in the form

$$1 + \frac{1}{2} + \frac{1}{3} + \cdots + \frac{1}{n} = \log n + \gamma + \epsilon_n$$

where $\lim_{n\to\infty} \epsilon_n = 0$. Use this fact to show that

(a) $1 - \frac{1}{2} + \frac{1}{3} - \frac{1}{4} + \cdots = \log 2$,

(b) $\lim_{n\to\infty} \left\{ 1 + \frac{1}{3} + \frac{1}{5} + \cdots + \frac{1}{2n-1} - \frac{1}{2} \log n \right\} = \frac{\gamma}{2} + \log 2$,

(c) $\displaystyle\sum_{n=1}^{\infty} \frac{1}{(2n-1)(2n)} = \log 2$,

(d) $\displaystyle\sum_{n=1}^{\infty} \frac{1}{n(2n+1)} = 2 - 2\log 2$.

11. Let $\displaystyle\sum_{n=1}^{\infty} a_n$ be a series of positive terms such that $a_n \geqslant a_{n+1}$ for every n. Show that the series converges if and only if the series

$$\sum_{n=0}^{\infty} 2^n a_{2^n} \equiv a_1 + 2a_2 + 4a_4 + 8a_8 + \cdots$$

converges. (This is usually called the *Cauchy condensation test*.)

12. Use the Cauchy condensation test to show that the series

$$\sum_{n=2}^{\infty} \frac{1}{n(\log n)^p}$$ converges if $p > 1$ and diverges if $p \leqslant 1$.

13. Let $\displaystyle\sum_{n=1}^{\infty} a_n$ be a series of positive terms such that $a_n \geqslant a_{n+1}$ for every n.

Show that if the series converges then $\displaystyle\lim_{n\to\infty} na_n = 0$. (Sometimes called

Pringsheim's test.) Give an example to show that a series may diverge and
yet still satisfy the condition $\displaystyle\lim_{n\to\infty} na_n = 0$.

14. Let $(a_n), (b_n)$ be infinite sequences of real numbers which are such that

$\displaystyle\sum_{n=1}^{\infty} a_n^2$ and $\displaystyle\sum_{n=1}^{\infty} b_n^2$ are both convergent. Prove that $\displaystyle\sum_{n=1}^{\infty} a_n b_n$ must be

absolutely convergent, and establish the inequality

$$\left(\sum_{n=1}^{\infty} (a_n + b_n)^2\right)^{\frac{1}{2}} \leqslant \left(\sum_{n=1}^{\infty} a_n^2\right)^{\frac{1}{2}} + \left(\sum_{n=1}^{\infty} b_n^2\right)^{\frac{1}{2}}$$

(See Miscellaneous Exercises, chapter 1, Nos. 6 and 7.)

15. Show that e is irrational. [Hint: use the fact, established in section 3.7.1,
that the error in taking just the first $(n + 1)$ terms of the exponential series
is less than $1/n(n!)$.]

16. Obtain Maclaurin expansions for the following functions:

    (a) $\cosh x \sin x$ (b) $e^x \cos x$ (c) $e^{\tan x}$

    (d) $\log \sec x$ (e) $\tanh x$ (f) $\log \cosh x$

17. Show that $y = \dfrac{\sin^{-1} x}{\sqrt{(1 - x^2)}}$ satisfies the differential equation

$$(1 - x^2)\frac{dy}{dx} - xy = 1$$

Hence, show that for $|x| < 1$

$$\frac{\sin^{-1} x}{\sqrt{(1 - x^2)}} = x + \frac{2}{3}x^3 + \frac{2.4}{3.5}x^5 + \frac{2.4.6}{3.5.7}x^7 + \cdots$$

4   FUNCTIONS OF MORE THAN ONE VARIABLE

4.1 Functions of two variables

We shall first consider functions of two variables or, more precisely, real valued functions of ordered pairs of real variables. Such a function will be denoted by $f(x, y)$ – with argument (x, y) – or by $\phi(\lambda, \mu)$ – with argument (λ, μ) and so on.
We may have for example

$$f(x, y) = ax^2 + bxy + cy^2, \text{ and}$$

$$g(\alpha, \beta) = \cos(\alpha + \beta^2)$$

It is difficult to illustrate such functions by two dimensional drawings, but they may be visualised with fair ease if we write

$$z = f(x, y)$$

where (x, y) are the coordinates of a point in a plane and z is taken as 'height' above that plane. The function then represents a surface 'covering' the domain of (x, y). For example, figure 4.1 shows a sketch of the function

$$z = 1 - \cos\{2\pi\sqrt{[1 - (x^2 + y^2)]}\}, \quad \text{for } x^2 + y^2 \leqslant 1.$$

We can think of this function as a function of x for each value of y or as a function of y for each value of x. Drawing a graph of z against x for a particular value of y – say $y = y_0$ – we obtain the curve defined by the intersection of the surface of the function with the plane $y = y_0$ (figure 4.2).
In this case, however, it is more fruitful to identify points in the domain of the argument by their polar coordinates instead of by their cartesian coordinates. Substituting $r = \sqrt{(x^2 + y^2)}$, we have

$$z = 1 - \cos\{2\pi\sqrt{(1 - r^2)}\}$$

It is immediately obvious that the surface has the z-axis as an axis of symmetry, and that taking a section with any plane containing the z-axis we always obtain the same curve (figure 4.3).

134

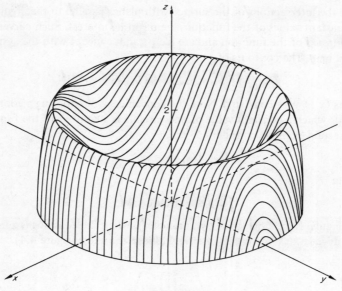

Fig. 4.1

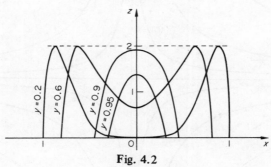

Fig. 4.2

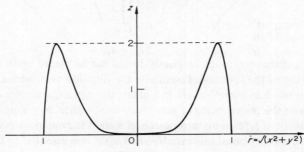

Fig. 4.3

Often the intersections of the surface with planes parallel to the argument plane (constant values of the function) are of prime interest. Such curves are called *contours* of the function and are identical in concept with the contour lines on a map. The contours of

$$f(x, y) = 1 - \cos\left\{2\pi \sqrt{[1 - (x^2 + y^2)]}\right\}$$

are circles ($x^2 + y^2$ = constant). Note the convenience of choosing a coordinate system for which a constant value of one variable is a contour of the function.

As a second example consider

$$f(x, y) = xy$$

A contour

$$xy = \text{constant} \neq 0$$

is a rectangular hyperbola (with two branches). When the constant is zero the contour degenerates into a pair of straight lines (the axes) (figure 4.4).

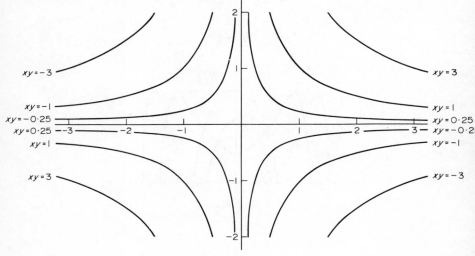

Fig. 4.4

It is clear that too much emphasis should not be placed upon the original formulation of the function. Essentially the function associates a real number with each point in some domain in a plane, the particular choice of coordinates to represent the points being of secondary importance. Nevertheless, the inadvisability of relying upon geometrical insight is even more marked than in the case of a function of one variable, and again it is essential to formalise ideas such as continuity and slope.

Exercise

For each of the following surfaces, sketch

(a)   the sections perpendicular to the x-axis,

(b)   the sections perpendicular to the y-axis, and

(c)   the contours (sections perpendicular to the z-axis).

(i) $z = x + 2y$,   (ii) $z = y - \sin \pi x$,

(iii) $z = y/x$,   (iv) $z = x^2$,

(v) $z = \sqrt{(2y + 4x)}$,   (vi) $z = \log (x + y)$,

(vii) $z = 1/(x^2 - y^2)$,   (viii) $z = (2x - 1)^2 + (y - 2)^2$

(ix) $z = (\cos \theta/r)^2$,   where (r, θ) are polar coordinates in the (x, y) plane.

In each case try to visualise the surface, and to describe some of its features.

4.1.1 *Limits*

Writing $f(P)$ to denote the value of a function at a point P in the plane of the argument, we may state the basic concept of a limit in its most general form:

$$f(P) \to L \text{ as } P \to P_0$$

if we can make $f(P)$ as close as we please to L by taking P sufficiently close to P_0.

Since $f(P)$ and L are real numbers we shall say that $f(P)$ is close to L if $|f(P) - L|$ is small, as with a function of one variable. In interpreting 'P close to P_0' we have a good deal of freedom, but at an elementary level we usually consider only the ordinary *Euclidean* distance so that P is close to P_0 if it lies inside a small circle centre P_0. (See exercise 2, page 170, and note 1.) If the coordinates of P are (x, y) and those of P_0 are (x_0, y_0), then

$$f(x, y) \to L \text{ as } (x, y) \to (x_0, y_0)$$

if, given any $\epsilon > 0$, there exists δ such that

$$|f(x, y) - L| < \epsilon$$

for all (x, y) such that

$$0 < \sqrt{\{(x - x_0)^2 + (y - y_0)^2\}} < \delta.$$

We also write $\lim\limits_{(x, y) \to (x_0, y_0)} f(x, y) = L.$

For sufficiently well behaved functions $\lim\limits_{x \to x_0} f(x, y)$ is a function of y which has a limit as $y \to y_0$. If this repeated limit $- \lim\limits_{y \to y_0} \lim\limits_{x \to x_0} f(x, y)$ exists, and

if also the double limit $\lim\limits_{(x,\,y)\,\rightarrow\,(x_0,\,y_0)} f(x, y)$ exists, then the two are equal.
We should note, however, that we cannot establish the existence of the limits
of $f(x, y)$ by considering only its behaviour as x and y vary separately. For
example, consider the behaviour near the origin of

$$f(x, y) = 2xy/(x^2 + y^2)$$

The repeated limits are

$$\lim\limits_{x\to 0}\ \lim\limits_{y\to 0}\ f(x, y) = \lim\limits_{x\to 0}\ 0 = 0, \text{ and } \lim\limits_{y\to 0}\ \lim\limits_{x\to 0}\ f(x, y) = \lim\limits_{y\to 0}\ 0 = 0.$$

Nevertheless, $\lim\limits_{(x,\,y)\,\rightarrow\,(0,\,0)} f(x, y)$ does not exist since the behaviour of $f(x, y)$
as x and y both become small depends upon the ratio of x to y.

It is equally true that the existence of the double limit does not of itself
ensure the existence of the repeated limits. For example, if

$$f(x, y) = \begin{cases} x & \text{for } y \geqslant 0, \\ -x & \text{for } y < 0 \end{cases}$$

then $f(x, y) \to 0$ as $(x, y) \to (0, 0)$; but $\lim\limits_{y\to 0} f(x, y)$ exists only for the one value
$x = 0$, and hence $\lim\limits_{x\to 0}\ \lim\limits_{y\to 0}\ f(x, y)$ is not a meaningful expression. It is true in
this case that $\lim\limits_{y\to 0}\ \lim\limits_{x\to 0}\ f(x, y)$ does exist and is equal to the double limit.

Many of the difficulties of practical mathematics would disappear if it were
always permissible freely to interchange the order of limiting processes, but a
discussion of when this is allowable is not always simple. (See note 2.)

Exercises

1. Investigate the continuity at the origin of the following functions, where in
   each case the value at the origin is defined to be zero:

   (i) $x^3y^3/(x^2 + y^2)$,   (ii) $1/(x^2 + y^2)$,

   (iii) $(x^4 - y^4)/(x^4 + y^4)$,   (iv) $x^2y^2/(x^4 + y^4)$.

2. If $f(x) \to L_1$ and $g(x) \to L_2$ as $x \to 0$, show that $f(x)g(y) \to L_1 L_2$ as
   $(x, y) \to (0, 0)$.

(Hint: consider $|f(x)g(x) - L_1 L_2| = |f(x)\{g(y) - L_2\} - L_2\{f(x) - L_1\}|.$)

4.1.2 *Continuity*

A function is said to be 'continuous' at a point (a, b) if

(i) $f(a, b)$ is defined and $\lim\limits_{(x,\,y)\,\rightarrow\,(a,\,b)} f(x, y)$ exists, and

(ii) these two values are equal.

The function $f(x, y) = 2xy/(x^2 + y^2)$, $(x, y) \neq (0, 0)$, is not continuous at the origin however we define it there, since $\lim\limits_{(x, y) \to (0, 0)} f(x, y)$ does not exist. Note, however, that if we define $f(0, 0)$ to be zero, then $f(x, y)$ is a continuous function of x for every value of y and also a continuous function of y for every value of x.

4.1.3 *Partial differentiation*

The rate of change of a function with respect to one of its variables whilst the other is held constant is called a 'partial derivative' (strictly 'first partial derivative') of the function. Geometrically the first partial derivatives of $f(x, y)$ measure the slope of the surface

$$z = f(x, y)$$

in directions parallel respectively to the x- and y-axes. This would appear to give a pre-eminence to a particular coordinate representation, but we shall see later that we can usually express the slope of the surface in any direction in terms of these partial derivatives.

We define, then, the partial derivative of $f(x, y)$ with respect to x at the point (x_0, y_0) as

$$\lim_{h \to 0} \frac{1}{h} [f(x_0 + h, y_0) - f(x_0, y_0)]$$

provided the limit exists. We denote this by $\partial f/\partial x$ or f_x or $(\partial f/\partial x)_{(x_0, y_0)}$ or $f_x(x_0, y_0)$. We similarly define the partial derivative with respect to y as

$$\frac{\partial f}{\partial y} = \lim_{h \to 0} \frac{1}{h} [f(x_0, y_0 + h) - f(x_0, y_0)]$$

If we write $\phi(x) = f(x, y_0)$, then

$$f_x(x_0, y_0) = \phi'(x_0)$$

and it is clear that we can use the properties of the derivatives of functions of one variable to give corresponding properties of partial derivatives. For example, if $\partial f/\partial x$ exists for all $a \leqslant x \leqslant b$ for a particular value of y, then we can apply the first mean value theorem (section 2.6.2) and write

$$f(b, y) - f(a, y) = (b - a) f_x(\xi, y)$$

where $a \leqslant \xi \leqslant b$. (But note that ξ is a function of y.) Clearly also

$$\frac{\partial}{\partial x} [f(x, y) + g(x, y)] = \frac{\partial f}{\partial x} + \frac{\partial g}{\partial x}$$

and similarly for partial derivatives of differences, products and quotients.

4.1.4 *Total differentiation*

To examine the slope of a surface in any direction — at (x_0, y_0), say — let a point (x, y) approach (x_0, y_0) along a curve S. Let d be the distance from (x_0, y_0) to (x, y), and suppose x and y are given as functions of d: $x(d)$ and $y(d)$. The slope of the resulting curve on the surface of $f(x, y)$ is then

$$D = \lim_{d \to 0} \frac{1}{d}\{f(x, y) - f(x_0, y_0)\}$$

To express this in terms of partial derivatives we write

$$\frac{1}{d}[f(x, y) - f(x_0, y_0)] = \frac{f(x, y) - f(x, y_0)}{d} + \frac{f(x, y_0) - f(x_0, y_0)}{x - x_0} \frac{x - x_0}{d}$$

We easily find the limit of the second of these terms. As $d \to 0$, so also does $(x - x_0) \to 0$ and hence

$$\frac{f(x, y_0) - f(x_0, y_0)}{x - x_0} \to f_x(x_0, y_0)$$

assuming the partial derivative to exist at (x_0, y_0). Also $(x - x_0)/d \to \cos \theta$, where θ is the angle between the tangent to S at (x_0, y_0) and the x-axis. (See figure 4.5.)

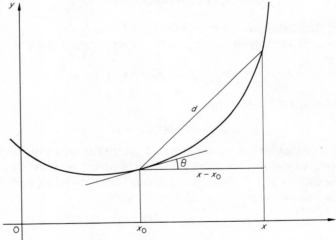

Fig. 4.5

However, the first of the two terms cannot be dealt with quite so simply, since not only $y \to y_0$, but also x varies as $d \to 0$. We proceed as follows. If $f_y(x, y_0)$ exists for all x close to x_0, then $f(x, y) - f(x, y_0) = f_y(x, \xi)(y - y_0)$ for some ξ lying between y and y_0. The first term is then $f_y(x, \xi)\{(y - y_0)/d\}$.

As $d \to 0$ so $x \to x_0$, and also $\xi \to y_0$ since ξ lies between y_0 and y and $y \to y_0$. Hence, provided $f_y(x, y)$ is a continuous function of (x, y) at (x_0, y_0), we have $f_y(x, \xi) \to f_y(x_0, y_0)$.

Since also $(y - y_0)/d \to \sin \theta$, we have

$$D = \lim_{d \to 0} \left[f_y(x, \xi) \frac{y - y_0}{d} + \frac{f(x, y_0) - f(x_0, y_0)}{x - x_0} \frac{x - x_0}{d} \right]$$

$$= f_y(x_0, y_0) \sin \theta + f_x(x_0, y_0) \cos \theta$$

Note that unless we have the required continuity of the first derivative there is no general expression for the slope in an arbitrary direction — which may not even exist.

Consider again the function

$$f(x, y) = \frac{2xy}{x^2 + y^2} \quad \text{for } (x, y) \neq (0, 0)$$

$$f(0, 0) = 0$$

We can write down without difficulty the partial derivatives at any point other than the origin. Treating y as a constant

$$\frac{\partial f}{\partial x} = \frac{(x^2 + y^2) \, 2y - 2xy \cdot 2x}{(x^2 + y^2)} = \frac{2y(x^2 - y^2)}{(x^2 + y^2)^2}$$

and similarly,

$$\frac{\partial f}{\partial y} = \frac{2x(y^2 - x^2)}{(x^2 + y^2)^2}$$

In fact the partial derivatives with respect to x and y also exist at the origin — in spite of the fact that the function is not continuous there.

We have $\qquad \dfrac{1}{\delta} \left\{ f(\delta, 0) - f(0, 0) \right\} = 0 \quad$ for all $\delta \neq 0$

and hence $\qquad f_x(0, 0) = 0$

Similarly $\qquad f_y(0, 0) = 0$

Note, however, that neither f_x nor f_y is continuous at the origin, and we cannot use the formula for slope derived above. If we try to evaluate directly the slope at the origin, we have (taking S as a straight line).

$$\frac{1}{d} \left[f(x, y) - f(x_0, y_0) \right] = \frac{1}{d} \left[f(d \cos \theta, d \sin \theta) - f(0, 0) \right]$$

$$= \frac{1}{d} \sin 2\theta \to \pm \infty \quad \text{as } d \to 0$$

except when $\sin 2\theta = 0$.

Exercises

1. Write down the partial derivatives of:

    (i) $f(x, y) = \cos(xy^2)$,   (ii) $f(x, y) = x^2 e^{(x+y)} + y$,

    (iii) $f(x, y) = \log(xy)$,   (iv) $f(x, y) = \tan^{-1}(y/x)$.

2. Investigate the continuity of the function, and of its partial derivatives at the origin, if

$$f(x, y) = 2xy/\sqrt{(x^2 + y^2)}, \quad (x, y) \neq (0, 0)$$

and $\quad\quad\quad f(0, 0) = 0$

Find the general expression for the slope of the function at the origin.

4.1.5 *Tangent plane and normal*

Let the line L be a tangent line to the surface $z = f(x, y)$ at the point P_0 (with coordinates (x_0, y_0, z_0)) on it, and let P be a point on L distant d from P_0. Let N be the foot of the perpendicular from P onto the plane $z = z_0$, and denote the angle $P\hat{P}_0 N$ by ϕ and the angle between $P_0 N$ and the x-axis by θ, so that the coordinates of P are

$$x = x_0 + d \cos \phi \cos \theta, \quad y = y_0 + d \cos \phi \sin \theta, \quad z = z_0 + d \sin \phi$$

(See figure 4.6.)

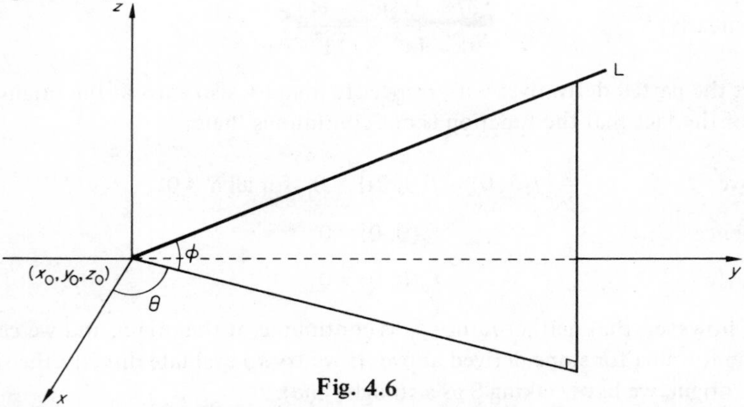

Fig. 4.6

If we assume that the first partial derivatives of $f(x, y)$ are continuous at $x = x_0, y = y_0$, then the slope of L is given by

$$\tan \phi = f_y \sin \theta + f_x \cos \theta$$

and using the previous three equations to eliminate θ and ϕ we have

$$z - z_0 = (x - x_0)f_x(x_0, y_0) + (y - y_0)f_y(x_0, y_0)$$

This is the equation of a plane — the *'tangent plane'* — containing all the tangent lines to the surface at (x_0, y_0, z_0).

If the partial derivatives are not continuous at (x_0, y_0) the equation linking ϕ and θ no longer holds and the tangents (if they exist) do not lie in a plane. For example

$$z = f(x, y) = \sqrt{(x^2 + y^2)} \qquad \text{(which represents a right circular cone)}$$

does not have a tangent plane at the origin. (The reader should prove this.) It is well-behaved everywhere else. We have for $(x_0, y_0) \neq (0, 0)$

$$f_x(x_0, y_0) = x_0/z_0 \quad \text{and} \quad f_y(x_0, y_0) = y_0/z_0$$

The tangent plane at (x_0, y_0, z_0) is

$$z_0(z - z_0) = (x - x_0)x_0 + (y - y_0)y_0$$

or more simply, since $z_0^2 = x_0^2 + y_0^2$

$$z_0 z = x_0 x + y_0 y$$

Note that all the tangent planes pass through the origin, the vertex of the cone.

The *'normal'* to a surface at a point is the line through the point and perpendicular to the tangent plane there. A line perpendicular to the plane

$$z - z_0 = (x - x_0)f_x + (y - y_0)f_y$$

has direction cosines

$$\alpha = f_x/\sqrt{(f_x^2 + f_y^2)}, \qquad \beta = f_y/\sqrt{(f_x^2 + f_y^2)}, \qquad \gamma = -1/\sqrt{(f_x^2 + f_y^2)}$$

The normal at (x_0, y_0, z_0) may then be written in parametric form

$$x = x_0 + \alpha d, \quad y = y_0 + \beta d, \quad z = z_0 + \gamma d$$

(See Appendix.)

Exercises

1. Write down the equation of the tangent plane when $x = 0$ and $y = 0$ for each of the following surfaces:

   (i) $z = ax + by$,
   (ii) $z = \sqrt{(x + y + 4)}$,
   (iii) $z = (y + 2) \log (x + 1)$,
   (iv) $z = (x + 1) e^{y(x + 2)}$

   (See also miscellaneous example No. 3.)

2. Find the equations of the tangent planes and the direction cosines of the normals to the following surfaces at the points indicated:

(i) $z = \dfrac{x^2}{4} + \dfrac{y^2}{9}$ at $(2, 3, 2)$

(ii) $z^2 = y - \dfrac{\sin \pi x}{\pi}$ at $(1, 1, 1)$

(iii) $z = \dfrac{y}{x}$ at $(1, 2, 2)$

4.1.6. Differentiation with respect to a parameter

Generalising the treatment of section 4.1.4, let u be any parameter varying along a curve S, and consider the rate of change of $z = f(x, y)$ with respect to u along a curve. At (x_0, y_0) — where $u = u_0$, say,

$$\frac{dz}{du} = \lim_{u \to u_0} \left\{ \frac{f(x, y) - f(x_0, y_0)}{u - u_0} \right\}$$

Treating this in a similar way as in section 4.1.4

$$\frac{dz}{du} = \lim_{u \to u_0} \left\{ f_y(x, \xi) \frac{y - y_0}{u - u_0} + \frac{f(x, y_0) - f(x_0, y_0)}{x - x_0} \cdot \frac{x - x_0}{u - u_0} \right\}$$

$$= f_y \frac{dy}{du} + f_x \frac{dx}{du} = \frac{\partial z}{\partial x} \frac{dx}{du} + \frac{\partial z}{\partial y} \frac{dy}{du}$$

the partial derivatives being evaluated at (x_0, y_0) and dy/du and dx/du at $u = u_0$. We have assumed that the partial derivatives are continuous at (x_0, y_0).

Theorems 6 and 7 of chapter 2 may now be seen as special cases by taking z as $x + y$, $x - y$, xy, x/y and $f(x)$ in turn.

4.1.7 Implicit differentiation

If y is defined implicitly as a function of x by the relationship

$$f(x, y) = \text{constant}$$

and if we wish to find dy/dx, then we take x as a special case of the parameter u in the previous section, so that

$$\frac{df}{dx} = f_x \cdot 1 + f_y \frac{dy}{dx}$$

But since the differentiation is carried out along a contour of f (f = constant), we have $df/dx = 0$, and hence dy/dx can be found from

$$f_x + f_y \frac{dy}{dx} = 0$$

If the equation linking x and y is not soluble for one of the variables in terms of the other then this is indeed the only way of finding dy/dx. For example, if

$$f(x, y) = \sin(x + 2y) - 2x - y = \text{constant},$$

then

$$\cos(x + 2y)\left(1 + 2\frac{dy}{dx}\right) - 2 - \frac{dy}{dx} = 0,$$

and hence

$$\frac{dy}{dx} = \frac{2 - \cos(x + 2y)}{2\cos(x + 2y) - 1}$$

It is not possible to express this result as a function of x alone, but dy/dx can be calculated at any point which is known to lie on a curve defined by the given relationship.

Even when it is possible to solve for y in terms of x it may be preferable to find dy/dx by differentiating an implicit relationship. For example, if we cons.der the ellipse:

$$y^2 + 2xy + 2x^2 = 1$$

we obtain by differentiating directly

$$2y\frac{dy}{dx} + 2y + 2x\frac{dy}{dx} + 4x = 0, \text{ and hence}$$

$$\frac{dy}{dx} = -\frac{y + 2x}{y + x}$$

which is an unambiguous expression for the slope of the tangent at any point on the ellipse. On the other hand, solving for y in terms of x and then differentiating we have the expression

$$\frac{dy}{dx} = -1 \pm \frac{x}{\sqrt{(1 - x^2)}}$$

in which we need to be careful to associate the appropriate sign with each part of the curve.

A pair of simultaneous equations such as

$$f(x, y, z) = \text{constant} \quad \text{and} \quad g(x, y, z) = \text{constant}$$

may yield a relationship between x and y by the elimination of x from the two equations. (The relationship obtained defines the projection on the (x, y)-plane of the intersection of the two surfaces defined by the given equations.) If the elimination cannot actually be carried out we may nevertheless find dy/dx by differentiating the implicit expressions.

We have
$$f_x + f_y \frac{dy}{dx} + f_z \frac{dz}{dx} = 0$$

and
$$g_x + g_y \frac{dy}{dx} + g_z \frac{dz}{dx} = 0$$

from which we can eliminate dz/dx to give dy/dx. For example, if

$$x + y + z = \exp(z), \text{ and}$$

$$x^2 + y^2 + z^2 = \exp(z^2), \text{ then}$$

$$1 + \frac{dy}{dx} + \frac{dz}{dx} = \exp(z)\frac{dz}{dx}, \text{ and}$$

$$2x + 2y\frac{dy}{dx} + 2z\frac{dz}{dx} = \exp(z^2)\frac{dz}{dx}$$

Eliminating dz/dx we have

$$\frac{dy}{dx} = \frac{z - x}{y - z}$$

Exercises

1. Find $\partial z/\partial x$ and $\partial z/\partial y$ at the points indicated for each of the following functions:

    (i) $x \cos z = y \sin z + 2(z - \pi)$ at $(0, 1, \pi)$,

    (ii) $\log z = x^2 + 2y$ at $(2, -2, 1)$,

    (iii) $5x^2 + 15y^3 = z^3$ at $(1, 2, 5)$,

    (iv) $\cos(xyz) + e^{(xz-1)} = \log(xy/\pi)$ at $(1, \pi, 1)$.

2. Given that

$$x^2 + y^2 = y(z^2 + z + 3), \text{ and}$$

$$\log(xyz/2) = x - y - z$$

find dy/dx when $x = 2$ and $y = 1$.

4.1.8 *The chain rule*

We consider now the relationship between the partial derivatives of a function with respect to two different coordinate systems. Changing from coordinates (x, y) to coordinates (u, v), we may suppose that x and y are given explicitly as functions of u and v

$$x = x(u, v) \qquad \text{and} \qquad y = y(u, v)$$

and also that these equations may be solved uniquely to give u and v as functions of x and y

$$u = u(x, y) \qquad \text{and} \qquad v = v(x, y)$$

We may draw curves of equal value of u and of v, and we consider in particular the curves $u(x, y) = u_0$ and $v(x, y) = v_0$, which intersect in the particular point under consideration: $x_0 = x(u_0, v_0)$ and $y_0 = y(u_0, v_0)$.

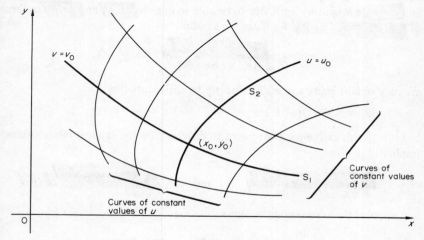

Fig. 4.7

As a point moves along S_1 (figure 4.7), v remains constant, whereas u may be taken as a parameter.

Given a function $z = f(x, y)$, we proceed as in section 4.1.6, except that derivatives with respect to u are now partial derivatives. We have

$$\frac{\mathrm{d}z}{\mathrm{d}u} = \lim_{u \to u_0} \left\{ \frac{f(x, y) - f(x_0, y_0)}{u - u_0} \right\}$$

$$= \lim_{u \to u_0} \left\{ f_y(x, \xi) \frac{y - y_0}{u - u_0} + \frac{f(x, y_0) - f(x_0, y_0)}{x - x_0} \cdot \frac{x - x_0}{u - u_0} \right\}$$

$$= f_y \frac{\partial y}{\partial u} + f_x \frac{\partial x}{\partial u}$$

That is
$$\frac{\partial z}{\partial u} = \frac{\partial z}{\partial x}\frac{\partial x}{\partial u} + \frac{\partial z}{\partial y}\frac{\partial y}{\partial u}$$

and similarly by differentiating along S_2:
$$\frac{\partial z}{\partial v} = \frac{\partial z}{\partial x}\frac{\partial x}{\partial v} + \frac{\partial z}{\partial y}\frac{\partial y}{\partial v}$$

The last two equations constitute the *chain rule* in two dimensions.

Example

Consider the change from Cartesian to polar coordinates. We have $x = r \cos \theta$ and $y = r \sin \theta$, and we wish also to be able to express $\partial z/\partial x$ and $\partial z/\partial y$ in terms of r, θ, $\partial z/\partial r$ and $\partial z/\partial \theta$. We have, for example
$$\frac{\partial z}{\partial x} = \frac{\partial z}{\partial r}\frac{\partial r}{\partial x} + \frac{\partial z}{\partial \theta}\frac{\partial \theta}{\partial x}$$

We may obtain $\partial r/\partial x$ and $\partial \theta/\partial x$ directly by differentiating
$$r = \sqrt{(x^2 + y^2)} \qquad \text{and} \qquad \theta = \tan^{-1}(y/x)$$

but it is in this case more convenient to differentiate the original relationships implicitly to give
$$1 = \frac{\partial r}{\partial x}\cos\theta - r\frac{\partial \theta}{\partial x}\sin\theta \qquad \text{and} \qquad 0 = \frac{\partial r}{\partial x}\sin\theta + r\frac{\partial \theta}{\partial x}\cos\theta$$

and to solve these equations to obtain
$$\frac{\partial r}{\partial x} = \cos\theta \qquad \text{and} \qquad \frac{\partial \theta}{\partial x} = -\frac{\sin\theta}{r}$$

Finally
$$\frac{\partial z}{\partial x} = \frac{\partial z}{\partial r}\cos\theta - \frac{\partial z}{\partial \theta}\frac{\sin\theta}{r}$$

and similarly
$$\frac{\partial z}{\partial y} = \frac{\partial z}{\partial r}\sin\theta + \frac{\partial z}{\partial \theta}\frac{\cos\theta}{r}$$

To change from polar to Cartesian coordinates we need to find $\partial x/\partial r$, $\partial x/\partial \theta$, $\partial y/\partial r$ and $\partial y/\partial \theta$. These are readily obtained from the original relationships between the pairs of coordinates. For example
$$\frac{\partial x}{\partial r} = \cos\theta \qquad \text{and} \qquad \frac{\partial x}{\partial \theta} = -r\sin\theta$$

and then, in terms of x and y,
$$\frac{\partial x}{\partial r} = \frac{x}{\sqrt{(x^2 + y^2)}} \qquad \text{and} \qquad \frac{\partial x}{\partial \theta} = -y$$

We must be vigilant to avoid falling into the trap of writing — say — $\partial x / \partial u$ in place of $1/(\partial u / \partial x)$. It is true that each of these is a limiting value of the ratio of a small change in x to a small change in u, but in the first place the limit is derived as a point moves on a line of constant v, whereas in the second it moves along a line of constant y. In the above example we saw that

$$\frac{\partial r}{\partial x} = \cos \theta \qquad \text{and} \qquad \frac{\partial x}{\partial r} = \cos \theta$$

Far from being reciprocal, $\partial r / \partial x$ and $\partial x / \partial r$ are in fact equal.

Exercises

1. If

$$z = \sin \left(\frac{x}{y} \right)$$

write down the partial derivatives of z with respect to the cartesian coordinates (x, y) and use the chain rule to find the partial derivatives of z with respect to the polar coordinates (r, θ). Verify the result by first substituting for x/y and then evaluating $\partial z / \partial r$ and $\partial z / \partial \theta$ directly.

2. Find the partial derivatives of a function with respect to the variables

$$u = xy \qquad \text{and} \qquad v = x^2 - y^2$$

in terms of those with respect to x and y. Also find the partial derivatives with respect to x and y in terms of those with respect to u and v, both by applying the chain rule directly and by solving the equations derived in the first part.

4.1.9 *Partial derivatives of higher order*

If the first partial derivative of a function $f(x, y)$ with respect to — say — x exists in some region of the (x, y) plane, it forms a function of two variables which is itself a candidate for partial differentiation. Provided that they exist, we may form from $f_x(x, y)$ the 'Second Partial Derivatives'

$$\frac{\partial}{\partial x} \left(\frac{\partial f}{\partial x} \right), \quad \text{which is written} \quad \frac{\partial^2 f}{\partial x^2} \text{ or } f_{xx}, \text{ and}$$

$$\frac{\partial}{\partial y} \left(\frac{\partial f}{\partial x} \right), \quad \text{which is written} \quad \frac{\partial^2 f}{\partial y \partial x} \text{ or } f_{xy}$$

Similarly, from $f_y(x, y)$ are formed

$$f_{yx} = \frac{\partial^2 f}{\partial x \partial y} = \frac{\partial}{\partial x}\left(\frac{\partial f}{\partial y}\right)$$

and

$$f_{yy} = \frac{\partial^2 f}{\partial y^2} = \frac{\partial}{\partial y}\left(\frac{\partial f}{\partial y}\right)$$

Example

$$f(x, y) = y^2 + x \exp(x + y)$$

$$f_x = (x + 1)\exp(x + y)$$

$$f_{xx} = (x + 2)\exp(x + y) \qquad \text{and} \qquad f_{xy} = (x + 1)\exp(x + y)$$

$$f_y = 2y + x \exp(x + y)$$

$$f_{yx} = (x + 1)\exp(x + y) \qquad \text{and} \qquad f_{yy} = 2 + x \exp(x + y)$$

We may observe in this example that f_{xy} and f_{yx} are identical. This is not a coincidence, and we have the following theorem.

Theorem 1. If f_{xy} and f_{yx} are both continuous at a point, then they have the same value there.

Note that continuity at a point implies existence in a neighbourhood of that point. To prove the theorem we consider the function of a single variable defined by

$$\phi(t) = f(x_0 + t, y_0 + t) - f(x_0, y_0 + t) - f(x_0 + t, y_0) + f(x_0, y_0)$$

and show that $\lim_{t \to 0}\{\phi(t)/t^2\}$ is equal both to $f_{xy}(x_0, y_0)$ and to $f_{yx}(x_0, y_0)$

Let

$$\lambda(\alpha) = f(x_0 + \alpha, y_0 + t) - f(x_0 + \alpha, y_0),$$

so that

$$\phi(t) = \lambda(t) - \lambda(0).$$

Applying the mean value theorem

$$\phi(t) = t\lambda'(\xi)$$

$$= t\{f_x(x_0 + \xi, y_0 + t) - f_x(x_0 + \xi, y_0)\}$$

where ξ lies between 0 and t. If now

$$\mu(\beta) = f_x(x_0 + \xi, y_0 + \beta), \quad \text{then}$$

$$\phi(t) = t\{\mu(t) - \mu(0)\} = t^2 \mu'(\eta)$$

$$= t^2 f_{xy}(x_0 + \xi, y_0 + \eta)$$

where η also lies between 0 and t. As $t \to 0$ so also $\xi \to 0$ and $\eta \to 0$. Since we assume that f_{xy} is continuous at (x_0, y_0), we have

$$\phi(t)/t^2 \to f_{xy}(x_0, y_0) \quad \text{as} \quad t \to 0$$

But equally well we can regroup the terms in $\phi(t)$ and write $\phi(t) = \lambda(t) - \lambda(0)$,

where $$\lambda(\alpha) = f(x_0 + t, y_0 + \alpha) - f(x_0, y_0 + \alpha)$$

We then find that also

$$\phi(t)/t^2 \to f_{yx}(x_0, y_0) \quad \text{as} \quad t \to 0,$$

and the proof is thus complete.

As an example of a function which does not everywhere satisfy this theorem we take

$$f(x, y) = y \sqrt{|y^2 - x^2|}$$

We find

$$f_{xy} = f_{yx} = \begin{cases} x^3/(x^2 - y^2)^{\frac{3}{2}} & \text{for } x^2 > y^2 \\ -x^3/(y^2 - x^2)^{\frac{3}{2}} & \text{for } y^2 > x^2 \end{cases}$$

On the lines $y = x$ and $y = -x$ the second partial derivatives exist at only a single point — the origin. The limits of f_{xy} and f_{yx} as $(x, y) \to (0, 0)$ do not exist, and hence they are not continuous there. The second partial derivatives are therefore not necessarily equal at the origin. In fact

$$f_{xy}(0, 0) = 0 \quad \text{but} \quad f_{yx}(0, 0) = 1$$

(The reader should derive these as an exercise.)

Derivatives of higher order than the second may be constructed by successive partial differentiation. For example, from $\partial^2 f/\partial x \partial y$ we may form the third partial derivatives

$$f_{yxx} = \frac{\partial^3 f}{\partial^2 x \partial y} = \frac{\partial}{\partial x} \left(\frac{\partial^2 f}{\partial x \partial y} \right)$$

and $$f_{yxy} = \frac{\partial^3 f}{\partial y \partial x \partial y} = \frac{\partial}{\partial y} \left(\frac{\partial^2 f}{\partial x \partial y} \right)$$

In all there are eight third order derivatives, but under suitable conditions we have only four distinct ones:

$$f_{xxx}, \quad f_{yyy},$$

$$f_{xxy} = f_{xyx} = f_{yxx}, \quad \text{and} \quad f_{xyy} = f_{yxy} = f_{yyx}$$

The relationships between second order derivatives in coordinate transformations may be established by repeated use of the chain rule. Changing from coordinates (x, y) to coordinates (u, v) we can write the chain rule symbolically as

$$\frac{\partial z}{\partial u} = \left(\frac{\partial x}{\partial u} \frac{\partial}{\partial x} + \frac{\partial y}{\partial u} \frac{\partial}{\partial y} \right) z,$$

and

$$\frac{\partial z}{\partial v} = \left(\frac{\partial x}{\partial v} \frac{\partial}{\partial x} + \frac{\partial y}{\partial v} \frac{\partial}{\partial y} \right) z$$

and we may then write, for example

$$\frac{\partial^2 z}{\partial u^2} = \left(\frac{\partial x}{\partial v} \frac{\partial}{\partial x} + \frac{\partial y}{\partial v} \frac{\partial}{\partial y} \right)^2 z = \left(\frac{\partial x}{\partial v} \frac{\partial}{\partial x} + \frac{\partial y}{\partial v} \frac{\partial}{\partial y} \right) \left(\frac{\partial x}{\partial v} \frac{\partial}{\partial x} + \frac{\partial y}{\partial v} \frac{\partial}{\partial y} \right) z$$

Note that when the differential operator is applied for the second time it must be remembered that $\partial x/\partial v$ and $\partial y/\partial v$ are not constant, so that, for example

$$\frac{\partial}{\partial y} \left(\frac{\partial x}{\partial v} \frac{\partial z}{\partial x} \right) = \frac{\partial x}{\partial v} \frac{\partial^2 z}{\partial y \partial x} + \frac{\partial}{\partial y} \left(\frac{\partial x}{\partial v} \right) \frac{\partial z}{\partial x}$$

However, it is more useful to consider a particular case than to expand in detail these general expressions, and we return to the change from cartesian to polar coordinates. We have seen that

$$\frac{\partial z}{\partial x} = \left(\cos \theta \frac{\partial}{\partial r} - \frac{\sin \theta}{r} \frac{\partial}{\partial \theta} \right) z, \text{ so that}$$

$$\frac{\partial^2 z}{\partial x^2} = \left(\cos \theta \frac{\partial}{\partial r} - \frac{\sin \theta}{r} \frac{\partial}{\partial \theta} \right)^2 z$$

$$= \left(\cos \theta \frac{\partial}{\partial r} - \frac{\sin \theta}{r} \frac{\partial}{\partial \theta} \right) \left(\cos \theta \frac{\partial z}{\partial r} - \frac{\sin \theta}{r} \frac{\partial z}{\partial \theta} \right)$$

$$= \cos \theta \frac{\partial}{\partial r} \left(\cos \theta \frac{\partial z}{\partial r} - \frac{\sin \theta}{r} \frac{\partial z}{\partial \theta} \right) - \frac{\sin \theta}{r} \frac{\partial}{\partial \theta} \left(\cos \theta \frac{\partial z}{\partial r} - \frac{\sin \theta}{r} \frac{\partial z}{\partial \theta} \right)$$

$$= \cos \theta \left(\cos \theta \frac{\partial^2 z}{\partial r^2} + \frac{\sin \theta}{r^2} \frac{\partial z}{\partial \theta} - \frac{\sin \theta}{r} \frac{\partial^2 z}{\partial r \partial \theta} \right)$$

$$- \frac{\sin \theta}{r} \left(- \sin \theta \frac{\partial z}{\partial r} + \cos \theta \frac{\partial^2 z}{\partial \theta \partial r} - \frac{\cos \theta}{r} \frac{\partial z}{\partial \theta} - \frac{\sin \theta}{r} \frac{\partial^2 z}{\partial \theta^2} \right)$$

$$= \cos^2 \theta \frac{\partial^2 z}{\partial r^2} - \frac{2 \cos \theta \sin \theta}{r} \frac{\partial^2 z}{\partial \theta \partial r} + \frac{\sin^2 \theta}{r^2} \frac{\partial^2 z}{\partial \theta^2} + \frac{\sin^2 \theta}{r} \frac{\partial z}{\partial r} + \frac{2 \sin \theta \cos \theta}{r} \frac{\partial z}{\partial \theta}$$

Expressions for $\partial^2 z/\partial x \partial y$ and $\partial^2 z/\partial y^2$ may be derived similarly (see exercise 1 below).

To find $\partial^2 z/\partial r^2$, $\partial^2 z/\partial r \partial\theta$ and $\partial^2 z/\partial\theta^2$ in terms of partial derivatives with respect to x and y we may start with

$$\frac{\partial z}{\partial r} = \frac{\partial x}{\partial r}\frac{\partial z}{\partial x} + \frac{\partial y}{\partial r}\frac{\partial z}{\partial y} = \left(\frac{x}{\sqrt{(x^2+y^2)}}\frac{\partial}{\partial x} + \frac{y}{\sqrt{(x^2+y^2)}}\frac{\partial}{\partial y} \right) z, \text{ and}$$

$$\frac{\partial z}{\partial\theta} = \frac{\partial x}{\partial\theta}\frac{\partial z}{\partial x} + \frac{\partial y}{\partial\theta}\frac{\partial z}{\partial y} = \left(-y\frac{\partial}{\partial x} + x\frac{\partial}{\partial y} \right) z$$

However, it is comparatively clumsy to use these expressions repeatedly, and it is more convenient to proceed as follows.

$$\frac{\partial z}{\partial r} = \cos\theta\,\frac{\partial z}{\partial x} + \sin\theta\,\frac{\partial z}{\partial y}, \text{ and hence}$$

$$\frac{\partial^2 z}{\partial r^2} = \frac{\partial}{\partial r}\left\{ \cos\theta\,\frac{\partial z}{\partial x} + \sin\theta\,\frac{\partial z}{\partial y} \right\} = \cos\theta\,\frac{\partial}{\partial r}\left(\frac{\partial z}{\partial x}\right) + \sin\theta\,\frac{\partial}{\partial r}\left(\frac{\partial z}{\partial y}\right)$$

$$= \cos\theta\,\left\{ \cos\theta\,\frac{\partial}{\partial x} + \sin\theta\,\frac{\partial}{\partial y} \right\}\left(\frac{\partial z}{\partial x}\right) + \sin\theta\,\left\{ \cos\theta\,\frac{\partial}{\partial x} + \sin\theta\,\frac{\partial}{\partial y} \right\}\left(\frac{\partial z}{\partial y}\right)$$

$$= \cos^2\theta\,\frac{\partial^2 z}{\partial x^2} + 2\sin\theta\cos\theta\,\frac{\partial^2 z}{\partial x \partial y} + \sin^2\theta\,\frac{\partial^2 z}{\partial y^2}$$

$$= \left(x^2\,\frac{\partial^2 z}{\partial x^2} + 2xy\,\frac{\partial^2 z}{\partial x \partial y} + y^2\,\frac{\partial^2 z}{\partial y^2} \right)\Big/(x^2+y^2)$$

and similarly for $\partial^2 z/\partial r \partial\theta$ and $\partial^2 z/\partial\theta^2$.

Exercises
1. Write down all the second partial derivatives for each of the functions:

   (i) $f(x, y) = xe^{xy}$,   (ii) $f(x, y) = x/y$,

   (iii) $f(x, y) = y \log x$,   (iv) $f(x, y) = x \cos y - y \sin x$.

2. Derive expressions for $\partial^2 z/\partial y^2$ in terms of polar coordinates and for $\partial^2 z/\partial r \partial\theta$ and $\partial^2 z/\partial\theta^2$ in terms of cartesian coordinates. Show that

$$\frac{\partial^2 z}{\partial x^2} + \frac{\partial^2 z}{\partial y^2} = \frac{\partial^2 z}{\partial r^2} + \frac{1}{r^2}\frac{\partial^2 z}{\partial\theta^2} + \frac{1}{r}\frac{\partial z}{\partial r}$$

3. If $x^2 = u + v$ and $y^2 = u - v$, find $\partial z/\partial u$ and $\partial z/\partial v$ in terms of x, y, $\partial z/\partial x$ and $\partial z/\partial y$. If $z = 3x^2 y - 2y^3 + 2x^2 + y^2$, find

$$\frac{\partial^2 z}{\partial u^2}, \qquad \frac{\partial^2 z}{\partial u \partial v} \qquad \text{and} \qquad \frac{\partial^2 z}{\partial v^2}$$

4.2 Functions of many variables

We consider now the general case of a real-valued function in many dimensions. We shall generally write $f(x_1, x_2, \ldots, x_n)$ but may also write $f(\mathbf{x})$, where $\mathbf{x}$ is used as shorthand for the ordered n-tuple of real numbers $(x_1, x_2, \ldots, x_n)$ — in other words, as shorthand for a point in n-dimensional space. It is not, of course, possible to represent such a function graphically if n is greater than two. At best, in three-dimensional space we can think of a function as a space distribution — of, say, mass or electrical charge. The terminology of three dimensions will usually be used in an extended sense. For example, the set of points $(x_1, x_2, \ldots, x_n)$ which satisfy the condition

$$(x_1 - a_1)^2 + (x_2 - a_2)^2 + \cdots + (x_n - a_n)^2 \leqslant d^2$$

is a sphere centre (a_1, a_2, a_3) and radius d when $n = 3$, and we shall continue to refer to such a set as a sphere when $n > 3$. We shall sometimes write $\rho(\mathbf{x}, \mathbf{y})$ to denote a measure of distance between points $\mathbf{x}$ and $\mathbf{y}$.

As in two dimensions, it is in theory possible to choose amongst many satisfactory ways of measuring distance between points (see note 1), but most obviously we generalise the Euclidean measure of distance and write

$$\rho(\mathbf{x}, \mathbf{y}) = \sqrt{\{(x_1 - y_1)^2 + (x_2 - y_2)^2 + \cdots + (x_n - y_n)^2\}}$$

4.2.1 *Limits and continuity*

In section 4.1.1 we wrote '$f(P) \to L$ as $P \to P_0$ if we can make $f(P)$ as close as we please to L by taking P sufficiently close to P_0', and we have no need to change this statement now. In terms of the notation introduced above we may write this as

$f(\mathbf{x}) \to L$ as $\mathbf{x} \to \mathbf{a}$ if, given any $\epsilon > 0$, there exists δ such that $|f(\mathbf{x}) - L| <$ for all $\mathbf{x}$ satisfying $\rho(\mathbf{x}, \mathbf{a}) < \delta$.

This last condition can equally well be stated, 'for all $\mathbf{x}$ lying inside the sphere centre $\mathbf{a}$ and radius δ'.

We also write

$$\lim_{\mathbf{x} \to \mathbf{a}} f(\mathbf{x}) = L$$

For sufficiently well-behaved functions this multiple limit is equal to appropriate repeated limits. For example, in three dimensions we may have

$$\lim_{\mathbf{x} \to \mathbf{a}} f(\mathbf{x}) = \lim_{x_1 \to a_1} \lim_{x_2 \to a_2} \lim_{x_3 \to a_3} f(x_1, x_2, x_3)$$

$$= \lim_{x \to a_1} \lim_{x_3 \to a_3} \lim_{x_2 \to a_2} f(x_1, x_2, x_3)$$

$$= \text{and so on.}$$

But any or all of these equalities may be falsified in a particular case.

The definition of continuity follows in exactly the same way as for functions of one and two variables. If $\lim_{x \to a} f(x)$ exists and is equal to $f(a)$ (which must therefore be defined), then $f(x)$ is said to be 'continuous' at $x = a$.

The possible types of discontinuous behaviour become more and more numerous as the number of dimensions increases.

4.2.2 *Partial differentiation*

There are no difficulties in extending the definition of partial differentiation to more than two variables. We define

$$f_r = f_{x_r} = \frac{\partial f}{\partial x_r} = \lim_{\delta \to 0} \frac{1}{\delta} \Big\{ f(x_1, x_2, \ldots, x_{r-1}, x_r + \delta, \ldots, x_n) \\ - f(x_1, x_2, \ldots, x_r, \ldots, x_n) \Big\}$$

assuming, of course, that the limit exists. The suffix r may take values 1 to n inclusive, and hence there are n first partial derivatives:

In general, each first partial derivative may be differentiated again with respect to each of the variables, giving n^2 second partial derivatives.

$$f_{rs} = \frac{\partial^2 f}{\partial x_s \partial x_r}, \qquad 1 \leqslant r, s \leqslant n$$

With suitable conditions of continuity

$$\frac{\partial^2 f}{\partial x_r \partial x_s} = \frac{\partial^2 f}{\partial x_s \partial x_r}$$

and there may be only $\frac{1}{2} n(n + 1)$ distinct second order partial derivatives

4.2.3 *The chain rule*

If $x_1, x_2, \ldots, x_n$ are given as specific functions of a single parameter u (we can write $x = x(u)$) the points defined as u varies form a 'curve' in n dimensions. Then if f is a function of $x_1, x_2, \ldots, x_n$ we can, under suitable conditions, express df/du in terms of the partial derivatives of f. Extending the proof given in section 4.1.6 in an obvious way, we find

$$\frac{df}{du} = \frac{\partial f}{\partial x_1} \frac{dx_1}{du} + \frac{\partial f}{\partial x_2} \frac{dx_2}{du} + \cdots + \frac{\partial f}{\partial x_n} \frac{dx_n}{du}$$

assuming $\partial f/\partial x_1, \partial f/\partial x_2 \cdots \partial f/\partial x_n$ all to be continuous at the point at which it is required to evaluate df/du.

To consider the effect on partial derivatives of changing from a set of coordinates $(x_1, x_2, \ldots, x_n)$ to $(u_1, u_2, \ldots, u_n)$, we find the rate of change of a function along a curve on which $u_i(\mathbf{x}) = k_i$ (a constant) all $i \neq r$. Then

$$\frac{\partial f}{\partial u_r} = \frac{\partial f}{\partial x_1} \frac{\partial x_1}{\partial u_r} + \frac{\partial f}{\partial x_2} \frac{\partial x_2}{\partial u_r} + \cdots + \frac{\partial f}{\partial x_n} \frac{\partial x_n}{\partial u_r}$$

We can do this for each r and thus derive n relationships for n first partial derivatives with respect to the u-coordinates. We may summarise these as

$$\frac{\partial f}{\partial u_r} = \sum_{s=1}^{n} \frac{\partial f}{\partial x_s} \frac{\partial x_s}{\partial x_r} \quad \text{for } r = 1, 2, \ldots, n$$

An important transformation in three dimensions is that from cartesian coordinates (x, y, z) to spherical polar coordinates (r, θ, ϕ). We have

$$x = r \sin \phi \cos \theta, \qquad y = r \sin \phi \sin \theta, \qquad z = r \cos \phi$$

and the reader should confirm that the relationship between the two sets of partial derivatives may be written

$$\frac{\partial f}{\partial r} = \sin \phi \cos \theta \frac{\partial f}{\partial x} + \sin \phi \sin \theta \frac{\partial f}{\partial y} + \cos \theta \frac{\partial f}{\partial z},$$

$$\frac{\partial f}{\partial \theta} = -r \sin \phi \sin \theta \frac{\partial f}{\partial x} + r \sin \phi \cos \theta \frac{\partial f}{\partial y}, \quad \text{and}$$

$$\frac{\partial f}{\partial \phi} = r \cos \phi \cos \theta \frac{\partial f}{\partial x} + r \cos \phi \sin \theta \frac{\partial f}{\partial y} - r \sin \theta \frac{\partial f}{\partial z}$$

The coefficients of the partial derivatives can be written in terms of x, y and z, but the expressions are then comparatively clumsy. The equations can be solved to give $\partial f/\partial x$, $\partial f/\partial y$ and $\partial f/\partial z$ in terms of $\partial f/\partial r$, $\partial f/\partial \theta$ and $\partial f/\partial \phi$. (See note 3.)

Exercise

If the independent variables (x, y, z) are replaced by the new variables $u = -x + y + z$, $v = x - y + z$, and $w = x + y - z$, find the first partial derivatives of a function f with respect to u, v and w in terms of those with respect to x, y and z. Show that

$$\frac{\partial^2 f}{\partial u \partial v} - 2 \frac{\partial^2 f}{\partial v \partial w} + \frac{\partial^2 f}{\partial w \partial u} = \frac{1}{4} \left(\frac{\partial^2 f}{\partial y^2} + \frac{\partial^2 f}{\partial z^2} - 2 \frac{\partial^2 f}{\partial x^2} \right)$$

Check your results by considering the function

$$f(u, v, w) = uv + vw + wu$$

4.3 Taylor's theorem

We consider the case of a function of two variables initially. Under suitable conditions we can expand the function about a point in terms of the partial derivatives there. To express the value of $f(x, y)$ at the point $(x_0 + h, y_0 + k)$ in terms of its behaviour at (x_0, y_0), we introduce the function of one variable

$$\phi(\lambda) = f(x_0 + \lambda h, y_0 + \lambda k)$$

so that $\qquad \phi(0) = f(x_0, y_0) \qquad$ and $\qquad \phi(1) = f(x_0 + h, y_0 + k)$

If f_x and f_y exist and are continuous on the line joining (x_0, y_0) and $(x_0 + h, y_0 + k)$ then $\phi'(\lambda)$ exists for all $0 \leqslant \lambda \leqslant 1$ and $\phi'(\lambda) = hf_x + kf_y$. If also the second partial derivatives exist and are continuous then

$$\phi''(\lambda) = h \frac{\mathrm{d}}{\mathrm{d}\lambda} f_x(x_0 + \lambda h, y_0 + \lambda k) + k \frac{\mathrm{d}}{\mathrm{d}\lambda} f_y(x_0 + \lambda h, y_0 + \lambda k)$$

$$= h^2 f_{xx} + 2hk f_{xy} + k^2 f_{yy}$$

We can conveniently write this as

$$\phi''(\lambda) = \left(h \frac{\partial}{\partial x} + k \frac{\partial}{\partial y} \right)^2 f$$

and in general if the nth order partial derivatives exist and are continuous on the line then

$$\phi^{(n)}(\lambda) = \left(h \frac{\partial}{\partial x} + k \frac{\partial}{\partial y} \right)^n f$$

Using these expressions for the derivatives of $\phi(\lambda)$ in the one-dimensional Taylor's expansion

$$\phi(1) = \phi(0) + \phi'(0) + \frac{1}{2} \phi''(0) + \cdots \cdots \frac{1}{n!} \phi^{(n)}(\xi)$$

we obtain

$$f(x_0 + h, y_0 + k) = f(x_0, y_0) + \left(h \frac{\partial}{\partial x} + k \frac{\partial}{\partial y} \right) f(x_0, y_0) +$$

$$\frac{1}{2} \left(h \frac{\partial}{\partial x} + k \frac{\partial}{\partial y} \right)^2 f(x_0, y_0) + \cdots \cdots + \frac{1}{n!} \left(h \frac{\partial}{\partial x} + k \frac{\partial}{\partial y} \right)^n f(x_0 + \xi h, y_0 + \xi k)$$

where ξ is some number in the interval $0 \leqslant \xi \leqslant 1$. [Note that

$\left(h \dfrac{\partial}{\partial x} + k \dfrac{\partial}{\partial y} \right)^2 f(x_0, y_0)$, for example, means that the expression

$\left(h \dfrac{\partial}{\partial x} + k \dfrac{\partial}{\partial y} \right)^2 f(x, y)$ is worked out and then evaluated at $x = x_0$, $y = y_0$. In

the last term above the expression is evaluated at $(x_0 + \xi h, y_0 + \xi k)$.]

In the case of several dimensions we carry out a similar expansion and write

$$f(\mathbf{x}_0 + \mathbf{h}) = f(\mathbf{x}_0) + \left(h_1 \frac{\partial}{\partial x_1} + h_2 \frac{\partial}{\partial x_2} + \cdots + h_n \frac{\partial}{\partial x_n} \right) f(\mathbf{x}_0)$$

$$+ \frac{1}{2} \left(h_1 \frac{\partial}{\partial x_1} + h_2 \frac{\partial}{\partial x_2} + \cdots + h_n \frac{\partial}{\partial x_n} \right)^2 f(\mathbf{x}_0) + \cdots$$

$$+ \frac{1}{m!} \left(h_1 \frac{\partial}{\partial x_1} + h_2 \frac{\partial}{\partial x_2} + \cdots + h_n \frac{\partial}{\partial x_n} \right)^m f(\mathbf{x}_0 + \xi \mathbf{h}),$$

where $\mathbf{h}$ represents $(h_1, h_2, \ldots, h_n)$.

Usually the general form of the remainder term is dauntingly complicated if more than two terms are included, and in many cases more convenient ways of expanding a function can be found. Nevertheless, the theorem is of theoretical importance, and we illustrate it by considering a simple function. Let

$$f(x, y, z) = x + y + xyz^2$$

$$\left(\alpha \frac{\partial}{\partial x} + \beta \frac{\partial}{\partial y} + \gamma \frac{\partial}{\partial z} \right) f = \alpha(1 + yz^2) + \beta(1 + xz^2) + \gamma(2xyz)$$

$$\left(\alpha \frac{\partial}{\partial x} + \beta \frac{\partial}{\partial y} + \gamma \frac{\partial}{\partial z} \right)^2 f = \alpha(\beta z^2 + 2\gamma yz) + \beta(\alpha z^2 + 2\gamma xz) + \gamma(2\alpha yz + 2\beta xz + 2\gamma xy)$$

$$= 2\alpha\beta z^2 + 4\alpha\gamma yz + 4\beta\gamma xz + 2\gamma^2 xy$$

$$\left(\alpha \frac{\partial}{\partial x} + \beta \frac{\partial}{\partial y} + \gamma \frac{\partial}{\partial z} \right)^3 f = \alpha(4\beta\gamma z + 2\gamma^2 y) + \beta(4\alpha\gamma z + 2\gamma^2 x) + \gamma(4\alpha\beta z + 4\alpha\gamma y + 4\beta\gamma x)$$

$$= 12\alpha\beta\gamma z + 6\alpha\gamma^2 y + 6\beta\gamma^2 x$$

Expanding about the point $(0, 1, 1)$.

$$f(0, 1, 1) = 1$$

$$\left(\alpha \frac{\partial}{\partial x} + \beta \frac{\partial}{\partial y} + \gamma \frac{\partial}{\partial z} \right) f = 2\alpha + \beta$$

$$\left(\alpha \frac{\partial}{\partial x} + \beta \frac{\partial}{\partial y} + \gamma \frac{\partial}{\partial z} \right)^2 f = 2\alpha\beta + 4\alpha\gamma$$

$$\left(\alpha \frac{\partial}{\partial x} + \beta \frac{\partial}{\partial y} + \gamma \frac{\partial}{\partial z} \right)^3 f(\alpha, 1 + \xi\beta, 1 + \xi\gamma) = 12\alpha\beta\gamma(1 + \xi\gamma) + 6\alpha\gamma^2(1 + \xi\beta)$$
$$+ 6\beta^2\gamma^2 \xi\alpha$$

$$= 12\alpha\beta\gamma + 6\alpha\gamma^2 + 24\alpha\beta\gamma^2 \xi$$

Hence

$$f(\alpha, 1 + \beta, 1 + \gamma) = 1 + 2\alpha + \beta + \frac{1}{2}(2\alpha\beta + 4\alpha\gamma) + \frac{1}{6}(12\alpha\beta\gamma + 6\alpha\gamma^2 + 24\alpha\beta\gamma^2\xi)$$

$$= 1 + 2\alpha + \beta + \alpha\beta + 2\alpha\gamma + 2\alpha\beta\gamma + \alpha\gamma^2 + 4\alpha\beta\gamma^2\xi$$

for $0 \leqslant \xi \leqslant 1$.

In this case we can express $f(\alpha, 1 + \beta, 1 + \gamma)$ exactly. We have

$$f(\alpha, 1 + \beta, 1 + \gamma) = \alpha + 1 + \beta + \alpha(1 + \beta)(1 + \gamma)^2$$

$$= 1 + 2\alpha + \beta + \alpha\beta + 2\alpha\gamma + 2\alpha\beta\gamma + \alpha\gamma^2 + \alpha\beta\gamma^2$$

We see that the previous expansion is in fact valid with $\xi = \frac{1}{4}$.

Taylor's theorem provides the theoretical justification for the estimation of the effects of small change in the variables. For example, to find the value of $\sqrt{(5.01^2 + 11.97^2)}$, we may write $f(x, y) = \sqrt{(x^2 + y^2)}$. Then

$$\sqrt{(5.01^2 + 11.97^2)} = f(5 + 0.01, 12 - 0.03)$$

$$\approx f(5, 12) + 0.01 f_x(5, 12) - 0.03 f_y(5, 12)$$

We have $f_x = x/\sqrt{(x^2 + y^2)}$ and $f_y = y/\sqrt{(x^2 + y^2)}$, so that

$$\sqrt{(5.01^2 + 11.97^2)} \approx 13 + 0.01 \times \frac{5}{13} - 0.03 \times \frac{12}{13}$$

$$= 12.976 \text{ to 3 decimal places}$$

The truncation error involved in the approximations is given by the remainder term

$$E = \frac{1}{2}[0.01^2 f_{xx}(\xi, \zeta) - 2 \times 0.01 \times 0.03 f_{xy}(\xi, \zeta) + 0.03^2 f_{yy}(\xi, \zeta)]$$

where $5 \leqslant \xi \leqslant 5.01$ and $11.97 \leqslant \zeta \leqslant 12$, but clearly this term will not be greatly in error if we take $\xi = 5$ and $\zeta = 12$. We find

$$f_{xx}(5, 12) = \frac{12^2}{13^3} \qquad f_{xy}(5, 12) = -\frac{5 \times 12}{13^3} \qquad \text{and} \qquad f_{yy}(5, 12) = \frac{5^2}{13^3}$$

and hence E is approximately equal to 2×10^{-7}.

The same technique is often useful in determining the effects of experimental error. For example, the velocity of a wave in some circumstances is given by the formula

$$v = \sqrt{\left\{\frac{g\lambda}{2\pi} + \frac{2\pi T}{p\lambda}\right\}}$$

where p and T are variables which may be in error in measurement by as much as 1 per cent; the percentage error in the calculated value of v will be approximately

$$\frac{100 \left| \dfrac{\partial v}{\partial p} \, \delta p + \dfrac{\partial v}{\partial T} \, \delta T \right|}{v} \leqslant \frac{100}{v} \left\{ \left| \dfrac{\partial v}{\partial p} \right| |\delta p| + \left| \dfrac{\partial v}{\partial T} \right| |\delta T| \right\}$$

$$\leqslant \frac{100}{v} \left\{ \left| -\frac{\pi T}{p^2 \lambda v} \right| \frac{p}{100} + \left| \frac{\pi}{pv\lambda} \right| \frac{T}{100} \right\}$$

$$= \frac{2\pi T}{p\lambda v^2}$$

4.4 Maxima, minima and saddle-points

We define a local maximum of a function of two variables in essentially the same way as with a function of one variable. If there is a neighbourhood of a point **a** within which the value of the function at **a** is greater than that at any other point, then we say that the function has a local maximum at **a**. That is, for $f(\mathbf{x})$ to have a local maximum at **a** we require that there should be some number $\delta > 0$ such that

$$f(\mathbf{x}) < f(\mathbf{a})$$

for all **x** satisfying

$$0 < \rho(\mathbf{x}, \mathbf{a}) < \delta$$

A local minimum is similarly defined by requiring $f(\mathbf{x}) > f(\mathbf{a})$.

The general n-dimensional case is investigated by using Taylor's theorem, but first we shall use a more geometrically obvious method to examine the conditions for maxima and minima in two dimensions.

4.4.1 *Two dimensions*

Let $f(x, y)$ have a local maximum at (x_0, y_0). Then as (x, y) moves on any straight line through (x_0, y_0), $f(x, y)$ has a one-dimensional maximum at (x_0, y_0). If the line makes an angle α with the x-axis, we can write (x, y) in terms of a parameter λ as

$$x = x_0 + \lambda \cos \alpha, \qquad y = y_0 + \lambda \sin \alpha$$

It follows that for any α, the function

$$\phi(\lambda) = f(\lambda \cos \alpha, \lambda \sin \alpha)$$

has a local maximum at $\lambda = 0$. If f_x and f_y are continuous at (x_0, y_0) then

$$\phi'(0) = f_x(x_0, y_0) \cos \alpha + f_y(x_0, y_0) \sin \alpha = 0$$

for all α and hence

$$f_x(x_0, y_0) = f_y(x_0, y_0) = 0$$

Such a point is called a *critical point*.

If the second partial derivatives exist and are continuous at (x_0, y_0) then

$$\phi''(0) = \cos^2 \alpha \, f_{xx} + 2 \cos \alpha \sin \alpha \, f_{xy} + \sin^2 \alpha \, f_{yy}$$

and if this is strictly negative for all α then $\phi(\lambda)$ has a maximum at $\lambda = 0$ for all α and hence $f(x, y)$ has a maximum at (x_0, y_0). By taking $\alpha = 0$ and $\alpha = \pi/2$ this condition implies $f_{xx} < 0$ and $f_{yy} < 0$. Then multiplying the inequality by f_{xx} we obtain

$$(f_{xx} \cos \alpha + f_{xy} \sin \alpha)^2 + \sin^2 \alpha (f_{xx} f_{yy} - f_{xy}^2) > 0$$

It is always possible to choose α so that the first bracket is zero, and hence it is necessary that

$$f_{xx} f_{yy} - f_{xy}^2 > 0$$

But this condition is also sufficient for the inequality to be satisfied for all α.

Examining a minimum in the same way we again find the condition

$$f_{xx} f_{yy} - f_{xy}^2 > 0,$$

but this time with $f_{xx} > 0$ and $f_{yy} > 0$. If $f_{xx} f_{yy} < f_{xy}^2$ the point is called a *saddle-point*. We may summarise this as follows.

Theorem 2. If at a point (x_0, y_0), $f_x = f_y = 0$ and $\Delta = f_{xx} f_{yy} - f_{xy}^2 \neq 0$, then

(i) if $\Delta > 0$ and $f_{xx} < 0$ (or $f_{yy} < 0$), (x_0, y_0) is a local maximum of f,

(ii) if $\Delta > 0$ and $f_{xx} > 0$ (or $f_{yy} > 0$), (x_0, y_0) is a local minimum of f,

(iii) if $\Delta < 0$, (x_0, y_0) is a saddle-point of f.

At a saddle-point, $\Delta < 0$, the equation

$$\phi''(\lambda) = \cos^2 \alpha \, f_{xx} + 2 \cos \alpha \sin \alpha \, f_{xy} + \sin^2 \alpha \, f_{yy} = 0$$

defines a pair of lines which divide the planes into four regions (see figure 4.8) — in two of which (x_0, y_0) is a local minimum and in the other two it is a local maximum.

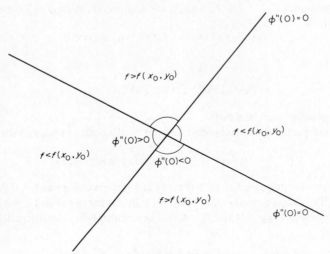

Fig. 4.8

Example. We consider the function $f(x, y) = x^2 + 2xy + \lambda y^2$

$$f_x = 2x + 2y \qquad \text{and} \qquad f_y = 2x + 2\lambda y$$

$f_x = f_y = 0$ at $(0, 0)$, and so we examine this point:

$$f_{xx} = 2, \quad f_{xy} = 2, \quad f_{yy} = 2\lambda$$

$$\therefore \ \Delta = f_{xx}f_{yy} - f_{xy}^2 = 4(\lambda - 1)$$

$\lambda > 1$: $\Delta > 0$ and $f_{xx} > 0$ and $f_{yy} > 0$, and hence a local maximum. Examining $f(x, y)$ directly in this case:

$$f(x, y) = (x + y)^2 + (\lambda - 1)y^2 > 0 \quad \text{for all} \quad (x, y) \neq (0, 0)$$

and therefore $(0, 0)$ is a local minimum.

$\lambda > 1$: $\Delta < 0$ and hence a saddle-point.
Writing $k = \sqrt{(1 - \lambda)}$:

$$f(x, y) = x^2 + 2xy + (1 - k^2)y = [x + (1 - k)y] \ [x + (1 + k)y]$$

On the lines $\qquad x + (1 - k)y = 0$

and $\qquad x + (1 + k)y = 0$

f is zero, and they bound regions in which f is greater than zero or less than zero. Figure 4.9 illustrates this case when $\lambda = -3 \ (k = -2)$.

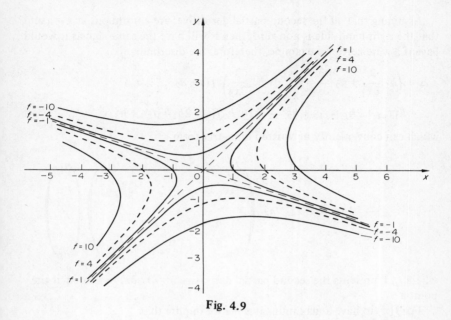

Fig. 4.9

*4.4.2 *More than two dimensions*

Readers who do not have a previous knowledge of matrix algebra should read chapter 7 before this section.

Consider now the case of n dimensions, where n may be more than two. If $f(\mathbf{x})$ has a local maximum at $\mathbf{x} = \mathbf{a}$ then, in particular,

$$\phi(\lambda) = f(a_1, a_2, \ldots, a_i + \lambda, a_{i+1}, \ldots, a_n)$$

has a one-dimensional local maximum at $\lambda = 0$, for each i from 1 to n. Assuming the existence of the partial derivatives this implies that

$$\frac{\partial f}{\partial x_i} = 0 \quad \text{for} \quad i = 1, 2, \ldots, n \quad \text{at} \quad \mathbf{x} = \mathbf{a}$$

Such a point is called a critical point. To find sufficient conditions that a critical point should be a maximum — or should be a minimum — we use Taylor's theorem. At a critical point

$$f(a_1 + h_1, a_2 + h_2, \ldots, a_n + h_n) - f(a_1, a_2, \ldots, a_n)$$

$$= \frac{1}{2} \left(h_1 \frac{\partial}{\partial x_1} + h_2 \frac{\partial}{\partial x_2} + \cdots + h_n \frac{\partial}{\partial x_n} \right)^2 f(a_1 + \xi h_1, a_2 + \xi h_2, \ldots, a_n + \xi h_n)$$

for some ξ such that $0 \leqslant \xi \leqslant 1$.

Assuming that all the second partial derivatives are continuous at $\mathbf{x} = \mathbf{a}$ and that the right-hand side is non-zero, then it will have the same sign as it would have if ξ were zero. We examine, therefore, the discriminant

$$\Delta = \left(h_1 \frac{\partial}{\partial x_1} + h_2 \frac{\partial}{\partial x_2} + \cdots + h_n \frac{\partial}{\partial x_n}\right)^2 f(a_1, a_2, \ldots, a_n)$$

$$= h_1^2 f_{11} + 2h_1 h_2 f_{12} + h_2^2 f_{22} + 2h_1 h_3 f_{13} + 2h_2 h_3 f_{23} + h_3^2 f_{33} + \ldots,$$

which can conveniently be written in matrix form

$$\Delta = (h_1, h_2, \ldots, h_n) \begin{pmatrix} f_{11} & f_{12} & f_{13} & \cdots & f_{1n} \\ f_{21} & f_{22} & & & \\ \cdot & & & & \\ \cdot & & & & \\ f_{n1} & & & & f_{nn} \end{pmatrix} \begin{pmatrix} h_1 \\ h_2 \\ \cdot \\ \cdot \\ h_n \end{pmatrix}$$

where f_{ij} represents the second partial derivative $\partial^2 f/\partial x_j \partial x_i$ evaluated at the point $\mathbf{a}$.

For $f(\mathbf{x})$ to have a maximum at $\mathbf{x} = \mathbf{a}$ we require that

$$f(a_1 + h_1, a_2 + h_2, \ldots, a_n + h_n) - f(a_1, a_2, \ldots, a_n) < 0$$

for all sufficiently small $h_1, h_2, \ldots, h_n$. That is, we require $\Delta < 0$ for all $h_1, h_2, \ldots, h_n$ not all zero.

If a square matrix A has the property that for every non-zero column vector $\mathbf{v}$ the product $\mathbf{v}'A\mathbf{v}$ is strictly less than zero, then A is said to be a *negative definite* matrix. If $\mathbf{v}'A\mathbf{v}$ is strictly positive for all non-zero $\mathbf{v}$ then A is called *positive definite*. The condition for a maximum is, therefore, that the matrix

$$H = \begin{pmatrix} f_{11} & f_{12} & \cdots & f_{1n} \\ f_{21} & f_{22} & \cdots & f_{2n} \\ \cdot & & & \\ \cdot & & & \\ f_{n1} & f_{n2} & \cdots & f_{nn} \end{pmatrix}$$

should be negative definite, and similarly the condition for a minimum at the critical point is that H should be positive definite.

If we define the *leading principal minor* of order r of a matrix A (of order $n \geqslant r$) as the determinant of the matrix obtained by taking only the first r rows and the first r columns of A, then a sufficient condition for A to be positive definite is that all its leading principal minors should be strictly positive. Thus, if f is a function of three variables, and if

$$f_{11} > 0, \quad \begin{vmatrix} f_{11} & f_{12} \\ f_{21} & f_{22} \end{vmatrix} > 0 \quad \text{and} \quad \begin{vmatrix} f_{11} & f_{12} & f_{13} \\ f_{21} & f_{22} & f_{23} \\ f_{31} & f_{32} & f_{33} \end{vmatrix} > 0$$

at a critical point, then f has a minimum at that point. Applying the given condition for positive definiteness in the case of two variables gives

$$f_{11} > 0 \quad \text{and} \quad f_{11}f_{22} - f_{12}^2 > 0$$

which is precisely the criterion for a minimum derived in section 4.4.1.

Example

$$f = x^3 - 3x + y^3 - 9y + z^3 - 9z + 6zy$$

has critical points where

$$3x^3 - 3 = 3y^2 - 9 + 6z = 3z^2 - 9 + 6y = 0$$

There are four such real points

$$(1, 1, 1) \qquad (1, -3, -3) \qquad (-1, 1, 1) \qquad \text{and} \qquad (-1, -3, -3)$$

The discriminant is

$$\Delta = (h_1 \quad h_2 \quad h_3) \begin{pmatrix} 6x & 0 & 0 \\ 0 & 6y & 6 \\ 0 & 6 & 6z \end{pmatrix} \begin{pmatrix} h_1 \\ h_2 \\ h_3 \end{pmatrix} = 6(xh_1^2 + yh_2^2 + 2h_2 h_3 + zh_3^2)$$

For a minimum we require $xh_1^2 > 0$ (and hence $x > 0$) and $yh_2^2 + 2h_2 h_3 + zh_3^2 > 0$ (and hence $y > 0, z > 0$ and $zy > 1$); for a maximum, $x < 0, y < 0, z < 0$ and $zy > 1$. Thus, there are no minima, the point $(-1, -3, -3)$ is a maximum and the other critical points are neither maxima nor minima.

Exercises

Examine the critical points of

1. $f = x^3 - 3x^2 - 4y^2 + 1$

2. $f = (x^2 + y^2)^2 - 2a^2(x^2 - y^2)$

4.4.3 *Notes on the numerical evaluation of maxima and minima*

In general the equations

$$\partial f(x_1, x_2, \ldots, x_n)/\partial x_i = 0 \qquad \text{for } i = 1, 2, \ldots, n$$

are not soluble analytically, and finding a minimum or maximum of $f(\mathbf{x})$ may depend upon finding a satisfactory numerical method of solving these equations. In one dimension there are several classical methods available, such as Newton's method (see section 6.3.1), and they may often be used in a straightforward way in two dimensions. With many variables special methods have been developed for the minimisation of functions.

We should note that not infrequently there is no analytical expression available for the function to be minimised, which can only be evaluated numerically (or possibly only experimentally) for individual specific values of its arguments. This usually means that there is no direct way of evaluating the partial derivatives, and it is then advisable to use a direct method of minimisation rather than to try to solve the equations $\partial f/\partial x_i = 0$.

NOTES ON CHAPTER 4

1. Metric spaces

We remarked in Note 2 of chapter 2 that the definition of a limit of a function of one variable may be stated in terms of neighbourhoods, and we can repeat this definition for functions of two or more variables. We have $f(\mathbf{x}) \rightarrow$ L as $\mathbf{x} \rightarrow \mathbf{a}$ if, given any neighbourhood N_L of L, there is a neighbourhood N_a of $\mathbf{a}$ such that $f(\mathbf{x})$ belongs to N_L whenever $\mathbf{x}$ belongs to N_a.

At an elementary level a neighbourhood of a point in n-dimensional space is taken as a hypersphere with the point as centre, so that N_a, for example, would be the set of points $\mathbf{x}$ satisfying (for some δ)

$$\rho(\mathbf{x}, \mathbf{a}) = \sqrt{\{(x_1 - a_1)^2 + (x_2 - a_2)^2 + \cdots + (x_n - a_n)^2\}} < \delta$$

However, we see from exercise 2, page 170, that, at least in the case of two dimensions, we may equally well use $\rho(\mathbf{x}, \mathbf{a}) = |x_1 - a_1| + |x_2 - a_2| < \delta$.

In the second case a neighbourhood of $\mathbf{a}$ is a square, centre $\mathbf{a}$, rather than a circle, and the two choices of ρ lead to the same limits since within any square we can construct a circle with the same centre, and vice versa.

Whenever neighbourhoods are defined in terms of some function which measures, possibly in a very generalised sense, the distance between two elements (points) in the space, then the space is called a *metric space*, and the function used as a measure of distance is called a *metric*.

Formally, a metric $\rho(\alpha, \beta)$ may be defined as a single-valued, non-negative, real function of α and beta which satisfies the following three axioms:

(i) $\rho(\alpha, \beta) = \rho(\beta, \alpha)$

(ii) $\rho(\alpha, \beta) = 0$ if and only if $\alpha = \beta$.

(iii) $\rho(\beta, \gamma) \leqslant \rho(\alpha, \beta) + \rho(\alpha, \gamma)$.

In n-dimensional space there is little need for any metric other than the Euclidean metric used in the body of this chapter (although some other definition of distance may occasionally be more convenient), but the concept of a metric may be extended to apply to more general spaces than those consisting of n-tuples of real numbers. We may consider, for example, the space of all functions $f(x)$ which are continuous on $0 \leqslant x \leqslant 1$. A metric measuring the distance between two such functions f and g and corresponding closely to the Euclidean metric in n-dimensions would be

$$\rho(f, g) = \sqrt{\left\{ \int_0^1 [f(x) - g(x)]^2 \, dx \right\}}$$

but for some purposes it would be a good deal more convenient to use the metric

$$\rho(f, g) = \text{the least upper bound of } |f(x) - g(x)| \quad \text{for } 0 \leqslant x \leqslant 1$$

(See E. T. Copson: *Metric Spaces*, C.U.P.)

2. The uniform limit of a function

Uniform convergence of sequences and series is dealt with in section 3.5. We define the uniform limit of a function similarly, thus: $f(x, y) \to g(x)$ as $y \to y_0$ uniformly with respect to x in the range $a \leqslant x \leqslant b$ if, given any $\epsilon > 0$, there exists $\delta(\epsilon)$ such that for all x in the range $a \leqslant x \leqslant b$, $|f(x, y) - g(x)| < \epsilon$ for all y satisfying $|y - y_0| < \delta$. Note the requirement that δ should be independent of x.

We have seen that there are functions $f(x, y)$ such that $\lim\limits_{x \to x_0} \lim\limits_{y \to y_0} f(x, y)$ and $\lim\limits_{y \to y_0} \lim\limits_{x \to x_0} f(x, y)$ both exist but are not equal. However, if $\lim\limits_{y \to y_0} f(x, y)$ is uniform with respect to x in some neighbourhood of x_0, then the two repeated limits are equal (and equal to the double limit).

Let $\qquad f(x, y) \to g(x)$ as $y \to y_0$ uniformly in $x_0 - a \leqslant x \leqslant x_0 + a$

Let $\qquad\qquad\qquad\qquad g(x) \to L$ as $x \to x_0$

We have $\qquad\qquad |f(x, y) - L| \leqslant |f(x, y) - g(x)| + |g(x) - L|$

The first of these terms can be made as small as we please by taking y sufficiently close to y_0 (provided only x lies in the interval $[x_0 - a, x_0 + a]$), and the second can be made as small as we please by taking x sufficiently close to x_0. It follows that we can make $|f(x, y) - L|$ as small as we please by taking (x, y) sufficiently close to (x_0, y_0), and hence $\lim_{(x,\, y) \to (x_0,\, y_0)} f(x, y)$ exists (equal to L). It follows that both repeated limits exist and are equal to the double limit, and hence to each other. (The reader is advised to write out in detail the above outline proof.)

A necessary and sufficient condition that $f(x, y) \to g(x)$ as $y \to y_0$ uniformly in $a \leqslant x \leqslant b$ is that $\sup_{a \,\leqslant\, x \,\leqslant\, b} |f(x, y) - g(x)| \to 0$ as $y \to y_0$.

A necessary and sufficient condition for the existence of a double limit in terms of polar coordinates is conveniently stated in terms of uniform convergence. Let

$$x - x_0 = r \cos \theta \qquad \text{and} \qquad y - y_0 = r \sin \theta$$

then the double limit $\lim_{(x,\, y) \to (x_0,\, y_0)} f(x, y)$ exists if and only if $f(x_0 + r \cos \theta, y_0 + r \sin \theta)$ converges uniformly as $r \to 0$ uniformly for $0 \leqslant \theta \leqslant 2\pi$. (See exercise 1, page 170.)

3. Matrix formulation of the chain rule

The chain rule for a change of coordinates in many dimensions (section 4.2.3) can conveniently be written in matrix form. In three dimensions the vector with components $\partial f/\partial x$, $\partial f/\partial y$ and $\partial f/\partial z$, where f is any function of x, y and z, is called the 'gradient' of f and written ∇f. We shall extend the use of the notation to n-dimensions and to more than one set of coordinates, and write

$$\nabla_u f = \begin{pmatrix} \partial f/\partial u_1 \\ \partial f/\partial u_2 \\ \cdot \\ \cdot \\ \cdot \\ \partial f/\partial u_n \end{pmatrix} \qquad \text{and} \qquad \nabla_x f = \begin{pmatrix} \partial f/\partial x_1 \\ \partial f/\partial x_2 \\ \cdot \\ \cdot \\ \cdot \\ \partial f/\partial x_n \end{pmatrix}$$

Then the chain-rule becomes

$$\nabla_u f = A \nabla_x f,$$

where A is the square matrix

$$A^{\cdot} = \begin{pmatrix} \partial x_1/\partial u_1 & \partial x_2/\partial u_1 & \ldots & \partial x_n/\partial u_1 \\ \partial x_1/\partial u_2 & \partial x_2/\partial u_2 & \ldots & \partial x_n/\partial u_2 \\ \cdot & \cdot & & \cdot \\ \cdot & \cdot & & \cdot \\ \cdot & \cdot & & \cdot \\ \partial x_1/\partial u_n & \partial x_2/\partial u_n & \ldots & \partial x_n/\partial u_n \end{pmatrix}$$

We also have

$$\nabla_x f = B \nabla_u f$$

where

$$B = \begin{pmatrix} \partial u_1/\partial x_1 & \partial u_2/\partial x_1 & \ldots & \partial u_n/\partial x_1 \\ \partial u_1/\partial x_2 & \partial u_2/\partial x_2 & \ldots & \partial u_n/\partial x_2 \\ \cdot & \cdot & & \cdot \\ \cdot & \cdot & & \cdot \\ \cdot & \cdot & & \cdot \\ \partial u_1/\partial x_n & \partial u_2/\partial x_n & \ldots & \partial u_n/\partial x_n \end{pmatrix}$$

It is clear that A and B are inverse to each other. We may verify this directly by noting that the (i, j)th element in the product AB is

$$\sum_{k=1}^{n} \frac{\partial x_k}{\partial u_i} \frac{\partial u_j}{\partial x_k} = \frac{\partial u_j}{\partial u_i} \begin{cases} 0 \text{ if } j \neq i \\ 1 \text{ if } j = i \end{cases}$$

The second partial derivatives may be transformed by using the chain rule a second time. We have

$$\frac{\partial^2 f}{\partial u_q \partial u_r} = \sum_{t=1}^{n} \frac{\partial x_t}{\partial u_q} \frac{\partial}{\partial x_t} \left(\frac{\partial f}{\partial u_r} \right) = \sum_{t=1}^{n} \frac{\partial x_t}{\partial u_q} \frac{\partial}{\partial x_t} \left(\sum_{s=1}^{n} \frac{\partial x_s}{\partial u_r} \frac{\partial f}{\partial x_s} \right)$$

$$= \sum_{t=1}^{n} \sum_{s=1}^{n} \frac{\partial x_t}{\partial u_q} \frac{\partial x_s}{\partial u_r} \frac{\partial^2 f}{\partial x_t \partial x_s} + \sum_{t=1}^{n} \sum_{s=1}^{n} \frac{\partial x_t}{\partial u_q} \frac{\partial f}{\partial x_s} \frac{\partial}{\partial x_t} \left(\frac{\partial x_s}{\partial u_r} \right)$$

The second term arises since in general the partial derivatives $\partial x_s/\partial u_r$ are not constant. If the transformation is linear so that

$$x_i = \sum_{j=1}^{n} a_{ij} u_j \quad \text{say,}$$

then $\quad \dfrac{\partial x_i}{\partial u_j} = a_{ij} \quad$ and $\quad A = (a_{ij})$

We have in matrix form

$$\mathbf{x} = \mathbf{Au}$$

and also $\qquad \nabla_u f = \mathbf{A}\nabla_x f, \qquad$ or $\qquad \nabla_x f = \mathbf{A}^{-1}\nabla_u f$

In this case the second partial derivatives of a function in one set of coordinates can be written in terms of those in the other together with the constants of the transformation

$$\frac{\partial^2 f}{\partial u_q \partial u_r} = \sum_{t=1}^{n} \sum_{s=1}^{n} a_{ts}\, a_{sr}\, \frac{\partial^2 f}{\partial x_t \partial x_s}$$

If H_u denotes the square matrix with (i, j) component $\partial^2 f/\partial u_i \partial u_j$, and H_x that with (i, j) component $\partial^2 f/\partial x_i \partial x_j$, then this equation can be written

$$H_u = \mathbf{A}' H_x \mathbf{A}$$

Miscellaneous Exercises

1. Show that $f(x, y) \to L$ as $(x, y) \to (0, 0)$ if and only if

$$\sup_{0 \leqslant \theta < 2\pi} |f(r\cos\theta, r\sin\theta) - L| \to 0 \quad \text{as} \quad r \to 0+$$

    If $\qquad f(x, y) = \dfrac{(x^2 + y^2)^2}{2x^2 y}$ for $x \neq 0$ and $y \neq 0$

    $f(x, 0) = 0$ for all x, and $f(0, y) = 0$ for all y

    then show that $\lim\limits_{r \to 0} f(r\cos\theta, r\sin\theta) = 0$ for all θ, but $\lim\limits_{(x, y) \to (0, 0)} f(x, y)$ does not exist.

2. In the definition of the limit of a function of two variables we used as a measure of distance between (x, y) and (x_0, y_0) the expression

$$\rho_1(x, y) = \sqrt{\{(x - x_0)^2 + (y - y_0)^2\}}$$

    It would appear superficially that replacing this by

$$\rho_2(x, y) = |x - x_0| + |y - y_0|$$

    would lead to a different definition. However, show that as $(x, y) \to (x_0, y_0$ $f(x, y)$ tends to L using ρ_1 if and only if it also tends to L using ρ_2. [Hint: within any circle centre (x_0, y_0) it is possible to draw a square with the same centre, and vice-versa.]

3. A point starts at the origin of the (x, y) plane and moves away from it in a direction making an angle θ with the positive direction of the x-axis and an angle $(\pi/2 - \theta)$ with that of the y-axis.

    For each of the following functions, use the partial derivatives at the origin to write down the initial rate of change of $f(x, y)$ as a function of θ.

    (i) $f(x, y) = 3x + 4y,$ (ii) $f(x, y) = \sqrt{(x + y + 4)},$

    (iii) $f(x, y) = (y + 2) \log (x + 1),$ (iv) $f(x, y) = (x + 1) e^{y(x + 2)}.$

    In each case find the value of θ for which the initial rate of change is a maximum and the value of the maximum rate of change.

    Show that in general the maximum rate of change of $f(x, y)$ at the point (a, b) is $\sqrt{\{f_x^2(a, b) + f_y^2(a, b)\}}$.

4. Show that the tangent plane to the general quadric surface:

    $$ax^2 + by^2 + cz^2 + d + 2exy + 2fxz + 2gyz + 2hx + 2jy + 2kz = 0$$

    at the point (x_0, y_0, z_0) on it, is

    $$ax_0x + by_0y + cz_0z + d + e(x_0y + y_0x) + f(x_0z + z_0x) + g(y_0z + z_0y)$$
    $$+ h(x + x_0) + j(y + y_0) + k(z + z_0) = 0$$

5. Find all the first and second partial derivatives of

    (i) $z = \sin (x - y) e^{x+y},$ and

    (ii) $w = x \log yz.$

6. If a surface is axially symmetric about the x-axis it may be written in the form

    $$z^2 = 2f(x) - y^2$$

    Show that all its normals intersect the x-axis.

7. Prove that the equation

    $$\frac{\partial^2 f}{\partial x^2} + \frac{\partial^2 f}{\partial y^2} + \frac{\partial^2 f}{\partial z^2} + \frac{2f}{x^2 + y^2 + z^2} = 0$$

    is satisfied by

    $$f = \frac{x + y + z}{x^2 + y^2 + z^2}$$

8. If
$$z = x\phi(y/x) + \psi(y/x)$$

where ϕ and ψ are arbitrary functions, show that

$$x^2 \frac{\partial^2 z}{\partial x^2} + 2xy \frac{\partial^2 z}{\partial x \partial y} + y^2 \frac{\partial^2 z}{\partial y^2} = 0$$

9. A function y of x is defined implicitly by the equation $f(x, y) = 0$. Express dy/dx and $d^2 y/dx^2$ in terms of the first and second partial derivatives of $f(x, y)$.

Find dy/dx and $d^2 y/dx^2$ if $y^2 + xy = a$.

10. If
$$w^2 + x^2 + y^2 + z^2 = 1,$$
$$w + x + y + z = 1, \text{ and}$$
$$wxyz = 1$$

show that

$$\frac{dw}{dx} = -\frac{w(x - y)(x - z)}{x(w - y)(w - z)}$$

11. The area Δ of a triangle is found from measurements of the side a and the angles B, C. Prove that the error $\delta\Delta$ in the calculated value of the area due to small errors δa, δB, δC is given approximately by

$$\frac{\delta\Delta}{\Delta} = 2\frac{\delta a}{a} + \frac{c}{a}\frac{\delta B}{\sin B} + \frac{b}{a}\frac{\delta C}{\sin C}$$

12. If $f(x, y, z) = $ constant, show that

$$\left(\frac{dx}{dy}\right)_z \times \left(\frac{dy}{dz}\right)_x \times \left(\frac{dz}{dx}\right)_y = -1$$

(The variable written as a suffix is treated as a constant during that particular differentiation.)

13. Show that when the arguments of $f(x, y)$ are transformed by

$$x = u, \ y = uv \text{ then}$$

$$\frac{\partial f}{\partial x} = \frac{\partial f}{\partial u} - \frac{v}{u}\frac{\partial f}{\partial v} \qquad \frac{\partial f}{\partial y} = \frac{1}{u}\frac{\partial f}{\partial v}$$

Hence evaluate $\left(x \dfrac{\partial f}{\partial x} + y \dfrac{\partial f}{\partial y} \right)$ and show that

$$x^2 \frac{\partial^2 f}{\partial x^2} + 2xy \frac{\partial^2 f}{\partial x \partial y} + y^2 \frac{\partial^2 f}{\partial y^2} = u^2 \frac{\partial^2 f}{\partial u^2}$$

14. Show that if

$$x = e^s \cos t, \qquad y = e^s \sin t,$$

then $\qquad \dfrac{\partial^2 F}{\partial x^2} + \dfrac{\partial^2 F}{\partial y^2} = e^{-2s} \left(\dfrac{\partial^2 F}{\partial s^2} + \dfrac{\partial^2 F}{\partial t^2} \right)$

15. If the independent variables x, y in $f(x, y)$ are transformed to ξ, η, where

$$\xi = x + y, \qquad \eta = x - y$$

so that $f(x, y)$ becomes $g(\xi, \eta)$, prove that

$$\frac{\partial^2 f}{\partial x^2} - \frac{\partial^2 f}{\partial y^2} = 4 \frac{\partial^2 g}{\partial \xi \partial \eta}$$

Deduce that if $x + y = \log (u + v)$, $x - y = \log (u - v)$ and $f(x, y) = h(u, v)$, then

$$\frac{\partial^2 f}{\partial x^2} - \frac{\partial^2 f}{\partial y^2} = (u^2 - v^2) \left(\frac{\partial^2 h}{\partial u^2} - \frac{\partial^2 h}{\partial v^2} \right)$$

16. Examine the critical points of

(i) $\cosh (x^2 y + xy - 3x^2/2 - 3x - 2y)$,

(ii) $(x^2 + y^2 + 2x + 1)/(x + y)$,

(iii) $(ax^2 - by^2) e^{(x + y)}$,

(iv) $x^4 + y^4 - 2(x - y)^2$,

(v) $\sin (x^2 + xy - y^2 - 4x + 3y) - x^2 - xy + y^2 + 4x - 3y$.

5 INTEGRATION

5.0 Introduction

The basic problem of the integral calculus may be stated as follows. A segment of a plane curve is defined by the equation $y = f(t)$, where t ranges over the finite interval $a \leqslant t \leqslant b$. It is required to find the area enclosed by the curve, the t-axis, and the ordinates $t = a$ and $t = b$. For a plane region bounded by straight lines there is, of course, no real difficulty; such a region can always be divided into a finite number of rectangles and triangles, and the areas of these can be obtained from elementary geometrical considerations. When the boundaries consist partly or wholly of curved lines, however, it becomes necessary to introduce some form of limiting process in order to make the concept of area meaningful.

5.1 Theory of the integral

5.1.1 *Definition of the integral*

Let $f(t)$ be a function of the real variable t which is defined, bounded, and non-negative for all t such that $a \leqslant t \leqslant b$. By a *partition*, P, of this interval we shall mean a subdivision into n (not necessarily equal) sub-intervals by arbitrarily chosen points t_k, where

$$a = t_0 < t_1 < t_2 < \cdots < t_{n-1} < t_n = b$$

For $k = 1, 2, \ldots, n$, let m_k and M_k denote respectively the greatest lower bound and the least upper bound of the function $f(t)$ in the sub-interval $t_{k-1} \leqslant t \leqslant t_k$. Now form the following sums

$$L(P) = m_1(t_1 - t_0) + m_2(t_2 - t_1) + \cdots + m_n(t_n - t_{n-1}) = \sum_{k=1}^{n} m_k \, \delta t_k \qquad (1)$$

$$U(P) = M_1(t_1 - t_0) + M_2(t_2 - t_1) + \cdots + M_n(t_n - t_{n-1}) = \sum_{k=1}^{n} M_k \, \delta t_k \qquad (2)$$

174

where we write δt_k for $t_k - t_{k-1}$. If the function $f(t)$ is sufficiently smooth we can represent it by the curve $y = f(t)$, as in figure 5.1, and the sums L(P) and U(P) are seen to be the areas of the regions defined respectively by the full lines and broken lines in that figure. The area of the region bounded by the curve $y = f(t)$, the t-axis, and the ordinates $t = a$ and $t = b$ will lie somewhere between L(P) and

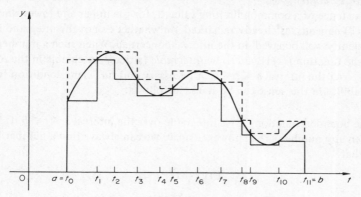

Fig. 5.1

U(P). Now let the number n of subdivisions increase in such a way that, for each k, the number $\delta_k = t_k - t_{k-1}$ becomes arbitrarily small. It seems clear that, provided the function $f(t)$ is sufficiently well-behaved, the corresponding sums L(P) and U(P) will approach a common limiting value I. It is this number I which measures the area enclosed by the curve and the t-axis, and which we call the *integral of the function f(t) taken over the interval* $a \leqslant t \leqslant b$:

$$I = \int_a^b f(t)\, dt \tag{3}$$

The function $f(t)$ is referred to as the *integrand* and the interval $a \leqslant t \leqslant b$ as the *range of integration*.

Remark. In an expression like $\int_a^b f(t)\, dt$ the so-called 'variable of integration', t, is just a *dummy variable.* The integral $I = \int_a^b f(t)\, dt$ is simply a number which depends on the lower and upper limits a and b, and on the particular function $f(t)$ which constitutes the integrand. (For this reason it is often referred to as a *definite* integral.) Thus, we may write

$$I = \int_a^b f(t)\, dt = \int_a^b f(x)\, dx = \int_a^b f(u)\, du$$

and so on. The variable of integration has, in fact, only the same significance as

the running index k in an expression like $\displaystyle\sum_{k=1}^{N} a_k$.

*5.1.2. Integrability

The existence of a common limiting value, I, for the upper and lower sums U(P) and L(P) depends, as already remarked, on whether or not the integrand is 'sufficiently well-behaved' in the interval concerned. When such a number I does exist the function $f(t)$ is said to be *integrable* (strictly, integrable in the *Riemann* sense), over the interval $a \leqslant t \leqslant b$. A necessary and sufficient condition for integrability in this sense can be stated as follows:

The bounded function $f(t)$ is integrable over the interval $a \leqslant t \leqslant b$ if, and only if, given any number $\epsilon > 0$, however small, we can always find a number $\delta > 0$ such that

$$U(P) - L(P) < \epsilon$$

for every partition P of the interval such that $\delta t_k < \delta$ for all k.

Suppose, in particular, that $f(t)$ is continuous on $a \leqslant t \leqslant b$. Then $f(t)$ is *uniformly continuous* there, that is given any $\epsilon > 0$ we can always find $\delta > 0$ such that

$$|f(t) - f(t')| < \epsilon/(b - a)$$

for all points t and t' in $a \leqslant t \leqslant b$ which are such that

$$|t - t'| < \delta$$

Moreover, for a continuous function $f(t)$ the bounds M_k and m_k in the sub-interval $t_{k-1} \leqslant t \leqslant t_k$ will simply be the maximum and minimum values attained by $f(t)$ in that sub-interval; that is, there exist points τ_k and τ_k' in $t_{k-1} \leqslant t \leqslant t_k$ such that

$$M_k = f(\tau_k) \qquad \text{and} \qquad m_k = f(\tau_k')$$

It follows that if we take any partition P of $a \leqslant t \leqslant b$ in which $\delta t_k < \delta$ for every k then we will have

$$U(P) - L(P) = \sum_{k=1}^{n} (M_k - m_k)\delta t_k = \sum_{k=1}^{n} [f(\tau_k) - f(\tau_k')]\,\delta t_k < \frac{\epsilon}{b - a} \sum_{k=1}^{n} \delta t_k$$

Thus every function continuous on $a \leqslant t \leqslant b$ is certainly integrable over that interval.

Now suppose that $f(t)$ is continuous on $a \leqslant t \leqslant b$ save for a simple discontinuity at $t = c$, where $a < c < b$. Specifically, let

$$\lim_{\epsilon \to 0} f(c - \epsilon) = A \qquad \text{and} \qquad \lim_{\epsilon \to 0} f(c + \epsilon) = B$$

where A and B are finite and $A \neq B$. In any partition of $a \leqslant t \leqslant b$ the point c appears in at most two sub-intervals. The contribution to $U(P) - L(P)$ made by these sub-intervals cannot exceed

$$2(M - m) \left\{ \max_k (\delta t_k) \right\}$$

where M and m denote respectively the least upper bound and the greatest lower bound of $f(t)$ in the whole interval $a \leqslant t \leqslant b$. Clearly this can be made as small as we please by choosing a partition in which $\max_k (\delta t_k)$ is sufficiently small. Hence $f(t)$ is integrable over $a \leqslant t \leqslant b$. More generally the same reasoning can be used to show that if $f(t)$ has only a finite number of simple discontinuities in $a \leqslant t \leqslant b$ then it is integrable over than interval.

This does not, in fact, exhaust the class of all functions integrable over a finite interval in this elementary, or Riemann, sense. There is little point in pursuing the investigation further however. Functions whose behaviour is wilder than that of those discussed here are only rarely of interest in any practical applications and, moreover, are best dealt with in terms of a more sophisticated theory of integration. Nevertheless one point should be borne in mind. The theory of the integral outlined here is concerned with the integration of *bounded* functions over *finite* intervals. Later, we shall require to relax these conditions and derive an extended concept of integration. The integrals we obtain in this way will be distinguished by the adjective 'improper'.

5.1.3 *The integral as a limit*

Let $f(t)$ be integrable on $a \leqslant t \leqslant b$ and let P denote some partition of this interval by points t_k, where $0 \leqslant k \leqslant n$. In each sub-interval $t_{k-1} \leqslant t \leqslant t_k$ choose some point τ_k arbitrarily and form the sum

$$f(\tau_1)(t_1 - t_0) + f(\tau_2)(t_2 - t_1) + \cdots + f(\tau_n)(t_n - t_{n-1})$$

$$\equiv \sum_{k=1}^{n} f(\tau_k) \, \delta t_k \tag{4}$$

Geometrically this sum is the total area of the rectangles in figure 5.2. It is usually referred to as a *Riemann sum* for the function $f(t)$.

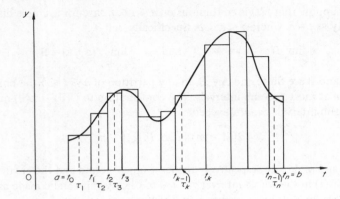

Fig. 5.2

Clearly it is always true that

$$L(P) = \sum_{k=1}^{n} m_k\, \delta t_k \leqslant \sum_{k=1}^{n} f(\tau_k)\, \delta t_k \leqslant \sum_{k=1}^{n} M_k \delta t_k = U(P) \tag{5}$$

no matter how the points τ_k may be chosen in the sub-intervals of the partition. It follows that, given any positive number ϵ, however small, we can always find a corresponding positive number δ such that

$$\left| \int_a^b f(t)\, dt - \sum_{k=1}^{n} f(\tau_k)\delta t_k \right| < \epsilon \tag{6}$$

provided only that $\delta t_k < \delta$ for all k concerned.

It is tempting to write this result in the form

$$\int_a^b f(t)\, dt = \lim_{\delta t_k \to 0} \sum_{k=1}^{n} f(\tau_k)\, \delta t_k \tag{7}$$

However, this is not a limit in the true sense. All that we can properly say is that the inequality (6) can be satisfied no matter how the points of subdivision t_k are chosen for a particular value of n (subject only to the condition $\delta t_k < \delta$), nor how the points τ_k are chosen in the resulting sub-intervals. We can express the integral as a true limit by specifying, for each integer n, some particular way of subdividing $a \leqslant t \leqslant b$, and some definite rule for choosing each τ_k in the appropriate sub-interval. In particular we might at each stage agree to divide

$a \leqslant t \leqslant b$ into n *equal* sub-intervals. The choice of the points τ_k could then be made according to any one of the following rules:

(a)   Let τ_k be the left-hand end-point of $t_{k-1} \leqslant t \leqslant t_k$. This would yield, for each integer n, a uniquely defined sum of the form

$$\Sigma_1(n) = \delta \left[f(a) + f(a + \delta) + f(a + 2\delta) + \cdots + f(a + (n-1)\delta) \right] \tag{8}$$

where $\delta = (b - a)/n$.

(b)   Let τ_k be the right-hand end-point of $t_{k-1} \leqslant t \leqslant t_k$. This would give,

$$\Sigma_2(n) = \delta \left[f(a + \delta) + f(a + 2\delta) + \cdots + f(b) \right] \tag{9}$$

(c)   If $f(t)$ is continuous we can choose τ_k such that $f(\tau_k) = M_k$, or τ'_k such that $f(\tau'_k) = m_k$, and so obtain the following sums

$$\Sigma_3(n) = \sum_{k=1}^{n} f(\tau_k) \delta = \delta \sum_{k=1}^{n} M_k \tag{10}$$

$$\Sigma_4(n) = \sum_{k=1}^{n} f(\tau'_k) \delta = \delta \sum_{k=1}^{n} m_k \tag{11}$$

In any one of these situations we could legitimately write

$$\int_a^b f(t)\, dt = \lim_{n \to \infty} \Sigma(n) \tag{12}$$

Example. To evaluate the integral $\displaystyle \int_0^\pi \sin t\, dt$ from first principles we divide the range of integration, $0 \leqslant t \leqslant \pi$, into n sub-intervals, each of length $\delta = \pi/n$. Taking, for example, the sum $\Sigma_2(n)$ defined in (9) above we get,

$$\int_0^\pi \sin t\, dt = \lim_{n \to \infty} \frac{\pi}{n} \sum_{k=1}^{n} \sin \frac{k\pi}{n}$$

From elementary trigonometry we know that, for any integer k

$$\cos \frac{(2k-1)\pi}{2n} - \cos \frac{(2k+1)\pi}{2n} = 2 \sin \frac{k\pi}{n} \sin \frac{\pi}{2n}$$

Hence,

$$\int_0^\pi \sin t \, dt = \lim_{n \to \infty} \frac{\pi}{n} \sum_{k=1}^n \frac{1}{2 \sin \dfrac{\pi}{2n}} \left\{ \cos \frac{(2k-1)\pi}{2n} - \cos \frac{(2k+1)\pi}{2n} \right\}$$

$$= \lim_{n \to \infty} \left\{ \frac{\pi/2n}{\sin \pi/2n} \right\} \left\{ \left(\cos \frac{\pi}{2n} - \cos \frac{3\pi}{2n} \right) + \left(\cos \frac{3\pi}{2n} - \cos \frac{5\pi}{2n} \right) + \cdots \right.$$

$$\left. + \left(\cos \frac{(2n-1)\pi}{2n} - \cos \frac{(2n+1)\pi}{2n} \right) \right\}$$

$$= \lim_{n \to \infty} \left\{ \frac{\pi/2n}{\sin \pi/2n} \right\} \left\{ \cos \frac{\pi}{2n} - \cos \frac{(2n+1)\pi}{2n} \right\} = \cos 0 - \cos \pi = 2$$

Exercises

By dividing the range of integration into equal sub-intervals and then forming the appropriate Riemann sums, obtain each of the following results:

1. $\displaystyle\int_0^b t^2 \, dt = \frac{1}{3} b^3$ [Hint: to find $\displaystyle\sum_{m=1}^n m^2$, use the identity $(m+1)^3 - m^3 = 3m^2 + 3m + 1$, $m = 1, 2, \ldots, n$.]

2. $\displaystyle\int_a^b e^{kt} \, dt = \frac{1}{k}(e^{bk} - e^{ak})$

3. $\displaystyle\int_0^{\pi/2} \cos t \, dt = 1$

5.2 Properties of the integral

The following properties are simple consequences of the definition of the integral and are, for the most part, fairly obvious. Where necessary sketch proofs of the more important results are given.

5.2.1 *Linearity*

Integration is a *linear* operation. That is to say, if $f_1(t)$ and $f_2(t)$ are any two bounded functions, each integrable over the interval $a \leqslant t \leqslant b$, and if α and β are any real numbers then,

$$\int_a^b \{\alpha f_1(t) + \beta f_2(t)\} dt = \alpha \int_a^b f_1(t) \, dt + \beta \int_a^b f_2(t) \, dt \qquad (13$$

In the initial discussion of the definition of the integral in 5.1.1 we stipulated that $f(t)$ should be bounded and *non-negative* on $a \leqslant t \leqslant b$. The boundedness of the integrand is, at this stage, crucial to the argument. However, a glance at the subsequent development will show that we make no use whatever of the non-negative property of $f(t)$ except in relating the analytic concept of integral to the geometric one of the area enclosed by a curve. Now, any bounded function $f(t)$ can be expressed as the difference of two non-negative functions. To see this we have only to define associated functions $f^+(t)$ and $f^-(t)$ as follows

$$f^+(t) = \max\{f(t), 0\}; \qquad f^-(t) = \max\{-f(t), 0\} \tag{14}$$

Then we must have

$$f(t) = f^+(t) - f^-(t) \qquad \text{for all } t$$

where $f^+(t) \geqslant 0$ and $f^-(t) \geqslant 0$ everywhere.

If we take the initial definition of integration as applying to non-negative integrands then we can extend it to the case of a general function by writing, as a definition,

$$\int_a^b f(t)\,dt \equiv \int_a^b f^+(t)\,dt - \int_a^b f^-(t)\,dt \tag{15}$$

On the other hand we could omit altogether the restriction that $f(t)$ be non-negative, and then (15) would occur naturally as a consequence of the linearity of the integral. In either case, however, the integral must be interpreted as measuring the *net* area enclosed by the curve $y = f(t)$ and the t-axis. The first term in (15), $\int_a^b f^+(t)\,dt$, measures the area enclosed by the t-axis and that portion of the curve which lies above it; the second term, $\int_a^b f^-(t)\,dt$, measures the area enclosed by the t-axis and that portion of the curve lying below it. The whole integral is the difference between these two numbers; that is, the area enclosed by the curve below the t-axis appears as a *negative* contribution to $\int_a^b f(t)\,dt$.

As a further consequence of (14) we have

$$|f(t)| = f^+(t) + f^-(t)$$

from which it follows at once that if $f(t)$ is integrable over $a \leqslant t \leqslant b$ then so also is the function $|f(t)|$. This is usually expressed by saying that $f(t)$ is *absolutely* integrable over $a \leqslant t \leqslant b$. Moreover, the following important inequality always holds

$$\left| \int_a^b f(t) \, dt \right| = \left| \int_a^b f^+(t) \, dt - \int_a^b f^-(t) \, dt \right|$$

$$\leqslant \int_a^b f^+(t) \, dt + \int_a^b f^-(t) \, dt = \int_a^b |f(t)| \, dt \qquad (16)$$

5.2.2 *Range of integration*

If $f(t)$ is integrable over $a \leqslant t \leqslant b$ and if c is any point such that $a < c < b$ then $f(t)$ is integrable over each of the intervals $a \leqslant t \leqslant c$ and $c \leqslant t \leqslant b$, and we have

$$\int_a^b f(t) \, dt = \int_a^c f(t) \, dt + \int_c^b f(t) \, dt \qquad (17)$$

This result is a trivial consequence of the definition of the integral.

Now consider a formal interchange of the limits, a and b, of the integral.

Hitherto we have made the natural assumption that when we write $\int_a^b f(t) \, dt$ the lower limit a is less than the upper limit b. This corresponds to the fact that, in computing any Riemann sum $\sum_{k=1}^{n} f(\tau_k) \, \delta t_k$, each of the quantities δt_k is positive. To be consistent we must then interpret $\int_b^a f(t) \, dt$ as the limit of Riemann sums in which each of the δt_k is negative, that is t must be considered as varying in the reverse, or negative, sense from b to a. Accordingly, provided we agree that

$$\int_b^a f(t) \, dt = - \int_a^b f(t) \, dt \qquad (18)$$

we shall obtain a consistent notation which allows an unrestricted use of limits.

5.2.3 *The mean-value theorem*

Let M and m denote respectively the least upper bound and the greatest lower bound of $f(t)$ in the interval $a \leqslant t \leqslant b$. Then for any given partition of this interval we will have

$$m\delta t_k \leqslant f(\tau_k) \, \delta t_k \leqslant M\delta t_k, \qquad 1 \leqslant k \leqslant n$$

and so

$$m \sum_{k=1}^{n} \delta t_k \leqslant \sum_{k=1}^{n} f(\tau_k) \, \delta t_k \leqslant M \sum_{k=1}^{n} \delta t_k$$

that is
$$m(b-a) \leqslant \sum_{k=1}^{n} f(\tau_k)\, \delta t_k \leqslant M(b-a)$$

If $f(t)$ is integrable over $a \leqslant t \leqslant b$ then it follows that

$$m(b-a) \leqslant \int_a^b f(t)\, \mathrm{d}t \leqslant M(b-a) \tag{19}$$

Suppose further that $f(t)$ is continuous on $a \leqslant t \leqslant b$. Then it takes on every value between m and M, its least and greatest values there. Now from (19) we know that

$$m \leqslant \frac{1}{b-a} \int_a^b f(t)\, \mathrm{d}t \leqslant M$$

Hence, there must exist a number ξ, such that $a < \xi < b$, for which

$$f(\xi) = \frac{1}{b-a} \int_a^b f(t)\, \mathrm{d}t \tag{20}$$

This result is known as the first mean-value theorem of the integral calculus, and is of very considerable importance. Its geometrical significance, as shown in figure 5.3, is fairly obvious: the area enclosed by the continuous curve $y = f(t)$, the t-axis and the ordinates $t = a$ and $t = b$, is the same as that of a rectangle of length $(b - a)$ and height $f(\xi)$.

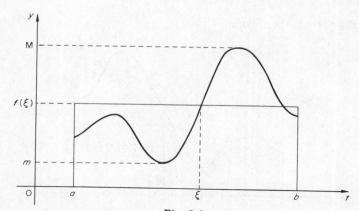

Fig. 5.3

5.2.4 *The fundamental theorem of the calculus*

The key result linking integration with differentiation is a consequence of the mean-value theorem. First, let $f(t)$ be integrable over $a \leqslant t \leqslant b$ and define $F(t)$ on this interval by writing

$$F(t) = \int_a^t f(\tau)\,d\tau \qquad (21)$$

Recall that if $f(t)$ is integrable over $a \leqslant t \leqslant b$ then so also is $|f(t)|$. Let M' denote the least upper bound of $|f(t)|$ in the interval. Then, if t and $t + h$ are any two points in $a \leqslant t \leqslant b$,

$$|F(t + h) - F(t)| = \left| \int_a^{t+h} f(\tau)\,d\tau - \int_a^t f(\tau)\,d\tau \right|$$

$$= \left| \int_t^{t+h} f(\tau)\,d\tau \right| \leqslant \left| \int_t^{t+h} |f(\tau)|\,d\tau \right| \leqslant M'\,|h|$$

Thus we can make $|F(t + h) - F(t)|$ as small as we please by taking $|h|$ sufficiently small. This shows that, no matter what discontinuities the integrand $f(t)$ may have, the function $F(t)$ defined by (21) is always *continuous* on $a \leqslant t \leqslant b$.

Now suppose that $f(t)$ is itself continuous on $a \leqslant t \leqslant b$. Once again, for any two points t and $t + h$ in this interval, we get

$$F(t + h) - F(t) = \int_a^{t+h} f(\tau)\,d\tau - \int_a^t f(\tau)\,d\tau$$

$$= \int_t^{t+h} f(\tau)\,d\tau = hf(\xi),$$

where $t < \xi < t + h$. (See figure 5.4.)

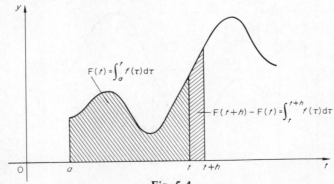

Fig. 5.4

Using the fact that $f(t)$ is continuous we get,

$$\lim_{h \to 0} \left\{ \frac{F(t+h) - F(t)}{h} \right\} = \lim_{h \to 0} f(\xi) = f(t)$$

Thus, for a continuous integrand $f(t)$ the function $F(t)$ defined by (21) is not merely continuous but is actually differentiable on $a \leqslant t \leqslant b$, and its derivative is the original integrand. Formally we may state this result as follows:

Fundamental theorem of the calculus. If $f(t)$ is continuous on $a \leqslant t \leqslant b$ then $\dfrac{d}{dt} \displaystyle\int_a^t f(\tau) \, d\tau$ exists and is equal to $f(t)$.

i.e.
$$\frac{d}{dt} \int_a^t f(\tau) \, d\tau = f(t) \tag{22}$$

5.2.5 *The anti-derivative*

Given a function $f(t)$, bounded and continuous on a finite interval $a \leqslant t \leqslant b$, let $F(t)$ be *any* function defined on this interval which is such that

$$F'(t) = f(t)$$

From the fundamental theorem of the calculus we know that

$$\frac{d}{dt} \left\{ \int_a^t f(\tau) \, d\tau - F(t) \right\} = f(t) - F'(t) = 0$$

But if a function has a zero derivative throughout an interval then it must be constant in that interval, that is we can write

$$F(t) = \int_a^t f(\tau) \, d\tau + C, \qquad \text{for } a \leqslant t \leqslant b$$

where C is a constant. Putting $t = a$ in this gives

$$F(a) = \int_a^a f(t) \, dt + C = C$$

Hence, putting $t = b$, we obtain the result

$$\int_a^b f(t) \, dt = F(b) - F(a) \tag{23}$$

It is on equation (23) that elementary methods of integration are based. For a given integrand $f(t)$ we try to find a function $F(t)$ whose derivative is *known* to be $f(t)$, and then evaluate the integral $\int_a^b f(t)\,dt$ by using (23). A function $F(t)$ whose derivative is $f(t)$ is called a *primitive* or an *anti-derivative* of $f(t)$. By a somewhat unfortunate abuse of terminology and of notation the term 'indefinite integral' is often used instead, and it is customary to write

$$F(t) = \int f(t)\,dt \qquad (24)$$

Using known results from the differential calculus the following table of anti-derivatives can be drawn up.

1. $\displaystyle\int t^n\,dt = \frac{1}{n+1}\,t^{n+1} \qquad (n \neq -1)$

2. $\displaystyle\int \frac{dt}{t} = \log |t|$

3. $\displaystyle\int e^{at}\,dt = \frac{1}{a}e^{at}$

4. $\displaystyle\int \sin t\,dt = -\cos t; \qquad \int \cos t\,dt = \sin t$

5. $\displaystyle\int \sec^2 t\,dt = \tan t; \qquad \int \mathrm{cosec}^2 t\,dt = -\cot t$

6. $\displaystyle\int \sinh t\,dt = \cosh t; \qquad \int \cosh t\,dt = \sinh t$

7. $\displaystyle\int \mathrm{sech}^2 t\,dt = \tanh t; \qquad \int \mathrm{cosech}^2 t\,dt = -\coth t$

8. $\displaystyle\int \frac{dt}{t^2 + a^2} = \frac{1}{a}\tan^{-1}\frac{t}{a}$

9. $\displaystyle\int \frac{dt}{a^2 - t^2} = \frac{1}{2a}\log\frac{a+t}{a-t}$ if $|t| < a$

$\displaystyle\qquad = \frac{1}{2a}\log\frac{t+a}{t-a}$ if $|t| > a > 0$

10. $\displaystyle\int \frac{dt}{\sqrt{(a^2 - t^2)}} = \sin^{-1}\frac{t}{a}$ or, $-\cos^{-1}\frac{t}{a}$

11. $\int \dfrac{dt}{\pm\sqrt{(t^2 + a^2)}} = \pm \sinh^{-1} \dfrac{t}{a} = \log |t \pm \sqrt{(t^2 + a^2)}|$

12. $\int \dfrac{dt}{\pm\sqrt{(t^2 - a^2)}} = \pm \cosh^{-1} \left|\dfrac{t}{a}\right| = \log |t \pm \sqrt{(t^2 - a^2)}|$

Notes

(a) In respect of formula (2) in the table recall that when we write

$$\frac{d}{dt} \log t = \frac{1}{t}$$

it is understood that t is positive, since the logarithm of a negative number is not real. If we write $x = -t$ then the function $y = \log x$ is well-defined for all $x > 0$, and hence for all $t < 0$. Also

$$\frac{dy}{dt} = -\frac{dy}{dx} = -\frac{1}{x} = \frac{1}{t}$$

so that when t is negative we have

$$\int \frac{dt}{t} = \log(-t)$$

(b) The inverse trigonometrical functions appearing in formulae (8) and (10) are single-valued; $\tan^{-1} t$ and $\sin^{-1} t$ are the angles lying between $-\pi/2$ and $\pi/2$ whose tangent and sine respectively are x, whereas $\cos^{-1} x$ is the angle between 0 and π whose cosine is x. Similarly the inverse hyperbolic function $\cosh^{-1} |t/a|$ in (12) defines the *positive* number y which is such that $|t/a| = \cosh y$.

Exercises

1. If $f(t)$ and $g(t)$ are integrable over $a \leqslant t \leqslant b$ and if $f(t) \leqslant g(t)$ in that interval, show that

$$\int_a^b f(t)dt \leqslant \int_a^b g(t)dt$$

2. (a)   Show that, for every value of n,

$$\left|\int_0^1 \frac{\sin nt}{t + 1} dt\right| \leqslant \log 2$$

   (b)   Show that

$$\lim_{n \to \infty} \int_0^{2\pi} \frac{\sin nt}{t^2 + n^2} dt = 0$$

3. In each of the following cases find ξ such that

$$a < \xi < b \qquad \text{and} \qquad \int_a^b f(t)\mathrm{d}t = (b - a)f(\xi)$$

(a) $f(t) = t$ (b) $f(t) = t^2$ (c) $f(t) = \dfrac{1}{t^2}$

4. Prove the following generalisation of the mean value theorem: If $f(t)$ and $g(t)$ are continuous for $a \leqslant t \leqslant b$ and if $g(t) > 0$ throughout that interval, then there exists some point ξ, such that $a < \xi < b$, for which

$$\int_a^b f(t)g(t)\mathrm{d}t = f(\xi) \int_a^b g(t)\mathrm{d}t$$

5. Show that there exist values ξ_1 and ξ_2 in $0 < t < 1$ for which

$$\int_0^1 \frac{e^{-t}}{1 + t^2}\,\mathrm{d}t = \frac{e - 1}{e(1 + \xi_1^2)} = \frac{\pi}{4e^{\xi_2}}$$

6. Use the fact that the integral of a continuous function can be expressed as the limit of Riemann sums to evaluate

(a) $\displaystyle\lim_{n\to\infty} \left\{ \frac{1}{n^2} + \frac{2}{n^2} + \cdots + \frac{n}{n^2} \right\}$

(b) $\displaystyle\lim_{n\to\infty} \left\{ \frac{\sqrt{(n + 1)} + \sqrt{(n + 2)} + \cdots + \sqrt{(2n)}}{n^{3/2}} \right\}$

5.3 Systematic integration

5.3.1 *Change of variable*

The general technique for evaluating integrals by means of the fundamental theorem of the calculus is to reduce the integrand to one of the forms given in the table of anti-derivatives, or to a linear combination of such forms. (We do not, of course, suggest that the table is exhaustive.) The following result is often very useful in this connection:

If $t = \phi(x)$, where $\phi(x)$ is a single-valued, differentiable function of x, then

$$\int_a^b f(t)\mathrm{d}t = \int_c^d f\{\phi(x)\}\phi'(x)\mathrm{d}x \qquad (25)$$

where c and d are given by the relations

$$a = \phi(c) \qquad \text{and} \qquad b = \phi(d)$$

Proof. If $F(t)$ is an anti-derivative of $f(t)$ then, by the fundamental theorem

$$\int_a^b f(t)dt = F(b) - F(a) = F\{\phi(d)\} - F\{\phi(c)\}$$

On the other hand, using the rule for differentiating a function of a function,

$$\frac{d}{dx} F\{\phi(x)\} = f\{\phi(x)\}\phi'(x)$$

so that

$$\int_c^d f\{\phi(x)\}\phi'(x)dx = F\{\phi(d)\} - F\{\phi(c)\}$$

and the result follows.

For example, the substitution $x = at + b$ allows us to write down results such as

$$\int (at + b)^n dt = \frac{1}{a} \int x^n dx = \frac{1}{a}\frac{(at + b)^{n+1}}{n + 1}$$

$$\int \sin (at + b)dt = \frac{1}{a} \int \sin x \, dx = -\frac{1}{a} \cos (at + b)$$

and so on.

In practice, of course, the usual object is to recognise situations in which an integrand can be expressed in the form $f[\phi(x)]\phi'(x)$ and then to make the substitution $t = \phi(x)$. Two important special cases of this are

(i)
$$\int \frac{f'(x)}{f(x)} \, dx = \int \frac{dt}{t} = \log |t| = \log |f(x)|$$

and (ii)
$$\int \frac{f'(x)}{[f(x)]^n} \, dx = \int \frac{dt}{t^n} = \frac{t^{1-n}}{1-n} = \frac{[f(x)]^{1-n}}{1-n}$$

where $n \neq 1$.

Remark. In applying a change of variable to a definite integral it should not be forgotten that the limits are generally modified by the substitution. For example, if we put $t = a \sin \theta$ in the integral $\int_0^1 \sqrt{(a^2 - t^2)} \, dt$ then we get $dt/d\theta = a \cos \theta$ and $\sqrt{(a^2 - t^2)} = a \cos \theta$. Since $\theta = 0$ when $t = 0$, and $\theta = \pi/2$ when $t = 1$, the integral becomes

$$\int_0^{\pi/2} a^2 \cos^2 \theta \, d\theta$$

5.3.2 *Integration by parts*

From the rule for differentiating a product we have

$$\frac{d}{dt} [u(t)v(t)] = u'(t)v(t) + u(t)v'(t)$$

Hence $\qquad \int [u'(t)v(t) + u(t)v'(t)] \, dt = u(t)v(t)$

and so $\qquad \int u'(t)v(t)dt = u(t)v(t) - \int u(t)v'(t)dt \qquad (26)$

Now suppose we have to evaluate $\int_a^b f(t)g(t)dt$ where an anti-derivative $F(t)$ of $f(t)$ is known but where the integration of the product $f(t)g(t)$ presents difficulty. Using (26) we can write

$$\int_a^b f(t)g(t)dt = \left[F(t)g(t) \right]_a^b - \int_a^b F(t)g'(t)dt \qquad (27)$$

and the problem is reduced to the evaluation of $\int_a^b F(t)g'(t)dt$ instead. As an example, if $f(t) = \cos t$ and $g(t) = t$ we have

$$\int t \cos t \, dt = t \sin t - \int \sin t \, dt = t \sin t + \cos t$$

Again, if $f(t) = 1$ and $g(t) = \log t$

$$\int \log t \, dt = t \log t - \int t \, \frac{1}{t} \, dt = t \log t - t$$

5.3.3 *Systematic integration*

Most texts on elementary calculus contain detailed accounts of methods of reducing various types of integrals to standard forms. We confine ourselves here to a brief review of the more important cases.

(i) *Rational integrands.* If the denominator is no worse than a quadratic the integration presents no real difficulty. For, by expressing $t^2 + pt + q$ as $(t - \alpha)^2 \pm \beta^2$, the integrand can easily be reduced to a combination of standard forms. Otherwise it is necessary to expand the integrand into partial fractions. (See Appendix.)

Examples

1. $\displaystyle \int \frac{t^2 + t + 1}{t^2 - t + 1}\, dt = \int \left\{ 1 + \frac{2t}{t^2 - t + 1} \right\} dt = \int \left\{ t + \frac{2t - 1}{t^2 - t + 1} + \frac{1}{(t - \frac{1}{2})^2 + \frac{3}{4}} \right\} dt$

$$= t + \log|t^2 - t + 1| + \frac{2}{\sqrt{3}} \tan^{-1} \frac{2t - 1}{\sqrt{3}}$$

2. $\displaystyle \int \frac{dt}{t^2(t - 1)} = \int \left\{ \frac{1}{t - 1} - \frac{1}{t} - \frac{1}{t^2} \right\} dt = \log|t - 1| - \log|t| + \frac{1}{t}$

3. $\displaystyle \int \frac{dt}{(t^2 + 1)^2} = \int \frac{(t^2 + 1) - t^2}{(t^2 + 1)^2}\, dt = \int \frac{dt}{t^2 + 1} - \int \frac{t^2\, dt}{(t^2 + 1)^2}$

$$= \tan^{-1} t + \frac{t}{2(t^2 + 1)} - \frac{1}{2} \int \frac{dt}{t^2 + 1} \quad \text{(integrating by parts)}$$

$$= \frac{1}{2} \tan^{-1} t + \frac{t}{2(t^2 + 1)}$$

(ii) *Trigonometric integrands.* Products of trigonometric functions involving multiple angles can be expressed as sums and differences of sines and cosines. For example, if $m \neq n$ we have

$$\int \sin mt \cos nt\, dt = \frac{1}{2} \int \left\{ \sin(m + n)t + \sin(m - n)t \right\} dt$$

$$= -\frac{1}{2} \left\{ \frac{\cos(m + n)t}{m + n} + \frac{\cos(m - n)t}{m - n} \right\} \qquad (28)$$

If $m = n$ then

$$\int \sin^2 nt \, dt = \frac{t}{2} - \frac{1}{4n} \sin 2nt,$$

and

$$\int \cos^2 nt \, dt = \frac{t}{2} + \frac{1}{4n} \sin 2nt.$$

If the integrand is a rational function $F(\sin t, \cos t)$ of $\sin t$ and $\cos t$ then the substitution $x = \tan t/2$ reduces it to a rational function of x, for we have

$$\frac{dt}{dx} = \frac{2}{1 + x^2}, \quad \sin t = \frac{2x}{1 + x^2}, \quad \cos t = \frac{1 - x^2}{1 + x^2}$$

Then,

$$\int F\left\{\sin t, \cos t\right\} dt = \int F\left\{\frac{2x}{1 + x^2}, \frac{1 - x^2}{1 + x^2}\right\} \frac{2}{1 + x^2} \, dx \tag{29}$$

For integrands involving powers of trigonometric functions, successive integration by parts can sometimes be used to reduce the powers without altering the form of the integrand. The result is then a recursive relation for the integral, known as a *reduction formula*.

Example. Reduction formula for $\int \sin^m t \cos^n t \, dt$.

Let

$$I(m, n) = \int \sin^m t \cos^n t \, dt = \int (\sin^m t \cos t)(\cos^{n-1} t) dt$$

Integrating by parts

$$I(m, n) = \frac{\sin^{m+1} t \cos^{n-1} t}{m + 1} + \frac{n - 1}{m + 1} \int \sin^{m+2} t \cos^{n-2} t \, dt$$

$$= \frac{\sin^{m+1} t \cos^{n-1} t}{m + 1} + \frac{n - 1}{m + 1} \int \sin^m t \{1 - \cos^2 t\} \cos^{n-2} t \, dt$$

$$= \frac{\sin^{m+1} t \cos^{n-1} t}{m + 1} + \frac{n - 1}{m + 1} [I(m, n - 2) - I(m, n)]$$

This gives the reduction formula

$$\int \sin^m t \cos^n t \, dt = \frac{\sin^{m+1} t \cos^{n-1} t}{m + n} + \frac{n - 1}{m + n} \int \sin^m t \cos^{n-2} t \, dt \tag{30}$$

(iii) *Integration of certain irrational functions.* When the integrand is a rational function it is always possible to find an anti-derivative and hence to evaluate the integral by using the fundamental theorem of the calculus.† The situation is quite different when it comes to irrational integrands. It is not possible, for example, to express in terms of elementary functions such general integrals as

$$\int \frac{dt}{\sqrt{(a_n t^n + a_{n-1} t^{n-1} + \cdots + a_0)}} \quad \text{or} \quad \int \sqrt{(a_n t^n + a_{n-1} t^{n-1} + \cdots + a_0)}\, dt$$

In certain special cases, however, the integrand can be reduced to a standard form or transformed, by a suitable substitution, to a rational function.

Examples

1. $\int \dfrac{3t + 1}{\sqrt{(t^2 + 2t + 3)}}\, dt = 3 \int \dfrac{t + 1}{\sqrt{(t^2 + 2t + 3)}}\, dt - 2 \int \dfrac{dt}{\sqrt{(t^2 + 2t + 3)}}$

$\qquad = 3\sqrt{(t^2 + 2t + 3)} - 2 \int \dfrac{dt}{\sqrt{[(t + 1)^2 + 2]}} = 3\sqrt{(t^2 + 2t + 3)} - 2 \sinh^{-1}\left(\dfrac{t + 1}{\sqrt{2}}\right)$

2. $\int \dfrac{dt}{(3 + t)\sqrt{(1 + t)}}.$ Put $1 + t = x^2$ so that $\dfrac{dt}{dx} = 2x.$

   The integral becomes $\int \dfrac{2x\, dx}{(2 + x^2)x} = \tan^{-1}\dfrac{x}{\sqrt{2}} = \tan^{-1}\sqrt{\left(\dfrac{1 + t}{2}\right)}$

3. $\int \sqrt{\left(\dfrac{1 + x}{1 - x}\right)}\, dx = \int \sqrt{\left(\dfrac{(1 + x)^2}{1 - x^2}\right)}\, dx$

   $\qquad = \int \dfrac{dx}{\sqrt{(1 - x^2)}} + \int \dfrac{x\, dx}{\sqrt{(1 - x^2)}} = \sin^{-1} x - \sqrt{(1 - x^2)}$

5.3.4 *Miscellaneous special techniques*
(i) By a simple change of variable we have

$$\int_0^a f(t)\, dt = \int_0^a f(a - t)\, dt \qquad\qquad (31)$$

---

† Note: In practice, of course, integration of a rational function by elementary means depends on our ability to factorise the denominator.

In particular,
$$\int_0^{\pi/2} f(\sin \theta) \, d\theta = \int_0^{\pi/2} f(\cos \theta) \, d\theta \qquad (32)$$

As a simple example of the use of this relation, note that since

$$\int_0^{\pi/2} \sin^2 \theta \, d\theta = \int_0^{\pi/2} \cos^2 \theta \, d\theta$$

it follows at once that each of these integrals must have the value

$$\frac{1}{2} \int_0^{\pi/2} (\sin^2 \theta + \cos^2 \theta) d\theta = \frac{1}{2} \int_0^{\pi/2} d\theta = \frac{\pi}{4}$$

Similarly, the following relation is often useful

$$\int_0^{2a} f(t) \, dt = \int_0^a f(t) \, dt + \int_a^{2a} f(t) \, dt$$

$$= \int_0^a f(t) \, dt + \int_a^0 f(2a - x)(-dx) = \int_0^a f(t) \, dt + \int_0^a f(2a - t) \, dt$$

$$= \int_0^a \{f(t) + f(2a - t)\} dt$$

Thus
$$\int_0^{2a} f(t) \, dt = 2 \int_0^a f(t) \, dt \quad \text{if} \quad f(2a - t) = f(t)$$

In particular, this gives

$$\int_0^{\pi} f(\sin \theta) \, d\theta = 2 \int_0^{\pi/2} f(\sin \theta) \, d\theta$$

(ii) A function $f(t)$ is said to be *even* if $f(t) = f(-t)$ for all t; it is said to be *odd* if $f(-t) = -f(t)$. For example, $\cos t$ is even and $\sin t$ is odd. An arbitrary function $f(t)$ admits a decomposition into even and odd components which is in many ways analogous to the decomposition into positive and negative parts (as in section 5.2.1):

Define

$$f_E(t) \equiv \tfrac{1}{2}\{f(t) + f(-t)\} \quad \text{and} \quad f_0(t) \equiv \tfrac{1}{2}\{f(t) - f(-t)\} \qquad (33)$$

Then $f_E(t)$ is even, $f_0(t)$ is odd, and, for all t

$$f(t) = f_E(t) + f_0(t) \quad \text{and} \quad f(-t) = f_E(t) - f_0(t) \tag{34}$$

Further

$$\int_{-a}^{a} f(t)\,dt = \int_{0}^{a} f(t)\,dt + \int_{-a}^{0} f(t)\,dt = \int_{0}^{a} f(t)\,dt + \int_{0}^{a} f(-t)\,dt$$

and it follows that

(a) if $f(t)$ is even, then $\displaystyle\int_{-a}^{a} f(t)\,dt = 2\int_{0}^{a} f(t)\,dt$

(b) if $f(t)$ is odd, then $\displaystyle\int_{-a}^{a} f(t)\,dt = 0$

and (c) in general, $\displaystyle\int_{-a}^{a} f(t)\,dt = 2\int_{0}^{a} f_E(t)\,dt$

(iii) Suppose that $\phi(t)$ is a complex-valued function of a single real variable. Then we can always express $\phi(t)$ in the form

$$\phi(t) = f(t) + ig(t)$$

where $f(t)$ and $g(t)$ are real-valued functions. We define the integral of $\phi(t)$ over the interval $a \leqslant t \leqslant b$ by

$$\int_{a}^{b} \phi(t)\,dt = \int_{a}^{b} \{f(t) + ig(t)\}\,dt \equiv \int_{a}^{b} f(t)\,dt + i\int_{a}^{b} g(t)\,dt \tag{35}$$

The properties of such integrals are simple consequences of those of ordinary real integrals. In particular, using equation (16) we can show that

$$\left| \int_{a}^{b} \phi(t)\,dt \right| = \left| \int_{a}^{b} f(t)\,dt + i\int_{a}^{b} g(t)\,dt \right| \leqslant \int_{a}^{b} |\phi(t)|\,dt \tag{36}$$

The evaluation of certain integrals involving trigonometric functions can be simplified by considering the appropriate complex exponentials instead, and equating real and imaginary parts. For example the rather complicated results

$$\int e^{\sigma t} \cos \omega t\,dt = e^{\sigma t} \left\{ \frac{\sigma \cos \omega t + \omega \sin \omega t}{\sigma^2 + \omega^2} \right\}$$

and
$$\int e^{\sigma t} \sin \omega t \, dt = e^{\sigma t} \left\{ \frac{\sigma \sin \omega t - \omega \cos \omega t}{\sigma^2 + \omega^2} \right\}$$

are both contained in the simple statement that

$$\int e^{\alpha t} \, dt = \frac{1}{\alpha} e^{\alpha t}$$

where $\alpha = \sigma + i\omega$.

Exercises

1. Find anti-derivatives in each of the following cases:

(i) $\displaystyle\int \frac{t^2 + t + 1}{t^2 - t - 1} \, dt$ (ii) $\displaystyle\int \frac{t + 1}{(t - 1)^2} \, dt$ (iii) $\displaystyle\int \frac{t^2 \, dt}{(t - 1)(t - 2)(t - 3)}$

(iv) $\displaystyle\int \frac{dt}{(t^2 + 2)(t^2 + 3)}$ (v) $\displaystyle\int \frac{t^2 \, dt}{(t^2 + 2)(t^2 + 3)}$ (vi) $\displaystyle\int \frac{dt}{t^4 + 1}$ (vii) $\displaystyle\int \frac{t^2 \, dt}{t^4 + 1}$

(viii) $\displaystyle\int \frac{dt}{\sqrt{(1 + 2t - 3t^2)}}$ (ix) $\displaystyle\int \frac{dt}{(1 - t)\sqrt{t}}$ (x) $\displaystyle\int \frac{dt}{(1 - t^2)\sqrt{(1 + t^2)}}$

(xi) $\displaystyle\int \frac{dt}{\sin t \cos^3 t}$ (xii) $\displaystyle\int t \tan^{-1} t \, dt$ (xiii) $\displaystyle\int t^4 \sin t \, dt$

(xiv) $\displaystyle\int \frac{dt}{a^2 \sin^2 t + b^2 \cos^2 t}$ (xv) $\displaystyle\int \frac{t + \sin t}{1 + \cos t} dt$ (xvi) $\displaystyle\int \sinh t \cos t \, dt$

2. Establish the following recurrence formulae:

(i) If $I_n = \displaystyle\int (1 + ax^2)^n \, dx$ then $(2n + 1)I_n - 2nI_{n-1} = x(1 + ax^2)^n$,

(ii) If $I_n = \displaystyle\int x^n \cosh x \, dx$ and $J_n = \displaystyle\int x^n \sinh x \, dx$ then

$$I_n = x^n \sinh x - nJ_{n-1} \text{ and } J_n = x^n \cosh x - nI_{n-1},$$

(iii) $\displaystyle\int \cos^m x \cos nx \, dx = \frac{1}{m + n} \cos^m x \sin nx + \frac{m}{m + n} \int \cos^{m-1} x \cos(n - 1)x \, d$

3. (i) Use the substitution $x = \sin^2 \theta$ to find the value of

$$\int_0^1 x^m (1 - x)^n \, dx$$

where m and n are positive integers.

(ii) Use the substitution $x = t + \alpha$, where $\tan \alpha = a/b$, to show that

$$\int \frac{dt}{a \cos t + b \sin t} = \frac{1}{\sqrt{(a^2 + b^2)}} \log |\tan \tfrac{1}{2}(t + \alpha)|$$

4. By using the relation

$$\int_0^a f(a - \theta) \, d\theta = \int_0^a f(\theta) \, d\theta$$

show that the integral $\int_0^{\pi/4} \log (1 + \tan \theta) \, d\theta$ may be evaluated without finding any anti-derivative.

5.4 Improper integrals

5.4.1 Improper integrals of the first kind

Let $f(t)$ be a bounded integrable function of t over every interval $a \leqslant t \leqslant x$, where a is some fixed number and x is any number greater than a. We define

the *infinite*, or *improper*, integral $\int_a^\infty f(t) \, dt$ by the relation

$$\int_a^\infty f(t) \, dt \equiv \lim_{x \to \infty} \int_a^x f(t) \, dt = \lim_{x \to \infty} F(x) - F(a) \qquad (37)$$

where $F(t)$ is any indefinite integral of $f(t)$. If the limit is finite then the integral is said to *converge*; otherwise it is said to *diverge*. An integral of this type, in which the range of integration becomes infinite but the integrand remains bounded, is called an *improper integral of the first kind*. For integrals over the range $(-\infty, +\infty)$ we adopt the following definition

$$\int_{-\infty}^{+\infty} f(t) \, dt \equiv \lim_{y \to -\infty} \int_y^a f(t) \, dt + \lim_{x \to \infty} \int_a^x f(t) \, dt \qquad (38)$$

where x and y tend to $+\infty$ and to $-\infty$ independently. Note that here a may be any finite number we please since

$$\lim_{y \to -\infty} \int_y^a f(t)\,dt + \lim_{x \to \infty} \int_a^x f(t)\,dt = F(a) - \lim_{y \to \infty} F(y) + \lim_{x \to \infty} F(x) - F(a)$$

Examples
1. If $a > 0$ and $p \neq 1$, then

$$\int_a^\infty \frac{dt}{t^p} = \lim_{x \to \infty} \int_a^x \frac{dt}{t^p} = \lim_{x \to \infty} \left[\frac{t^{1-p}}{1-p} \right]_a^x$$

This converges to the value $a^{1-p}/(p-1)$ if $p > 1$, and diverges to $+\infty$ if $p < 1$.

Again, if $a > 0$ and $p = 1$ then

$$\int_a^\infty \frac{dt}{t^p} = \lim_{x \to \infty} \int_a^x \frac{dt}{t} = \lim_{x \to \infty} \left[\log x - \log a \right]$$

which diverges to $+\infty$.

2. $$\int_{-\infty}^{+\infty} \frac{dt}{1+t^2} = \lim_{y \to -\infty} \int_y^0 \frac{dt}{1+t^2} + \lim_{x \to \infty} \int_0^x \frac{dt}{1+t^2}$$

$$= \tan^{-1} 0 - \lim_{y \to -\infty} \tan^{-1} y + \lim_{x \to \infty} \tan^{-1} x - \tan^{-1} 0 = \pi$$

The above examples are easy to discuss just because in each case we can evaluate $\int_a^x f(t)\,dt$ by elementary methods and obtain an explicit formula for $F(x)$. Frequently this cannot be done — just as we cannot always find an explicit expression for the nth partial sum of an infinite series. However, just as in the series case, we can often establish the convergence (or divergence) of an infinite integral by comparing it with some other 'test' integral whose behaviour is already known.

Comparison test for integrals of the first kind. Let $f(t)$ and $g(t)$ be bounded integrable functions of t for $a \leqslant t \leqslant x$, and suppose that

$$0 \leqslant f(t) \leqslant g(t)$$

throughout this range. Then

(i) if $\displaystyle\int_a^\infty g(t)\,\mathrm{d}t$ converges, so also does $\displaystyle\int_a^\infty f(t)\,\mathrm{d}t$,

(ii) if $\displaystyle\int_a^\infty f(t)\,\mathrm{d}t$ diverges, so also does $\displaystyle\int_a^\infty g(t)\,\mathrm{d}t$.

In particular, if we take the integral $\displaystyle\int_a^\infty \frac{\mathrm{d}t}{t^p}$ (discussed in Example 1 above) as a

test integral then we obtain the very simple and useful 'p-test' for improper integrals of the first kind:

'p-test' for integrals of the first kind. Let $f(t)$ be bounded, continuous, and non-negative for $t \geqslant a$. If we can find a number p such that $\displaystyle\lim_{t\to\infty} t^p . f(t) = A$, then,

(i) $\displaystyle\int_a^\infty f(t)\,\mathrm{d}t$ converges if $p > 1$ and A is finite

(ii) $\displaystyle\int_a^\infty f(t)\,\mathrm{d}t$ diverges if $p \leqslant 1$ and $A > 0$, (possibly infinite).

The analogy with the p-test for infinite series of positive terms is obvious. Note that for a rational integrand the test becomes particularly easy to apply. Suppose that $f(t) = N(t)/D(t)$, where $N(t)$ and $D(t)$ are real polynomials and $D(t)$ has no real zeros for $t \geqslant a$. (We may assume, without loss of generality, that $f(t) > 0$ for all $t \geqslant a$.) Then $\displaystyle\int_a^\infty f(t)\,\mathrm{d}t$ converges if and only if the degree of $D(t)$ exceeds that of $N(t)$ by at least 2.

Examples
1.
$$\int_0^\infty \frac{2x^2 + x + 3}{x^6 + 1}\,\mathrm{d}x$$

The denominator, $x^6 + 1$, has no real zeros and the integrand is a bounded continuous function of x. The integral converges by the p-test, since when $p = 4$, we have

$$\lim_{x\to\infty} x^4 \left\{ \frac{2x^2 + x + 3}{x^6 + 1} \right\} = 2$$

More briefly we would say that the integral converges since the integrand 'behaves like $2/x^4$' for large x.

2.
$$\int_2^\infty \frac{x\,dx}{\sqrt{(x^4 - 1)}}$$

The denominator has no real zeros within the range of integration and the integrand is again bounded and continuous within this range. The p-test shows that the integral diverges since, when $p = 1$, we get

$$\lim_{x \to \infty} x \left\{ \frac{x}{\sqrt{(x^4 - 1)}} \right\} = 1$$

(Alternatively: divergent since the integrand 'behaves like $1/x$' for large x.)

*5.4.2 *Absolute and conditional convergence*

If $\displaystyle\int_a^\infty |f(t)|\,dt$ converges then $\displaystyle\int_a^\infty f(t)\,dt$ must also converge; the convergence of

$\displaystyle\int_a^\infty f(t)\,dt$ in this case is said to be *absolute*. This result follows, as in the series

case, from the decomposition of the (bounded) function $f(t)$ into its positive and negative components:

$$f(t) = f^+(t) - f^-(t) \quad \text{and} \quad |f(t)| = f^+(t) + f^-(t)$$

where $\qquad f^+(t) = \tfrac{1}{2}\{|f(t)| + f(t)\} \quad$ and $\quad f^-(t) = \tfrac{1}{2}\{|f(t)| - f(t)\}$

Clearly, $\displaystyle\int_a^\infty |f(t)|\,dt \equiv \int_a^\infty f^+(t)\,dt + \int_a^\infty f^-(t)\,dt$ converges if and only if *both*

the integrals $\displaystyle\int_a^\infty f^+(t)\,dt$ and $\displaystyle\int_a^\infty f^-(t)\,dt$ converge. In that case the integral

$\displaystyle\int_a^\infty f(t)\,dt \equiv \int_a^\infty f^+(t)\,dt - \int_a^\infty f^-(t)\,dt$ must also converge. The comparison test

and the p-test apply to integrals with non-negative integrands and hence may be used to investigate absolute convergence.

If $\displaystyle\int_a^\infty |f(t)|\,dt$ diverges then at least one of the integrals $\displaystyle\int_a^\infty f^+(t)\,dt$ and

$\displaystyle\int_a^\infty f^-(t)\,dt$ must diverge. If both these integrals diverge it may nevertheless happen that $\displaystyle\int_a^\infty f(t)\ \mathrm{d}t$ converges to a finite limit; in such a case the convergence is said to be *conditional*.

Example. The function $(\sin t)/t$ is bounded and continuous. Hence the integral $\displaystyle\int_0^\infty \frac{\sin t}{t}\ \mathrm{d}t$ is an improper integral of the first kind. We shall show that it is conditionally convergent.

$$\int_0^\infty \frac{\sin t}{t}\ \mathrm{d}t = \lim_{n\to\infty}\int_0^{n\pi}\frac{\sin t}{t}\ \mathrm{d}t = \sum_{n=0}^\infty \int_{n\pi}^{(n+1)\pi}\frac{\sin t}{t}\ \mathrm{d}t$$

$$= \sum_{n=0}^\infty (-1)^n \int_0^\pi \frac{\sin x}{x+n\pi}\ \mathrm{d}x \qquad \text{(putting } t = x + n\pi\text{)}$$

Now
$$\int_0^\pi \frac{\sin x}{x+n\pi}\ \mathrm{d}x \geqslant \int_0^\pi \frac{\sin x}{x+(n+1)\pi}\ \mathrm{d}x$$

and
$$0 \leqslant \lim_{n\to\infty}\int_0^\pi \frac{\sin x}{x+n\pi}\ \mathrm{d}x \leqslant \lim_{n\to\infty}\frac{1}{n\pi}\int_0^\pi \mathrm{d}x = 0$$

so that the infinite series is an alternating series which satisfies the conditions for Leibnitz's test (section 3.4.3). This shows that the integral

$$\int_0^\infty \frac{\sin t}{t}\ \mathrm{d}t$$

converges.

But, by the same procedure as before, we can show that

$$\int_0^\infty \left|\frac{\sin t}{t}\right|\ \mathrm{d}t = \sum_{n=0}^\infty \int_{n\pi}^{(n+1)\pi}\left|\frac{\sin t}{t}\right|\ \mathrm{d}t = \sum_{n=0}^\infty \int_0^\pi \frac{\sin x}{x+n\pi}\ \mathrm{d}x$$

This time we have
$$\int_0^\pi \frac{\sin x}{x+n\pi}\ \mathrm{d}x \geqslant \frac{1}{(n+1)\pi}\int_0^\pi \sin x\ \mathrm{d}x = \frac{2}{(n+1)\pi}$$

Since $\displaystyle\sum_{n=0}^{\infty} \frac{2}{(n+1)\pi}$ diverges, it follows that $\displaystyle\int_0^\infty \left| \frac{\sin t}{t} \right| \, dt$ diverges, and therefore

that the convergence of $\displaystyle\int_0^\infty \frac{\sin t}{t} \, dt$ is conditional.

5.4.3 *Improper integrals of the second kind*

If $f(t)$ becomes unbounded as t tends to a in $a \leqslant t \leqslant b$ then we define

$$\int_a^b f(t) \, dt \equiv \lim_{\epsilon \to 0} \int_{a+\epsilon}^b f(t) \, dt \qquad (\epsilon > 0) \qquad (39)$$

whenever this limit exists. Similarly if $f(t)$ becomes unbounded as t tends to b in $a \leqslant t \leqslant b$ then we define

$$\int_a^b f(t) \, dt \equiv \lim_{\epsilon \to 0} \int_a^{b-\epsilon} f(t) \, dt \qquad (\epsilon > 0) \qquad (40)$$

Now suppose that x is a number such that $a < x_0 < b$ and that $f(t)$ becomes unbounded in the neighbourhood of x_0. The improper integral $\displaystyle\int_a^b f(t) \, dt$ is said to converge to the value

$$\lim_{\epsilon_1 \to 0} \int_a^{x_0 - \epsilon_1} f(t) \, dt + \lim_{\epsilon_2 \to 0} \int_{x_0 + \epsilon_2}^b f(t) \, dt \qquad (41)$$

provided that the *limits exist independently*. (i.e. ϵ_1 and ϵ_2 must be allowed to tend to zero independently of one another). That is to say, we require that *both* the integrals

$$\int_a^{x_0} f(t) \, dt \qquad \text{and} \qquad \int_{x_0}^b f(t) \, dt$$

should converge.

Integrals in which the range of integration is finite but the integrand becomes unbounded at one or more points of that range are called *improper integrals of the second kind*.

Example. If $p \neq 1$ then

$$\int_0^1 \frac{dt}{t^p} = \lim_{\epsilon \to 0} \int_\epsilon^1 \frac{dt}{t^p} = \frac{1}{1-p} - \lim_{\epsilon \to 0} \left[\frac{\epsilon^{1-p}}{1-p} \right]$$

This converges to the value $1/(1-p)$ if $p < 1$, and diverges to $+\infty$ if $p > 1$. Further, if $p = 1$ then we have

$$\int_0^1 \frac{dt}{t^p} = \lim_{\epsilon \to 0} \int_\epsilon^1 \frac{dt}{t} = \log 1 - \lim_{\epsilon \to 0} \{\log \epsilon\}$$

which diverges to $+\infty$.

Many of the theorems and results concerning improper integrals of the first kind have straightforward analogues which apply to integrals of the second kind.

For example, an improper integral of the second kind, say $\int_a^b f(t)\, dt$, is said to be absolutely convergent if the integral $\int_a^b |f(t)|\, dt$ converges, and it is easily shown that absolute convergence implies convergence. Again, there is a comparison test for integrals of the second kind which closely resembles that for integrals of the first kind:

Comparison test for integrals of the second kind. Let $f(t)$ and $g(t)$ be continuous for $a < t \leqslant b$, and suppose that

$$0 \leqslant f(t) \leqslant g(t)$$

throughout this range. If both $f(t)$ and $g(t)$ become unbounded as t tends to a, then

(i) if $\int_a^b g(t)\, dt$ converges, so also does $\int_a^b f(t)\, dt$,

(ii) if $\int_a^b f(t)\, dt$ diverges, so also does $\int_a^b g(t)\, dt$.

However, there are significant differences. Consider, in particular, the 'p-test' for integrals of the second kind, obtained by applying the comparison test with the integral $\int_0^1 \frac{dt}{t^p}$ as a test integral:

'p-test' for integrals of the second kind. Let $f(t)$ be continuous and non-negative for $a < t \leqslant b$ and suppose that $f(t)$ becomes unbounded as t tends to a. If we can find a number p such that $\lim_{t \to a+} (t - a)^p f(t) = A$, then

(i) $\displaystyle\int_a^b f(t) \, dt$ converges if $p < 1$ and A is finite,

(ii) $\displaystyle\int_a^b f(t) \, dt$ diverges if $p \geqslant 1$ and $A > 0$ (possibly infinite).

The application of this test and the difference between it and the corresponding p-test for integrals of the first kind is best shown by means of a specific example.

Consider the integral $\displaystyle\int_0^\infty \frac{dx}{\sqrt[3]{(x^4 + x^2)}}$. The range of integration is infinite and the integrand becomes unbounded in the neighbourhood of the point $x = 0$. An integral like this, which possesses the characteristics both of an integral of the first kind and of the second kind, is said to be an *improper integral of the third kind.* By dividing the range of integration into two parts the problem is reduced to that of one integral of the first kind and another of the second kind:

$$\int_0^\infty \frac{dx}{\sqrt[3]{(x^4 + x^2)}} = \int_0^1 \frac{dx}{\sqrt[3]{(x^4 + x^2)}} + \int_1^\infty \frac{dx}{\sqrt[3]{(x^4 + x^2)}} = I_1 + I_2$$

I_1 is an integral of the second kind, and the p-test shows it to be convergent, for we have

$$\lim_{x \to 0} x^p \left[\frac{1}{\sqrt[3]{(x^4 + x^2)}} \right] = 1 \qquad \text{if } p = \frac{2}{3} < 1$$

Essentially this corresponds to the fact that, for *small x,* x^2 dominates x^4 so that the integrand behaves like $x^{-2/3}$ near the origin. As a result, the integrand goes to infinity 'slowly enough', as x approaches the origin, to ensure that I_1 has a finite value.

I_2 is an integral of the first kind, and the appropriate p-test shows that it is convergent. For we have

$$\lim_{x \to \infty} x^p \left[\frac{1}{\sqrt[3]{(x^4 + x^2)}} \right]$$

if $p = 4/3 > 1$. Once again we can interpret this by saying that, for *large x,* x^4 dominates x^2 so that the integrand behaves like $x^{-4/3}$. Hence, the integrand goes to zero 'rapidly enough', as x tends to infinity, to ensure that I_2 has a finite value.

*5.4.4 *Cauchy principal value*

Let $f(t)$ be unbounded in the neighbourhood of a point x_0, where $a < x_0 < b$,

and suppose that $\int_a^b f(t)\, dt$ diverges. It may happen that although the limits

$$\lim_{\epsilon_1 \to 0} \int_a^{x_0 - \epsilon_1} f(t)\, dt \qquad \text{and} \qquad \lim_{\epsilon_2 \to 0} \int_{x_0 + \epsilon_2}^b f(t)\, dt$$

do not exist independently, we may set $\epsilon_1 = \epsilon_2 = \epsilon$ and then find that the unbounded parts of the two integrals cancel each other out. This gives a finite answer, called the *Cauchy principal value* of the integral. It is usual to write

$$P\int_a^b f(t)\, dt = \lim_{\epsilon \to 0} \left[\int_a^{x_0 - \epsilon} f(t)\, dt + \int_{x_0 + \epsilon}^b f(t)\, dt \right]$$

Example

$$\int_1^4 \frac{dx}{(x-2)^3} = \lim_{\epsilon_1 \to 0} \int_1^{2 - \epsilon_1} \frac{dx}{(x-2)^3} + \lim_{\epsilon_2 \to 0} \int_{2 + \epsilon_2}^4 \frac{dx}{(x-2)^3}$$

$$= \lim_{\epsilon_1 \to 0} \left(\frac{1}{2} - \frac{1}{2\epsilon_1^2} \right) + \lim_{\epsilon_2 \to 0} \left(\frac{1}{2\epsilon_2^2} - \frac{1}{8} \right)$$

These limits do not exist and so the integral diverges. However,

$$P\int_1^4 \frac{dx}{(x-2)^3} = \lim_{\epsilon \to 0} \left\{ \frac{1}{2} - \frac{1}{2\epsilon^2} + \frac{1}{2\epsilon^2} - \frac{1}{8} \right\} = \frac{3}{8}$$

and this number is the Cauchy principal value.

Exercises

1. Show that $\int_0^\infty e^{-kx}\, dx$ converges if $k > 0$ and diverges if $k \leqslant 0$.

2. Show that (a) $\int_0^\infty e^{-x^2}\, dx$ converges, (b) $\int_2^\infty \frac{dx}{\log x}$ diverges.

3. State whether each of the following integrals is of the first, second, or third kind. Establish whether they converge or diverge by applying appropriate p-tests.

(i) $\displaystyle\int_{-\infty}^{+\infty} \frac{x^2\,dx}{x^4 + 2}$ (ii) $\displaystyle\int_{2}^{\infty} \frac{x^3\,dx}{x^4 - 1}$ (iii) $\displaystyle\int_{0}^{\infty} \frac{dx}{(1 + x)\sqrt{x}}$

(iv) $\displaystyle\int_{-\infty}^{+\infty} \frac{t^2 + t + 1}{3t^6 + 7}\,dt$ (v) $\displaystyle\int_{0}^{1} \frac{dt}{(t + 1)\sqrt{(1 - t^2)}}$ (vi) $\displaystyle\int_{0}^{\infty} \frac{x^{\alpha-1}}{1 + x}\,dx\ (0 < \alpha < 1),$

(vii) $\displaystyle\int_{0}^{1} \theta^{m-1}(1 - \theta)^{n-1}\,d\theta,$ where $m > 0, n > 0$.

*5.5 Integration and convergence — uniform convergence

For $n = 0, 1, 2, 3, \ldots,$ let $f_n(t)$ denote a function which is defined for all t in the finite closed interval $a \leqslant t \leqslant b$. If, for each value of t in this interval, the sequence of real numbers $f_n(t)$ converges to a definite limit as n goes to infinity, then this limit will itself be a function of t, say $f(t)$, and we may write

$$f(t) = \lim_{n \to \infty} f_n(t) \qquad \text{for } a \leqslant t \leqslant b \qquad (42)$$

The question now arises of whether or not various important and desirable proper of the functions $f_n(t)$ are preserved under the limit operation. In particular, suppose that each of the functions $f_n(t)$ is integrable over the interval $a \leqslant t \leqslant b$. Does it necessarily follow that the limit function $f(t)$ is also integrable over this interval? And, supposing this to be the case, under what circumstances can we go on to conclude that the integral of the limit function is equal to the limit of th integrals of the functions $f_n(t)$? That is to say, when we can write

$$\int_{a}^{b} \lim_{n \to \infty} f_n(t)\,dt = \lim_{n \to \infty} \int_{a}^{b} f_n(t)\,dt \ ?$$

A general discussion of the problem is far from easy. In what follows we shall concentrate on a very special mode of convergence for which the situation is relatively straightforward. Its importance can be gauged from the fact that it includes the case of a power series within its interval of convergence.

5.5.1 *Uniform convergence of sequences of functions*

We consider a function $f(t)$ defined, as in equation (42), as the limit of a sequence of functions $f_n(t)$ on a finite closed interval $a \leqslant t \leqslant b$. From the definition of convergence given in chapter 3 we can write (42) in the following, more explicit, form:

If t is any particular point in $a \leqslant t \leqslant b$ and if ϵ is any given positive number, however small, we can find an integer N such that

$$|f(t) - f_n(t)| < \epsilon \tag{43}$$

for all $n > \mathrm{N}$.

In general this integer N will depend not only on ϵ but also on t. Suppose, however, that we can determine N *independently* of t so that, provided only that $n > \mathrm{N}$, the inequality (43) holds for all t in the interval $a \leqslant t \leqslant b$. Under these circumstances the convergence of the sequence of function $f_n(t)$ to the limit function $f(t)$ is of a very important and special kind and is known as *uniform convergence*. The nature of uniform convergence and the properties associated with it are more easily understood if we re-phrase the definition in an alternative form.

First consider the case when $f_n(t)$ converges to zero for all t in the interval $a \leqslant t \leqslant b$. The convergence will be uniform provided that given any $\epsilon > 0$ we can always find an integer N such that

$$|f_n(t)| < \epsilon$$

for all $n > \mathrm{N}$ and all t in $a \leqslant t \leqslant b$. But this will be the case if and only if

$$\lim_{n \to \infty} \left\{ \text{l.u.b. } |f_n(t)| \right\} = 0 \tag{44}$$

where, for each n, the least upper bound is taken over the interval $a \leqslant t \leqslant b$. For the general situation in which a sequence of functions $f_n(t)$ converges to a limit function $f(t)$ (not identically zero) we need only write

$$g_n(t) \equiv f(t) - f_n(t)$$

Clearly, the functions $f_n(t)$ converge uniformly to the limit $f(t)$ on $a \leqslant t \leqslant b$ if and only if the functions $g_n(t)$ converge uniformly to zero on that interval. Hence we may state the following general definition:

Uniform convergence. The function $f(t)$ is said to be the *uniform limit* of the sequence of functions $f_n(t)$ on the interval $a \leqslant t \leqslant b$ if, and only if, given any positive number ϵ, however small, we can always find a corresponding integer N such that

$$\underset{a \leqslant t \leqslant b}{\text{l.u.b.}} \ |f(t) - f_n(t)| < \epsilon$$

for all $n > N$. Equivalently, the sequence of functions $f_n(t)$ is said to *converge uniformly* to $f(t)$ on $a \leqslant t \leqslant b$.

Example 1. For $n = 0, 1, 2, 3, \ldots$, let the functions $\phi_n(t)$ be defined as follows

$$\phi_n(t) = \begin{cases} \dfrac{2^{n+1}}{n+2}\, t \text{ for } 0 \leqslant t \leqslant 1/2^n \\[2mm] \dfrac{4}{n+2}\,(1 - 2^{n-1}t) \text{ for } 1/2^n \leqslant t \leqslant 1/2^{n-1} \\[2mm] 0 \text{ otherwise} \end{cases}$$

(see figure 5.5). It is clear that

$$\lim_{n \to \infty} \phi_n(t) = 0$$

for all values of t in the interval $0 \leqslant t \leqslant 2$.

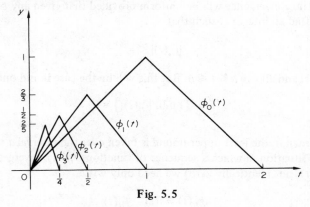

Fig. 5.5

Moreover, taking the least upper bounds over this interval, we have

$$\underset{0 \leqslant t \leqslant 2}{\text{l.u.b.}} \ |\phi(t) - \phi_n(t)| = \underset{0 \leqslant t \leqslant 2}{\text{l.u.b.}} \ |\phi_n(t)| = \frac{2}{n+2}$$

Since this tends to 0 as n goes to infinity it follows that the sequence $\{\phi_n(t)\}$ converges uniformly to zero on the interval $0 \leqslant t \leqslant 2$ (and, in fact, on any interval of the t-axis, however large).

Example 2. For $n = 0, 1, 2, 3, \ldots$, let the functions $\psi_n(t)$ be defined as follows:

$$\psi_n(t) = \begin{cases} (n+1)^2 t \text{ for } 0 \leqslant t \leqslant 1/(n+1) \\ 2(n+1) - (n+1)^2 t \text{ for } 1/(n+1) \leqslant t \leqslant 2/(n+1) \\ 0 \text{ otherwise} \end{cases}$$

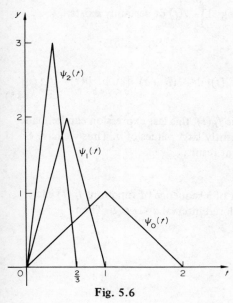

Fig. 5.6

If t is any point such that $0 < t \leqslant 2$ (see figure 5.6) then $\psi_n(t) = 0$ for every n such that

$$n > \frac{2}{t} - 1$$

Also $\psi_n(0) = 0$ for every n. Hence the sequence $\psi_n(t)$ converges to zero for all t in $0 \leqslant t \leqslant 2$. On the other hand,

$$\underset{0 \leqslant t \leqslant 2}{\text{l.u.b.}} |\psi_n(t)| = n$$

so that the convergence is not uniform.

5.5.2 *Integration of uniformly convergent sequences*

For each n let the functions $f_n(t)$ be continuous on the finite closed interval $a \leqslant t \leqslant b$ and suppose that they converge uniformly to $f(t)$ on this interval. If t and $t + h$ are any two points in $a \leqslant t \leqslant b$ then we have, for any n

$$|f(t+h) - f(t)| = |f(t+h) - f_n(t+h) + f_n(t+h) - f_n(t) + f_n(t) - f(t)|$$

$$\leqslant |f(t+h) - f_n(t+h)| + |f_n(t+h) - f_n(t)| + |f_n(t) - f(t)|$$

Since the convergence is uniform we can always choose a value of n for which $|f_n(t) - f(t)| < \epsilon/3$ for all t in $a \leqslant t \leqslant b$, where ϵ is any pre-assigned positive number. For this value of n, since $f_n(t)$ is continuous, we can choose $\delta > 0$ such that

$$|f_n(t+h) - f_n(t)| < \epsilon/3$$

provided only that $|h| < \delta$. Combining these inequalities we have the result that,

$$|f(t + h) - f(t)| < \epsilon$$

for any points $t + h$ and t in the interval $a \leqslant t \leqslant b$ such that $|h| < \delta$. In other words *the uniform limit of a sequence of functions each continuous on a closed interval is itself continuous on that interval.*

In particular this shows that the integral $\int_a^b f(t) \, dt$ certainly exists.

Moreover,

$$\left| \int_a^b f(t) \, dt - \int_a^b f_n(t) \, dt \right| \leqslant \int_a^b |f(t) - f_n(t)| \, dt \leqslant (b - a) \; \left[\underset{a \leqslant x \leqslant b}{\text{l.u.b.}} |f(t) - f_n(t)| \right] \tag{45}$$

and, by the uniform convergence of the $f_n(t)$, this last expression can be made as small as we wish by choosing sufficiently large values of n. Thus we have established the following very important result:

Theorem. Let $f(t)$ be the uniform limit of a sequence of functions $f_n(t)$ each of which is continuous on the finite, closed interval $a \leqslant t \leqslant b$. Then

(i) $f(t)$ is itself continuous on $a \leqslant t \leqslant b$,

and (ii) $\int_a^b f(t) \, dt = \lim_{n \to \infty} \int_a^b f_n(t) \, dt$

Corollary. Suppose further that each of the functions $f_n(t)$ has a continuous derivative $f_n'(t)$ on $a \leqslant t \leqslant b$, and that the functions $f_n'(t)$ themselves converge uniformly to the limit $\phi(t)$ on this interval. Then $\phi(t) = f'(t)$.

That is

$$\lim_{n \to \infty} f_n'(t) = \frac{d}{dt} \left\{ \lim_{n \to \infty} f_n(t) \right\}$$

(For we have, for any t in $a \leqslant t \leqslant b$

$$\int_a^t \phi(\tau) \, d\tau = \lim_{n \to \infty} \int_a^t f_n'(\tau) \, d\tau$$

$$= \lim_{n \to \infty} \left\{ f_n(t) - f_n(a) \right\} = f(t) - f(a).)$$

Remarks

(i) The sequences discussed in section 5.5.1 provide useful and simple illustrations of the results established above. The sequence $\{\phi_n(t)\}$ of example 1 converges uniformly to the (continuous) limit function $\phi(t) \equiv 0$ on the interval $0 \leqslant t \leqslant 2$, and a simple calculation shows that

$$\int_0^2 \phi_n(t) \, dt = \frac{1}{2}\left(\frac{2}{n+2}\right) \frac{1}{2^{n-1}} = \frac{1}{2^{n-1}} \frac{1}{n+2}$$

Hence

$$\lim_{n \to \infty} \int_0^2 \phi_n(t) \, dt = \int_0^2 \lim_{n \to \infty} \phi_n(t) \, dt = 0$$

The sequence $\psi_n(t)$ of example 2 converges to the same limit function on the interval $0 \leqslant t \leqslant 2$ as does the sequence $\phi_n(t)$, but this time the convergence is not uniform. We have

$$\int_0^2 \psi_n(t) \, dt = \frac{1}{2}\left(\frac{2}{n+1}\right)(n+1) = 1, \quad \text{for every } n$$

so that,

$$\lim_{n \to \infty} \int_0^2 \psi_n(t) \, dt \neq \int_0^2 \lim_{n \to \infty} \psi_n(t) \, dt$$

Note, however, that the integral of the limit of a sequence of functions may be equal to the limit of the integrals even though the convergence is not uniform; uniform convergence is a *sufficient* condition in this context but not a *necessary* one.

(ii) The uniform convergence of a sequence $\{f_n(t)\}$ of differentiable functions does not imply the convergence (uniform or otherwise) of the sequence of derivatives $\{f_n'(t)\}$. On the other hand, the corollary to the theorem proved in this section can be replaced by the following, stronger, result:

Let $\{f_n(t)\}$ be a sequence of functions, each differentiable on a finite closed interval $a \leqslant t \leqslant b$, such that $\{f_n(t_0)\}$ converges for some particular point t_0 in $a \leqslant t \leqslant b$. If the sequence $\{f_n'(t)\}$ converges uniformly on $a \leqslant t \leqslant b$ then $\{f_n(t)\}$ converges uniformly on this interval to a function $f(t)$, and

$$f'(t) = \lim_{n \to \infty} f_n'(t) \quad \text{for} \quad a \leqslant t \leqslant b$$

5.5.3 *Uniform convergence of series*

For $n = 0, 1, 2, 3, \ldots$, let $a_n(x)$ denote a function of the real variable x which is defined on the interval $a \leqslant x \leqslant b$, and write

$$A_n(x) = \sum_{k=0}^{n} a_k(x) \tag{46}$$

The infinite series

$$\sum_{n=0}^{\infty} a_n(x) \equiv a_0(x) + a_1(x) + a_2(x) + \cdots + a_n(x) + \cdots \tag{47}$$

is said to converge uniformly to the sum $\alpha(x)$ on $a \leqslant x \leqslant b$ if and only if $\alpha(x)$ is the uniform limit of the functions $A_n(x)$ on that interval. An application of the Cauchy criterion of convergence for series (see theorem 5, section 3.5.1) shows that a necessary and sufficient condition for the uniform convergence of

$\sum_{n=0}^{\infty} a_n(x)$ can be stated as follows:

Given $\epsilon > 0$ we can always find a corresponding integer N such that, for all x in $a \leqslant x \leqslant b$,

$$|A_m(x) - A_n(x)| \equiv \left| \sum_{k=n+1}^{m} a_k(x) \right| < \epsilon$$

provided only that $n > N$ and $m \geqslant n + 1$.

This allows us to derive a simple and very useful test for uniform convergence:

Theorem (Weierstrass M-test). If $\sum_{n=0}^{\infty} M_n$ is a convergent series of positive terms such that

$$|a_n(x)| \leqslant M_n \quad \text{for } a \leqslant x \leqslant b$$

then the series $\sum_{n=0}^{\infty} a_n(x)$ is uniformly convergent on $a \leqslant x \leqslant b$.

Proof. Given any $\epsilon > 0$ we can choose N such that

$$M_{n+1} + M_{n+2} + \cdots + M_m < \epsilon$$

for any m and n such that $m \geqslant n > N$. The result follows since

$$\left| \sum_{k=n+1}^{m} a_k(x) \right| \leqslant \sum_{k=n+1}^{m} |a_k(x)| \leqslant \sum_{k=n+1}^{m} M_k < \epsilon$$

As an immediate application of the Weierstrass M-test we consider the case of a real power series, $\sum_{n=0}^{\infty} a_n x^n$, with radius of convergence R. Let ρ be any positive number less than R. Then the series $\sum_{n=0}^{\infty} |a_n| \rho^n$ is certainly convergent.

Also, for any x such that $|x| \leqslant \rho$, it is the case that

$$|a_n x^n| \leqslant |a_n| \rho^n$$

It follows by the M-test that the power series is uniformly convergent on the interval $-\rho \leqslant x \leqslant \rho$. Since this will be true for *any* number ρ such that $0 < \rho < R$ we can conclude at once that a power series can be integrated term by term provided only that the limits of integration lie strictly within the interval of convergence $-R < x < +R$. Since the power series $\sum_{n=1}^{\infty} n a_n x^{n-1}$ has the same radius of convergence, R, we can go on to confirm the result of section 3.6.3 that a power series may be differentiated term by term at any point within its interval of convergence.

Exercises

1. For $n = 1, 2, 3, \ldots$, let $f_n(x) = nx\, e^{-nx^2}$. Show that

$$\lim_{n \to \infty} f_n(x) = 0 \qquad \text{for all } x \text{ in } 0 \leqslant x \leqslant 1$$

but that

$$\lim_{n \to \infty} \int_0^1 f_n(x)\, dx \neq 0$$

2. For $n = 1, 2, 3, \ldots$, let $f_n(x) = nx/(1 + n^2 x^2)$. Show that

(a) the sequence converges to a continuous limit $f(x)$ on $0 \leqslant x \leqslant 1$,

(b) $\lim_{n \to \infty} \int_0^1 f_n(x)\, dx = \int_0^1 f(x)\, dx$

but, (c) the convergence is not uniform.

3. Find, in each case, the range of values of x for which the following series
   converge uniformly:

   (a) $\displaystyle\sum_{n=1}^{\infty} \frac{x^n}{n^n}$ (b) $\displaystyle\sum_{n=1}^{\infty} \frac{\sin nx}{n^2}$ (c) $\displaystyle\sum_{n=1}^{\infty} \frac{x}{(1+x)^n}$, $x \geqslant 0$

5.6 Multiple integrals

5.6.1 *Double integral over a rectangle*

Let R denote the rectangle in the (x, y)-plane with sides $x = a$, $x = b$, $y = c$,
$y = d$, and let $f(x, y)$ be a bounded continuous function of (x, y); for simplicity
we shall assume to begin with that $f(x, y)$ is positive at all points within and
on the boundary of R. We wish to find the volume of the spatial region bounded
by the (x, y)-plane, the cylinder with base R, and the surface $u = f(x, y)$
(figure 5.7).

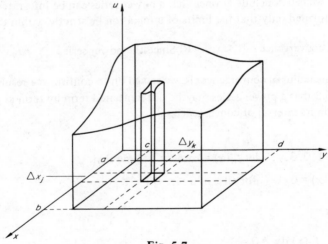

Fig. 5.7

Subdivide the interval $a \leqslant x \leqslant b$ by points x_j; $0 \leqslant j \leqslant m$, where

$$a = x_0 < x_1 < x_2 < \cdots < x_m = b$$

and similarly subdivide $c \leqslant y \leqslant d$ by points y_k, $0 \leqslant k \leqslant n$, where

$$c = y_0 < y_1 < y_2 < \cdots < y_n = d$$

This divides the rectangle R into mn small rectangular regions. In the small
rectangle whose sides are $x = x_{j-1}$, $x = x_j$, $y = y_{k-1}$, $y = y_k$, choose a point

(ξ_{jk}, η_{jk}) arbitrarily. Then the volume of the cuboid with this rectangle as base and with height $f(\xi_{jk}, \eta_{jk})$ is

$$f(\xi_{jk}, \eta_{jk})\Delta x_j \Delta y_k$$

where $\Delta x_j = x_j - x_{j-1}$ and $\Delta y_k = y_k - y_{k-1}$. Summing such expressions over the mn small rectangles into which R is divided will give a total volume approximately equal to the volume V of the region in which we are interested. It is intuitively clear that as m and n are taken larger and larger, in such a way that the area of each of the rectangular sub-divisions of R tends to zero, so the sums

$$\sum_{\substack{j=1,\ldots,m \\ k=1,\ldots,n}} f(\xi_{jk}, \eta_{jk})\Delta x_j \Delta y_k \tag{48}$$

approach the value V more and more closely. More precisely it is the case that, given any number $\epsilon > 0$, however small, we can always find a corresponding number $\delta > 0$ such that

$$\left| V - \sum_{j, k} f(\xi_{jk}, \eta_{jk})\Delta x_j \Delta y_k \right| < \epsilon \tag{49}$$

provided only that $\max_j \Delta x_j < \delta$ and $\max_k \Delta y_k < \delta$.

This number V is, by definition, the *double integral of the function $f(x, y)$ taken over the rectangle* R, and we write

$$V = \iint_R f(x, y) \, dxdy \tag{50}$$

Bearing in mind the remarks made in section 5.1.3 on the abuse of notation involved, we can express the result of (49) in the form

$$\iint_R f(x, y) \, dxdy = \lim_{\substack{m \to \infty \\ n \to \infty}} \sum_{\substack{j=1,\ldots,m \\ k=1,\ldots,n}} f(\xi_{jk}, \eta_{jk})\Delta x_j \Delta y_k$$

The rectangle R is usually referred to as the *field of integration*.

Remark. The existence of the double integral (50) can be established by an argument analogous to that used earlier in the case of an ordinary integral with a continuous integrand. That is to say, for each division of the rectangle R into small rectangles we construct upper and lower sums U and L by choosing respectively the least upper bound and greatest lower bound of $f(x, y)$ in each of these rectangles. The fact that L and U can be made as close as we wish by choosing a sufficiently fine sub-division of R then follows, as before, from the (uniform) continuity of the integrand. As in the single real variable case, the existence of the integral may be established even when the continuity constraint on the integrand is relaxed somewhat.

5.6.2 *Repeated integrals*

Referring once more to figure 7, let us again form the sum (48) but this time carry out the summation in a specific order. If we keep j fixed and sum the cuboids from $k = 1$ to $k = n$ then we obtain an approximation to the volume of the slice of the region lying between the planes $x = x_{j-1}$ and $x = x_j$. If Δx_j is sufficiently small then this sum is approximately equal to

$$\Delta x_j \left\{ \sum_{k=1,\ldots,n} f(x_j, \eta_{jk}) \Delta y_k \right\} \tag{51}$$

As n tends to infinity, and each Δy_k tends to zero, this becomes

$$\Delta x_j \int_{y=c}^{y=d} f(x_j, y) \, \mathrm{d}y$$

To complete the summation we need to add the volumes of all the slices corresponding to $j = 1, 2, \ldots, m$.

$$\sum_{j=1,2,\ldots,m} \left[\int_c^d f(x_j, y) \, \mathrm{d}y \right] \Delta x_j$$

As m tends to infinity, and each Δx_j tends to zero, this becomes

$$\int_a^b \left[\int_c^d f(x, y) \, \mathrm{d}y \right] \mathrm{d}x \tag{52}$$

Alternatively we could choose quite a different order of summation: keep k fixed and sum all the cuboids from $j = 1$ to $j = m$ to obtain an approximation to the volume of the slice lying between $y = y_{k-1}$ and $y = y_k$. This means we would have to deal with sums of the form

$$\Delta y_k \left\{ \sum_{y=1,\ldots,m} f(\xi_{jk}, y_k) \Delta y_k \right\} \tag{53}$$

instead of expressions like (51). Proceeding in the same way as before, we would end up with the following

$$\int_c^d \left[\int_a^b f(x, y)\, dx \right] dy \tag{54}$$

Expressions like (52) and (54) are said to be *repeated integrals*. In (52), the function $f(x, y)$ is first integrated with respect to y from $y = c$ to $y = d$, x being held constant. The resulting function of x is then integrated (with respect to x) from $x = a$ to $x = b$. There are two alternative conventions for indicating this sequence of integrations:

$$\int_a^b \left[\int_c^d f(x, y)\, dy \right] dx \equiv \int_a^b \int_c^d f(x, y)\, dy dx \equiv \int_a^b dx \int_c^d f(x, y)\, dy \tag{55}$$

In the case of (54), on the other hand, we first integrate $f(x, y)$ with respect to x from $x = a$ to $x = b$ and then integrate the resulting function of y from $y = c$ to $y = d$:

$$\int_c^d \left[\int_a^b f(x, y)\, dx \right] dy \equiv \int_c^d \int_a^b f(x, y)\, dx dy \equiv \int_c^d dy \int_a^b f(x, y)\, dx \tag{56}$$

In either case the result is the volume of the region bounded by the (x, y)-plane, the cylinder with R as base, and the surface $u = f(x, y)$. This is the same as saying that the double integral over R can be evaluated either as the repeated integral (55), or equally well, as the repeated integral (56):

$$\iint_R f(x, y)\, dx dy = \int_a^b dx \int_c^d f(x, y)\, dy = \int_c^d dy \int_a^b f(x, y)\, dx \tag{57}$$

The situation becomes particularly simple if the integrand $f(x, y)$ is of the form

$$f(x, y) \equiv g(x)h(y)$$

where $g(x)$ and $h(y)$ are continuous functions of a single real variable. Then we have

$$\begin{aligned}
\iint_R f(x, y)\, dx dy &= \int_a^b dx \int_c^d g(x)h(y)\, dy \\
&= \int_a^b \left[g(x) \int_c^d h(y)\, dy \right] dx \\
&= \left\{ \int_a^b g(x)\, dx \right\}\left\{ \int_c^d h(y)\, dy \right\} \tag{58}
\end{aligned}$$

so that the double integral reduces to the product of two ordinary integrals.

5.6.3 *Double integral over a general plane region*

We turn now to the problem of integrating a function $f(x, y)$ over plane regions more general in nature than the simple rectangles considered so far. The field of integration is, typically, a region enclosed by a simple closed curve, ABCD, as illustrated in figure 5.8.

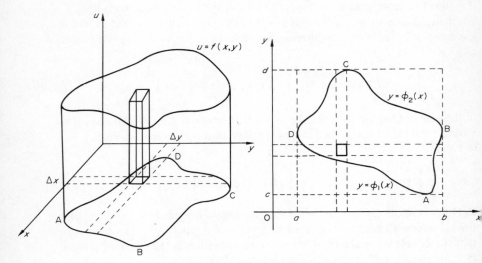

Fig. 5.8

We assume first that this region, R, is such that any line parallel to the y-axis meets the bounding curve ABCD in at most two points (as is, in fact, the case in figure 5.8), and that the arcs DAB and DCB are given respectively by the relation $y = \phi_1(x)$ and $y = \phi_2(x)$. (The functions $\phi_1(x)$ and $\phi_2(x)$ are single-valued and continuous.) Now let $f_R(x, y)$ be defined as follows

$$f_R(x, y) = \begin{cases} f(x, y), & \text{if } (x, y) \text{ lies within R or on the bounding curve ABCD,} \\ 0, & \text{otherwise.} \end{cases}$$

If we now enclose the region R by a rectangle R_0 with sides $x = a$, $x = b$, $y = c$, $y = d$, then $f_R(x, y)$ is a function which is continuous within R_0 except possibly at points of the curve ABCD. Provided this curve is reasonably well-behaved (in a sense to be elaborated below) we may invoke the results of the preceding sections and define the double integral of the function $f(x, y)$ over the region R to be equal to the double integral of the function $f_R(x, y)$ over the rectangular region

R_0. Bearing in mind the fact that $f_R(x, y)$ vanishes identically at all points of the rectangle which lie outside the curve ABCD, this gives us

$$\iint_R f(x, y)\,dxdy \equiv \iint_{R_0} f_R(x, y)\,dxdy = \int_a^b dx \int_c^d f_R(x, y)\,dy$$

$$= \int_a^b dx \int_{y=\phi_1(x)}^{y=\phi_2(x)} f(x, y)\,dy \tag{59}$$

Suppose further that the field of integration, R, is such that any line parallel to the x-axis meets the bounding curve ABCD in at most two points (as is again the case in figure 5.8), and that the arcs ADC and ABC are given respectively by $x = \psi_1(y)$ and $x = \psi_2(y)$. Then

$$\iint_R f(x, y)\,dxdy \equiv \iint_{R_0} f_R(x, y)\,dxdy = \int_c^d dy \int_a^b f_R(x, y)\,dx$$

$$= \int_c^d dy \int_{x=\psi_1(y)}^{x=\psi_2(y)} f(x, y)\,dx \tag{60}$$

Example 1. Find the volume enclosed by the coordinate planes and that portion of the plane

$$x + y + z = 1$$

which lies in the first octant.

The field of integration is the triangular region bounded by the lines $x = 0$, $y = 0$, $y = 1 - x$ (figure 5.9). Also we have

$$z \equiv f(x, y) = 1 - x - y$$

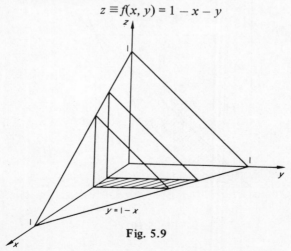

Fig. 5.9

and so the required volume is

$$\iint\limits_{R} (1 - x - y) \, dx dy = \int_0^1 dx \int_{y=0}^{y=1-x} (1 - x - y) \, dy$$

$$= \int_0^1 \left[(1-x)y - y^2/2 \right]_{y=0}^{y=1-x} dx = \int_0^1 \frac{1}{2} (1-x)^2 \, dx = \frac{1}{6}$$

Example 2. Evaluate the double integral

$$\iint xy(x + y) \, dx dy$$

over the region enclosed by the curves $y = x$ and $y = x^2$ (figure 5.10).

$$\iint\limits_{R} xy(x + y) \, dx dy = \int_0^1 dx \int_{x^2}^{x} xy(x + y) \, dy = \int_0^1 \left[\frac{x^2 y^2}{2} + \frac{x y^3}{3} \right]_{y=x^2}^{y=x} dx$$

$$= \int_0^1 \left(\frac{5x^4}{6} - \frac{x^6}{2} - \frac{x^7}{3} \right) dx = \frac{3}{56}$$

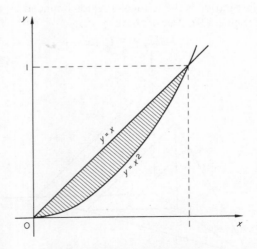

Fig. 5.10

Example 3. Invert the order of integration and then evaluate the repeated integral

$$\int_0^1 dx \int_x^{2-x} \frac{x}{y} \, dy$$

The field of integration is sketched in figure 5.11. If we invert the order of integration and integrate first with respect to x then the limits for x vary according to the range of values of y: if $0 \leqslant y \leqslant 1$ then we go from $x = 0$ to $x = y$; if $1 \leqslant y \leqslant 2$ then we go from $x = 0$ to $x = 2 - y$. Hence the integral can be regarded as the sum of two distinct parts:

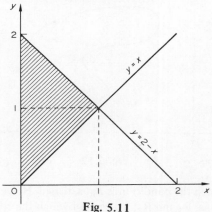

Fig. 5.11

$$\int_0^1 dx \int_x^{2-x} \frac{x}{y} \, dy = \int_0^1 dy \int_0^y \frac{x}{y} \, dx + \int_1^2 dy \int_0^{2-y} \frac{x}{y} \, dy$$

$$= \int_0^1 \left(\frac{x^2}{2y}\right)_0^y dy + \int_1^2 \left(\frac{x^2}{2y}\right)_0^{2-y} dy$$

$$= \int_0^1 \frac{y}{2} \, dy + \int_1^2 \frac{(4 - 4y + y^2)}{2y} \, dy = \left(\frac{y^2}{4}\right)_0^1 + \left(2 \log y - 2y + \frac{y^2}{4}\right)_1^2$$

$$= \tfrac{1}{4} + 2 \log 2 - 4 + 1 + 2 - \tfrac{1}{4} = 2 \log 2 - 1.$$

5.6.4 *Note on integrability*
We have assumed that the integrand $f(x, y)$ is a positive (or at least a non-negative) function on the field of integration. This condition is easily removed once we note

that negative values of $f(x, y)$ correspond to portions of the surface $u = f(x, y)$ which lie *below* the (x, y)-plane. If we adopt the convention that volumes lying below this plane are to be taken as negative then the double integral defined for integrands of variable sign can always be interpreted as a measure of the *net* volume concerned. (Compare the remarks on area in section 5.2.1.)

Again, it is easy to see that we may relax the condition that any line parallel to one or other of the coordinate axes should cut the boundary of the field of integration in at most two points. Figure 5.12 shows an example of an otherwise

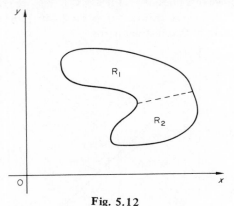

Fig. 5.12

simple region for which the condition is not satisfied. However we can easily divide this into regions, R_1 and R_2, for each of which the condition is fulfilled. The double integral over the whole region R is then taken to be the sum of the double integrals over each of the component regions

$$\iint_R f(x, y)\, dxdy = \iint_{R_1} f(x, y)\, dxdy + \iint_{R_2} f(x, y)\, dxdy$$

On the other hand, it must be borne in mind that the existence of the double integral of a function $f(x, y)$ over a region R depends very much both on the nature of the function and of the field of integration. To pursue either of these points in any detail is beyond the scope of this text; we shall do no more here than describe a relatively simple set of conditions which are sufficient to ensure existence.

First, let $x = \phi(t)$ and $y = \psi(t)$, where $\phi(t)$ and $\psi(t)$ are real, single-valued, continuous functions of the real variable t, defined over the range $\alpha \leqslant t \leqslant \beta$. As t varies from α to β so the point

$$(x, y) \equiv \{\phi(t), \psi(t)\}$$

describes a curve in the (x, y)-plane called a *continuous arc*. If two different values of t in the given range define identical values of x and y, then these values are said to give a *multiple point* of the curve. An arc with no multiple points (that is, one which does not intersect itself) is called a *simple arc*. If, in addition, the points corresponding to the initial value, α, and the final value, β, of t coincide then the arc (which has now just one multiple point) is called a *simple closed curve*. An arc is said to be *smooth* if the functions $\phi(t)$ and $\psi(t)$ have continuous derivatives, $\phi'(t)$ and $\psi'(t)$; the length of a smooth arc is given by

$$\int_\alpha^\beta \sqrt{[\{\phi'(t)\}^2 + \{\psi'(t)\}^2]}\, dt$$

We can now state (without proof) a fundamental *existence theorem* for the double integral:

Let R be a finite region of the (x, y)-plane which is bounded by a simple closed curve C consisting of a finite number of smooth arcs. Let $f(x, y)$ be bounded within the region R and on the bounding curve C, and continuous in R save possibly on a finite number of arcs lying in R. Then the double integral

$$\iint_R f(x, y)\, dx dy$$

exists as a well defined finite number.

Example. A sufficient condition under which the order of integration in a repeated integral may be inverted is that the double integral over the corresponding region should exist. It is instructive to consider, in contrast, the following pair of repeated integrals:

$$I_1 = \int_0^1 dx \int_0^1 \frac{x - y}{(x + y)^3}\, dy \qquad I_2 = \int_0^1 dy \int_0^1 \frac{x - y}{(x + y)^3}\, dx$$

The function $f(x, y) = (x - y)/(x + y)^3$ is unbounded in the neighbourhood of $(0, 0)$ and the double integral $\iint_R \frac{x - y}{(x + y)^3}\, dx dy$, where R is the rectangular region

$0 \leqslant x \leqslant 1, 0 \leqslant y \leqslant 1$, does not exist. However, if ϵ_1 and ϵ_2 are any positive numbers then the double integral of $f(x, y)$ over the region $\epsilon_1 \leqslant x \leqslant 1, \epsilon_2 \leqslant y \leqslant 1$ does exist and we have

$$\int_{\epsilon_1}^1 dx \int_{\epsilon_2}^1 \frac{x-y}{(x+y)^3} \, dy = \int_{\epsilon_1}^1 dx \int_{\epsilon_2}^1 \frac{2x - (x+y)}{(x+y)^3} \, dy$$

$$= \int_{\epsilon_1}^1 dx \int_{\epsilon_2}^1 \left\{ \frac{2x}{(x+y)^3} - \frac{1}{(x+y)^2} \right\} \, dy = \int_{\epsilon_1}^1 \left(-\frac{x}{(x+y)^2} + \frac{1}{x+y} \right)_{y=\epsilon_2}^{y=1} dy$$

$$= \int_{\epsilon_1}^1 \left\{ \frac{1}{(x+1)^2} - \frac{\epsilon_2}{(x+\epsilon_2)^2} \right\} \, dx = -\frac{1}{2} + \frac{1}{1+\epsilon_1} + \frac{\epsilon_2}{1+\epsilon_2} - \frac{\epsilon_2}{\epsilon_1 + \epsilon_2}$$

As a direct evaluation will confirm, the same value is obtained for

$\int_{\epsilon_2}^1 dy \int_{\epsilon_1}^1 \frac{x-y}{(x+y)^3} \, dx$. However, when we turn to the *improper integrals* which

result when ϵ_1 and ϵ_2 are allowed to tend to zero, the order of operations becomes crucial

$$\lim_{\epsilon_1 \to 0} \left\{ \lim_{\epsilon_2 \to 0} \int_{\epsilon_1}^1 dx \int_{\epsilon_2}^1 \frac{x-y}{(x+y)^3} \, dy \right\} = \lim_{\epsilon_1 \to 0} \left\{ -\frac{1}{2} + \frac{1}{1+\epsilon_1} \right\} = \frac{1}{2}$$

$$\lim_{\epsilon_2 \to 0} \left\{ \lim_{\epsilon_1 \to 0} \int_{\epsilon_2}^1 dy \int_{\epsilon_1}^1 \frac{x-y}{(x+y)^3} \, dx \right\} = \lim_{\epsilon_2 \to 0} \left\{ -\frac{1}{2} + 1 + \frac{\epsilon_2}{1+\epsilon_2} - 1 \right\} = -\frac{1}{2}$$

5.6.5 *Change of variable*
The evaluation of an integral with respect to a single real variable is often made easier by a suitable substitution (see section 5.3.1). Similarly it is often desirable

to express a double integral $\iint_R f(x, y) \, dxdy$ as a double integral with respect to

two new variables u and v. That is to say we consider a substitution of the form

$$x = x(u, v), \qquad y = y(u, v) \tag{61}$$

We assume that the equations (61) can be solved for u and v in terms of x and y so that the transformation from (x, y) coordinates to (u, v) coordinates is one-to-one.

The double integral $\iint\limits_{R} f(x, y)\,dxdy$ has been defined as a limiting form of certain finite sums; these sums were obtained as a result of dividing the field of integration, R, into small sub-regions by means of lines x = constant, y = constant, parallel to one or other of the coordinate axes. For the double integral with respect to u and v we would have to consider the division of the field of integration by curves corresponding to the equations u = constant, v = constant. A typical sub-region ΔR of the field would thus have the four vertices

$$\{x(u, v), y(u, v)\}, \qquad \{x(u + \Delta u, v), y(u + \Delta u, v)\},$$

and

$$\{x(u + \Delta u, v + \Delta v), y(u + \Delta u, v + \Delta v)\}, \qquad \{x(u, v + \Delta v), y(u, v + \Delta v)\}$$

Now by Taylor's theorem we have

$$x(u + \Delta u, v) = x(u, v) + \frac{\partial x}{\partial u}\,\Delta u + \text{terms involving higher powers of } \Delta u,$$

$$x(u + \Delta u, v + \Delta v) = x(u, v) + \frac{\partial x}{\partial u}\,\Delta u + \frac{\partial x}{\partial v}\,\Delta v + \text{terms involving higher powers of}$$

$$\Delta u \text{ and } \Delta v,$$

and so on. This means that for sufficiently small values of Δu and Δv the four vertices of ΔR are given approximately by

$$(x, y), \qquad \left(x + \frac{\partial x}{\partial u}\,\Delta u,\, y + \frac{\partial y}{\partial u}\,\Delta u\right),$$

$$\left(x + \frac{\partial x}{\partial u}\,\Delta u + \frac{\partial x}{\partial v}\,\Delta v,\, y + \frac{\partial y}{\partial u}\,\Delta u + \frac{\partial y}{\partial v}\,\Delta v\right), \qquad \left(x + \frac{\partial x}{\partial v}\,\Delta v,\, y + \frac{\partial y}{\partial v}\,\Delta v\right)$$

Further, when Δu and Δv are very small, the area of this sub-region is approximately equal to twice the area of the triangle with vertices

$$(x, y), \qquad \left(x + \frac{\partial x}{\partial u}\,\Delta u,\, y + \frac{\partial y}{\partial u}\,\Delta u\right), \qquad \left(x + \frac{\partial x}{\partial v}\,\Delta v,\, y + \frac{\partial y}{\partial v}\,\Delta v\right)$$

Using determinantal notation (see chapter 7), this can be written

$$\Delta R \approx 2 \times \tfrac{1}{2} \begin{vmatrix} 1 & 1 & 1 \\ x & x + \dfrac{\partial x}{\partial u}\,\Delta u & x + \dfrac{\partial x}{\partial v}\,\Delta v \\ y & y + \dfrac{\partial y}{\partial u}\,\Delta u & y + \dfrac{\partial y}{\partial v}\,\Delta v \end{vmatrix} = \begin{vmatrix} \dfrac{\partial x}{\partial u} & \dfrac{\partial x}{\partial v} \\ \dfrac{\partial y}{\partial u} & \dfrac{\partial y}{\partial v} \end{vmatrix} \Delta u \Delta v$$

The quantity $\begin{vmatrix} \dfrac{\partial x}{\partial u} & \dfrac{\partial x}{\partial v} \\[2mm] \dfrac{\partial y}{\partial u} & \dfrac{\partial y}{\partial v} \end{vmatrix}$ is often written symbolically as $\dfrac{\partial(x, y)}{\partial(u, v)}$ and is called

the *Jacobian* of the transformation $x = x(u, v), y = y(u, v)$. Summing over all such sub-regions ΔR and proceeding to the limit we obtain the result

$$\iint\limits_{R} f(x, y)\, dxdy = \iint\limits_{R} f\{x(u, v), y(u, v)\}\, \frac{\partial(x, y)}{\partial(u, v)}\, dudv \tag{62}$$

Example. To find the volume of the sphere $x^2 + y^2 + z^2 = a^2$.

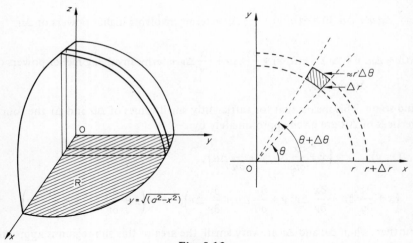

Fig. 5.13

The required volume is 8 times that enclosed in the first octant, and, if we work in cartesian coordinates, the result is the following double integral

$$V = 8 \iint\limits_{R} \sqrt{(a^2 - x^2 - y^2)}\, dxdy = 8 \int_0^a dx \int_0^{\sqrt{(a^2 - x^2)}} \sqrt{(a^2 - x^2 - y^2)}\, dy$$

(see figure 5.13). While it is perfectly possible to evaluate this repeated integral as it stands, it is easier to transform to polar coordinates

$$x = r \cos \theta, \qquad y = r \sin \theta$$

The Jacobian in this case becomes

$$\frac{\partial(x, y)}{\partial(r, \theta)} \equiv \begin{vmatrix} \cos\theta & \sin\theta \\ -r\sin\theta & r\cos\theta \end{vmatrix} = r \tag{63}$$

and a glance at the sketch in figure 5.13 confirms that the polar element of area is given by $r\Delta\theta\,\Delta r$, for small values of Δr and $\Delta\theta$. Since $f(x, y) \equiv \sqrt{(a^2 - x^2 - y^2)}$ transforms into $f(r, \theta) \equiv \sqrt{(a^2 - r^2)}$ the integral reduces to

$$V = 8 \iint_R \sqrt{(a^2 - r^2)}\,r\,dr\,d\theta = 8 \int_0^{\pi/2} d\theta \int_0^a r\sqrt{(a^2 - r^2)}\,dr$$

$$= 8 \int_0^{\pi/2} \left[-\frac{1}{3}(a^2 - r^2)^{3/2} \right]_{r=0}^{r=a} d\theta = 8 \int_0^{\pi/2} \frac{1}{3}a^3\,d\theta = \frac{4}{3}\pi a^3$$

5.6.6 Triple integrals

Once the double integral has been formulated, the extension to higher dimensional situations is relatively straightforward. For the triple integral we have an integrand $f(x, y, z)$, which is a function of three independent variables, and a field of integration which consists of a certain closed region, V, of three-dimensional space. Division of the field into small parallelepipeds by planes $x = x_r$, $y = y_s$, $z = z_t$, gives rise to sums of the form

$$\Sigma f(\xi_{rst}, \eta_{rst}, \zeta_{rst})\Delta x_r\,\Delta y_s\,\Delta z_t$$

and the triple integral of $f(x, y, z)$ over the region V is the limiting value to which these sums tend as Δx_r, Δy_s and Δz_t tend to zero. In the same way as for a double integral we usually need to express a triple integral as a repeated integral in order to evaluate it:

$$\iiint_V f(x, y, z)\,dx\,dy\,dz = \int_a^b dx \int_{\phi_1(x)}^{\phi_2(x)} dx \int_{\psi_1(x,y)}^{\psi_2(x,y)} f(x, y, z)\,dz \tag{64}$$

As in the case of the double integral, the existence of the triple integral is enough to ensure the equivalence of the six possible repeated integrals which we can obtain. The following example should make clear the way in which the limits of integration are determined.

Example. Integrate the function $f(x, y, z) = x^2 + y^2 + z^2$ over the region bounded by the coordinate planes and the plane $x + y + z = 1$.

If we integrate first with respect to z, then x and y are held constant and z varies from an initial value $z = 0$ to the final value $z = 1 - x - y$. Integrating next with respect to y we keep x fixed and allow y to vary from $y = 0$ to $y = 1 - x$. In the final integration x simply goes from 0 to 1 (figure 5.14).

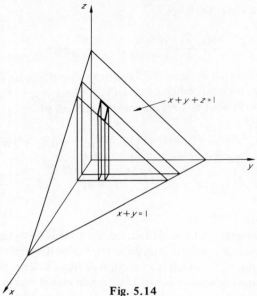

Fig. 5.14

Then

$$\iiint\limits_V (x^2 + y^2 + z^2)\, \mathrm{d}x\mathrm{d}y\mathrm{d}z = \int_0^1 \mathrm{d}x \int_0^{1-x} \mathrm{d}y \int_0^{1-x-y} (x^2 + y^2 + z^2)\, \mathrm{d}z$$

$$= \int_0^1 \mathrm{d}x \int_0^{1-x} \left(x^2 z + y^2 z + \frac{z}{3} \right)_{z=0}^{1-x-y} \mathrm{d}y$$

$$= \int_0^1 \mathrm{d}x \int_0^{1-x} \left\{ x^2(1-x)^2 - x^2 y + (1-x)y^2 - y^3 + \frac{1}{3}(1-x-y)^3 \right\} \mathrm{d}y$$

$$= \int_0^1 \left[x^2(1-x)y - \frac{x^2 y^2}{2} + \frac{(1-x)y^3}{3} - \frac{y^4}{4} - \frac{(1-x-y)^4}{12} \right]_{y=0}^{1-x} \mathrm{d}x$$

$$= \int_0^1 \left\{ x^2(1-x)^2 - \frac{x^2}{2}(1-x)^2 + \frac{(1-x)^4}{3} - \frac{(1-x)^4}{4} + \frac{(1-x)^4}{12} \right\} \mathrm{d}x$$

$$= \int_0^1 \left\{ \frac{x^2(1-x)^2}{2} + \frac{(1-x)^4}{6} \right\} \mathrm{d}x = \frac{1}{20}$$

Exercises

1. Evaluate the following repeated integrals

(a) $\displaystyle\int_0^{\pi/4} dx \int_0^{\pi/2} \sin(x+y)\,dy$ (b) $\displaystyle\int_1^4 dx \int_0^{\sqrt{(4-x)}} xy\,dy$

(c) $\displaystyle\int_0^1 dx \int_x^1 \frac{y^2\,dy}{\sqrt{(x^2+y^2)}}$ (d) $\displaystyle\int_0^a dy \int_0^{\sqrt{(a^2-y^2)}} e^{-(x^2+y^2)}\,dx$

2. (a) Use the transformation $x+y = u,\ y = uv$, to evaluate the integral

$$\int_0^1 dx \int_x^{1-x} e^{y/(x+y)}\,dy$$

(b) Use the transformation $x - y = u,\ v = y$, to evaluate the integral

$$\int_0^2 dx \int_0^2 \{4 + (x-y)^2\}^{-\frac{1}{2}}\,dy$$

3. Integrate the function xy over the region enclosed by the curves

$$y^2 = 2x, \quad y^2 = x, \quad x^2 = 2y, \quad x^2 = y$$

4. Show that the volume of the portion of the cylinder $x^2 + y^2 - 2ax = 0$ cut off by the cylinder $z^2 = 2ax$ is $128a^3/15$.

5. Evaluate the triple integral $\displaystyle\iiint_R \frac{1}{(x^2+y^2+z^2)^{3/2}}\,dxdydz$ over the region R bounded by the spheres $x^2 + y^2 + z^2 = 9,\ x^2 + y^2 + z^2 = 1$.

5.7 Differentiation under the integral sign

In section 5.6.3 it was shown that the double integral of a continuous function $f(x, y)$ over a certain region R could generally be evaluated by expressing it as a repeated integral. Essentially this meant that the problem was reduced to that of evaluating an integral of the form $\displaystyle\int_a^b F(x)\,dx$ where $F(x)$ is a function defined as follows

$$F(x) = \int_{\phi_1(x)}^{\phi_2(x)} f(x, y)\,dy \qquad a \leqslant x \leqslant b \tag{65}$$

The value of F(x) at any particular point x in the range $a \leqslant x \leqslant b$ thus depends on the integrand, $f(x, y)$, and on both the lower and the upper limit of integration. In fact, we may write

$$F(x) \equiv F(u, v, x)$$

where $u = \phi_1(x)$ and $v = \phi_2(x)$. The existence of the repeated integral clearly presupposes that F(x), as defined by equation (65), is actually an integrable function of x for the range concerned. In what follows we shall look at the corresponding problem of *differentiating* functions defined in this way.

First suppose that $f(x, y)$ is a continuously differentiable function of x and y in the region R (that is, that the derivatives f_x and f_y both exist and are continuous at all points of this region). Suppose also that $u = \phi_1(x)$ and $v = \phi_2(x)$ are functions which have continuous derivatives for $a \leqslant x \leqslant b$. Then, by the chain rule

$$\frac{dF}{dx} = \frac{\partial F}{\partial x} + \frac{\partial F}{\partial u}\frac{du}{dx} + \frac{\partial F}{\partial v}\frac{dv}{dx} \tag{66}$$

From the fundamental theorem of the calculus it follows readily enough that

$$\frac{\partial F}{\partial u} \equiv \frac{\partial}{\partial u}\int_u^v f(x, y)\, dy = -f(x, u)$$

and that

$$\frac{\partial F}{\partial v} \equiv \frac{\partial}{\partial v}\int_u^v f(x, y)\, dy = f(x, v)$$

Now to obtain $\dfrac{\partial F}{\partial x}$ we need to differentiate the integral $\displaystyle\int_u^v f(x, y)\, dy$ with respect to x, while holding the limits u, v, constant

$$\frac{\partial F}{\partial x} = \lim_{h\to 0}\left\{\int_u^v f(x + h, y)\, dy - \int_u^v f(x, y)\, dy\right\}\bigg/ h$$

$$= \lim_{h\to 0}\int_u^v \frac{1}{h}\{f(x + h, y) - f(x, y)\}\, dy = \lim_{h\to 0}\int_u^v f_x(x + \theta h, y)\, dy$$

where $0 < \theta < 1$ (using the first mean-value theorem of the differential calculus).

Since $f_x(x, y)$ is assumed continuous in $a \leqslant x \leqslant b$ we can write

$$f_x(x + \theta h, y) = f_x(x, y) + \delta$$

where $|\delta|$ tends to zero with h. It follows that

$$\frac{\partial F}{\partial x} = \int_u^v \frac{\partial}{\partial x} f(x, y)\, dy$$

Substituting these results in (66) we obtain what is sometimes known as *Leibnitz's rule* for differentiating an integral with respect to a parameter

$$\frac{d}{dx}\int_{\phi_1(x)}^{\phi_2(x)} f(x, y)\, dy = \int_{\phi_1(x)}^{\phi_2(x)} \frac{\partial}{\partial x} f(x, y)\, dy - \phi_1'(x)\, f\{x, \phi_1(x)\}$$

$$+ \phi_2'(x)\, f\{x, \phi_2(x)\} \tag{67}$$

Example 1. If $F(x) = \displaystyle\int_0^{x^2} \tan^{-1}\frac{y}{x}\, dx$, find $\dfrac{dF}{dx}$.

We could integrate by parts to get

$$F(x) = \left(y\, \tan^{-1}\frac{y}{x}\right)_0^{x^2} - \int_0^{x^2} \frac{xy}{x^2+y^2}\, dy = x^2 \tan^{-1} x - \frac{x}{2}\log(1+x^2)$$

whence $\qquad F'(x) = 2x \tan^{-1} x + \dfrac{x^2}{1+x^2} - \dfrac{x}{2}\dfrac{2x}{1+x^2} - \dfrac{1}{2}\log(1+x^2)$

On the other hand, Leibnitz's rule gives us immediately

$$F'(x) = \int_0^{x^2} \frac{-y}{x^2+y^2}\, dy + 2x \tan^{-1}\frac{x^2}{x} = 2x \tan^{-1} x - \frac{1}{2}\log(1+x^2)$$

Example 2. Evaluate the integral $\displaystyle\int_0^1 \frac{y^x - 1}{\log y}\, dy,\ x \geqslant 0$.

By Leibnitz's rule

$$\frac{d}{dx}\int_0^1 \frac{y^x - 1}{\log y}\, dy = \int_0^1 \frac{y^x \log y}{\log y}\, dy = \int_0^1 y^x dy = \frac{1}{1+x}$$

Hence $\qquad\qquad \displaystyle\int_0^1 \frac{y^x - 1}{\log y}\, dy = \log(1+x) + C$

By setting $x = 0$ it is easily seen that the constant of integration, C, must have the value zero.

Exercises

1. Show that,

(a) $\dfrac{d}{dx}\displaystyle\int_{x}^{x^2} \cos t^2 \, dt = 2x \cos x^4 - \cos x^2,$

(b) $\dfrac{d}{dx}\displaystyle\int_{0}^{x} \sin xy \, dy = \int_{0}^{x} y \cos(xy) \, dy + \sin x^2,$

(c) $\dfrac{d}{dx}\displaystyle\int_{x}^{x^2} \dfrac{\sin \theta}{\theta} \, d\theta = \dfrac{2 \sin x^2 - \sin x}{x}.$

2. If $y = \dfrac{1}{n}\displaystyle\int_{a}^{x} f(t) \sin n \, (x - t) \, dt$, show that y satisfies the differential equation

$$\frac{d^2 y}{dx^2} + n^2 y = f(x)$$

3. Given that $\displaystyle\int_{0}^{\pi} \dfrac{dx}{\alpha - \cos x} = \dfrac{\pi}{\sqrt{(\alpha^2 - 1)}}$, for $\alpha > 1$, deduce the value of

$\displaystyle\int_{0}^{\pi} \dfrac{dx}{(\alpha - \cos x)^2}$ when $\alpha = 2$.

4. By differentiating the integral $\displaystyle\int_{0}^{1} x^\alpha dx, (\alpha > -1)$, with respect to α, evaluate

the integral $\displaystyle\int_{0}^{1} x^\alpha (\log x)^2 \, dx.$

5. Solve each of the following integral equations:

(a) $u(x) = \cos x + 2 \sin x + \displaystyle\int_{0}^{x} \sin (x - y)u(y) \, dy,$

(b) $y(x) = e^{-x} + \displaystyle\int_{x}^{1} e^{-(t - x)}y(t) \, dt.$

NOTES ON CHAPTER 5

1. Integration theory

For a fuller account of the Riemann theory of integration outlined in section 5.1.1 the reader is referred to R. P. Gillespie: *Integration,* Oliver and Boyd. This also contains a treatment of the theory of the Riemann double integral.

The Riemann integral can be generalised in a very simple manner. Let $\sigma(t)$ be a function defined and monotone increasing on $[a, b]$, and write

$$\delta \sigma_k \equiv \sigma(t_k) - \sigma(t_{k-1})$$

Then, if $f(t)$ is any function defined and bounded on $[a, b]$ and if P is any partition of $[a, b]$, we can form generalised versions of the upper and lower sums, U(P) and L(P), used in section 5.1.1 to define the ordinary Riemann integral:

$$U(P, \sigma) \equiv \sum_{k=1}^{n} M_k \delta \sigma_k \qquad \text{and} \qquad L(P, \sigma) \equiv \sum_{k=1}^{n} m_k \delta \sigma_k$$

If these sums approach a common limiting value as the sub-divisions of $[a, b]$ are made smaller and smaller then the function $f(t)$ is said to be integrable in the *Riemann–Stieltjes sense* over $[a, b]$ with respect to the monotone function $\sigma(t)$.

The common limit, written as $\int_a^b f(t) \, d\sigma(t)$, is called the Riemann–Stieltjes integral of $f(t)$, with respect to $\sigma(t)$, over the interval $[a, b]$. A clear and concise account of the theory of the Riemann–Stieltjes integral is to be found in W. Rudin: *Principles of Mathematical Analysis,* McGraw-Hill. The ordinary Riemann integral then appears as the special case of the Riemann–Stieltjes integral in which $\sigma(t) = t$.

One application of the Riemann–Stieltjes theory is of particular importance. Note first that if $\sigma(t)$ has a continuous derivative, $\sigma'(t)$, then the Riemann–Stieltjes integral with respect to $\sigma(t)$ reduces to an ordinary integral

$$\int_a^b f(t) \, d\sigma(t) = \int_a^b f(t)\sigma'(t) \, dt$$

In contrast, take for $\sigma(t)$ the discontinuous function $u(t)$ which has the value 1 when $t > 0$ and the value 0 when $t < 0$. Then, if $f(t)$ is continuous at the origin, it can be shown that

$$\int_{-R}^{R} f(t) \, du(t) = f(0)$$

for any $R > 0$. Although an abuse of notation is involved, it is customary to write this result in the form

$$\int_{-\infty}^{+\infty} f(t)\delta(t)\,\mathrm{d}t = f(0)$$

in which $\delta(t)$, the so-called *delta function,* is interpreted in a symbolic sense as the 'derivative' of the discontinuous function $u(t)$. (See also exercise 27, chapter 9.)

2. Numerical integration

The function e^{-t^2} is bounded and continuous over every finite interval and therefore certainly has a well defined integral over any given range $a \leqslant t \leqslant b$. But it is not possible to find any finite combination of known elementary functions of which e^{-t^2} is the derivative. The definition of integration in terms of Riemann sums suggests an obvious way of obtaining an approximate value for an integral like $\int_0^1 e^{-t^2}\,\mathrm{d}t$. Using the notation of section 5.1.3 we can divide the interval $[0, 1]$ into equal sub-intervals of length $1/n$ and compute the sums

$$\sum_1 (n) = \frac{1}{n}\sum_{k=0}^{n-1} \exp\left\{-(k/n)^2\right\} \qquad \text{and} \qquad \sum_2 (n) = \frac{1}{n}\sum_{k=1}^{n} \exp\left\{-(k/n)^2\right\}$$

The integrand is monotone decreasing on $[0, 1]$ and so, for each n

$$\sum_2 (n) < \int_0^1 e^{-t^2}\,\mathrm{d}t < \sum_1 (n)$$

For $n = 10, 100, 1000$, the following results are obtained.

$$\Sigma_2(10) = 0.714605 \qquad \Sigma_1(10) = 0.777817$$

$$\Sigma_2(100) = 0.743657 \qquad \Sigma_1(100) = 0.749979$$

$$\Sigma_2(1000) = 0.746508 \qquad \Sigma_1(1000) = 0.747140$$

To improve the accuracy of the estimate we could either go on increasing the value of n, or else use some better approximation to the actual integrand in the sub-intervals. It is the latter approach which gives rise to the study of what is usually called *numerical integration.* Essentially the idea is to replace the actual integrand by a function which is relatively easy to integrate. The use of polynomia in this connection is discussed in section 6.5.2.

3. The Lebesgue integral

The Riemann theory of integration outlined in section 5.1 is adequate for most applications but it is deficient in some rather important respects. A classical example of its limitations is afforded by the function $f(t)$ defined as follows

$$f(t) = \begin{cases} 1 \text{ for rational values of } t \text{ in } [0, 1] \\ 0 \text{ for irrational values of } t \text{ in } [0, 1] \end{cases}$$

If we take any partition, P, of the interval $[0, 1]$ then, since there will be both rational and irrational points in any sub-interval (however small), we find that

$$U(P) = 1 \qquad \text{and} \qquad L(P) = 0$$

(where U(P) and L(P) are respectively the upper and lower sums of $f(t)$, corresponding to the partition P). Thus, the Riemann integral of $f(t)$ over the interval $[0, 1]$ is not defined at all. This is not particularly surprising in itself, perhaps, since $f(t)$ is a function whose behaviour is extremely wild — it is, in fact, discontinuous at every point. What is rather more disturbing is the fact that $f(t)$ can be represented as the limit of a sequence of functions each of which has a perfectly well defined integral on $[0, 1]$:

$$f(t) = \lim_{m \to \infty} f_m(t) \qquad \text{where} \qquad f_m(t) = \lim_{n \to \infty} \left\{ \cos m! \pi t \right\}^{2n}$$

To see this, note that $\left\{ \cos m! \pi t \right\}^2 = 1$ only for those values of t for which $m!t$ is an integer, while for all other values of t we have $0 \leqslant \left\{ \cos m! \pi t \right\}^2 < 1$. Hence, $f_m(t) = 0$ on $[0, 1]$ except for finitely many points at which it has the value 1. It follows that $\int_0^1 f_m(t) \, dt = 0$, $m = 1, 2, 3, \ldots$. Finally, if t is irrational then $m!t$ cannot be an integer for any integral value of m, and so $\lim_{m \to \infty} f_m(t) = 0$; if, on the other hand, t is rational, say $t = p/q$, then $m!t$ will be an integer for all $m \geqslant q$ and so $\lim_{m \to \infty} f_m(t) = 1$.

It is primarily this failure of the Riemann integral under comparatively simple limiting processes which makes a more sophisticated theory of integration desirable. The theory of the integral which supersedes that of Riemann, and which is now accepted as the standard theory in modern analysis, is due to *Lebesgue*. It is not possible to give even an outline of the theory here but the following points should be noted:

(i) If $f(t)$ is any bounded function which is integrable in the ordinary Riemann sense over an interval $[a, b]$ then it is integrable in the Lebesgue sense over that interval, and the values of the Riemann and of the Lebesgue integrals are the same.

(ii) The Riemann theory is properly confined to the integration of bounded functions over finite intervals. The Lebesgue theory, on the other hand, can deal at the outset with unbounded integrands and infinite ranges of integration. In fact, any improper Riemann integral (of either the first or the second kind) which is *absolutely convergent* becomes a proper integral in the Lebesgue sense.

Thus the Lebesgue theory in no way conflicts with the Riemann theory. On the other hand, the scope of integration is extended since there exist functions, integrable in the Lebesgue sense, for which the Riemann definition of integral fails. There are many ways of developing the Lebesgue theory, all of which demand a reasonably thorough grounding in analysis. Of the books currently available the following is perhaps the most straightforward: E. J. McShane: *Integration*, Princeton.

Miscellaneous exercises

1. If $0 < a < b$ and m is an integer $\neq -1$, establish the result

$$\int_a^b x^m \, dx = \frac{b^{m+1} - a^{m+1}}{m+1}$$

from first principles. [Hint: subdivide the interval $a \leqslant x \leqslant b$ by points a, ad, $ad^2, \ldots,$ and $ad^n = b$.]

2. Use the definition of the integral as the limit of approximating Riemann sums to evaluate each of the following:

(a) $\displaystyle\lim_{n \to \infty} \sum_{k=1}^n \frac{\pi}{2n} \sin \frac{k\pi}{2n}$, (b) $\displaystyle\lim_{n \to \infty} \sum_{k=1}^n \frac{n}{n^2 + k^2}$, (c) $\displaystyle\lim_{n \to \infty} \sqrt[n]{\left(\frac{n!}{n^n}\right)}$.

$\left[\text{Hint: in (c) note first that } \log \sqrt[n]{\left(\frac{n!}{n^n}\right)} = \frac{1}{n} \sum_{k=0}^{n-1} \log \left(1 - \frac{k}{n}\right).\right]$

3. Establish the following results for any continuous function $f(t)$:

(a) $\displaystyle\int_a^b f(a + b - t) \, dt = \int_a^b f(t) \, dt$,

(b) $\displaystyle\int_a^b t \, f''(t) \, dt = bf'(b) - f(b) - af'(a) + f(a)$,

(c) $\displaystyle\int_{-a}^a f(t^2) \, dt = 2 \int_0^a f(t^2) \, dt$, $\displaystyle\int_{-a}^a tf(t^2) \, dt = 0$.

4. Let $f(x)$ be defined on the interval $0 \leqslant x \leqslant 1$ as follows

$$f(x) = \begin{cases} 0 \text{ if } x \text{ is irrational} \\ 1/q \text{ if } x = p/q \end{cases}$$

Show that $\displaystyle\int_0^x f(t) \, dt$ exists for every value of x in the interval $0 \leqslant x \leqslant 1$ but

that $\displaystyle\frac{d}{dx}\int_0^x f(t) \, dt = f(x)$ only if x is irrational.

5. Use appropriate substitutions to show that

(a) $\displaystyle\int \sqrt{(x^2 + a^2)} \, dx = \frac{1}{2}x\sqrt{(x^2 + a^2)} + \frac{1}{2}a^2 \log |x + \sqrt{(x^2 + a^2)}|,$

(b) $\displaystyle\int \sqrt{(x^2 - a^2)} \, dx = \frac{1}{2}x\sqrt{(x^2 - a^2)} - \frac{1}{2}a^2 \log |x + \sqrt{(x^2 - a^2)}|,$

(c) $\displaystyle\int \sqrt{(a^2 - x^2)} \, dx = \frac{1}{2}x\sqrt{(a^2 - x^2)} + \frac{1}{2}a^2 \sin^{-1} \frac{x}{a},$

and confirm these results by using integration by parts.

6. Evaluate $\displaystyle\int_0^1 \frac{x^3}{(x^2 + 1)^3} \, dx$ by means of the substitutions

(a) $t = x^2 + 1$,   (b) $x = \tan \theta$.

7. Show that the following integrands may be reduced to rational functions by means of the substitutions suggested:

(a) Integrand a rational function of $\cosh x$ and $\sinh x$; put $t = \tanh \dfrac{x}{2}$,

(b) Integrand a rational function of x and $\sqrt[n]{\left(\dfrac{ax + b}{cx + d}\right)}$; put $t^n = \dfrac{ax + b}{cx + d}$.

8. Prove that, $\displaystyle\int_{-1}^{+1} (1 + x)^m (1 - x)^n \, dx = 2^{m+n+2}\int_0^{\pi/2} \sin^{2n+1}\theta \cos^{2m+1}\theta \, d\theta$

for any positive integers m and n.

9. If n is a positive integer and $m > -1$ show that

$$\int_0^1 x^m (\log x)^n \, dx = (-1)^n \frac{n!}{(m+1)^{n+1}}$$

10. If $I_n = \int (a + b \cos \theta)^{-n} \, d\theta$, where n is a positive integer, show that

$$(n-1)(a^2 - b^2)I_n = -b \sin \theta \, (a + b \cos \theta)^{-(n-1)} + (2n-3)aI_{n-1} - (n-2)I_{n-}$$

11. Without finding any indefinite integrals show that

(a) $\int_0^{\pi/2} \frac{\sin^m x}{\sin^m x + \cos^m x} \, dx = \frac{\pi}{4}$, where m is any real number

(b) $\int_0^{\pi/2} \log \frac{1 + \sin x}{1 + \cos x} \, dx = 0$

(c) $\int_0^{\pi/2} \log \sin x \, dx = -\frac{\pi}{2} \log 2$

12. If $f(t)$ and $g(t)$ are bounded continuous functions on $a \leqslant t \leqslant b$ establish the *Schwarz inequality*

$$\left[\int_a^b f(t)g(t) \, dt \right]^2 \leqslant \int_a^b f^2(t) \, dt \int_a^b g^2(t) \, dt$$

and the *Minkowski inequality*

$$\left[\int_a^b \{f(t) + g(t)\}^2 \, dt \right]^{\frac{1}{2}} \leqslant \left[\int_a^b f^2(t) \, dt \right]^{\frac{1}{2}} + \left[\int_a^b g^2(t) \, dt \right]^{\frac{1}{2}}$$

(See Miscellaneous Exercises, chapter 1, Nos. 5 and 6, and Miscellaneous Exercises, chapter 3, No. 14.)

13. By using the identity

$$\frac{1}{1+t^2} = 1 - t^2 + t^4 - \cdots + (-1)^{n-1}t^{2n-1} + (-1)^n \frac{t^{2n}}{1+t^2}$$

and integrating from 0 to x, obtain a power series expansion for $\tan^{-1} x$. (The range of values of x for which the expansion is valid should be established by examining the remainder term.) Devise a similar method for the function $\log (1 + x)$.

14. Discuss the following contradictions

(i) If $I_1 = \int_{-1}^{+1} \frac{dx}{x^2}$ then, since $\frac{1}{x^2} \geqslant 1$ for all x in the range of integration we should have $I_1 > 0$.

But $\qquad \int_{-1}^{+1} \frac{dx}{x^2} = \left(-\frac{1}{x}\right)_{-1}^{+1} = (-1) - (+1) = -2$

(ii) If $I_2 = -\int_{-1}^{+1} \frac{dx}{1+x^2}$ then, using the substitution $x = 1/y$, we get

$$I_2 = -\int_{-1}^{+1} \frac{1}{1+y^{-2}} \frac{dy}{y^2} = -\int_{-1}^{+1} \frac{dy}{1+y^2} = -I_2$$

Hence, the only possible value for I_2 is 0.

But $\qquad I_2 = \int_{-1}^{+1} \frac{dx}{1+x^2} = \left(\tan^{-1} x\right)_{-1}^{+1} = \frac{\pi}{4} - \left(-\frac{\pi}{4}\right) = \frac{\pi}{2}$

15. Find, in each case, the range of values of the parameter α for which the following integrals converge

(a) $I = \int_0^\infty \frac{x^\alpha}{1+x^2} \, dx$ (b) $J = \int_0^1 x^\alpha (1-x)^{1-\alpha} \, dx$

16. State whether the following integrals are of the First, Second, or Third kinds, and establish whether or not they converge:

(a) $\int_0^\infty \frac{dx}{x^2+x+1}$ (b) $\int_0^\infty \frac{\sin 2x}{x^3+1} \, dx$ (c) $\int_0^\infty \frac{1-\cos^2 x}{x^2} \, dx$

(d) $\int_0^1 \frac{x}{(1-x)^3} \, dx$

17. Show that each of the following integrals converges:

(a) $\int_0^\infty \sin x^2 \, dx$ (b) $\int_0^\infty \cos x^2 \, dx$ (c) $\int_0^\infty x \cos x^4 \, dx$

18. Show that the following integrals diverge and find, in each case, the Cauchy principal value:

(a) $\int_0^5 \dfrac{dx}{4-x}$ (b) $\int_{-\pi/4}^{\pi/2} \cot x \, dx$ (c) $\int_0^2 \dfrac{x^2}{1-x^2} \, dx$

19. Show that $I \equiv \displaystyle\int_0^\infty \dfrac{e^{-bx} - e^{-ax}}{x} \, dx = \log \dfrac{a}{b}$, (where $a, b > 0$).

[Hint: express I as a repeated integral of the form,

$$\lim_{R \to \infty} \int_0^R dx \int_b^a f(x, y) \, dy$$

and change the order of integration.]

20. Evaluate the triple integral $\displaystyle\int_0^1 dx \int_0^1 dy \int_{\sqrt{x^2+y^2}}^2 xyz \, dz$.

6 POLYNOMIALS AND THEIR APPLICATIONS

6.0 Introduction

The polynomial is, in many respects, the best-behaved of all mathematical functions. It is continuous, differentiable, and easy to evaluate for all values of its argument. It may readily be differentiated or integrated, the result of either operation being, moreover, another polynomial. Well-established methods exist for the location of its zeros, and the problem of locating its maxima or minima is simply that of finding the zeros of a derived polynomial.

By contrast, the functions which arise in the analysis of physical problems often lack most or all of these virtues. Such functions may be very complicated and mathematically intractable, or they may only be available in the form of a set of tabulated values. In the former case, analytical operations such as integration or differentiation may be difficult, if not impossible; in the latter case, they are clearly always impossible, since limiting processes cannot be carried out on a function which is only defined at a discrete set of points. If progress is hampered by the presence of such awkward functions, their approximation by other functions of a simpler mathematical nature often enables an analysis to proceed. Polynomials are frequently used as approximating functions in situations of this kind, firstly because they possess the desirable properties cited in the first paragraph, and secondly because any function which is continuous over some finite interval of its argument may be represented as closely as may be desired over that interval by a polynomial of sufficiently high degree. This conclusion is precisely embodied in a theorem due to Weierstrass, quoted here without proof:

Theorem 1: Let $f(x)$ be continuous on the finite interval $a \leqslant x \leqslant b$. Then, for any positive number ϵ, however small, there exists a polynomial $P(x)$ such that $|f(x) - P(x)| < \epsilon$ throughout $a \leqslant x \leqslant b$.

An introduction to polynomial interpolation and approximation, which underlie much of classical numerical analysis, is given in the later part of this chapter. Firstly, however, we will establish some basic properties of polynomials and outline some methods which may be used to solve polynomial equations.

6.1 Polynomials and polynomial equations

To emphasise the fact that much of what follows is equally valid for polynomial functions of either real or complex variables, the basic definitions and theorems will be stated in terms of a complex variable $z = x + iy$.

Definition 1. A function of z of the form

$$P(z) = a_0 + a_1 z + a_2 z^2 + \cdots + a_n z^n$$

in which $a_n \neq 0$, is called a *polynomial of degree n* in z. If the coefficients $a_0, a_1, \ldots, a_n$ are all real, it is said to be a *real polynomial*.

Definition 2. For any polynomial $P(z)$, a real or complex number α such that $P(\alpha) = 0$ is said to be a *zero* of $P(z)$, or a *root* or *solution* of the polynomial equation $P(z) = 0$.

Having defined our terms, we will now prove a number of important theorems concerning polynomial equations and their roots.

Theorem 2 (*remainder theorem*): If α is any constant and $P(z)$ is any polynomial, then the remainder obtained on dividing $P(z)$ by $(z - \alpha)$ is $P(\alpha)$.

Proof: The division will give rise to a quotient polynomial $Q(z)$ and a constant remainder R. Then

$$P(z) = (z - \alpha)Q(z) + R$$

whence, on setting $z = \alpha$ we find, as required

$$P(\alpha) = R$$

Corollary: If α is a root of $P(z) = 0$, then $P(z)$ is exactly divisible by $(z - \alpha)$.

Proof: Division of $P(z)$ by $(z - \alpha)$ gives zero remainder, since $R = P(\alpha) = 0$.

Example: Consider the division of $P(z) = 2z^3 + 3z^2 + 8z + 12$ by $z + i$

We have

$$
\begin{array}{r}
2z^2 + (3-2i)z\ + (6-3i) \\
z + i\ |\overline{2z^3 + 3z^2 + 8z + 12}
\end{array}
$$

$$
\underline{2z^3 + 2iz^2}
$$

$$
(3-2i)z^2 + 8z
$$

$$
\underline{(3-2i)z^2 +(2+3i)z}
$$

$$
(6-3i)z + 12
$$

$$
\underline{(6-3i)z + (3+6i)}
$$

$$
9 - 6i
$$

so that the quotient $Q(z)$ is $2z^2 + (3-2i)z + (6-3i)$ and the remainder is $R = 9 - 6i$. We also find $P(-i) = 2i - 3 - 8i + 12 = 9 - 6i = R$, in accordance with the remainder theorem.

If $P(z)$ is divided by $z + 2i$ in a similar manner, the remainder proves to be zero, since $-2i$ is a root of $P(z) = 0$.

Theorem 3 (fundamental theorem of algebra): A polynomial equation $P(z) = 0$, of degree $n \geqslant 1$, has at least one root.

This is clearly true for polynomial equations of odd degree (see Exercise 5 at the end of this section), but the simplest general proof of the theorem makes use of the theory of functions of a complex variable (but see Note 1). The reader is meanwhile requested to take the validity of the fundamental theorem on trust, since it has the following far-reaching implication:

Corollary: Any polynomial equation $P(z) = 0$, of degree $n \geqslant 1$, has exactly n roots.

Proof: By theorem 3, the equation has at least one root, which we will call α. Then, by the corollary to theorem 2, $P(z)$ is exactly divisible by $(z - \alpha)$, and we may write $P(z) = (z - \alpha)Q(z)$, where $Q(z)$ is a polynomial of degree $n - 1$. But similarly, $Q(z) = 0$ has at least one root, β (which is not necessarily different from α) and so

$$
P(z) = (z - \alpha)(z - \beta)R(z)
$$

where $R(z)$ is a polynomial of degree $n - 2$.

If this argument is repeated $n - 1$ times, we find that $P(z)$ can be factorised as the product of $n - 1$ linear factors and a polynomial of degree 1, which is yet another linear factor. If any one of these n factors is zero, $P(z) = 0$; the equation therefore has exactly n roots.†

† If z_0 is any given complex number, the problem of finding $\sqrt[n]{z_0}$ is equivalent to that of solving the polynomial equation $z^n - z_0 = 0$. It has already been demonstrated in chapter 1 that this particular type of polynomial equation always has n roots.

It was noted in the course of the foregoing proof that the roots of a polynomial equation are not necessarily all different. Consider, as an example, the sixth-degree equation

$$z^6 - 3z^5 + 6z^3 - 3z^2 - 3z + 2 = 0$$

which can be factorised as

$$(z - 1)^3(z + 1)^2(z - 2) = 0.$$

The six roots of this equation are 1 (three times), -1 (twice) and 2. The multiple or repeated roots are classified according to their *multiplicity*; thus 1 is said to be a root of multiplicity 3 of the equation, while -1 is root of multiplicity 2. The root 2, which occurs only once, is called a *simple root*.

Theorem 4. If α is a root of multiplicity $m > 1$ of the polynomial equation $P(z) = 0$, then α is a root of multiplicity $m - 1$ of $P'(z) = 0$.

Proof: Let the degree of $P(z)$ be n. Since α is a root of multiplicity m of $P(z) = 0$ we have

$$P(z) = (z - \alpha)^m Q(z) = 0$$

where $Q(z)$ is a polynomial of degree $n - m$, and α is not a root of $Q(z) = 0$. On equating $P'(z)$ to zero, we obtain

$$P'(z) = m(z - \alpha)^{m-1} Q(z) + (z - \alpha)^m Q'(z) = 0$$

or

$$P'(z) = (z - \alpha)^{m-1}\{mQ(z) + (z - \alpha)Q'(z)\} = 0$$

We have already noted that α is not a zero of $Q(z)$, and therefore the expression in curly brackets does not possess a factor $(z - \alpha)$, since for $z = \alpha$ it becomes $mQ(\alpha) \neq 0$. Then the factor $(z - \alpha)$ occurs precisely $m - 1$ times in $P'(z)$, and α is a root of multiplicity $m - 1$ of $P'(z) = 0$. From a geometrical point of view, this theorem shows that the graph of $P(x)$, for real x, is tangential to the x-axis wherever $P(x) = 0$ has a multiple root.

Example: The equation of the last example,

$$P(z) = z^6 - 3z^5 + 6z^3 - 3z^2 - 3z + 2 = 0$$

or

$$P(z) = (z - 1)^3(z + 1)^2(z - 2) = 0$$

has a root $z = 1$ of multiplicity 3 and a root $z = -1$ of multiplicity 2. The equation $P'(z) = 0$ is

$$P'(z) = 6z^5 - 15z^4 + 18z^2 - 6z - 3 = 0$$

or

$$P'(z) = 6(z - 1)^2(z + 1)(z - \tfrac{1}{4}\{3 + \sqrt{17}\})(z - \tfrac{1}{4}\{3 - \sqrt{17}\}) = 0$$

which has a root $z = 1$ of multiplicity 2 and a non-repeated root $z = -1$.

Up to the present, the material covered in this section has applied equally to real polynomials and to polynomials with complex coefficients. In either case, the roots which arise may be either real or complex. The following theorem concerns complex roots of real polynomial equations:

Theorem 5. If $\alpha = u + iv$ is a complex root of a real polynomial equation $P(z) = 0$, then $\overline{\alpha} = u - iv$ is also a root.

Proof: A necessary and sufficient condition for both α and its complex conjugate $\overline{\alpha}$ to be roots is that $P(z)$ must be exactly divisible by $(z - \alpha)(z - \overline{\alpha})$. Now

$$(z - \alpha)(z - \overline{\alpha}) = (z - u - iv)(z - u + iv)$$
$$= (z^2 - 2uz + u^2 + v^2)$$

If the division of $P(z)$ by this real quadratic function gives a quotient $Q(z)$ and a remainder $\lambda z + \mu$, then

$$P(z) = (z^2 - 2uz + u^2 + v^2)Q(z) + \lambda z + \mu$$

Since $\alpha = u + iv$ is a root, we have

$$P(u + iv) = \lambda(u + iv) + \mu = 0$$

Now λ and μ are real, since all the coefficients of the dividend and divisor are real. If $v \neq 0$, then $\lambda = 0$, and it follows that $\mu = 0$. The remainder is therefore zero, and we conclude that $P(z)$ is exactly divisible by $(z - \alpha)(z - \overline{\alpha})$. If α is a root of $P(z) = 0$, then, so is $\overline{\alpha}$.

Since the expansion of $(z - \alpha)(z - \overline{\alpha})$ gives rise to a quadratic with real coefficients, we also have the result which follows:

Corollary: A real polynomial may always be expressed as the product of real linear and real quadratic factors.

The occurrence of complex roots in conjugate pairs leads to the further conclusion:

Corollary: A real polynomial equation of odd degree has at least one real root.

We will conclude this section with a brief discussion of the relations between the roots and the coefficients of a polynomial equation. Consider the fourth-degree equation

$$a_4 z^4 + a_3 z^3 + a_2 z^2 + a_1 z + a_0 = 0$$

If its four roots are α, β, γ and δ, the equation may be written in the factorised form

$$a_4(z - \alpha)(z - \beta)(z - \gamma)(z - \delta) = 0$$

which, on expansion, gives

$$a_4\{z^4 - (\alpha + \beta + \gamma + \delta)z^3 + (\alpha\beta + \alpha\gamma + \alpha\delta + \beta\gamma + \beta\delta + \gamma\delta)z^2$$
$$- (\alpha\beta\gamma + \beta\gamma\delta + \gamma\delta\alpha + \delta\alpha\beta)z + \alpha\beta\gamma\delta\} = 0$$

Comparison of this equation with the original reveals that

$$a_3 = -(\alpha + \beta + \gamma + \delta)a_4$$
$$a_2 = (\alpha\beta + \alpha\gamma + \alpha\delta + \beta\gamma + \beta\delta + \gamma\delta)a_4$$
$$a_1 = -(\alpha\beta\gamma + \beta\gamma\delta + \gamma\delta\alpha + \delta\alpha\beta)a_4$$

and $$a_0 = \alpha\beta\gamma\delta a_4$$

It is evident that a_3 involves the sum of all the roots, a_2 involves the sum of all the possible products of pairs of roots, and so on. Furthermore, alternating signs are associated with successive sums.

Generalisation of the foregoing procedure is not difficult, and the conclusions reached are summarised in the following theorem:

Theorem 6 (*relations between coefficients and roots*): Let the roots of the nth-degree polynomial equation

$$P(z) = a_n z^n + a_{n-1}z^{n-1} + \cdots + a_1 z + a_0 = 0$$

be $\alpha_1, \alpha_2, \alpha_3, \ldots, \alpha_n$. Then

$$\frac{a_0}{a_n} = (-1)^n \, \alpha_1 \alpha_2 \ldots \alpha_n$$

$$\frac{a_1}{a_n} = (-1)^{n-1} \sum \begin{array}{l} \text{(all possible products of roots} \\ \text{taken } n-1 \text{ at a time)} \end{array}$$

. . . .

$$\frac{a_{n-2}}{a_n} = (-1)^2 \sum \begin{array}{l} \text{(all possible products of roots} \\ \text{taken 2 at a time)} \end{array}$$

and $$\frac{a_{n-1}}{a_n} = (-1) \sum \text{(all the roots)}$$

The relations do not, of themselves, provide a means for solving a polynomial equation, for they contain no more information than the equation itself. They do, however, provide a useful means of checking calculated roots of equations. Sometimes, certain prior information is available concerning the roots of an equation, and the relations may then be used to obtain a complete solution, as in the example which follows.

Example: The equation $8x^3 - 36x^2 + 46x - 15 = 0$ has three roots which are in arithmetic progression. It is required to evaluate these roots.

Let the roots be α, $\alpha + \theta$ and $\alpha + 2\theta$. Using the relations between coefficients and roots, we have

$$-\frac{36}{8} = -(\text{sum of the roots}) = -3\alpha - 3\theta$$

or

$$\alpha = \frac{3}{2} - \theta$$

But also

$$\frac{46}{8} = \sum \begin{array}{l} \text{(all possible products of roots} \\ \text{taken 2 at a time)} \end{array}$$

$$= \alpha(\alpha + \theta) + (\alpha + \theta)(\alpha + 2\theta) + (\alpha + 2\theta)\alpha$$

$$= 3\alpha^2 + 6\alpha\theta + 2\theta^2$$

Substitution for α now gives

$$\frac{46}{8} = \frac{27}{4} - 9\theta + 3\theta^2 + 9\theta - 6\theta^2 + 2\theta^2 = \frac{27}{4} - \theta^2$$

or

$$\theta^2 = 1$$

whence

$$\theta = \pm 1$$

If we take $\theta = 1$, we obtain $\alpha = \frac{1}{2}$, so that the roots of the equation are $\frac{1}{2}, \frac{3}{2}$ and $\frac{5}{2}$. Taking $\theta = -1$ gives the same three roots in the reverse order.

Exercises

1. Use algebraic long division to calculate the remainder when $x^5 + 3x^4 - 4x^3 + x - 1$ is divided by (i) $(x + 2)$, (ii) $(x - 1)$ and (iii) $(2x - 3)$. Check your results using the remainder theorem.

2. Use algebraic long division to show that $P(x) = 2x^4 - x^3 - 12x^2 + 13x - 2$ is exactly divisible by $2x^2 + 5x - 1$. Hence find all the roots of $P(x) = 0$.

3. The equation $x^3 - x^2 - 8x + 12 = 0$ has a repeated root. Use this fact to solve the equation completely.

4. Given that one of the roots of $x^4 - x^3 + 4x^2 + 3x + 5 = 0$ is $1 + 2i$, find the other three roots.

5. Given that two of the roots of $6x^3 + 23x^2 + 16x + 3 = 0$ are mutually reciprocal, solve the equation completely.

6. If $ax^3 + bx^2 + cx + d = 0$ has a repeated root α, show that $-[(2b/3a) + \alpha]$ is a root of $3ax^2 + 2bx + c = 0$.

7. Solve the equation $4x^3 - 49x + 60 = 0$, given that two of its roots differ by 1.

8. The equation $ax^4 + bx^3 + cx^2 + dx + e = 0$, in which all the coefficients are real, has a complex root of multiplicity 2. Show that $d\sqrt{a} = b\sqrt{e}$ and $4ac = b^2 + 8a^{\frac{3}{2}}\sqrt{e}$.

9. The argument of one of the complex roots of the equation $x^3 + x^2 - 2x + k = 0$, where k is real, is known to be $\pi/3$. Using this fact, solve the equation completely and determine the value of k.

10. Let x be a real variable and $P(x)$ a real polynomial of odd degree. By considering the behaviour of $P(x)$ for large positive and negative values of x, show that $P(x) = 0$ has at least one real root.

Show similarly that if $Q(x) = a_0 + a_1 x + \cdots + a_n x^n$ is a real polynomial of even degree in which a_0 and a_n differ in sign, then $Q(x) = 0$ has at least two real roots.

6.2 Exact methods for the solution of polynomial equations

A method appropriate to the degree of a polynomial equation must be used when exact solutions are sought:

(i) *First-degree (linear) equations.* The solution of the general first-degree equation $a_1 z + a_0 = 0$ is immediately seen to be $z = - a_0/a_1$.

(ii) *Second-degree (quadratic) equations.* The equation $a_2 z^2 + a_1 z + a_0 = 0$ may be solved by dividing by a_2 and adding $\frac{1}{4}(a_1/a_2)^2 - a_0/a_2$ to both sides; the left-hand side is then $[z + \frac{1}{2}(a_1/a_2)]^2$, and hence

$$z + \frac{1}{2}\left(\frac{a_1}{a_2}\right) = \pm \sqrt{\left\{\frac{1}{4}\left(\frac{a_1}{a_2}\right)^2 - \frac{a_0}{a_2}\right\}}$$

This leads to the well-known formula

$$z = \frac{-a_1 \pm \sqrt{(a_1^2 - 4a_0 a_2)}}{2a_2}$$

There are two roots, z_1 and z_2, whose nature depends upon the expression under the square root sign. If $a_1^2 - 4a_0 a_2$ is positive, the roots are real and distinct; if it is negative they are complex, while if it is zero the roots are real and equal. It is clear that the roots obey the relations

$$z_1 + z_2 = -\frac{a_1}{a_2} \qquad \text{and} \qquad z_1 z_2 = \frac{a_0}{a_2}$$

in accordance with theorem 6.

(iii) *Third-degree (cubic) equations.* The first steps in the solution of $a_3 z^3 + a_2 z^2 + a_1 z + a_0 = 0$ are division by a_3, followed by the substitution $z = \zeta - \frac{1}{3}(a_2/a_3)$. The resulting equation is of the standard form

$$\zeta^3 + G\zeta + H = 0 \tag{1}$$

containing no term in ζ^2; the numbers G and H depend on the coefficients of the original equation. Various methods are now available; that of *Tartaglia and Cardan,* for instance, makes use of the identity

$$\zeta^3 - 3uv\zeta - (u^3 + v^3) = (\zeta - u - v)(\zeta - \omega u - \omega^2 v)(\zeta - \omega^2 u - \omega v) \tag{2}$$

in which ω is one of the complex cube roots of unity, $-\frac{1}{2}(1 \pm i\sqrt{3})$, and which holds for any values of u and v. This may be confirmed by expansion of the right-hand side. (See exercise 22 on p. 37). The left-hand side of equation (2) is compared with that of equation (1), and values for u and v determined such that

$$\left. \begin{array}{r} -3uv = G \\ -(u^3 + v^3) = H \end{array} \right\} \tag{3}$$

and

For these particular values of u and v the two left-hand sides are exactly equivalent, and the solutions of equation (1) are found by requiring that the right-hand side of equation (2) shall be zero. The three solutions are clearly

$$\left. \begin{array}{l} \zeta_1 = u + v \\ \zeta_2 = \omega u + \omega^2 v \\ \zeta_3 = \omega^2 u + \omega v \end{array} \right\} \tag{4}$$

and

The solution of the original equation in z is now found by setting

$$z_k = \zeta_k - \tfrac{1}{3}(a_2/a_3) \quad \text{for} \quad k = 1, 2, 3$$

This method for solving cubic equations is always successful, but it may involve a good deal of tedious complex algebra. Elimination of v between

equations (3) leads to a quadratic equation in u^3; if $H^2 + 4G^3 < 0$ this
equation has complex roots, and the determination of u then requires the
extraction of a complex cube root. Such a situation always arises if all
three roots of the original equation are real. Other methods exist for
the exact solution of cubic equations, but they, too, are all rather laborious,
and it is probably preferable in most instances (particularly if a calculating
machine is to hand) to find a real root by using a numerical technique,
divide the equation through by the appropriate linear factor, and solve the
resulting quadratic equation for the two remaining roots. The three
solutions found should satisfy the relations

$$z_1 + z_2 + z_3 = -\frac{a_0}{a_3}, \quad z_1 z_2 + z_3 z_3 + z_3 z_1 = \frac{a_1}{a_3} \quad \text{and} \quad z_1 z_2 z_3 = -\frac{a_0}{a_3}$$

in agreement with theorem 6.

(iv) *Fourth-degree (quartic) equations.* Here again, an exact method of
solution exists, in which the roots of the quartic equation are made to
depend upon the roots of a so-called resolvent cubic equation. This
procedure is extremely lengthy, and a numerical method is much to be
preferred, particularly when real roots are present.

(v) *Fifth and higher degree equations.* It has been proved that exact methods
do not exist for the solution of general polynomial equations of the fifth
and higher degrees. In particular cases it may be possible to find an exact
solution, but usually there is no alternative but to resort to numerical
means.

6.3 Numerical solution of polynomial and other nonlinear equations

6.3.1 *Iterative methods*
Many of the simpler techniques for the numerical solution of polynomial
equations may also be used to solve other types of nonlinear equations. Perhaps
the most elementary method is the *interval bisection* method, which may be used
for determining real roots of an equation $f(x) = 0$ to any desired accuracy. In
this method, it is first necessary to find two numbers x_0 and x_1 such that $f(x_0)$
and $f(x_1)$ differ in sign, while $f(x)$ is continuous in the interval $x_0 \leqslant x \leqslant x_1$. If
this is so, $f(x)$ must be zero at one or more points in the interval. The sign of
$f(x)$ is now determined at $x = x_2 = \frac{1}{2}(x_0/x_1)$, the mid-point of the interval. It may
chance that $f(x_2) = 0$, in which case a root has been hit upon fortuitously;
otherwise, the desired root lies in the subinterval $x_0 < x < x_2$ if $f(x_0)f(x_2) < 0$ or
in the subinterval $x_2 < x < x_1$ if $f(x_1)f(x_2) < 0$. A further bisection of the

relevant subinterval localises the root still more precisely, and the process may be continued until the required accuracy is attained. After n bisections the subinterval containing the root will be of length $2^{-n}I$, where $I = x_1 - x_0$, and the value of x_{n+1} will therefore differ from the true root by less than this amount.

Example: It is proposed to find a real root of the polynomial equation

$$P(x) = x^5 + 3x^3 + x^2 - 1 = 0$$

to an accuracy of 0.001.

Take $x_0 = 0$ and $x_1 = 1$; since $P(0) = -1$ and $P(1) = 4$, a real root exists in the interval $0 < x < 1$. Bisecting the interval at $x_2 = \frac{1}{2}$, we find $P(\frac{1}{2}) \simeq -0.344$, which locates the root in the subinterval $\frac{1}{2} < x < 1$. A further bisection at $x_3 = \frac{3}{4}$ shows that the root lies between $\frac{1}{2}$ and $\frac{3}{4}$, since $P(\frac{3}{4}) \simeq 1.065$. In order to achieve the stipulated accuracy we must perform 10 bisections, since 10 is the smallest integral value of n such that $2^{-n} < 0.001$. The results are, to four decimal places

$$x_0 = 0.0000$$
$$x_1 = 1.0000$$
$$x_2 = 0.5000$$
$$x_3 = 0.7500$$
$$x_4 = 0.6250$$
$$x_5 = 0.5625$$
$$x_6 = 0.5938$$
$$x_7 = 0.5781$$
$$x_8 = 0.5859$$
$$x_9 = 0.5820$$
$$x_{10} = 0.5840$$
$$x_{11} = 0.5830$$

The difference between x_{11} and the true root is smaller than 0.001; the root is in fact 0.582645, to six decimal places.

The bisection method is slow but sure; although it does not converge rapidly upon the required root, it has the great virtue that, provided the function concerned is continuous, convergence is assured. Most of the more rapidly convergent methods, including the next one to be discussed, do not possess this property.

The *Newton-Raphson method* for the numerical solution of an equation $f(x) = 0$ is of great importance. Suppose that $\bar{x}$ is an exact root of the equation, and that x_n is an approximation to $\bar{x}$, so that $|\bar{x} - x_n|$ is small. On expanding $f(\bar{x})$ in a Taylor series about $x = x_n$ we have

$$f(\bar{x}) = f(x_n) + (\bar{x} - x_n)f'(x_n) + \frac{1}{2}(\bar{x} - x_n)^2 f''(x_n) + \cdots$$

Since $|\bar{x} - x_n|$ is small, we may neglect second and higher powers on the right-hand side; furthermore, since $\bar{x}$ is a root of $f(x) = 0$, we have $f(\bar{x}) = 0$. We are left with

$$f(x_n) + (\bar{x} - x_n)f'(x_n) \simeq 0 \tag{5}$$

Provided that $f'(x_n) \neq 0$, this equation may be solved for $\bar{x}$, with the result

$$\bar{x} \cong x_{n+1} = x_n - \frac{f(x_n)}{f'(x_n)} \tag{6}$$

Here we may reasonably expect that x_{n+1} is a better approximation to $\bar{x}$ than was x_n. The iterative process based on the recurrence formula (6) is known as the Newton-Raphson process.

A simple geometrical interpretation of the Newton-Raphson method is shown in figure 6.1:

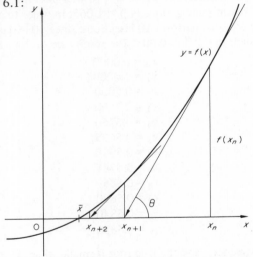

Fig. 6.1 The geometrical basis of the Newton-Raphson method

If x_n is an approximation to the true root $\bar{x}$, the tangent to the curve $y = f(x)$ at $x = x_n$ will usually cut the x-axis at a point x_{n+1} lying between x_n and $\bar{x}$, so that $|\bar{x} - x_{n+1}| < |\bar{x} - x_n|$. From the figure, we see that

$$\tan \theta = f'(x_n) = \frac{f(x_n)}{x_n - x_{n+1}}$$

or

$$x_{n+1} = x_n - \frac{f(x_n)}{f'(x_n)}$$

which is the Newton-Raphson iterative formula once again.

Example. We will again solve the equation of the last example

$$x^5 + 3x^3 + x^2 - 1 = 0$$

It was noted prviously that this equation has a real root lying between 0 and 1; accordingly, we take $x_0 = \frac{1}{2}$ as an initial approximation in the Newton-Raphson process. The recurrence formula is

$$x_{n+1} = x_n - \frac{x_n^5 + 3x_n^3 + x_n^2 - 1}{5x_n^4 + 9x_n^2 + 2x_n}$$

and the results of the first few iterations are, to six decimal places

$$x_0 = 0.500000$$
$$x_1 = 0.596491$$
$$x_2 = 0.582965$$
$$x_3 = 0.582645$$
$$x_4 = 0.582645$$

Further iterations simply generate the same result, and the process has given the root correct to six decimal places after only three iterations; more iterations would be necessary if greater accuracy were required. Such rapid convergence is characteristic of the Newton-Raphson method. It is not difficult to show that under most circumstances the error in x_{n+1} is roughly proportional to the square of the error in x_n; provided, therefore, that x_0 is sufficiently well chosen, the error quickly diminishes as the number of iterations increases. The process may be terminated when two successive iterates differ by less than some specified small number, or when $f(x_n)$ is found to be less than some specified small number.

Unlike the bisection method, the Newton-Raphson method can also be used to find complex roots. A complex starting value must be used, and complex arithmetic employed, but otherwise no modification is necessary. Unfortunately, the approximate location of complex roots is difficult, and it is often necessary to take a stab in the dark as regards x_0 and hope that convergence will result.

Example: We will find a solution of the equation $z^3 - 1 = 0$, arbitrarily taking $z_0 = i$ as a starting value. The iterative formula is $z_{n+1} = z_n - (z_n^3 - 1)/3z_n^2$ and the following results are obtained:

$$z_0 = 0.000000 + 1.000000i$$
$$z_1 = -0.333333 + 0.666667i$$
$$z_2 = -0.582222 + 0.924444i$$
$$z_3 = -0.508791 + 0.868165i$$
$$z_4 = -0.500069 + 0.865982i$$
$$z_5 = -0.500000 + 0.866025i$$
$$z_6 = -0.500000 + 0.866025i$$

Here z_5 and z_6 agree to six decimal places, and we are in fact converging upon one of the complex cube roots of unity, namely

$$-\frac{1}{2}+\frac{\sqrt{3}}{2}i$$

As mentioned earlier, the Newton-Raphson method is not infallible. Convergence may not be obtained if the initial approximation is poorly chosen, and similar trouble may be encountered if $f''(x)$ happens to change sign near a real root. These situations are illustrated in figures 6.2 and 6.3. When the root

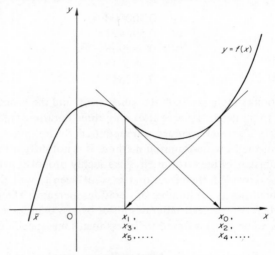

Fig. 6.2

sought is of multiplicity greater than one, the method is only slowly convergent (see exercise 5 at the end of this section), and slow convergence is also likely if two or more roots lie close together. Under most circumstances, however, the Newton-Raphson process is very satisfactory in operation.

6.3.2 *Approximate location of real roots*

In some instances a satisfactory starting approximation for an iterative solution of $f(x) = 0$ may be obtained simply by evaluating $f(x)$ for a few sample values of x and sketching a graph of the function. Equivalently, $f(x)$ may be split into two components which are sketched separately; rough solutions of $e^{-x} - \sin x = 0$ may be found, for example, by locating the intersections of the curves $y = e^{-x}$ and $y = \sin x$. Where non-polynomial equations are concerned,

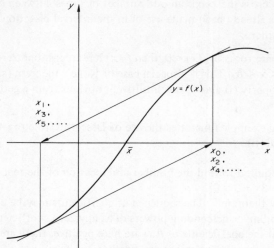

Fig. 6.3

some such method is often the only one available, short of embarking on a computer search for approximate roots over a wide range of values of x. In cases involving polynomial equations, on the other hand, we can often elicit some useful information concerning the approximate whereabouts of real roots by applying the following theorem and its corollary:

Theorem 7 (Descartes' rule of signs). The number of positive real roots of a polynomial equation $f(x) = 0$ is equal to, or less than by an even integer, the number of sign changes in the sequence of coefficients of $f(x)$.

The proof of this theorem is to be found in standard textbooks on algebra. It is important to note that the roots should be counted in their multiplicity (for example, a root of multiplicity three counts as three roots for the purposes of the theorem).

Corollary. The number of negative real roots of a polynomial equation $f(x) = 0$ is equal to, or less than by an even integer, the number of sign changes in the sequence of coefficients of $f(-x)$.

In addition to using Descartes' rule and its corollary, we may also take advantage of certain consequences of the fact that a polynomial $f(x)$ is continuous and differentiable for all finite x:

(i) If $f(a)$ and $f(b)$ differ in sign, then at least one root of $f(x) = 0$ lies in the interval $a < x < b$. The number of roots must in fact be odd, since the graph of $f(x)$ must cross the x-axis an odd number of times between a and b. This property has already been made use of in the interval bisection method discussed earlier.

(ii) If α_1 and α_2 are roots of $f(x) = 0$, then $f'(x)$ has at least one zero in the interval $\alpha_1 < x < \alpha_2$. This is a special case of Rolle's theorem (see section 2.5.1 and, like property (i) above, it is intuitively obvious from a geometrical point of view.

The following example illustrates the use of Descartes' rule together with properties (i) and (ii).

Example. It is required to find the number and location of the real roots of $f(x) = x^3 + 4x^2 + 8x + 3 = 0$.

We first apply theorem 7. The sequence of coefficients may be considered in order of ascending or descending powers of x, any zero coefficients being ignored. Since all the coefficients of $f(x)$ are here positive, there are no sign changes and hence no positive real roots. Further, we have $f(-x) = -x^3 + 4x^2 - 8x + 3$; the signs of the coefficients change three times, and the corollary indicates that there are either three or one negative real roots.

If there are three real roots, property (ii) requires that $f'(x)$ must have two or more real zeros, at least one between each pair of roots. But $f'(x) = 3x^2 + 8x + 8$ has only the complex zeros $\frac{2}{3}(-2 \pm \sqrt{2}i)$, and hence $f(x) = 0$ can only have one real root, which must be negative, from what has gone before.

Evaluation of $f(x)$ for some sample non-positive values of x shows that $f(0) = 3, f(-1) = -2$. The root therefore lies between 0 and -1; use of the Newton-Raphson method with $x_0 = -0.5$ gives its value to six decimal places as $x = -0.474043$.

6.3.3 *Some computational considerations*

Whenever we wish to find more than one root of a polynomial equation, it is worthwhile to decrease the degree of the equation, after the determination of each root α, by dividing it by the linear factor $(x - \alpha)$. The computational labour of finding each successive root is thereby diminished, and, if the process is taken far enough, the last two roots are eventually found by solving a quadratic equation. The method for accomplishing the algebraic division of a polynomial by a linear expression on a computer is called *synthetic division*.

Consider the division of the polynomial $f(x) = a_n x^n + a_{n-1} x^{n-1} + \cdots + a_0$ by the linear expression $(x - \alpha)$. The quotient will be a polynomial of degree $n - 1$,

$$q(x) = b_{n-1} x^{n-1} + b_{n-2} x^{n-2} + \cdots + b_0$$

and, unless α is a root of $f(x) = 0$, there will be a constant remainder r. Then

$$f(x) \equiv (x - \alpha)q(x) + r$$

or

$$a_n x^n + a_{n-1} x^{n-1} + \cdots + a_0 \equiv (x - \alpha)(b_{n-1} x^{n-1} + b_{n-2} x^{n-2} + \cdots + b_0) + r$$

By equating corresponding powers of x in this latter identity, we find successively

$$b_{n-1} = a_n$$
$$b_{n-2} = a_{n-1} + \alpha b_{n-1}$$
$$b_{n-3} = a_{n-2} + \alpha b_{n-2}$$
$$\cdots\cdots\cdots\cdots\cdots\cdots\cdots$$
$$b_0 = a_1 + \alpha b_1$$
$$r = a_0 + \alpha b_0$$

These relations, used in the order shown above, generate all the coefficients of the quotient $q(x)$ and the value of the remainder r. The whole process may conveniently be summarised in the recurrence relation

$$\left.\begin{array}{l} b_{n-1} = a_n \\ b_{k-1} = a_k + \alpha b_k \end{array}\right\} \quad k = (n-1), (n-2), \ldots, 0 \qquad (7)$$

if we define $b_{-1} = r$.

A related method exists for synthetic division by a quadratic factor, having application where a pair of complex conjugate roots of a polynomial equation have been found; such a pair of roots gives rise to a real quadratic factor, as mentioned in section 6.1.

The numerical solution of a polynomial equation $f(x) = 0$ entails the repeated evaluation of $f(x)$ (and, in the Newton-Raphson process, $f'(x)$ also), for particular values of x. Now the remainder theorem (theorem 2) states that the remainder r resulting from the division of a polynomial $f(x)$ by $(x - \alpha)$ is equal to $f(\alpha)$. Thus the synthetic division process outlined above yields not only the quotient polynomial but also the value of $f(\alpha)$, which is given by r.

6.2.7 *Example.* Evaluate $f(x) = 4x^3 + 3x^2 + 2x + 1$ for $x = 2$. The polynomial is of degree 3; accordingly, we take $n = 3$ and $\alpha = 2$ in the recurrence equation (7):

$$b_2 = a_3 \qquad\quad = 4$$
$$b_1 = a_2 + 2b_2 = 11$$
$$b_0 = a_1 + 2b_1 = 24$$
$$r = b_{-1} = a_0 + 2b_0 = 49$$

Then $f(2) = r = 49$. Furthermore, we have elicited the information that the quotient resulting from the division of $f(x)$ by $(x - 2)$ is

$$q(x) = b_2 x^2 + b_1 x + b_0 = 4x^2 + 11x + 24$$

Finally, let us examine the computational efficiency of the foregoing method for evaluating a polynomial. If, in the above example, we had commenced by calculating each term of the polynomial separately, we would have needed five multiplications (two to calculate x^2 and x^3 and three to multiply by the relevant coefficients) followed by three additions. The method actually used required only three multiplications and three additions. It is not difficult to see that this method is equivalent to the evaluation of the *nested* form of the polynomial, $((4x + 3)x + 2)x + 1$, by expansion outwards from the innermost bracket. In this simple example, we have saved the computing time necessary for two multiplications; in a lengthy computer calculation involving many polynomial evaluations, such small economies may lead to a significant saving in total computing time. Generally, a polynomial $f(x)$ of degree n requires n multiplications for its evaluation by the method outlined above, against $2n - 1$ for a term-by-term evaluation. Apropos the Newton–Raphson method, which requires the evaluation of $f'(x)$, it is worth noting that the recurrence relation

$$\left. \begin{array}{l} b'_{n-1} = na_n \\ b'_{k-1} = ka_k + \alpha b'_k \end{array} \right\} \quad k = (n - 1), \ldots, 1$$

gives $f'(\alpha)$ as the value of b'_0; it is therefore unnecessary for the computer to store the coefficients of the derived polynomial $f'(x)$ as well as those of $f(x)$ itself.

Exercises

1. Solve the following quadratic equations:
    (i) $x^2 + ix + 2 = 0$
    (ii) $2x^2 + (2 + 2i)x - (2 - i) = 0$

2. Solve the following cubic equations, using the method of Tartaglia and Cardan:

    (i) $8x^3 - 12x^2 + 54x - 81 = 0$
    (ii) $9x^3 - 18x^2 - 13x + 36 = 0$
    (iii) $27x^3 + 27x^2 - 153x + 55 = 0$
    (iv) $x^3 - 6x + 7i = 0$

3. On the basis of section 6.3.2, what statements can be made concerning the numbers of real and of complex roots of the following polynomial equations?

    (i) $x^3 - x - 1 = 0$
    (ii) $x^3 + x - 1 = 0$
    (iii) $x^5 + 3x + 1 = 0$
    (iv) $x^6 - 3x^3 - 4 = 0$

4. Find all the real solutions of the following equations, to four decimal places, by numerical means:

   (i) $x^3 - 10x + 1 = 0$
  (ii) $x^4 - 7x + 5 = 0$
 (iii) $x \log_e x = 3/2$
 (iv) $e^x + x^2 - 2 = 0$
  (v) $x^3 - x^2 + 1 = 0$
 (vi) $x \sec x - 1 = 0$

In cases (ii) and (v), find also the complex roots.

5. Use the Newton-Raphson method, with $x_0 = 1$, to calculate a root of the equation $4x^3 + 8x^2 - 29x + 12 = 0$. Hence obtain the two remaining roots. Explain the convergence of the iterative process to a root which is further from the initial approximation than either of the other two roots.

6. Write down the Newton–Raphson recurrence formula for the equation $x^3 + 1 = 0$, and perform two iterations, using exact complex arithmetic, taking $x_0 = i$. To which solution of the equation does the process appear to be converging?

7. Use synthetic division to calculate the values of the following polynomials for the given values of x:

   (i) $x^4 - 4x^3 + 5x^2 - 2; \quad x = -3$
  (ii) $2x^3 + 2x^2 - x - 3; \quad x = 2$
 (iii) $3x^5 - 4x^4 - x^3 + x + 1; \quad x = -1$
 (iv) $x^4 + 2x^3 + 2x^2 - 4x - 5; \quad x = 1 - i$

8. Obtain a 3-term recurrence relation representing the synthetic division of a polynomial $f(x) = a_n x^n + a_{n-1} x^{n-1} + \cdots + a_0$ by the quadratic expression $x^2 + \beta x + \gamma$. Hence find the quotient and remainder when $x^5 + 3x^4 - 2x^2 + 1$ is divided by $x^2 - x + 2$.

9. Using a computer, two roots of the equation $8x^3 + 24x^2 + 6x - 1 = 0$ are found to be -0.4076 and -2.7057, to 4 decimal places. Use the relations between roots and coefficients to calculate the third root. Explain why, in using a procedure of this type, it is important in the interests of accuracy to compute roots of the largest modulus first.

10. Let $\bar{x}$ be a solution of $f(x) = 0$, and suppose that x_n is an approximation to $\bar{x}$, such that $\epsilon_n \equiv (x_n - \bar{x})$ is small. The *order* of an iterative process for solving $f(x) = 0$ is defined as the exponent k in the relation $\epsilon_{n+1} \simeq A\epsilon_n^k$, where A is some constant. The order thus characterises the

rate of diminution of the error from one iterated solution to the next, and hence determines the rate of convergence of the process.

By expanding the right-hand side of the Newton–Raphson iterative relation about $x = \bar{x}$ in a Taylor series, show that the convergence of this method is generally of second order. Show also that, in the particular case where $\bar{x}$ is a root of multiplicity $m > 1$ of $f(x) = 0$, the rate of convergence is reduced to first order. For this case, examine the order of the process

$$x_{n+1} = x_n - m \frac{f(x_n)}{f'(x_n)}$$

6.4 Interpolation using polynomials

6.4.1 *Lagrangean interpolation*

It was pointed out in the introduction to this chapter that a frequent recourse of numerical analysis is the use of a polynomial to approximate a function which is defined only by its values at a number of discrete points. Two fairly distinct cases arise of the problem of finding such a polynomial. In the first, the data available can be relied upon to contain only small inaccuracies; this would be the case, for instance, if a set of function values were taken from standard tables, or if they resulted from a good numerical solution of a differential equation (see chapter 8). In such circumstances, the approximating polynomial may be required to pass through all the data points defining the function. The second case arises, typically, where the data to be fitted result from some experimental procedure, so that they are subject to statistical errors which are not negligible. An insistence on fitting all the data points exactly will now almost certainly lead to trouble, since the statistical fluctuations of the observed quantity will be impressed upon (and probably amplified by) the approximating function, when what is really required is that these fluctuations should be smoothed out. Under these circumstances, then, it is usual to require that the approximating function passes close to all data points, but not necessarily through any of them. The procedures adopted in the two foregoing situations are referred to, respectively, as *interpolation* and *curve fitting*. We turn our attention first to the problem of interpolation..

Suppose that the values of a single-valued function $y(x)$ are specified at $n + 1$ discrete values of its argument, namely x_i, where $i = 0, 1, 2, \ldots, n$. The corresponding function values will be denoted by y_i, where $y_i \equiv y(x_i)$. The problem of interpolation is effectively that of finding a value for y at some point x in the interval $x_0 < x < x_n$ which does not coincide with one of the x_i. A crude interpolation may be made between, say, x_i and x_{i+1} by assuming that the variation of y over this interval is approximately linear; if we set

$$y \simeq P_1(x) = ax + b$$

we can determine a and b from the relations

$$y_i = ax_i \quad + b$$

and
$$y_{i+1} = ax_{i+1} + b$$

since we wish $y(x)$ and $P_1(x)$ to assume the same values at the points (x_i, y_i) and (x_{i+1}, y_{i+1}). A more accurate interpolation might be achieved on approximating y by a second-degree polynomial

$$P_2(x) = ax^2 + bx + c$$

passing through the points (x_i, y_i), (x_{i+1}, y_{i+1}) and (x_{i+2}, y_{i+2}). The coefficients a, b and c are now the solutions of the three linear equations

$$y_i = ax_i^2 \quad + bx_i \quad + c$$

$$y_{i+1} = ax_{i+1}^2 + bx_{i+1} + c$$

$$y_{i+2} = ax_{i+2}^2 + bx_{i+2} + c$$

Similarly, a third-degree interpolating polynomial may be constructed by using four of the given function values, and so on. If, in fact, we take advantage of the total information available, we may use all the $n + 1$ given function values to construct a polynomial $P_n(x)$, of degree n. This polynomial will approximate $y(x)$ over the entire range of x covered by the table, and will agree in value with y at all the tabulation points x_i. Any required interpolated value of y may be obtained simply by evaluating $P_n(x)$ for the relevant value of x.

The method indicated above is not the best way of finding an interpolating polynomial, since for large n the process of solving n linear equations for the coefficients of $P_n(x)$ is somewhat lengthy. An alternative method will shortly be outlined, and it will also be shown that it is often possible to use the properties of $P_n(x)$ to obtain required results without ever finding it explicitly. However, regardless of what method is employed to construct an interpolating polynomial fitting a given set of points, the result will be the same:

Theorem 8. If $n + 1$ points (x_i, y_i) are given, the polynomial $P(x)$ of degree $\leqslant n$ which has the property that $P(x_i) = y_i$ for $i = 0, 1, 2, \ldots, n$ is unique.

Proof. Suppose that P and Q are two polynomials both having the specified property; their difference $D = P - Q$ will then also be a polynomial of degree $\leqslant n$. Moreover, at the $n + 1$ points x_i we have $D(x_i) = P(x_i) - Q(x_i) = 0$, since P and Q both have the value y_i at these points. But D, being a polynomial of degree $\leqslant n$, can only have at most n zeros, and hence D must be identically zero. It follows that $P = Q$.

Corollary. If $y(x)$, the tabulated function, is itself a polynomial of degree $\leqslant n$, interpolation by P(x) is exact.

A convenient method of obtaining an interpolating polynomial explicitly is that of *Lagrange*. The polynomial can be expressed in the form

$$P(x) = L_0(x)y_0 + L_1(x)y_1 + \cdots + L_n(x)y_n \tag{8}$$

where y_i, $i = 0, 1, 2, \ldots, n$, are the $n + 1$ given values of $y(x)$ and the $L_i(x)$ are polynomials of degree $\leqslant n$ in x, as is P(x) itself. Now at each of the tabulation points x_k we wish P(x_k) to have the value y_k, and this will be so if we can arrange that

$$\text{(i)} \quad L_i(x_k) = 0, \quad i \neq k$$

and $\qquad$ (ii) $\quad L_k(x_k) = 1$

since then for $x = x_k$ only one non-zero term remains on the right-hand side of equation (8), this term having the value y_k. Condition (i) above is fulfilled by setting

$$L_i(x) = A_i(x - x_0)(x - x_1) \cdots (x - x_{i-1})(x - x_{i+1}) \cdots (x - x_n)$$

where A_i is a constant, since this gives L_i the desired polynomial form and ensures that it is zero at all the tabular points x_k for $i \neq k$. Condition (ii) above determines the value of A_i; we find that

$$L_i(x) = \frac{(x - x_0)(x - x_1) \cdots (x - x_{i-1})(x - x_{i+1}) \cdots (x - x_n)}{(x_i - x_0)(x_i - x_1) \cdots (x_i - x_{i-1})(x_i - x_{i+1}) \cdots (x_i - x_n)}$$

$$= \prod_{\substack{k=0 \\ k \neq i}}^{n} \frac{(x - x_k)}{(x_i - x_k)} \tag{9}$$

has the required property, since for $x = x_i$ corresponding factors in the numerator and denominator cancel, giving $L_i(x_i) = 1$. Our interpolating polynomial is then

$$P(x) = \sum_{i=0}^{n} L_i(x)y_i \tag{10}$$

where the $L_i(x)$ (the *Lagrangean interpolating coefficients*) are given by equation (9).

Example. It is required to find the value of the following tabulated function for
$x = 4$:

i	x_i	y_i
0	1	1.500
1	2	1.914
2	5	2.736
3	9	3.500

Note that the tabulation points x_i need not be equally spaced. Since we are given
the value of $y(x)$ at four points, we can construct a third-degree interpolating
polynomial. Using equations (9) and (10), we obtain

$$P(x) = \frac{(x - x_1)(x - x_2)(x - x_3)}{(x_0 - x_1)(x_0 - x_2)(x_0 - x_3)} y_0 + \frac{(x - x_0)(x - x_2)(x - x_3)}{(x_1 - x_0)(x_1 - x_2)(x_1 - x_3)} y_1$$

$$+ \frac{(x - x_0)(x - x_1)(x - x_3)}{(x_2 - x_0)(x_2 - x_1)(x_2 - x_3)} y_2 + \frac{(x - x_0)(x - x_1)(x - x_2)}{(x_3 - x_0)(x_3 - x_1)(x_3 - x_2)} y_3$$

$$= - \frac{1.500}{32} (x - 2)(x - 5)(x - 9) + \frac{1.914}{21} (x - 1)(x - 5)(x - 9)$$

$$- \frac{2.736}{48} (x - 1)(x - 2)(x - 9) + \frac{3.500}{224} (x - 1)(x - 2)(x - 5) \qquad (11)$$

At this point, each term could be expanded and like powers of x added to put
$P(x)$ in the form

$$P(x) = a_3 x^3 + a_2 x^2 + a_1 x + a_0$$

but in order to determine $y(4)$ it is simpler to substitute $x = 4$ directly into
equation (11), to obtain

$$y(4) \simeq P(4) = - \frac{10}{32} 1.500 + \frac{15}{21} 1.914 + \frac{30}{48} 2.736 - \frac{6}{224} 3.500 = 2.515$$

The given table was actually constructed using $y = \sqrt{x} + \frac{1}{2}$, and the exact value
of $y(4)$ is therefore 2.5.

Although Lagrange's interpolation formula is of considerable theoretical
importance in the derivation of other methods of numerical analysis, it must be
used with caution in practice, because of the difficulty of assessing the accuracy
with which $P(x)$ approximates $y(x)$ over the interval of interest. Although the
values of the two functions coincide at the tabulation points, it is apparent that

y may be subjected to drastic alterations at intermediate points without any resulting change in the polynomial P. The misleading results which may be obtained using Langrangean interpolation are illustrated in figure 6.4, in which the cubic interpolating polynomial passing through the four points $(0, 0)$, $(1, 1)$, $(8, 2)$ and $(27, 3)$ is compared with the function $y = x^{1/3}$ from which these points were obtained.

6.4.2 *Finite differences*
Having indicated the disadvantage of the Lagrangean method of interpolation, we now introduce *finite differences,* with the intention of developing some interpolation formulae which are less prone to this type of gross error. In what follows, it will be assumed that the tabulation points x_i of the function y are equidistantly spaced, so that $x_{i+1} - x_i = h$ = constant. The formation of a difference table is best illustrated by an example:

x_i	y_i	Differences			
		1st	2nd	3rd	4th
0	−4				
		2			
1	−2		2		
		4		6	
2	2		8		0
		12		6	
3	14		14		0
		26		6	
4	40		20		
		46			
5	86				

The numbers in the column of *first differences* are obtained by subtracting each function value in turn from the one following it. The next three columns contain *second, third* and *fourth differences,* the numbers in each column being obtained in a similar manner from the preceding column. It is customary to write each difference on a level intermediate in the table between the two numbers from which it is derived.

Finite difference interpolation formulae are based upon the following theorem:

Theorem 9. If a polynomial $P(x)$ of degree n is tabulated at equal intervals in x, then all its nth differences will be constant.

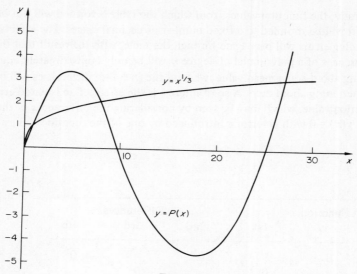

Fig. 6.4

Proof. Let $P(x) = a_n x^n + a_{n-1} x^{n-1} + \ldots + a_0$

Then, since $x_{i+1} = x_i + h$ where h is the tabulation interval (or *step length*), a first difference of P is given by

$$P(x_{i+1}) - P(x_i) = P(x_i + h) - P(x_i)$$
$$= a_n(x_i + h)^n + a_{n-1}(x_i + h)^{n-1} + \ldots + a_0$$
$$-a_n x_i^n - a_{n-1} x_i^{n-1} - \ldots - a_0$$
$$= Q(x_i)$$

The function $Q(x)$ is a polynomial of degree $n - 1$, whose coefficients are functions of the coefficients of $P(x)$ and of the step length h; the first differences of $P(x)$ are given by $Q(x)$ evaluated at the tabulation points x_i. Repeated application of the foregoing argument shows that all the nth differences of $P(x)$ are given by a polynomial of degree zero, which is a constant.

Theorem 9 is illustrated by the difference table given earlier, in which the function tabulated was the third-degree polynomial $x^3 - 2x^2 + 3x - 4$. The third differences are all seen to be constant, and the fourth differences consequently zero.

Generally, the function values from which the table is formed will not be exact, but will be rounded to a fixed number of decimal places. The effects of the rounding errors will propagate through the table, with the result that the nth differences of a polynomial of degree n will be only approximately equal, fluctuating about some mean value, whereas the $(n + 1)$th differences will be small, fluctuating about zero. Also of interest is the effect of an isolated error in a function value, which may be seen by considering the differences of the function $y(x) = 0$ with an error ϵ introduced by one of the function values:

Function y_i	1st	2nd	3rd	4th
0		0		0
	0		0	
0		0		ϵ
	0		ϵ	
0		ϵ		-4ϵ
	ϵ		-3ϵ	
ϵ		-2ϵ		6ϵ
	$-\epsilon$		3ϵ	
0		ϵ		-4ϵ
	0		$-\epsilon$	
0		0		ϵ
	0		0	
0		0		0

The effect of the error is seen to spread out fanwise and to increase in magnitude with increasing order of differences. In the column of nth differences, the coefficients of ϵ correspond to the coefficients arising in the binomial expansion of $(1 - \beta)^n$. This fact affords a means of locating and correcting errors in a table, as illustrated in the following example.

Example. Locate and correct the error in the following table of values of $\log_{10} x$:

x	y	Differences			
6.00	0.7781513				
		36041			
6.05	0.7817554		−297		
		35744		6	
6.10	0.7853298		−291		−2
		35453		4	
6.15	0.7888751		−287		0
		35166		4	
6.20	0.7923917		−283		1
		34883		5	
6.25	0.7958800		−278		20
		34605		25	
6.30	0.7993405		−253		−81
		34352		−56	
6.35	0.8027757		−309		119
		34043		63	
6.40	0.8061800		−246		−79
		33797		−14	
6.45	0.8095597		−260		16
		33537		2	
6.50	0.8129134		−258		3
		33279		5	
6.55	0.8162413		−253		−1
		33026		4	
6.60	0.8195439		−249		
		32777			
6.65	0.8228216				

A table has been formed of differences up to the fourth order; note that it is customary to write differences as integers, omitting decimal points and leading zeros.

The third differences in the table above are roughly equal, with a mean value of about $4\frac{1}{2}$, apart from a group of four anomalous larger terms. The fourth differences are small, fluctuating about zero, with the exception of a group of five larger terms.

The conclusions to be drawn are that

(i) although $\log_{10} x$ is not a polynomial, it behaves very much like a polynomial of degree 3 over the interval $6.00 \leqslant x \leqslant 6.65$;

(ii) an isolated error is present in one of the function values. Since the effects of such an error propagate symmetrically through the table, the incorrect entry is clearly that for $x = 6.35$. The anomalous terms in the fourth difference column are approximately 20 times the set of coefficients $1, -4, 6, -4, 1$; the implication is that $y(6.35)$ is in error by 0.0000020. Reference to tables confirms that the correct value of $\log_{10} 6.35$ is indeed 0.8027737.

An important consequence of conclusion (i) above is that since $\log_{10} x$ behaves like a cubic polynomial over the range of the table, an accurate interpolation may be made using a cubic interpolating polynomial fitting any four successive function values. We shall now develop some difference formulae which accomplish this purpose. Three distinct standard notations exist for differences, the most convenient to use being determined by the particular application. If we are dealing with a table of values of a function $y(x)$, we have the notation of *forward differences*, in which $\Delta y_n \equiv y_{n+1} - y_n$:

x_{-2}	y_{-2}				
		Δy_{-2}			
x_{-1}	y_{-1}		$\Delta^2 y_{-2}$		
		Δy_{-1}		$\Delta^3 y_{-2}$	
x_0	y_0		$\Delta^2 y_{-1}$		$\Delta^4 y_{-2}$
		Δy_0		$\Delta^3 y_{-1}$	
x_1	y_1		$\Delta^2 y_0$		
		Δy_1			
x_2	y_2				

the notation of *backward differences*, in which $\nabla y_n \equiv y_n - y_{n-1}$:

x_{-2}	y_{-2}				
		∇y_{-1}			
x_{-1}	y_{-1}		$\nabla^2 y_0$		
		∇y_0		$\nabla^3 y_1$	
x_0	y_0		$\nabla^2 y_1$		$\nabla^4 y_2$
		∇y_1		$\nabla^3 y_2$	
x_1	y_1		$\nabla^2 y_2$		
		∇y_2			
x_2	y_2				

and the notation of *central differences*, in which $\delta y_{n+\frac{1}{2}} \equiv y_{n+1} - y_n$:

x_{-2}	y_{-2}							
		$\delta y_{-\frac{3}{2}}$						
x_{-1}	y_{-1}		$\delta^2 y_{-1}$					
		$\delta y_{-\frac{1}{2}}$		$\delta^3 y_{-\frac{1}{2}}$				
x_0	y_0		$\delta^2 y_0$		$\delta^4 y_0$			
		$\delta y_{\frac{1}{2}}$		$\delta^3 y_{\frac{1}{2}}$				
x_1	y_1		$\delta^2 y_1$					
		$\delta y_{\frac{3}{2}}$						
x_2	y_2							

For a given set of values of y, the actual numbers in each table will be the same. The three notations differ in the way in which the suffixes are allocated; in forward differences they are constant along lines sloping downwards to the right, in backward differences the lines of constant suffixes slope upwards, while in central differences they are horizontal. The three notations exist because many difference formulae take the form of a series of differences which all have the same suffix. Reference to the three foregoing difference schemes shows that near the beginning of the tables there are more forward differences with suffix, say, -1 than backward or central differences. The greatest accuracy will therefore result if a forward difference formula is used for interpolation near the beginning of a table, since this enables more terms of the difference series to be used. Similarly, backward differences are employed near the end of a table and central differences in the body of a table.

Interpolation formulae involving differences are most easily derived by the use of a symbolic method in which Δ, ∇ and δ are treated as *operators* which, when operating upon a function value y_i transform it into Δy_i, ∇v_i and δy_i respectively. Two other useful operators are the *differential operator* D, defined by

$$\mathrm{D} y_i = \left(\frac{\mathrm{d}y}{\mathrm{d}x}\right)_{x=x_i} = y_i'$$

and the *shifting operator* E, defined by

$$\mathrm{E} y_i = y_{i+1}$$

The operator E thus has the effect of increasing a suffix by one. Each of the five operators may be expressed in terms of any one of the others; for instance

$$\Delta y_0 = y_1 - y_0 = (\mathrm{E} - 1)y_0$$

so that $\qquad\qquad \Delta \equiv \mathrm{E} - 1 \qquad\qquad\qquad (12)$

In a similar manner, we find that

$$\nabla \equiv 1 - E^{-1} \tag{13}$$

Since E increases a suffix by 1, we may take $E^{\frac{1}{2}}$ to be the operator increasing a suffix by $\frac{1}{2}$ If we now define

$$\delta \equiv E^{\frac{1}{2}} - E^{-\frac{1}{2}}, \tag{14}$$

we see that

$$\delta y_{\frac{1}{2}} = E^{\frac{1}{2}} y_{\frac{1}{2}} - E^{-\frac{1}{2}} y_{\frac{1}{2}} = y_1 - y_0$$

and conclude that equation (14) correctly expresses the central difference operator δ in terms of E. Another important relation is obtained by expanding $y_1 = y(x_1) = y(x_0 + h)$ (where h, it will be remembered, is the constant step length or tabulation interval) in a Taylor series about x_0:

$$y_1 = y(x_0 + h) = y_0 + hDy_0 + \frac{h^2 D^2}{2!} y_0 + \frac{h^3 D^3}{3!} y_0 + \cdots$$

or

$$y_1 = Ey_0 = e^{hD} y_0$$

whence

$$E \equiv e^{hD} \tag{15}$$

Using equations (14) and (15) we obtain further

$$\delta \equiv e^{\frac{1}{2}hD} - e^{-\frac{1}{2}hD} \equiv 2 \sinh \left(\tfrac{1}{2} hD \right) \tag{16}$$

Other relations are similarly derived, and a complete summary is given in the following table:

	E	Δ	δ	∇	hD
E	E	$1 + \Delta$	$1 + \tfrac{1}{2}\delta^2 + \delta\sqrt{(1 + \tfrac{1}{4}\delta^2)}$	$(1 - \nabla)^{-1}$	e^{hD}
Δ	$E - 1$	Δ	$\delta\sqrt{(1 + \tfrac{1}{4}\delta^2)} + \tfrac{1}{2}\delta^2$	$\nabla(1 - \nabla)^{-1}$	$e^{hD} - 1$
δ	$E^{\frac{1}{2}} - E^{-\frac{1}{2}}$	$\Delta(1 + \Delta)^{-\frac{1}{2}}$	δ	$\nabla(1 - \nabla)^{-\frac{1}{2}}$	$2 \sinh \tfrac{1}{2} hD$
∇	$1 - E^{-1}$	$\Delta(1 + \Delta)^{-1}$	$\delta\sqrt{(1 + \tfrac{1}{4}\delta^2)} - \tfrac{1}{2}\delta^2$	∇	$1 - e^{-hD}$
hD	$\log E$	$\log(1 + \Delta)$	$2 \sinh^{-1}(\tfrac{1}{2}\delta)$	$-\log(1 - \nabla)$	hD

Interrelations between difference operators

An equation such as (15) or (16) should be regarded merely as a shorthand expression of an infinite power series of difference operators, whose use may be justified if (i) the series operates on a polynomial, and (ii) it is expressed in powers of Δ, δ, ∇ or D (but not E), which, when operating upon a polynomial, reduce its degree. The resulting series then terminates after a finite number of terms, and questions of convergence do not arise. In applying these operator formulae to non-polynomial functions, we should therefore regard ourselves as operating upon an interpolating polynomial rather than upon the function itself.

6.4.3 *Interpolation using finite differences*

Let us now suppose that we wish to interpolate between x_0 and x_1 in a table of values of y, at a point $x = x_0 + \theta h$, where $0 \leqslant \theta \leqslant 1$.

On expanding $y(x_0 + \theta h)$ in a Taylor series about x_0 we have

$$y(x_0 + \theta h) = y_0 + \theta h D y_0 + \frac{\theta^2 h^2 D^2}{2!} y_0 + \frac{\theta^3 h^3 D^3}{3!} y_0 + \cdots$$

$$= e^{\theta h D} y_0 \qquad (17)$$

But from equations (12) and (15) we have

$$e^{hD} = 1 + \Delta$$

and equation (17) becomes

$$y(x_0 + \theta h) = (1 + \Delta)^\theta y_0$$

or, on expanding by the binomial theorem,

$$y(x_0 + \theta h) = y_0 + \theta \Delta y_0 + \frac{1}{2!} \theta(\theta - 1)\Delta^2 y_0 + \frac{1}{3!} \theta(\theta - 1)(\theta - 2)\Delta^3 y_0 + \cdots \qquad (18)$$

Equation (18) is known as the *Newton-Gregory* forward difference interpolation formula, and it is used for interpolating near the beginning of a table. For successful interpolation, successive terms should decrease in magnitude until they become negligible. Curtailment of the series after $n + 1$ terms is exactly equivalent to fitting an nth degree Lagrangean interpolating polynomial; for instance, if only the first three terms are retained, the substitutions

$$\theta = (x - x_0)/h, \quad \Delta y_0 = y_1 - y_0 \quad \text{and} \quad \Delta^2 y_0 = \Delta y_1 - \Delta y_0 = y_2 - 2y_1 + y_0$$

lead to a quadratic polynomial in x, whose coefficients involve y_0, y_1 and y_2. This polynomial fits the three points (x_0, y_0), (x_1, y_1) and (x_2, y_2), and must therefore, according to theorem 8, be identical with the corresponding Lagrangean interpolating polynomial.

The Newton-Gregory backward formula, which should be used near the end of a table, is obtained by substituting $e^{hD} = (1 - \nabla)^{-1}$ in equation (17). We then find

$$y(x_0 + \theta h) = y_0 + \theta \nabla y_0 + \frac{1}{2!} \theta(\theta + 1)\nabla^2 y_0 + \frac{1}{3!} \theta(\theta + 1)(\theta + 2)\nabla^3 y_0 + \cdots \qquad (19)$$

While the forward formula is generally used with $0 \leq \theta \leq 1$, it is often better with the backward formula to use θ in the range $-1 \leq \theta \leq 0$, as in the example which follows.

Example. Given the following table of values of e^{-x}, find the value of $e^{-1.9}$.

x	$y = e^{-x}$	∇y	$\nabla^2 y$	$\nabla^3 y$	$\nabla^4 y$
1.00	0.3679				
		−814			
1.25	0.2865		180		
		−634		−39	
1.50	0.2231		141		6
		−493		−33	
1.75	0.1738		108		
		−385			
2.00	0.1353				

The difference table has been formed. For interpolation near the end of the table we must use the Newton-Gregory backward formula. The step length is $h = 0.25$, and we may therefore take either (i) $x_0 = 1.75$ and $\theta = 0.6$ or (ii) $x_0 = 2.00$ and $\theta = -0.4$. The first choice permits the use of differences up to the third order, while with the second choice we may use a fourth difference, which should give better accuracy. Accordingly, we find

$$e^{-1.9} = e^{-(x_0 - 0.4h)} \simeq y_0 - \frac{2}{5} \nabla y_0 - \frac{3}{25} \nabla^2 y_0 - \frac{8}{125} \nabla^3 y_0 - \frac{26}{625} \nabla^4 y_0$$

$$= 0.1353 + 0.0154 - 0.00130 + 0.00021 - 0.00002$$

$$= 0.1496$$

to four decimal places, on substituting the values of the backward differences from the table. The result is in fact correct to four figures.

One of a number of similar central difference interpolation formulae, which are suitable for use in the body of a table, is that due to *Everett*. This formula contains only even order differences of the function values y_0 and y_1 at either end of the interpolation interval. If, as before, we define $\theta = (x - x_0)/h$, where $0 \leqslant \theta \leqslant 1$, and also set $\bar{\theta} = 1 - \theta$, Everett's formula has the form

$$y(x_0 + \theta h) = \bar{\theta}y_0 + \theta y_1 + E_2\delta^2 y_0 + F_2\delta^2 y_1 + E_4\delta^4 y_0 + F_4\delta^4 y_1 + \cdots \tag{20}$$

where E_2, F_2 and so on are functions of θ and $\bar{\theta}$. These *Everett coefficients* are found by writing equation (20) entirely in terms of y_0 and the forward difference operator Δ; reference to the table on p. 270 shows that we may replace y_1 by $Ey_0 = (1 + \Delta)y_0$ and that $\delta = \Delta(1 + \Delta)^{\frac{1}{2}}$. The resulting formula must be equivalent to the Newton-Gregory forward formula, equation (18), and the Everett coefficients are found by equating coefficients of powers of Δ in the two relations. The result is

$$y(x_0 + \theta h) = \bar{\theta}y_0 + \frac{(\bar{\theta} + 1)\bar{\theta}(\bar{\theta} - 1)}{3!}\delta^2 y_0 + \frac{(\bar{\theta} + 2)(\bar{\theta} + 1)\bar{\theta}(\bar{\theta} - 1)(\bar{\theta} - 2)}{5!}\delta^4 y_0 + \cdots$$

$$+ \theta y_1 + \frac{(\theta + 1)\theta(\theta - 1)}{3!}\delta^2 y_1 + \frac{(\theta + 2)(\theta + 1)\theta(\theta - 1)(\theta - 2)}{5!}\delta^4 y_1 + \cdots$$

$$\tag{21}$$

Everett's formula usually gives good accuracy, firstly because the coefficients diminish rapidly with increasing order of differences, and secondly because the information it uses is symmetrically distributed about the interval of interpolation and not biased in one direction or the other as in the case of the Newton-Gregory formulae. Furthermore, the use of differences of both y_0 and y_1 permits the calculation of the cubic interpolating polynomial using differences of no higher order than the second, as may easily be seen by dropping fourth and higher differences and expressing what remains in Lagrangean form by writing

$$\delta^2 y_0 = \delta y_{\frac{1}{2}} - \delta y_{-\frac{1}{2}} = y_1 - 2y_0 + y_{-1}$$

and

$$\delta^2 y_1 = \delta y_{\frac{3}{2}} - \delta y_{\frac{1}{2}} = y_2 - 2y_1 + y_0$$

Exercises

1. Construct the interpolating polynomial passing through the points $(-1, 2)$, $(1, 2)$, $(2, -1)$, $(4, 2)$, and hence find the value of y when $x = 1.2$.

2. For $x = 2.0, 2.5, 3.0, 3.5$ the values of $\log_{10} x$ are respectively 0.3010, 0.3979, 0.4771, 0.5441. Use Lagrange's method of interpolation to calculate a value for $\log_{10} 2.63$.

3. The exact values of a quartic polynomial $p(x)$ for $x = 1.0, 1.1, \ldots, 1.4$ are 11.10000, 10.96641, 10.93616, 11.02701 and 11.25936 respectively. Using the properties of finite differences, extend the table of values over the range $x = 1.5, 1.6, \ldots, 2.0$.

4. The following table of solutions of $x^3 + x = a$ contains an error. Locate it, and estimate a correction by means of differences. Verify your corrected value using the Newton–Raphson method.

a	x	a	x
50	3.5936	56	3.7388
51	3.6186	57	3.7609
52	3.6432	58	3.7848
53	3.6676	59	3.8074
54	3.6916	60	3.8297
55	3.7153	61	3.8518

5. Locate and estimate a correction for the error in the following table:

x	$f(x)$	x	$f(x)$
1.0	1.0100	1.8	10.5559
1.1	1.4774	1.9	13.1007
1.2	2.0909	2.0	16.0800
1.3	2.8781	2.1	19.5407
1.4	3.8690	2.2	23.5321
1.5	5.0963	2.3	28.1058
1.6	6.5946	2.4	33.3158
1.7	8.4021	2.5	39.2188

Using the corrected table, calculate values for $f(1.06)$, $f(1.75)$ and $f(2.32)$ by employing appropriate finite difference formulae.

6. The values of $y = x^2 - 8/(x + 3)$ for integer values of x from 0 to 5 are, to three decimal places, -2.667, -1.000, 2.400, 7.667, 14.857 and 24.000. Calculate values for $y(1.2)$, $y(2.6)$ and $y(4.5)$ using

   (i) an appropriate Newton–Gregory formula, and
   (ii) Everett's formula (where possible).

   Compare your results with the exact values.

7. Using the data of question 6, but now treating x as a function of y, construct a suitable cubic interpolating polynomial and hence estimate the value of x for which $y = 0$. (This kind of procedure is called *inverse interpolation*.) Compare your result with the correct answer, obtained by the Newton–Raphson process.

8. The rounding of function values to a certain number of decimal places introduces errors of magnitude $\leqslant \frac{1}{2}$ unit in the last decimal place. Assuming the worst possible case, in which the errors in a set of tabulated values are alternatively $+\frac{1}{2}$ unit and $-\frac{1}{2}$ unit, show that the resulting errors in the column of nth differences alternate between -2^{n-1} and $+2^{n-1}$. Statistically, such a distribution of errors is extremely improbable, and the fluctuations due to rounding errors will in practice usually lie well inside these limits.

Tabulate $f(x) = x^3$ for $x = 1.0, 1.2, \ldots, 2.0$, rounding the function values to two decimal places. Verify that the fluctuations in the 4th differences lie within the limits stated above.

9. Prove that the Newton–Gregory forward interpolation formula, terminated after the term involving $\Delta^2 y_0$, is exactly equivalent to the Lagrangean interpolating polynomial passing through the points (x_0, y_0), (x_1, y_1) and (x_2, y_2).

10. Derive the operator relationship $\Delta = E - 1$.
Suppose that

$$u_0 - u_1 + u_2 - u_3 + \cdots$$

is a slowly convergent series whose sum is S. By first expressing the terms of the series in terms of u_0 and the shifting operator E, show that

$$S = \frac{1}{2 + \Delta} u_0 = \tfrac{1}{2}(1 - \tfrac{1}{2}\Delta + \tfrac{1}{4}\Delta^2 - \tfrac{1}{8}\Delta^3 + \cdots) u_0$$

Use this formula to estimate, to four decimal places, the sum of the series

$$1 - \frac{1}{2} + \frac{1}{3} - \frac{1}{4} + \cdots$$

from the values of its first six terms. The exact value of S is $\log_e 2$, or 0.6931, to four decimal places. (This process, known as *Euler's transformation*, frequently accelerates the convergence of an alternating series. The operator series should be viewed in the light of remarks made on such series in section 6.4.2.)

6.5 Numerical differentiation and integration

6.5.1 *Numerical differentiation*
Formulae for numerical differentiation and integration follow from the symbolic operator relations already developed; their use is tantamount to the performance of the corresponding analytical processes on an interpolating polynomial.

Numerical differentiation is, in general, not a very satisfactory process, and should be avoided whenever possible. Its disadvantage is illustrated by the following simple formula for the derivative of a tabulated function $y(x)$ at $x = x_0$:

$$y'_0 \simeq \frac{y_1 - y_0}{x_1 - x_0} = \frac{\Delta y_0}{h} \qquad (22)$$

Here y'_0 is approximated by the slope of the linear interpolating polynomial fitting the points (x_0, y_0) and (x_1, y_1). Clearly, we cannot expect the formula to be accurate for large values of h, though in principle it becomes exact in the limit as $h \to 0$. In practice, however, if we use a small value of h, y_1 will usually be very nearly equal to y_0, and in forming their difference a large relative error may be incurred, due to rounding errors in the function values. Division by the small quantity h may then lead to a considerable absolute error in y'_0.

Formulae which are more accurate than equation (22) are easily found using the relations between difference operators. In terms of forward differences, we find from the table on p. 270

$$hy'_0 = hDy_0 = \{\log(1 + \Delta)\}y_0$$
$$= \Delta y_0 - \tfrac{1}{2}\Delta^2 y_0 + \tfrac{1}{3}\Delta^3 y_0 - \cdots \qquad (23)$$

The corresponding backward difference formula is

$$hy'_0 = hDy_0 = -\{\log(1 - \nabla)\}y_0$$
$$= \nabla y_0 + \tfrac{1}{2}\nabla^2 y_0 + \tfrac{1}{3}\nabla^3 y_0 + \cdots \qquad (24)$$

It will be noted that if only the first term of equation (23) is retained, the result is equation (22). Since their coefficients only decrease slowly, neither of these formulae is likely to be very rapidly convergent. The first may be used near the beginning, and the second near the end of a table. Use of central differences leads to a more rapidly convergent formula:

$$hy'_0 = hDy_0 = \{2 \sinh^{-1} \tfrac{1}{2}\delta\} y_0$$
$$= \delta y_0 - \frac{1}{24} \delta^3 y_0 + \frac{3}{640} \delta^5 y_0 - \cdots$$

Here we have a problem in that odd-order central differences always have fractional suffixes, so that δy_0, $\delta^3 y_0$ and so on do not appear in our difference table. However, if we increase all the suffixes by $\tfrac{1}{2}$, we have

$$hy'_{\frac{1}{2}} = \delta y_{\frac{1}{2}} - \frac{1}{24} \delta^3 y_{\frac{1}{2}} + \frac{3}{640} \delta^5 y_{\frac{1}{2}} - \cdots \qquad (25)$$

where the left-hand side should be interpreted as the derivative of y at the mid-point of the interval $x_0 \leqslant x \leqslant x_1$ and all the differences on the right-hand side appear in the table. It seems, therefore, that first derivatives are more naturally evaluated at the mid-points of tabular intervals than at the tabulation points themselves; the same is true for all odd-order derivatives.† Even-order derivatives, on the other hand, are naturally evaluated at tabular points. We have, for instance

$$h^2 y_0'' = h^2 D^2 y_0 = \{2 \sinh^{-1} \tfrac{1}{2}\delta\}^2 y_0$$

$$= \delta^2 y_0 - \frac{1}{12} \delta^4 y_0 + \frac{1}{90} \delta^6 y_0 - \cdots \tag{26}$$

There is some advantage, then, in arranging a computation so that only even order derivatives are used. It is better still, if possible, to formulate a problem in such a way that numerical differentiation is not necessary.

6.5.2 *Numerical integration*

Numerical integration is a much more reliable process, and suitable formulae are conveniently derived by integrating the Newton-Gregory forward interpolation formula

$$y(x_0 + \theta h) = y_0 + \theta \Delta y_0 + \frac{1}{2!} \theta(\theta - 1)\Delta^2 y_0 + \frac{1}{3!} \theta(\theta - 1)(\theta - 2)\Delta^3 y_0 + \cdots$$

If we make the substitution $x = x_0 + \theta h$, we have

$$\int_{x_0}^{x_n} y(x)\mathrm{d}x = h \int_0^n y(x_0 + \theta h)\mathrm{d}\theta$$

$$= h\left[\theta y_0 + \frac{1}{2}\theta^2 \Delta y_0 + \frac{1}{2!}\left(\frac{1}{3}\theta^3 - \frac{1}{2}\theta^2 \right)\Delta^2 y_0 \right.$$

$$\left. + \frac{1}{3!}\left(\frac{1}{4}\theta^4 - \theta^3 + \theta^2 \right)\Delta^3 y_0 + \cdots \right]_0^n$$

$$= h\left\{ ny_0 + \frac{1}{2} n^2 \Delta y_0 + \left(\frac{1}{6} n^3 - \frac{1}{4} n^2 \right)\Delta^2 y_0 \right.$$

$$\left. + \left(\frac{1}{24} n^4 - \frac{1}{6} n^3 + \frac{1}{6} n^2 \right)\Delta^3 y_0 + \cdots \right\} \tag{27}$$

---

† A central-difference formula giving first derivatives at tabular points may be found if the *averaging operator* $\mu \equiv \frac{1}{2}(\mathrm{E}^{1/2} - \mathrm{E}^{-1/2}) \equiv \sqrt{(1 + \tfrac{1}{4}\delta^2)}$ is introduced, since now we may write

$$hy_0 = hDy_0 = \{2 \sinh^{-1} \tfrac{1}{2}\delta\} y_0 = \left\{ \frac{2\mu \sinh^{-1} \tfrac{1}{2}\delta}{\sqrt{(1 + \tfrac{1}{4}\delta^2)}} \right\} y_0$$

$$= \mu\delta y_0 - \frac{1}{6} \mu\delta^3 y_0 + \frac{1}{30} \mu\delta^5 y_0 - \cdots$$

where $\qquad \mu\delta^{2n+1} y_0 = \tfrac{1}{2}\{\delta^{2n+1} y_{\frac{1}{2}} + \delta^{2n+1} y_{-\frac{1}{2}}\}$

This formula is not very rapidly convergent.

Consider first the case when $n = 1$. Equation (27) becomes

$$\int_{x_0}^{x_1} y(x)\mathrm{d}x = h\{y_0 + \frac{1}{2}\Delta y_0 - \frac{1}{12}\Delta^2 y_0 + \frac{1}{24}\Delta^3 y_0 - \frac{19}{720}\Delta^4 y_0 + \cdots\} \quad (28)$$

Here we are integrating between the tabular points x_0 and x_1; if it so happens that we know the value of y only at these two points, we must curtail the formula after the term in Δy_0, since second and higher differences cannot be calculated. The result is

$$\int_{x_0}^{x_1} y(x)\mathrm{d}x \simeq h\{y_0 + \frac{1}{2}\Delta y_0\}$$

$$= \frac{1}{2}h\{y_0 + y_1\} \quad (29)$$

which is recognisable as the *trapezium rule,* whose use amounts to integration of the linear interpolating polynomial passing through (x_0, y_0) and (x_1, y_1). The trapezium rule therefore gives an exact result if the integrand is linear in x. If we next put $n = 2$ in equation (27), we find

$$\int_{x_0}^{x_2} y(x)\mathrm{d}x = h\left\{2y_0 + 2\Delta y_0 + \frac{1}{3}\Delta^2 y_0 - \frac{1}{90}\Delta^4 y_0 + \cdots\right\} \quad (30)$$

In order to evaluate third and higher differences we need function values lying outside the interval of integration; if these are not available we may curtail equation (30) after the term in $\Delta^2 y_0$

$$\int_{x_0}^{x_2} y(x)\mathrm{d}x \simeq h\{2y_0 + 2\Delta y_0 + \frac{1}{3}\Delta^2 y_0\}$$

$$= \frac{1}{3}h\{y_0 + 4y_1 + y_2\} \quad (31)$$

This formula is *Simpson's rule,* whose use is equivalent to integrating the quadratic interpolating polynomial passing through (x_0, y_0), (x_1, y_1) and (x_2, y_2). An exact result must therefore be obtained if $y(x)$ is a second degree polynomial. Better still, in fact, Simpson's rule is also exact for cubic integrands, owing to the absence of a $\Delta^3 y_0$ term in equation (30); in the transition to equation (31) all the terms neglected involve fourth or higher differences, which are zero for a cubic polynomial, by theorem 9.

The substitution of $n = k$, $k > 2$, in equation (27) leads to a formula for integration over k tabular intervals. The formula has the effect of integrating an interpolating polynomial of degree k, and it will therefore be exact if $y(x)$ is a polynomial of degree $\leqslant k$. Such formulae, characterised by their use of equally spaced function values, including the values at the extremes of the interval of integration, are called *Newton-Cotes closed* formulae. Simpson's rule, which combines simplicity with good accuracy, is much the most frequently used. It is easily extended to permit integration over any even number of tabular intervals:

$$\int_{x_0}^{x_{2n}} y(x)\,dx \simeq \frac{1}{3}h\{y_0 + 4y_1 + 2y_2 + 4y_3 + \cdots + 2y_{2n-2} + 4y_{2n-1} + y_{2n}\} \quad (32)$$

Here the interpolating function is *piecewise* quadratic, a different quadratic being fitted over each successive pair of intervals. The extended form of the trapezium rule is

$$\int_{x_0}^{x_n} y(x)\,dx \simeq \frac{1}{2}h\{y_0 + 2y_1 + 2y_2 + \cdots + 2y_{n-1} + y_n\} \quad (33)$$

the interpolating function here being piecewise linear.

The error incurred by the use of Simpson's rule may be estimated by noting that in proceeding from equation (30) to equation (31) the first of the terms dropped is $-(h/90)\Delta^4 y$. If $y(x)$ and its differences are well-behaved, this term will dominate the truncation error. It is often more convenient to have the error expressed in terms of a derivative, and to this end we may write

$$\left(\frac{d^k y}{dx^k}\right)_{x=x_0} = y_0^{(k)} = \frac{1}{h^k}(hD)^k y_0 = \frac{1}{h^k}\left\{\log(1+\Delta)\right\}^k y_0$$

$$= \frac{1}{h^k}\left\{\Delta - \frac{1}{2}\Delta^2 + \frac{1}{3}\Delta^3 - \cdots\right\}^k y_0$$

or
$$h^k y_0^{(k)} = \Delta^k y_0 - \frac{1}{2}k\Delta^{k+1}y_0 + \cdots$$

Assuming, again, that $y(x)$ is well-behaved and that k is not too large

$$\Delta^k y_0 \simeq h^k y^{(k)} \quad (34)$$

whence our estimate of the error in Simpson's rule becomes $-(h^5/90)y_0^{(4)}$. In the transition from equation (28) to equation (29) the dominant term dropped was $-(h/12)\Delta^2 y_0$, and the corresponding error estimate for the trapezium rule is hence $-(h^3/12)y_0''$.† These are estimates for single applications of the two rules.

---

† The argument used here should be regarded as no more than plausible. The results are confirmed by a more rigorous analysis, however, and in particular equations (35) and (36) can be shown to hold for the integration of any functions having derivatives up to 4th order and second order respectively on $a \leqslant x \leqslant b$.

Let us now suppose that the interval of integration is from a to b, and that it is divided into n segments of length h so that $nh = (b - a)$. Suppose also that $|y''(x)| \leqslant M_2$ and $|y^{(4)}(x)| \leqslant M_4$ throughout the interval. Then we can say of the errors incurred by the use of the extended formulae, equations (32) and (33), that

$$|\epsilon_S| \leqslant \frac{n}{2} \frac{h^5}{90} M_4 = (b - a) \frac{h^4}{180} M_4 \tag{35}$$

and

$$|\epsilon_T| \leqslant n \frac{h^3}{12} M_2 = (b - a) \frac{h^2}{12} M_2 \tag{36}$$

where the subscripts S and T refer to Simpson's rule and to the trapezium rule; the errors are said to be of order h^4 and h^2 respectively.

Example. Use Simpson's rule to evaluate $\displaystyle\int_1^3 \frac{e^{-x} \, dx}{x}$ to 4 decimal places.

Analytic evaluation of the integral is impossible. Using two intervals of length $h = 1$, Simpson's rule gives, to four decimal places

$$I_2 = \frac{1}{3}\left\{\frac{e^{-1}}{1} + 4\frac{e^{-2}}{2} + \frac{e^{-3}}{3}\right\} = 0.2184$$

Taking four intervals of length $h = 0.5$, we find

$$I_4 = \frac{1}{6}\left\{\frac{e^{-1}}{1} + 4\frac{e^{-1.5}}{1.5} + 2\frac{e^{-2}}{2} + 4\frac{e^{-2.5}}{2.5} + \frac{e^{-3}}{3}\right\} = 0.2077$$

If we continue to double the number of intervals, we obtain

$$I_8 = 0.2064$$
$$I_{16} = 0.2063$$
$$I_{32} = 0.2063$$

The desired value is apparently 0.2063. If greater accuracy were required, we could use still smaller step lengths, though a point would come where the cumulative effect of the rounding errors in the large number of function evaluations necessary would outweigh the gain in accuracy due to smaller truncation error. The reader may like to confirm that equation (35) gives the error in I_{32} to be less than $\frac{1}{2}$ unit in the last decimal place.

Exercises

1. Using four-figure tables, tabulate the function $f(x) = e^x$ from $x = 0$ to $x = 1$ at intervals of 0.2, and form a table of differences. Use forward, central and

backward difference formulae to obtain approximate values for $f'(x)$ at $x = 0$, $x = 0.5$ and $x = 1.0$ respectively. In the first and third cases show, by comparison with the exact results, that the most accurate approximations are obtained by omitting the fifth difference term — this is because the effects of rounding error increase towards higher orders of differences faster than the coefficients of the slowly convergent formulae decrease. (See exercise 8, p. 275.)

2. Use the trapezium rule with $h = 4$, 2 and 1, and Simpson's rule with $h = 2$ and 1 to obtain appoximate values for the integrals

$$\int_0^{12} x^{\frac{1}{2}} \, dx \qquad \text{and} \qquad \int_0^{12} \frac{dx}{1 + x}$$

Work to four decimal places. (The values of the integrals are 27.7128 and 2.5649 respectively, to four decimal places.)

3. The values of $\cos x$ for $x = 0.0, 0.5, \ldots, 2.5$ (radians), to three decimal places, are 1.000, 0.878, 0.540, 0.071, -0.416, -0.801. From these data, it is possible to construct a corresponding table of values of $\sin x$, using either of the relations

(i) $$\sin x = -\frac{d}{dx}(\cos x),$$

or (ii) $$\sin x = \int_0^x \cos x \, dx$$

Which approach is likely to give the more accurate results? Verify your answer by performing the computations for the first three values of x, using equation (28) for the integration and an appropriate difference formula for the differentiation.

4. Determine the smallest integer n which ensures that the evaluation of

$$\int_0^1 (1 + x)^{-1} \, dx$$

by Simpson's rule with step length 2^{-n} will be correct to three decimal places. Hence compute the integral to this accuracy. (Its exact value is $\log_e 2 \simeq 0.6931$.)

5. Derive the *three-eighths rule* for numerical integration

$$\int_{x_0}^{x_3} f(x) \, dx \simeq \frac{3}{8} h \left\{ f_0 + 3f_1 + 3f_2 + f_3 \right\}$$

and show that the error is approximately $-\frac{3}{80} h^5 f_0^{(iv)}$ (that is, that this rule is less accurate than Simpson's rule with the same step length, even though it uses four function values rather than only three.)

6.6 Least-square polynomial curve fitting

We turn now to the second of the two problems outlined at the beginning of section 6.4 — that of finding a polynomial which best fits a given set of data which is known to be only approximate. It is first necessary to examine the given data and to decide what degree of polynomial to fit; for instance, the points may appear to fall roughly on a straight line, in which case we could seek an approximating polynomial of the form $a_1 x + a_0$. The procedure usually followed once the form of the approximating function is decided upon will be illustrated by an example.

Example. Fit a suitable polynomial to the following set of data, in which the y_i are known to be approximate:

i	x_i	y_i
1	-2	-1.2
2	-1	-1.5
3	0	-1.3
4	1	1.9
5	2	7.1

It is evident from figure 6.5, where the points are plotted, that a straight line would not fit the data satisfactorily. The points might very well fall on a parabola, however, and we will accordingly fit a second-degree polynomial $p(x) = ax^2 + bx + c$. The *deviation* of the fitted curve from a data point is defined by

$$\delta_i = p(x_i) - y_i$$

and the most convenient criterion of 'best fit' is the requirement that $\Sigma \delta_i^2$, summed over all the tabulation points, is a minimum.† Thus, in the present case, we wish to determine values of a, b and c which minimise

$$S \equiv \sum_{i=1}^{5} \{ax_i^2 + bx_i + c - y_i\}^2 \tag{37}$$

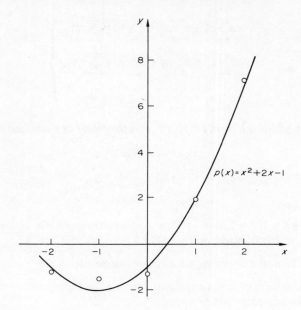

Fig. 6.5

This we achieve by setting

$$\frac{\partial S}{\partial a} = \frac{\partial S}{\partial b} = \frac{\partial S}{\partial c} = 0$$

If the x_i are all distinct, the resulting equations will have a unique solution which can only give a minimum of S, since however large S is we can always make it larger by moving the approximating function farther away from the data points. We obtain (omitting the limits on the summations, for clarity)

$$\left.\begin{aligned}
\frac{\partial S}{\partial a} &= 2\sum\{ax_i^2 + bx_i + c - y_i\}\,x_i^2 = 0 \\[2mm]
\frac{\partial S}{\partial b} &= 2\sum\{ax_i^2 + bx_i + c - y_i\}\,x_i = 0 \\[2mm]
\frac{\partial S}{\partial c} &= 2\sum\{ax_i^2 + bx_i + c - y_i\}\,1 = 0
\end{aligned}\right\}$$

† It is not satisfactory to minimise $\Sigma\delta_i$, since large positive and negative deviations may cancel; minimisation of $\Sigma|\delta_i|$ is a possibility, but the calculations become rather awkward. The chosen criterion not only makes for easier minimisation, but also discriminates against large deviations δ_i, which are statistically much less probable than small errors.

or
$$a\sum x_i^4 + b\sum x_i^3 + c\sum x_i^2 = \sum x_i^2 y_i$$
$$a\sum x_i^3 + b\sum x_i^2 + c\sum x_i = \sum x_i y_i$$
$$a\sum x_i^2 + b\sum x_i + c\sum 1 = \sum y_i$$

All the summations are from $i = 1$ to 5, and they may be evaluated from the initial data, giving

$$34a \quad\quad + 10c = 24$$
$$10b \quad\quad = 20 \tag{38}$$
$$10a \quad\quad + 5c = 5$$

with solution $a = 1$, $b = 2$, $c = -1$. The least-squares quadratic is therefore $x^2 + 2x - 1$, which is shown on figure 6.5.

Points to be noted regarding least-squares curve fitting are

(i) The system of linear equations which arises (compare equations (38)) is always symmetrical (see chapter 7);

(ii) If we find a best least-squares polynomial of degree n for $n + 1$ given points, it will prove to be identical with the nth-degree interpolating polynomial fitting those points. Usually, however, it is desired to fit a low-degree polynomial to a large number of points, so that an exact fit is not possible.

(iii) The method shown may be used to fit not only polynomials but any linear combination of functions to a given set of data. For example, the data of this example may be approximated by $\alpha + \beta e^{-x} + \gamma e^x$, when it will be found that $-2.235 + 0.110\,e^{-x} + 1.283\,e^x$ gives the best least-squares fit.

Exercises

1. Obtain least-squares fits to the data of the foregoing example using (i) a straight line, and (ii) a cubic polynomial.

2. Fit a function of the form $\alpha + \beta e^{-x} + \gamma e^x$ to the same data, and thus verify the statement made in (iii) above.

3. The following are values of y corresponding to $x = 0, 1, \ldots, 5$ respectively. Find the least-squares straight line in each case:

   (i) 1, 4, 7, 9, 12, 14
   (ii) 10, 8, 5, 0, −3, −9
   (iii) 1, 1, 2, 3, 2, 4

4. The following are values of y corresponding to $x = 0, 1, \ldots, 4$ respectively.
   Find the least-squares polynomial of degree 2 in each case:

   (i) $4, 1, -1, -2, -2$
   (ii) $10, 9, 7, 4, 0$
   (iii) $2, 1, 2, 4, 7$

5. Find a and b such that $a \cos x + b \sin x$ is a best least-squares fit to the points

$$(0, 2), \left(\frac{\pi}{2}, 1\right), (\pi, -3), \left(\frac{3\pi}{2}, -1\right), (2\pi, 1)$$

NOTES ON CHAPTER 6

1. It may seem surprising that the fundamental theorem of algebra (theorem 3), which underlies the whole of the theory of polynomials, possesses no simple algebraic proof. The fact that the most straightforward proof uses the theory of functions of a complex variable serves to illustrate the fundamental nature of this branch of mathematics. An alternative proof, given in G. H. Hardy: *A Course of Pure Mathematics* (Appendix II), runs in essence as follows:

Where $f(z)$ is any polynomial, $F(x, y) = |f(x + iy)| = |f(z)|$ is continuous and non-negative for all x, y. For an arbitrary complex number z' a real number N is determined such that $N > |f(z')|$; it is first proved that, however large N is, a real positive number R exists such that $F(x, y) > N$ for $|z| = \sqrt{(x^2 + y^2)} > R$. Inside the circle $|z| = R$, $F(x, y)$ must attain its greatest lower bound (that is, must have its minimum value), at some point which we will call $z_0 = x_0 + iy_0$. Assuming that $|f(z_0)| = F(x_0, y_0) \neq 0$, it is now shown that there exists a complex number ϵ such that $|f(z_0 + \epsilon)| < |f(z_0)|$. But this contradicts the assumption that $|f(z_0)|$ is the lower bound of $|f(z)|$, and the hypothesis that $|f(z_0)| \neq 0$ must therefore be false. Then there exists at least one point at which $|f(z)|$, and consequently $f(z)$, is zero.

The crux of this proof lies in a result from the analysis of functions of two real variables, namely that a continuous function $F(x, y)$ attains its greatest lower bound in any closed domain. Although the truth of this statement is intuitively fairly obvious, its rigorous demonstration is a somewhat delicate matter. The proof given by Hardy cannot, therefore, be regarded as elementary, though familiarity with the contents of chapters 1–4 of the present volume should enable the reader to master the details.

2. Only two of a multitude of methods for the numerical solution of a general nonlinear equation $f(x) = 0$ are described in this chapter – the bisection method because it is infallible whenever $f(x)$ is continuous, and the Newton-Raphson method because it combines simplicity with computational efficiency. The latter method is readily extended to the solution of systems of nonlinear equations in several variables, although such problems often present acute difficulties in the location of approximate roots and in the attainment of convergence (see either of the references below). Specialised methods of guaranteed convergence are available for finding real and complex roots of polynomial equations, notably the Lehmer-Schur method, which localises the roots by carrying out a systematic search of the entire complex plane, and the quotient-difference method, which finds all the roots of a polynomial equation simultaneously. The first is described in A. Ralston: *A First Course in Numerical Analysis*, McGraw-Hill, and the second in P. Henrici: *Elements of Numerical Analysis*, Wiley. The theory underlying these methods is not elementary. They require no starting approximation, and converge only slowly; it is therefore usual to use them in conjunction with a more rapidly convergent process such as Newton–Raphson iteration.

3. Apart from those mentioned in this chapter, other interpolation formulae include that of *Hermite,* which fits a polynomial of degree $2n - 1$ to n points at which both $y(x)$ and $y'(x)$ are specified, and formulae based on *divided differences,* analogous to the finite difference formulae already introduced but applicable in the case of unequally spaced data. There also exist formulae due to Aitken and Neville which are algebraically equivalent to the formulae developed earlier but which permit the progression to higher orders of interpolation to be carried out in an iterative manner particularly suited to machine computation. For details of all these methods see Z. Kopal: *Numerical Analysis,* Chapman and Hall, or F. B. Hildebrand: *Introduction to Numerical Analysis,* McGraw-Hill.

It is quite possible to interpolate using functions other than polynomials; for instance, a set of data exhibiting a periodic nature might be interpolated by a combination of trigonometric functions. Recently, interpolation by piecewise polynomial functions called *splines* has become popular – for example, the cubic spline $g(x)$ interpolating the values y_i at the points x_i, $i = 0, 1, \ldots, n$, has the properties that

(a) $g(x)$ is a cubic polynomial in each interval $x_i \leqslant x \leqslant x_{i+1}$;

(b) $g(x_i) = y_i$;

(c) $g'(x)$ and $g''(x)$ are continuous at $x = x_i, i = 1, 2, \ldots, (n - 1)$.

It may be shown that $g(x)$ is the smoothest possible function interpolating the given data, in the sense that it possesses the least mean-squared curvature over the interval $x_0 \leqslant x \leqslant x_n$. Further details may be found in B. Wendroff: *Theoretical Numerical Analysis,* Academic Press.

4. The methods of approximation described in this chapter apply when the function $f(x)$ to be approximated is defined only by its values at a finite number of points. For computational purposes, however, approximations are needed even for such familiar functions as $\sin x$ or e^x, which are defined for all values of x; computers do not contain tables of these functions, and their values are calculated from suitable approximate formulae whenever they are needed. Polynomial approximations for such functions may be derived by truncation of their Maclaurin series after a certain number of terms, but the resulting formulae have the disadvantage that the further x is from zero, the larger is the truncation error. A function $f(x)$ may be approximated more uniformly over some finite interval (a, b) by finding a polynomial $p(x)$ according to the least-

squares criterion that $\int_a^b \{(p(x) - f(x)\}^2 dx$ shall be a minimum. The integral may

be minimised in terms of the coefficients of $p(x)$ by a process similar to that used in section 6.5 to minimise a sum of squared deviations. More frequently used is a *minimax* criterion, which determines $p(x)$ such that the maximum value of $|p(x) - f(x)|$ in the interval (a, b) is a minimum for all approximating polynomials of the same degree as $p(x)$. The two latter methods of approximation are greatly facilitated by the use of certain sets of polynomials which are said to be *orthogonal*. A further use of orthogonal polynomials is in the derivation of a class of very powerful numerical integration formulae associated with the name of Gauss. Further information on these topics may be sought in Hildebrand, in the work quoted, where details are also given on various important non-polynomial approximation techniques.

5. Further coverage of the numerical methods described in this chapter is given in L. Fox and D. F. Mayers: *Computing Methods for Scientists and Engineers,* O.U.P., which also expands upon most of the topics mentioned in these notes.

Miscellaneous Exercises

1. Suppose that a, b, x, y are real numbers such that $x + iy$ is the square root of $a + ib$; show that $x^2 - y^2 = a$ and $2xy = b$, and hence obtain an explicit formula for $(a + ib)^{\frac{1}{2}}$ in terms of a and b. Use this result in solving the quadratic equations

   (i) $z^2 + (2 - i)z - 1 + 5i = 0$, and

   (ii) $(1 - i)z^2 - (5 - 3i)z + 10 = 0$.

2.   Show that for no real value of x does the value of the function $(x^2 - 3x + 1)/(x^2 + 3x - 1)$ lie between -1 and $-5/13$.

3.   The equation $6x^5 - 17x^4 + 11x^3 - 56x^2 + ax + b = 0$ has roots $x = 3$ and $x = \frac{1}{2}$. Determine a and b, and find the remaining three roots by the method of Tartaglia and Cardan.

4.   Given that α and $-\alpha$ are both real roots of $4x^4 + 12x^3 + 3x^2 + kx - 27 = 0$, solve the equation completely and determine the value of k.

5.   The real quartic equation $x^4 - 6x^3 + 26x^2 + kx + 32 = 0$ has a complex root of argument $\pi/3$ and a complex root of argument $\pi/4$. Use these facts to determine all the roots of the equation and to find the value of k.

6.   Prove that, if the equations $a_1 x^m + b_1 x^n + c_1 = 0$ and $a_2 x^m + b_2 x^n + c_2 = 0$ have a common root, then $(a_1 b_2 - b_1 a_2)^{m-n}(b_1 c_2 - c_1 b_2)^n = (c_1 a_2 - a_1 c_2)^m$.

7.   The equation $x^4 - (p + q)x^3 + (p - q)x - 1 = 0$ has a root α of multiplicity two. Show that $p^{\frac{2}{3}} - q^{\frac{2}{3}} = 2^{\frac{2}{3}}$ and that $\alpha = 2^{-\frac{1}{3}}(p^{\frac{1}{3}} - q^{\frac{1}{3}})$. Hence solve completely $16x^4 - 49x^3 + 76x - 16 = 0$.

8.   (a) Use appropriate methods to obtain real solutions, to four decimal places, of

     (i) $x^x = 20$, and
     (ii) $3^x - 3^{-x} = \frac{3}{2}$.

    (b) Find to four decimal places, the positive value of x for which $(\tan x)/x^2$ is a minimum.

9.   (a) Write down the Newton-Raphson recurrence formula for the equation $x^2 - a = 0$, and use it to calculate $\sqrt{a}$ to four decimal places for

     (i) $a = 6$, and
     (ii) $a = 72$.

    In both cases, take $x_0 = \frac{1}{2}a$. (This method is widely implemented on digital computers for the extraction of square roots.)

    (b) In a similar manner, compute $\sqrt[3]{2}$ to four decimal places, taking $x_0 = 1$.

10. Try the Newton-Raphson method on the equation $x^4 + 4x^3 - 8x - 16 = 0$, taking $x_0 = 0$. Why does the method fail?

    Solve the equation completely, to four decimal places, using the Newton-Raphson method with a better starting value, and reducing the degree of the equation by synthetic division after the determination of each real root.

Check your results by substituting $x = \zeta - 1$ in the original equation and solving the resulting equation exactly.

11. Find the polynomial of lowest degree which passes through the points $(0, 8), (1, 1), (2, -4), (3, 11), (4, 64)$ and $(5, 173)$.

12. If S_n denotes the partial sum to n terms of the slowly convergent series

$$1 - \frac{1}{3} + \frac{1}{5} - \frac{1}{7} + \frac{1}{9} - \cdots$$

calculate S_2, S_4 and S_6 to four decimal places. Construct the interpolating polynomial passing through the points $(\frac{1}{2}, S_2)$, $(\frac{1}{4}, S_4)$ and $(\frac{1}{6}, S_6)$, and use it to estimate the sum to infinity of the series. (The exact value of the sum is $\pi/4$.)

13. Having located and corrected the error in the table below, use appropriate difference formulae to evaluate the following, to four decimal places: $y(0.06), y(1.32), y(2.82), y'(2.80), y'(1.30), y''(2.00)$. Also evaluate $\int_1^3 y(x)dx$ using Simpson's rule with $h = 0.2$ and obtain an approximate solution of $y(x) = 0$ by approximating $x(y)$ with a cubic Lagrangean interpolating polynomial and setting $y = 0$.

x	y	x	y
0.0	−3.2066	1.6	+1.5043
0.2	−3.4941	1.8	3.7960
0.4	−3.6272	2.0	6.6260
0.6	−3.5580	2.2	10.0425
0.8	−3.2383	2.4	14.0934
1.0	−2.6203	2.6	18.8266
1.2	−1.6538	2.8	24.2903
1.4	−0.2969	3.0	30.5323

14. Find the cubic polynomial which has the values y_0, y_1 and the derivatives y'_0, y'_1 at the points $x = 0$ and $x = 1$ respectively. (This is a simple example of *Hermite's* method of interpolation. See Note 3.)

Use your result to derive a formula for numerical integration over the interval $0 \leqslant x \leqslant 1$ which uses the values of $y(0)$, $y'(0)$, $y(1)$ and $y'(1)$, giving an exact answer when the integrand is a polynomial of degree $\leqslant 3$.

Hence find an approximate value for $\int_0^1 \tan\left(\tfrac{1}{4}\pi x\right) dx$.

15. Prove the following operator relationships:

(i) $\Delta(f_i\, g_i) = f_i \Delta g_i + g_{i+1} \Delta f_i$,

(ii) $\Delta f_i^2 = (f_i + f_{i+1})\, \Delta f_i$,

(iii) $\Delta(f_i/g_i) = (g_i \Delta f_i - f_i \Delta g_i)/g_i\, g_{i+1}$,

(iv) $\Delta\left(\dfrac{1}{f_i}\right) = -\Delta f_i / f_i\, f_{i+1}$.

16. Evaluate the following integrals using Simpson's rule with step lengths $\frac{1}{2}(b-a)$, $\frac{1}{4}(b-a)$ and $\frac{1}{8}(b-a)$, where a and b are the lower and upper limits. In case (iv), the substitution $x = (1 + \zeta)/(1 - \zeta)$ will be found to give finite limits. The answers given are exact.

(i) $\displaystyle\int_0^1 (1 - x^2)/(1 + x^2)\, dx = \frac{\pi}{2} - 1 \simeq 0.5708$

(ii) $\displaystyle\int_0^\pi \log_e\left(\frac{5}{4} - \cos\theta\right) d\theta = 0$

(iii) $\displaystyle\int_0^{2\pi} (3 - 2\cos\theta + \sin\theta)^{-1}\, d\theta = \pi \simeq 3.1416$

(iv) $\displaystyle\int_0^\infty (1 + x^6)^{-1}\, dx = \frac{\pi}{3} \simeq 1.0472$

17. (a) Let $T(h)$, $S(h)$ denote the results of evaluating

$$I = \int_0^1 \frac{dx}{1 + x + x^2} \quad \left(= \frac{\pi}{\sqrt[3]{3}} \simeq 0.6046\right)$$

by the trapezium rule and by Simpson's rule respectively, with step length h. Evaluate $T(\tfrac{1}{2})$, $T(\tfrac{1}{4})$, $S(\tfrac{1}{2})$ and $S(\tfrac{1}{4})$ to four decimal places.

(b) Equation (36) indicates that the error in $T(\tfrac{1}{2})$ should be roughly four times that of $T(\tfrac{1}{4})$. Use this fact to calculate an improved value $T^*(\tfrac{1}{4})$.

Similarly, calculate an improved value $S^*(\tfrac{1}{4})$ from $S(\tfrac{1}{2})$ and $S(\tfrac{1}{4})$ on the basis of equation (35).

(c) If your calculations are correct, you will find that $T^*(\tfrac{1}{4}) = S(\tfrac{1}{4})$. Can you explain this?

18. Consider the numerical integration formula

$$\int_{-1}^{1} f(x)\ dx \simeq w_1 f(-1) + w_2 f(-\tfrac{1}{2}) + w_3 f(\tfrac{1}{2}) + w_4 f(1)$$

If we stipulate that the formula shall give an exact result in the four cases where $f(x) = 1, x, x^2$ and x^3, it will be exact for any linear combination of these functions, namely any cubic integrand. On this basis, determine the four constants w_1, w_2, w_3 and w_4.

Use the foregoing method to derive the trapezium rule with $h = 2$

$$\int_{-1}^{1} f(x)\ dx \simeq f(-1) + f(1)$$

and Simpson's rule with $h = 1$,

$$\int_{-1}^{1} f(x)\ dx \simeq \frac{1}{3}f(-1) + \frac{4}{3}f(0) + \frac{1}{3}f(1)$$

remembering that they must give exact results when $f(x)$ is respectively linear and quadratic in nature.

19. (a) Find the straight line and the quadratic of best least-squares fit to the data

x:	0	1	2	3	4	5
y:	3.00	2.40	2.00	1.65	1.35	1.10

(b) Fit a curve of the form $y = ae^{bx}$ to the above data by taking logarithms and using the method of least squares. (Why is it first necessary to take logarithms?)

20. By minimising the integral

$$\int_{0}^{1} (ax^2 + bx + c - \sin \pi x)^2\ dx$$

(see section 5.7), find the quadratic which is the best least-squares fit over the integral $0 \leqslant x \leqslant 1$ to the function $\sin \pi x$. (This is an example of a method of approximation referred to in Note 4.)

7 MATRIX ALGEBRA AND LINEAR EQUATIONS

7.0 Introduction

In many mathematical problems a situation arises in which the data may be arranged naturally in rows and columns. For example, a system of linear equations such as

$$2x + y + 3z = 4$$
$$3x - 2y + 2z = 1$$

has solutions which are determined by the rectangular array of coefficients $\begin{pmatrix} 2 & 1 & 3 \\ 3 & -2 & 2 \end{pmatrix}$ and by the array of constants $\begin{pmatrix} 4 \\ 1 \end{pmatrix}$ from the right-hand side of the equations.

As a further example, the transformation of rectangular cartesian coordinates obtained by rotating the axes through an angle θ is usually expressed in the form

$$x = x' \cos \theta - y' \sin \theta$$
$$y = x' \sin \theta + y' \cos \theta$$

and this transformation is completely specified by the rectangular array
$\begin{pmatrix} \cos \theta & -\sin \theta \\ \sin \theta & \cos \theta \end{pmatrix}$.

In dealing with complex numbers it is convenient to use the single symbol z to represent the complex number $x + iy$, or the ordered pair of real numbers (x, y); in a similar way it is convenient to represent the rectangular arrays or matrices such as those above by single symbols such as A, or B, and to develop a matrix algebra for performing certain operations on these entities.

The aim of this chapter is to introduce elementary matrix algebra and apply it to the theory of simultaneous linear equations (which is the most basic of all the many applications).

292

7.1 Elementary matrix algebra

7.1.1 *Basic definitions*

An $m \times n$ *matrix* is a rectangular array of $m \cdot n$ elements (usually numbers) arranged in m rows and n columns.

Conventionally, a matrix is denoted by a capital letter (for example, A), its individual elements being denoted by the corresponding small letter together with a pair of suffixes to indicate the position of the element in the matrix; the first of these suffixes refers to the row, and the second to the column (for example, a_{23} denotes the element in the second row and third column of matrix A). A typical element is usually denoted a_{ij}, signifying an element in the ith row and jth column of A where i and j are arbitrary numbers such that $1 \leqslant i \leqslant m$, $1 \leqslant j \leqslant n$.

Example

$$A = \begin{pmatrix} 2 & 3 & 4 & 1 \\ -1 & 2 & 0 & 5 \\ 4 & 1 & 7 & -2 \end{pmatrix}$$

is a 3×4 matrix with $a_{12} = 3$, $a_{21} = -1$, $a_{34} = -2$, etc.

Two matrices are said to be *equal* if they are of the same dimensions and if all pairs of corresponding elements are equal. More concisely this can be stated: A = B if A and B are of the same dimensions and if $a_{ij} = b_{ij}$ for all relevant i, j. Matrices of different dimensions cannot be compared.

7.1.2 *Addition and subtraction of matrices*

Definition 1. If A and B are both $m \times n$ matrices, we define an $m \times n$ matrix C = A + B by the equations $c_{ij} = a_{ij} + b_{ij}$, for all $i = 1, \ldots, m$, all $j = 1, \ldots, n$.

Example

$$A = \begin{pmatrix} 1 & 2 & 3 \\ 4 & -1 & 2 \end{pmatrix} \quad B = \begin{pmatrix} 2 & 1 & -3 \\ 5 & 2 & -1 \end{pmatrix} \quad A + B = \begin{pmatrix} 3 & 3 & 0 \\ 9 & 1 & 1 \end{pmatrix}$$

Note: Addition is only defined for matrices of the same size. The $m \times n$ *zero matrix*, 0, is defined as the $m \times n$ matrix with every element zero.† From the definitions the algebraic properties that follow can be easily proved.

† Strictly, we should distinguish between the zero matrix $0_{m, n}$ and the ordinary number 0. In practice, however, confusion does not arise.

(It is assumed that A, B, C are $m \times n$ matrices.)

(1) A + B = B + A (commutative law)
(2) A + (B + C) = (A + B) + C (associative law)
(3) A + 0 = A where 0 is the $m \times n$ zero matrix.
(4) Given any $m \times n$ matrix A there is an $m \times n$ matrix −A such that
     A + (−A) = 0.

Specimen proof. To prove any algebraic property of matrices it is necessary to establish three things: (a) that each side of the equation does in fact exist; (b) that the matrices obtained on each side are of the same size and hence comparable; (c) that the corresponding pairs of elements in these matrices are equal.

To prove (1): Let A + B = C,   + A = D.

Since A and B are both $m \times n$ matrices, A + B is defined and is an $m \times n$ matrix.

Similarly B + A is a well defined $m \times n$ matrix. Hence C and D both exist and are comparable.

$$c_{ij} = a_{ij} + b_{ij} = b_{ij} + a_{ij} = d_{ij} \quad \text{for all relevant } i, j.$$

Hence C = D or A + B = B + A.

Subtraction. Property (4) above provides a method of defining the subtraction of two $m \times n$ matrices. If A and B are both $m \times n$ matrices we define A − B as A + (−B) where −B is the $m \times n$ matrix whose 'typical' element is $-b_{ij}$.

7.1.3 *Multiplication by a scalar*

Definition 2. Let A be an $m \times n$ matrix and λ be a scalar (or number). An $m \times n$ matrix B = λA is then defined by the equations $b_{ij} = \lambda a_{ij}$ for all i, j such that $1 \leqslant i \leqslant m,\ 1 \leqslant j \leqslant n$.

Example.

$$A = \begin{pmatrix} 1 & 2 & 0 \\ -1 & 2 & 3 \end{pmatrix} \quad \lambda A = \begin{pmatrix} \lambda & 2\lambda & 0 \\ -\lambda & 2\lambda & 3\lambda \end{pmatrix}$$

In particular, taking $\lambda = 3$, we have

$$3A = \begin{pmatrix} 3 & 6 & 0 \\ -3 & 6 & 9 \end{pmatrix}$$

From the definition the following algebraic properties can be deduced:

(1) $\lambda(A + B) = \lambda A + \dot{\lambda} B$
(2) $(\lambda + \mu)A = \lambda A + \mu A$
(3) $0 \cdot A = 0_{m,n}$
(4) $\lambda(\mu A) = (\lambda\mu)A$
(5) $1 \cdot A = A$

(It is assumed that A and B are $m \times n$ matrices and λ, μ are scalars.)

7.1.4 *The product of two matrices*

The definitions given so far for equality, addition, subtraction and scalar multiplication of matrices will appear to be quite natural. It would be tempting to define the product of two matrices in a similar way (that is, by multiplying together pairs of corresponding elements). Although this would offer the simplest definition it would have few, if any, applications and a definition suited to the practical applications of matrices is therefore chosen.

Suppose we have three sets of variables $x_1, x_2; y_1, y_2, y_3; z_1, z_2$ related by the following linear equations

$$x_1 = a_{11}y_1 + a_{12}y_2 + a_{13}y_3 \qquad y_1 = b_{11}z_1 + b_{12}z_2$$
$$x_2 = a_{21}y_1 + a_{22}y_2 + a_{23}y_3 \qquad y_2 = b_{21}z_1 + b_{22}z_2$$
$$y_3 = b_{31}z_1 + b_{32}z_2$$

where a_{ij}, b_{ij} are constants for all relevant i, j.

Then the relationship between the variables $X = \begin{pmatrix} x_1 \\ x_2 \end{pmatrix}$ and $Y = \begin{pmatrix} y_1 \\ y_2 \\ y_3 \end{pmatrix}$ is determined by the 2×3 matrix $A = \begin{pmatrix} a_{11} & a_{12} & a_{13} \\ a_{21} & a_{22} & a_{23} \end{pmatrix}$. The relationship between Y and the variable $Z = \begin{pmatrix} z_1 \\ z_2 \end{pmatrix}$ is determined by the 3×2 matrix $B = \begin{pmatrix} b_{11} & b_{12} \\ b_{21} & b_{22} \\ b_{31} & b_{32} \end{pmatrix}$

These relations could be expressed more briefly as: $X = AY$, $Y = BZ$. (For the time being, $X = AY$ is merely a convenient shorthand notation for the above set of equations since the product of two matrices has yet to be defined.) There is an implicit relationship between the variables x_1, x_2 and the variables z_1, z_2; suppose this is expressed in terms of a matrix C as $X = CZ$. It would now be convenient to have the matrix product defined in such a way that $C = AB$ so that $X = A(BZ) = ABZ$. Carrying out the linear substitutions necessary to express X in terms of Z suggests the method of defining a matrix product.

Substitution for y_1, y_2, y_3 gives

$$x_1 = a_{11}(b_{11}z_1 + b_{12}z_2) + a_{12}(b_{21}z_1 + b_{22}z_2) + a_{13}(b_{31}z_1 + b_{32}z_2)$$
$$x_2 = a_{21}(b_{11}z_1 + b_{12}z_2) + a_{22}(b_{21}z_1 + b_{22}z_2) + a_{23}(b_{31}z_1 + b_{32}z_2)$$

These can be re-arranged to give

$$x_1 = (a_{11}b_{11} + a_{12}b_{21} + a_{13}b_{31})z_1 + (a_{11}b_{12} + a_{12}b_{22} + a_{13}b_{32})z_2$$
$$x_2 = (a_{21}b_{11} + a_{22}b_{21} + a_{23}b_{31})z_1 + (a_{21}b_{12} + a_{22}b_{22} + a_{23}b_{32})z_2$$

These equations can be compared with

$$x_1 = c_{11}z_1 + c_{12}z_2 \quad \text{or} \quad X = CZ$$
$$x_2 = c_{21}z_1 + c_{22}z_2$$

The comparison shows that, for example

$$c_{12} = a_{11}b_{12} + a_{12}b_{22} + a_{13}b_{32}$$
$$c_{22} = a_{21}b_{12} + a_{22}b_{22} + a_{23}b_{32}$$

and the general relationship between the coefficients is

$$c_{ij} = a_{i1}b_{1j} + a_{i2}b_{2j} + a_{i3}b_{3j} \quad \text{for } i = 1, 2; j = 1, 2$$

This equation is used to define the product of the 2 × 3 matrix A and the 3 × 2 matrix B to give the 2 × 2 matrix C = AB.

Formal definition. Let A be an $m \times n$ matrix and B an $n \times p$ matrix. The product C = AB is then an $m \times p$ matrix defined by the equations

$$c_{ij} = a_{i1}b_{1j} + a_{i2}b_{2j} + \cdots + a_{in}b_{nj}$$

$$= \sum_{k=1}^{n} a_{ik}b_{kj}$$

for $i = 1, 2, \ldots, m; j = 1, 2, \ldots, p$.

Notes. The element c_{ij} in the ith row and jth column of the product AB is obtained by adding together the products of pairs of corresponding elements of the ith row of A and the jth column of B. c_{ij} can then be considered as the 'product' of the ith row of A and the jth column of B (see figure 7.1).

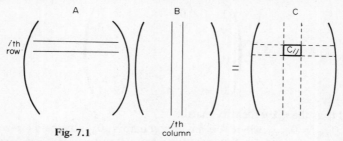

Fig. 7.1

The product AB is only defined if the number of columns of A is equal to the number of rows of B. If this condition is satisfied AB has the same number of rows as A and the same number of columns as B.

Examples

(i) $A = \begin{pmatrix} 2 & 3 & 4 \\ 1 & 2 & 0 \\ 2 & 3 & 1 \end{pmatrix}$ $B = \begin{pmatrix} 2 & 1 \\ -3 & 2 \\ 0 & -5 \end{pmatrix}$ $AB = \begin{pmatrix} -5 & -12 \\ -4 & 5 \\ -5 & 3 \end{pmatrix}$

BA is undefined since B has 2 columns and A has 3 rows.

(ii) $C = \begin{pmatrix} 1 & 2 \\ -1 & 3 \end{pmatrix}$ $D = \begin{pmatrix} 3 & 1 \\ 4 & 2 \end{pmatrix}$ $CD = \begin{pmatrix} 11 & 5 \\ 9 & 5 \end{pmatrix}$ $DC = \begin{pmatrix} 2 & 9 \\ 2 & 14 \end{pmatrix}$

(iii) $E = \begin{pmatrix} 2 & 3 & -1 \\ 1 & 4 & 6 \end{pmatrix}$ $I = \begin{pmatrix} 1 & 0 & 0 \\ 0 & 1 & 0 \\ 0 & 0 & 1 \end{pmatrix}$ $EI = \begin{pmatrix} 2 & 3 & -1 \\ 1 & 4 & 6 \end{pmatrix}$

Properties of matrix products. The definition of matrix products is not directly related to the multiplication of real numbers. Consequently it must not be automatically assumed that matrices will obey all the elementary algebraic laws. The following properties can be proved directly from the definition of the product of two matrices.

(1) (Associative law) $(AB)C = A(BC)$, where A is any $m \times n$ matrix, B any $n \times p$ matrix and C any $p \times q$ matrix.

(2) (Distributive laws) (i) $A(B + C) = AB + AC$, and (ii) $(D + E)A = DA + EA$, where A is any $m \times n$ matrix, B and C are any $n \times p$ matrices, and D and E are any $l \times m$ matrices.

(3) $I_m A = A$, $AI_n = A$, where A is any $m \times n$ matrix, I_m is the $m \times m$ *identity matrix*

$$I_m = \begin{pmatrix} 1 & 0 & 0 & . & . & . & 0 \\ 0 & 1 & 0 & . & . & . & 0 \\ . & & & & & & \\ . & & & & & & \\ . & & & & & & \\ 0 & . & . & . & . & 0 & 1 \end{pmatrix}$$

and I_n is the $n \times n$ identity matrix.

(4) $A \cdot 0_{n \times p} = 0_{m \times p}$, where A is any $m \times n$ matrix, $0_{n \times p}$ is the $n \times p$ zero matrix (with all its elements zero), and $0_{m \times p}$ is the $m \times p$ zero matrix.

(5) $A(\lambda B) = \lambda(AB) = (\lambda A) \cdot B$ for any $m \times n$ matrix A, any $n \times p$ matrix B and any scalar λ.

Specimen proofs

(2) (i) Suppose A is an $m \times n$ matrix, B, C are $n \times p$ matrices. Then $B + C = D$ is a well defined $n \times p$ matrix and the product $A(B + C) = AD$ exists, and is an $m \times p$ matrix.

Also $AB = F$, $AC = G$ are well defined $m \times p$ matrices, and $H = F + G$ is again an $m \times p$ matrix.

We have thus established that the two sides of equation $A(B + C) = AB + AC$ exist and are comparable.

Let $A(B + C) = AD = E$.

Then by the definition of a matrix product we have

$$e_{ij} = \sum_{k=1}^{n} a_{ik} d_{kj} = \sum_{k=1}^{n} a_{ik}(b_{kj} + c_{kj}) \quad \text{for } i = 1, 2, \ldots, m \\ j = 1, 2, \ldots, p$$

$$= \sum_{k=1}^{n} a_{ik} b_{kj} + \sum_{k=1}^{n} a_{ij} c_{kj} = f_{ij} + g_{ij} \quad \text{(since } F = AB \\ G = AC)$$

$$= h_{ij} \quad \text{(since } H = F + G).$$

Hence $E = H$ or $A(B + C) = AB + AC$.

(2) (ii) is proved in a similar way.

(3) To prove $I_m A = A$.

I_m is the $m \times m$ matrix whose typical element is δ_{ij}, where δ_{ij} (the *Kronecker delta*) is defined as

$$\delta_{ij} = 0 \quad \text{if } i \neq j$$
$$\delta_{ij} = 1 \quad \text{if } i = j$$

Since I_m is an $m \times m$ matrix and A is an $m \times n$ matrix the product $I_m A$ exists and is an $m \times n$ matrix. Let $I_m A = B$.

Then, from the definition of a matrix product, we have,

$$b_{ij} = \sum_{k=1}^{n} \delta_{ik} a_{kj} = \delta_{ii} a_{ij} = a_{ij} \quad \text{(since } \delta_{ik} = 0 \text{ unless } k = i\text{)}$$

Thus $\qquad\qquad$ B = A $\qquad$ or $\qquad$ $I_m A = A$

Similarly $\qquad\qquad\qquad\qquad$ $AI_n = A$

Note. It is usual to omit the suffixes *m, n,* and to write the equations IA = A, AI = A, it being understood that the appropriate size of square identity matrix I is chosen in each case.

Exceptional properties of matrices

(a) $AB \neq BA$

This is to say that in general AB will not be equal to BA. Unless A and B are both square matrices of the same size AB and BA will not be comparable (they need not even both exist; see example (i) above). In the special case when A and B are both $n \times n$ matrices it is still not generally true that AB = BA. A counter-example is provided by example (ii) above.

If, in fact AB = BA the pair of matrices A and B are said to *commute.* In particular, all square matrices commute with the identity matrix and the $n \times n$ zero matrix.

Since matrices do not in general commute care must be taken when manipulating matrix products to keep the matrices in the correct order; for example,

$$(A + B)^2 = A^2 + AB + BA + B^2 \neq A^2 + 2AB + B^2$$

and $\qquad\qquad\qquad\qquad$ $ABA \neq A^2 B$

(b) AB = 0 does not necessarily imply that A = 0 or B = 0

Real numbers have the well-known property that if *a* and *b* are numbers such that $a \cdot b = 0$ then either $a = 0$ or $b = 0$. This is expressed symbolically as $a \cdot b = 0 \Rightarrow a = 0$ or $b = 0$. The corresponding property is not in general true for matrices as the example below shows.

Let $A = \begin{pmatrix} 1 & 2 & 1 \\ 2 & 4 & 2 \\ -3 & -6 & -3 \end{pmatrix}$ and $B = \begin{pmatrix} -1 & 2 & 1 \\ 1 & -2 & -1 \\ -1 & 2 & 1 \end{pmatrix}$;

then $AB = 0$.

As a consequence of this property it is not always possible to conclude for matrices that if $AB = AC$ then $B = C$.

$(AB = AC \Rightarrow A(B - C) = 0$, but this may be possible with $B - C \neq 0)$

This cancellation law is only valid if A is a *non-singular* or *regular* matrix, terms which will be defined in section 7.3.

7.1.5 *The transpose of a matrix*

Let A be any $n \times m$ matrix; the *transpose of* A, denoted A' (or by some authors A^T), is an $n \times m$ matrix obtained from A by interchanging rows and columns. More precisely, if α_{ij} is the element in the ith row and jth column of A' then $\alpha_{ij} = a_{ji}$ for all i, j. A square matrix A such that $A' = A$ is said to be *symmetric*.

A square matrix B such that $B' = -B$ is said to be *skew-symmetric* or *anti-symmetric*.

Symmetric matrices play an important part in the theory of quadric surfaces in geometry and in the theory of moments and products of inertia.

Examples

$$A = \begin{pmatrix} 5 & 1 & 2 \\ 2 & 3 & 4 \end{pmatrix} A' = \begin{pmatrix} 5 & 2 \\ 1 & 3 \\ 2 & 4 \end{pmatrix}$$

$B = \begin{pmatrix} 1 & 2 & -1 \\ 2 & 2 & 5 \\ -1 & 5 & 4 \end{pmatrix}$ is a symmetric matrix, since $B' = B$

$C = \begin{pmatrix} 0 & 1 & -2 \\ -1 & 0 & 3 \\ 2 & -3 & 0 \end{pmatrix}$ is skew-symmetric, since $C' = -C$

Properties of the transpose
(1) $(A + B)' = A' + B'$, where A and B are $m \times n$ matrices
(2) $(AB)' = B'A'$ where A is an $m \times n$ matrix, B an $n \times p$ matrix

Exercises

1. $A = \begin{pmatrix} 2 & -1 & 2 \\ 3 & 4 & 7 \\ 2 & 1 & 2 \end{pmatrix}$ $B = \begin{pmatrix} 5 & 1 \\ 4 & 3 \\ -3 & -1 \end{pmatrix}$ $C = \begin{pmatrix} 3 & 1 \\ -4 & 2 \end{pmatrix}$

    State which of the products AB, BA, AC, BC, CA, CB are well defined. Find the values of those which are defined.

2. For the matrices given in question 1 verify that $(AB)C = A(BC)$.

3. Expand the following expressions, where A and B are $n \times n$ matrices which do not commute and I is the $n \times n$ identity matrix.

    (i) $(A + B)(A - B)$
    (ii) $(A - B)^3$
    (iii) $(A + I)^3$

4. Verify that the matrices $A = \begin{pmatrix} 1 & 0 & 1 \\ -1 & 2 & 0 \\ 1 & -1 & 1 \end{pmatrix}$ $B = \begin{pmatrix} 2 & -1 & 2 \\ -3 & 4 & -1 \\ 3 & -3 & 2 \end{pmatrix}$ commute.

5. A diagonal matrix is a square matrix A with $a_{ij} = 0$ if $i \neq j$. Prove that if D and E are any two $n \times n$ diagonal matrices then they commute.

6. A matrix P is said to be orthogonal if it satisfies the equation $PP' = I$. Verify that the matrix P given below is orthogonal

    $$P = \begin{pmatrix} \dfrac{1}{\sqrt{3}} & \dfrac{1}{\sqrt{6}} & -\dfrac{1}{\sqrt{2}} \\ \dfrac{1}{\sqrt{3}} & -\dfrac{2}{\sqrt{6}} & 0 \\ \dfrac{1}{\sqrt{3}} & \dfrac{1}{\sqrt{6}} & \dfrac{1}{\sqrt{2}} \end{pmatrix}$$

7. If A is any $n \times n$ matrix prove that the matrix $A + A'$ is symmetric and the matrix $A - A'$ is skew-symmetric. Deduce that A can always be expressed uniquely in the form $A = B + C$, where B is symmetric and C is skew-symmetric.

8. If $A = \begin{pmatrix} 1 & -2 & -6 \\ -3 & 2 & 9 \\ 2 & 0 & -3 \end{pmatrix}$

    find the values of A^2 and A^3. Deduce the values of A^{17} and A^{123}.

9. If $J = \begin{pmatrix} 0 & 1 \\ -1 & 0 \end{pmatrix}$ show that $J^2 = -I$.

    If α and β are scalars, prove that $(\alpha I + \beta J)^2 = (\alpha^2 - \beta^2)I + 2\alpha\beta J$. Hence find a 2×2 matrix X such that $X^2 = J$.

10. The trace of a square matrix A is defined to be the sum of the diagonal elements of A. Prove that if A and B are any 3×3 matrices then trace $(AB) =$ trace (BA).

7.2 Theory of linear equations

The system

$$a_{11}x_1 + a_{12}x_2 + \cdots + a_{1n}x_n = c_1$$
$$a_{21}x_1 + a_{22}x_2 + \cdots + a_{2n}x_n = c_2$$
$$\cdot$$
$$\cdot$$
$$\cdot$$
$$a_{m1}x_1 + a_{m2}x_2 + \cdots + a_{mn}x_n = c_m$$

of m linear equations in n unknowns can be written in matrix form as $AX = C$, where A is the $m \times n$ matrix of coefficients, X is the $n \times 1$ matrix or *column vector* $X = \begin{pmatrix} x_1 \\ x_2 \\ \cdot \\ \cdot \\ \cdot \\ x_n \end{pmatrix}$ and C is the constant column vector $C = \begin{pmatrix} c_1 \\ c_2 \\ \cdot \\ \cdot \\ \cdot \\ c_m \end{pmatrix}$

The solutions of the above system of equations are closely linked to those of the related *homogeneous* system $AX = 0$. This relationship is established in the first two theorems below.

7.2.1 *Theorem 1*

If $X = Y = \begin{pmatrix} y_1 \\ \cdot \\ \cdot \\ \cdot \\ y_n \end{pmatrix}$ is any solution to the homogeneous set of equations $AX = 0$,

then $X = \lambda Y$ is also a solution for any value of the scalar constant λ. If $X = Z$ is a further solution then so is $X = Y + Z$.

Proof. Since $X = Y$ is a solution of $AX = 0$, we have $AY = 0$. Substituting $X = \lambda Y$ into the equation gives $AX = A(\lambda Y) = \lambda(AY) = \lambda \cdot 0 = 0$, showing that λY is a solution for all values of λ.

Since $X = Y$, $X = Z$, are both solutions, we have $AY = 0$ and $AZ = 0$; substituting $X = Y + Z$ gives $AX = A(Y + Z) = AY + AZ = 0 + 0 = 0$. Hence, $X = Y + Z$ is a further solution.

Note. The equation $AX = 0$ is always soluble since $X = 0$ is a solution. This is called the *trivial solution*; any solution other than $X = 0$ is called a *non-trivial solution*. An immediate consequence of theorem 1 is that if the homogeneous system $AX = 0$ has a non-trivial solution then it has an infinite number of distinct solutions.

7.2.2 Theorem 2
If $X = Y$ is any particular solution to the non-homogeneous system $AX = C$, and if $X = Z$ is a non-trivial solution of the related homogeneous equations $AX = 0$, then a more general solution of the non-homogeneous equations is $X = Y + \lambda Z$, where λ is an arbitrarily chosen scalar.

Proof. Since $X = Y$ is a solution of $AX = C$ then $AY = C$. Since $X = Z$ is a solution of $AX = 0$ then by theorem 1 so is $X = \lambda Z$. Substitution of $X = Y + \lambda Z$ gives:

$$AX = A(Y + \lambda Z) = AY + A(\lambda Z) = C + 0 = C$$

Hence $X = Y + \lambda Z$ is a more general solution of $AX = C$.

Converse to Theorem 2. If the equations $AX = C$ have two distinct solutions then the corresponding homogeneous system has a non-trivial solution.

The proof of this result is left as an exercise for the reader.

Deductions from theorems 1 and 2. Consider the equations $AX = C$, where A is an $m \times n$ matrix. As a consequence of theorems 1 and 2 there are three mutually exclusive possibilities for the existence of solutions to these equations:

(i) $AX = C$ has a unique solution; in this case $AX = 0$ can have only the trivial solution.

(ii) $AX = C$ has no solution; the equations are incompatible.

(iii) $AX = C$ has an infinite number of solutions and $AX = 0$ has a non-trivial solution.

From this it can be seen that it is of critical importance to know whether or not $AX = 0$ has a non-trivial solution. This is the next problem to be considered.

Examples

1. The equations $2x_1 - x_2 + x_3 = 0$
   $$x_1 - x_2 + 2x_3 = 0$$
   $$x_1 + x_2 - 4x_3 = 0$$

have the non-trivial solution $x_1 = 1$, $x_2 = 3$, $x_3 = 1$,

or $X = \begin{pmatrix} 1 \\ 3 \\ 1 \end{pmatrix}$; then $X = \begin{pmatrix} \lambda \\ 3\lambda \\ \lambda \end{pmatrix}$, or $x_1 = \lambda$, $x_2 = 3\lambda$, $x_3 = \lambda$, is a solution of the

equations for any value of λ.

The equations $2x_1 - x_2 + x_3 = 3$
   $$x_1 - x_2 + 2x_3 = 1$$
   $$x_1 + x_2 - 4x_3 = 3$$

have the solution $x_1 = 2$, $x_2 = 1$, $x_3 = 0$; combining this with the solution of
the related homogeneous equations above we obtain, as a more general
solution, $x_1 = 2 + \lambda$, $x_2 = 1 + 3\lambda$, $x_3 = \lambda$, for any value of the parameter λ.
(This example illustrates the application of theorems 1 and 2.)

2. The equations $x_1 + x_2 = c_1$
   $$x_1 - x_2 = c_2$$

have the unique solution $x_1 = \dfrac{c_1 + c_2}{2}$, $x_2 = \dfrac{c_1 - c_2}{2}$, for any values of c_1 and c_2.

The related homogeneous equations

$$x_1 + x_2 = 0$$
$$x_1 - x_2 = 0$$

have only the trivial solution $x_1 = x_2 = 0$.

7.2.3 *Theorem 3*

The set of m homogeneous equations in n unknowns, $AX = 0$, always has a
non-trivial solution if $m < n$.

Proof. The proof is by induction on m.
When $m = 1$ the set of equations is

$$a_{11}x_1 + a_{12}x_2 + \cdots + a_{1n}x_n = 0$$

In this equation we assume that all coefficients are non-zero (otherwise the
corresponding variable would not appear).
   Then

$$x_1 = a_{12}, \quad x_2 = -a_{11}, \quad x_3 = \cdots = x_n = 0$$

gives a non-trivial solution.

Suppose now that the theorem is true for all sets of $m - 1$ equations in a greater number of unknowns. Consider the equations

$$a_{11}x_1 + a_{12}x_2 + \cdots + a_{1n}x_n = 0$$
$$a_{21}x_1 + a_{22}x_2 + \cdots + a_{2n}x_n = 0$$

where $n > m$

$$a_{m1}x_1 + a_{m2}x_2 + \cdots + a_{mn}x_n = 0$$

In at least one of these equations x_n must appear with a non-zero coefficient; rearranging the order of the equations, if necessary, we may assume that $a_{mn} \neq 0$. Let

$$x_n = \frac{-1}{a_{mn}}(a_{m1}x_1 + a_{m2}x_2 + \cdots + a_{mn-1}x_{n-1})$$

The final equation is then satisfied for any values of $x_1, x_2, \ldots, x_{n-1}$. Substitution of this value of x_n into the previous equations gives a set of $m - 1$ equations in the $n - 1$ unknowns $x_1, x_2, \ldots, x_{n-1}$.

But $m < n \Rightarrow m - 1 < n - 1$; hence by our assumption (the induction hypothesis) these equations have a non-trivial solution.

Substitution of this solution into the expression for x_n gives a non-trivial solution of the original set of m equations.

Hence, by induction, the theorem is proved.

Corollary. Combining the result of theorem 3 with the deductions from theorems 1 and 2 we have the following corollary:

The set $AX = C$ of m non-homogeneous equations in n unknowns can never have a unique solution if $m < n$.

7.2.4 *Case of n equations in n unknowns*

In this case the homogeneous equations $AX = 0$ may, or may not, have a non-trivial solution, depending upon the matrix of coefficients.

A simple example will suffice to show that on occasions n homogeneous equations in n unknowns can have a non-trivial solution.

Examples

(a) Equations: $\left.\begin{array}{l} x_1 - x_2 = 0 \\ x_1 + x_2 = 0 \end{array}\right\}$ have only the trivial solution

(b) Equations: $\left.\begin{array}{l} x_1 - 2x_2 = 0 \\ -2x_1 + 4x_2 = 0 \end{array}\right\}$ have the non-trivial solution $x_1 = 2, \; x_2 = 1$.

Considering the related non-homogeneous equations we have:

(a) $\left.\begin{array}{l} x_1 - x_2 = c_1 \\ x_1 + x_2 = c_2 \end{array}\right\}$ The solution $x_1 = \dfrac{c_1 + c_2}{2}$, $x_2 = \dfrac{c_1 - c_2}{2}$ exists and is unique for all c_1, c_2.

(b) $\left.\begin{array}{l} -x_1 + 2x_2 = -5 \\ -2x_1 + 4x_2 = \ 6 \end{array}\right\}$ These equations are insoluble.

$\left.\begin{array}{l} -x_1 + 2x_2 = -2 \\ -2x_1 + 4x_2 = -4 \end{array}\right\}$ These have solutions $x_1 = 4 + 2\lambda$, $x_2 = 1 + \lambda$ for any value of λ.

In this case the distinction between having no solutions and having an infinite number of solutions depends upon the values of the constants on the right-hand side of the equations. (In fact the coefficients in the second equation are precisely twice the coefficients in the first equation and unless the constants are similarly related the equations will be incompatible.) Geometrically the equations $x_1 - x_2 = c_1$, $x_1 + x_2 = c_2$ represent a pair of non-parallel lines in the (x_1, x_2) plane; for any values of c_1 and c_2 these lines are bound to meet at a unique point which is the solution of this pair of equations. On the other hand $x_1 - 2x_2 = k_1$, $-2x_1 + 4x_2 = k_2$, represent a pair of lines which are either parallel (if $k_2 \neq -2k_1$), or coincident, having an infinite number of common points, (if $k_2 = -2k_1$).

In the case of two equations in two unknowns it is a relatively easy matter to spot incompatible equations, but as the number of equations and unknowns increases this becomes very difficult unless a systematic method is used. Such a method of recognising incompatible equations, and at the same time obtaining solutions if the equations are compatible, is outlined below. The case of n homogeneous equations in n unknowns is considered further in section 7.2.6.

7.2.5 *Use of augmented matrix and row operations to solve linear equations*
The values of the solutions of the set $AX = C$ of m equations in n unknowns depends only upon the values of A and C; the actual symbols used for the unknowns are irrelevant. As a first step in the calculation the *augmented matrix* is introduced. This is the $m \times (n + 1)$ matrix

$$A_1 = \begin{pmatrix} a_{11} & a_{12} & . & . & . & a_{1n} & c_1 \\ a_{21} & a_{22} & . & . & . & a_{2n} & c_2 \\ . & . & . & . & . & . & . \\ a_{m1} & & & & & a_{mn} & c_m \end{pmatrix}$$

This augmented matrix contains all the information given by the system of equations.

In elementary methods of solving linear equations it is usual to attempt to eliminate some of the unknowns by means of one or more of the following operations:

(i) Re-arranging the order of the equations.
(ii) Multiplying (or dividing) any equation by a non-zero constant.
(iii) Adding (or subtracting) any multiple of one equation to (or from) another.

In the augmented matrix the rows correspond to the equations in the original system. The following *elementary row operations* are introduced, corresponding to the three operations listed above:

(I) Interchange two rows.
(II) Multiply by any row a non-zero constant.
(III) Add to any row a multiple of another.

If a matrix B_1 is obtained from a matrix A_1 by a sequence of elementary row operations we say that B_1 is *row-equivalent* to A_1.
Since the elementary row operations are reversible, A_1 is also row-equivalent to B_1.
Row-equivalent augmented matrices will correspond to equivalent systems of linear equations (that is, systems having precisely the same set of solutions).
The basis of the method is to use row operations to reduce the augmented matrix A_1 to a particularly simple form, called the *row-echelon* form, in which successive rows contain an increasing number of zeros in the leading positions. For an augmented matrix in echelon form it is a simple matter to obtain the solutions of the corresponding set of equations or to determine that the equations are incompatible. The method is best illustrated by examples.

Examples
(1) Solve, if possible, the equations

$$x_1 + 2x_2 - x_3 = 4$$
$$2x_1 + 3x_2 - x_3 = 2$$
$$-x_1 + x_2 + 3x_3 = -1$$

The corresponding augmented matrix is

$$A_1 = \begin{pmatrix} 1 & 2 & -1 & | & 4 \\ 2 & 3 & -1 & | & 2 \\ -1 & 1 & 3 & | & -1 \end{pmatrix}$$

The object is to reduce this matrix to row-echelon form by the use of elementary row operations. This is done systematically by first obtaining zeros in all positions lower than the first in the first column, then obtaining zeros in all positions lower than the second in the second column, and so on. At each stage of the calculation a note is made of the row operations performed. (For example, $R_2 - 2R_1$ refers to the operation of subtracting twice the first row from the second in order to obtain the next matrix.)

$$\begin{pmatrix} 1 & 2 & -1 & | & 4 \\ 2 & 3 & -1 & | & 2 \\ -1 & 1 & 3 & | & -1 \end{pmatrix} \begin{matrix} \\ \sim R_2 - 2R_1 \\ R_3 + R_1 \end{matrix} \begin{pmatrix} 1 & 2 & -1 & | & 4 \\ 0 & -1 & 1 & | & -6 \\ 0 & 3 & 2 & | & 3 \end{pmatrix} \begin{matrix} \\ \sim \\ R_3 + 3R_2 \end{matrix} \begin{pmatrix} 1 & 2 & -1 & | & 4 \\ 0 & -1 & 1 & | & -6 \\ 0 & 0 & 5 & | & -15 \end{pmatrix}$$

The final augmented matrix B_1 corresponds to the equations:

$$\left. \begin{matrix} x_1 + 2x_2 - x_3 = 4 \\ -x_2 + x_3 = -6 \\ 5x_3 = -15 \end{matrix} \right\}$$ By back substitution the solution is $x_3 = -3, x_2 = 3, x_1 = -5$.

Note. As far as possible the first row is used as an operator when introducing zeros into the first column, the second row for the second column, etc. If at any stage there is a zero in the critical position it is necessary to interchange this row with a lower row before continuing. Operations using the same row as operator may be carried out simultaneously. The symbol, $\sim$, denotes 'is row-equivalent to'.

(2) Solve, if possible, the equations

$$\begin{matrix} x_1 - x_2 + 2x_3 - x_4 = 1 \\ 2x_1 - 2x_2 + x_3 + 2x_4 = 3 \\ 3x_1 - 2x_2 - 3x_3 + 4x_4 = -1 \end{matrix}$$

Since this is a set of 3 equations in 4 unknowns the solution, if it exists, cannot be unique; however, the same method can be used to find this solution. The augmented matrix is

$$A_1 = \begin{pmatrix} 1 & -1 & 2 & -1 & | & 1 \\ 2 & -2 & 1 & 2 & | & 3 \\ 3 & -2 & -3 & 4 & | & -1 \end{pmatrix} \begin{matrix} \\ \sim R_2 - 2R_1 \\ R_3 - 3R_1 \end{matrix} \begin{pmatrix} 1 & -1 & 2 & -1 & | & 1 \\ 0 & 0 & -3 & 4 & | & 1 \\ 0 & 1 & -9 & 7 & | & -4 \end{pmatrix}$$

$$\sim R_2 \leftrightarrow R_3 \begin{pmatrix} 1 & -1 & 2 & -1 & | & 1 \\ 0 & 1 & -9 & 7 & | & -4 \\ 0 & 0 & -3 & 4 & | & 1 \end{pmatrix} = B_1$$

The matrix B_1 is now in echelon form and no further reduction is possible. The final row of B_1 now corresponds to the equation $-3x_3 + 4x_4 = 1$. This has no unique solution, but letting $x_4 = \lambda$ (an arbitrary constant) gives $x_3 = 4/3\lambda - 1/3$.

Substituting into the equations corresponding to the second and first rows of B_1 gives the general solution

$$x_1 = \frac{10}{3}\lambda - \frac{16}{3}, \quad x_2 = 5\lambda - 7, \quad x_3 = \frac{4}{3}\lambda - \frac{1}{3}, \quad x_4 = \lambda$$

(3) Show that the equations below are only compatible for one value of k. For this value of k find the solution.

$$x_1 + 3x_2 + 2x_3 = 3$$
$$3x_1 + 7x_2 + 5x_3 = 5$$
$$2x_1 + 4x_2 + 3x_3 = k$$

The augmented matrix is

$$A_1 = \begin{pmatrix} 1 & 3 & 2 & | & 3 \\ 3 & 7 & 5 & | & 5 \\ 2 & 4 & 3 & | & k \end{pmatrix} \underset{\substack{R_2-3R_1 \\ R_3-2R_1}}{\sim} \begin{pmatrix} 1 & 3 & 2 & | & 3 \\ 0 & -2 & -1 & | & -4 \\ 0 & -2 & -1 & | & k-6 \end{pmatrix} \underset{R_3-R_2}{\sim} \begin{pmatrix} 1 & 3 & 2 & | & 3 \\ 0 & -2 & -1 & | & -4 \\ 0 & 0 & 0 & | & k-2 \end{pmatrix}$$

Since the last row of the echelon matrix corresponds to the equation $0x_1 + 0x_2 + 0x_3 = k - 2$, the equations are incompatible unless $k = 2$. For $k = 2$ the solutions are: $x_3 = \lambda, x_2 = 2 - \lambda/2, x_1 = -3 - \lambda/2$.

Note. Examples (1) and (3) illustrate all the various alternative possibilities for the solution of 3 equations in 3 unknowns. Generalising these results to the case of n equations in n unknowns we have:

If the matrix A of coefficientes is row equivalent to an echelon matrix of the form:

$$\begin{pmatrix} b_{11} & b_{12} & b_{13} & \cdots & b_{1n} \\ 0 & b_{22} & b_{23} & \cdots & b_{2n} \\ 0 & 0 & b_{33} & \cdots & b_{3n} \\ \cdot & \cdot & \cdot & \cdots & \cdot \\ 0 & 0 & 0 & \cdots & b_{nn} \end{pmatrix}$$

where all the diagonal elements $b_{11}, b_{22}, \ldots, b_{nn}$ are non-zero, then a unique solution to the equations $AX = C$ can be obtained for all values of C (including $C = 0$). If, on the other hand, A is row equivalent to an echelon matrix with $b_{nn} = 0$ the existence of a solution will depend upon the values of $c_1, c_2, \ldots, c_n$ and will in any case not be unique. $AX = 0$ will in this case have a non-trivial solution (by theorem 3) since the system is equivalent to a set of $n - 1$ homogeneous equations in n unknowns.

7.2.6 *The determinant of an* $n \times n$ *matrix*

It has previously been noted that for a system of n homogeneous equations in n unknowns the existence, or otherwise, of a non-trivial solution depends upon the matrix of coefficients. The *determinant* of an $n \times n$ matrix is a number so defined that it is zero if the corresponding homogeneous equations have a non-trivial solution and is non-zero otherwise. We shall deduce the definition of a determinant from this property. The determinant of the $n \times n$ matrix A is denoted by $|A|$.

1 × 1 determinant. The equation $a_{11}x_1 = 0$ has a non-trivial solution only if $a_{11} = 0$; hence we define the 1×1 determinant as $|a_{11}| = a_{11}$.

2 × 2 determinant. Consider the equations

$$a_{11}x_1 + a_{12}x_2 = 0$$
$$a_{21}x_1 + a_{22}x_2 = 0$$

For these to have a non-trivial solution, the coefficient matrix A must be row-equivalent to an echelon matrix with zero final row.

$$\begin{pmatrix} a_{11} & a_{12} \\ a_{21} & a_{22} \end{pmatrix} \sim \begin{pmatrix} a_{11} & a_{12} \\ 0 & a_{22} \quad \dfrac{-a_{12}a_{21}}{a_{11}} \end{pmatrix} \quad \text{(provided } a_{11} \neq 0)$$

Hence, if $a_{11} \neq 0$, $AX = 0$ has a non-trivial solution only if $a_{11}a_{22} - a_{12}a_{21} = 0$.

Alternatively, if $a_{11} = 0$, A is row-equivalent to an echelon matrix with zero row only if $a_{12} = 0$ or $a_{21} = 0$, and once more this leads to the condition $a_{11}a_{22} - a_{12}a_{21} = 0$. Hence we define

$$\begin{vmatrix} a_{11} & a_{12} \\ a_{21} & a_{22} \end{vmatrix} = a_{11}a_{22} - a_{12}a_{21}$$

Cramer's rule for the solution of 2 simultaneous equations. Consider the equations

$$a_{11}x_1 + a_{12}x_2 = c_1$$
$$a_{21}x_1 + a_{22}x_2 = c_2$$

Suppose $|A| \neq 0$, $a_{11} \neq 0$.

Solving these equations by the augmented matrix method gives

$$\left(\begin{array}{cc|c} a_{11} & a_{12} & c_1 \\ a_{21} & a_{22} & c_2 \end{array} \right) \sim \left(\begin{array}{cc|c} a_{11} & a_{12} & c_1 \\ 0 & a_{22} - \dfrac{a_{12}a_{21}}{a_{11}} & c_2 - \dfrac{a_{21}c_1}{a_{11}} \end{array} \right)$$

and so

$$x_2 = \frac{c_2 - \dfrac{a_{21}}{a_{11}} c_1}{a_{22} - \dfrac{a_{12}}{a_{11}} a_{21}} = \frac{a_{11}c_2 - a_{21}c_1}{a_{11}a_{22} - a_{12}a_{21}} = \frac{\begin{vmatrix} a_{11} & c_1 \\ a_{21} & c_2 \end{vmatrix}}{|A|}$$

Similarly,
$$x_1 = \frac{\begin{vmatrix} a_{12} & c_1 \\ a_{22} & c_2 \end{vmatrix}}{\begin{vmatrix} a_{12} & a_{11} \\ a_{22} & a_{21} \end{vmatrix}} = \frac{\begin{vmatrix} c_1 & a_{12} \\ c_2 & a_{22} \end{vmatrix}}{|A|}$$

These solutions are usually expressed in the form

$$\frac{x_1}{\begin{vmatrix} c_1 & a_{12} \\ c_2 & a_{22} \end{vmatrix}} = \frac{x_2}{\begin{vmatrix} a_{11} & c_1 \\ a_{21} & c_2 \end{vmatrix}} = \frac{1}{|A|}$$

this result being a special case of *Cramer's rule*.

3 x 3 determinant. Suppose the equations

$$a_{11}x_1 + a_{12}x_2 + a_{13}x_3 = 0$$
$$a_{21}x_1 + a_{22}x_2 + a_{23}x_3 = 0$$
$$a_{31}x_1 + a_{32}x_2 + a_{33}x_3 = 0$$

have a non-trivial solution.

The last two equations can be re-written

$$a_{21}x_1 + a_{22}x_2 = -a_{23}x_3$$
$$a_{31}x_1 + a_{32}x_2 = -a_{33}x_3$$

Using Cramer's rule the solution of these is

$$\frac{x_1}{\begin{vmatrix} -a_{23} & a_{22} \\ -a_{33} & a_{32} \end{vmatrix}} = \frac{x_2}{\begin{vmatrix} a_{21} & -a_{23} \\ a_{31} & -a_{33} \end{vmatrix}} = \frac{x_3}{\begin{vmatrix} a_{21} & a_{22} \\ a_{31} & a_{32} \end{vmatrix}}$$

or, re-arranging the coefficients so that they appear in the same relative positions as in matrix A and using the easily verified fact that interchanging the columns of a 2 x 2 determinant has the effect of changing its sign; we obtain

$$\frac{x_1}{\begin{vmatrix} a_{22} & a_{23} \\ a_{32} & a_{33} \end{vmatrix}} = \frac{-x_2}{\begin{vmatrix} a_{21} & a_{23} \\ a_{31} & a_{33} \end{vmatrix}} = \frac{x_3}{\begin{vmatrix} a_{21} & a_{22} \\ a_{31} & a_{32} \end{vmatrix}}$$

Substituting these values for $x_1 : x_2 : x_3$ back into the first equation gives as a condition for the existence of a non-trivial solution

$$a_{11}\begin{vmatrix} a_{22} & a_{23} \\ a_{32} & a_{33} \end{vmatrix} - a_{12}\begin{vmatrix} a_{21} & a_{23} \\ a_{31} & a_{33} \end{vmatrix} + a_{13}\begin{vmatrix} a_{21} & a_{22} \\ a_{31} & a_{32} \end{vmatrix} = 0$$

The left-hand side of this equation defines the 3×3 determinant $|A|$.

Note. In this definition the coefficient of a_{11} is the 2×2 determinant obtained by omitting row 1 and column 1 from A, the coefficient of a_{12} is -1 times the 2×2 determinant obtained by omitting row 1 and column 2 from A and the coefficient of a_{13} the 2×2 determinant obtained by omitting row 1 and column 3 from A. A comparison with the definition of the 2×2 determinant shows that it can be expressed in a similar way as $a_{11}|a_{22}| - a_{12}|a_{21}|$.

$n \times n$ determinants. Logically we should now define a 4×4 determinant by first proving Cramer's rule for a set of 3 equations then using this to obtain a condition in terms of 3×3 determinants, for a homogeneous system of 4 equations in 4 unknowns to have a non-trivial solution. Continuing in this way we would obtain definitions of successively larger determinants. The general definition of an $n \times n$ determinant can in fact be written down by following carefully the pattern which emerged from the definitions of the 2×2 and 3×3 determinants above.

Definition.

$$\begin{vmatrix} a_{11} & a_{12} & \cdots & a_{1n} \\ a_{21} & a_{22} & \cdots & a_{2n} \\ \cdot & & & \\ \cdot & & & \\ \cdot & & & \\ a_{n1} & a_{n2} & \cdots & a_{nn} \end{vmatrix} = a_{11}\begin{vmatrix} a_{22} & \cdots & a_{2n} \\ a_{32} & & \\ \cdot & & \\ \cdot & & \\ a_{n2} & \cdots & a_{nn} \end{vmatrix}$$

$$- a_{12}\begin{vmatrix} a_{21} & a_{23} & \cdots & a_{2n} \\ & & & \\ & & & \\ a_{n1} & a_{n3} & \cdots & a_{nn} \end{vmatrix} + a_{13}\begin{vmatrix} a_{21} & a_{22} & a_{24} & \cdots & a_{2n} \\ & & & & \\ a_{n1} & & & & a_{nn} \end{vmatrix}$$

$$+ \cdots + (-1)^{n+1} a_{1n}\begin{vmatrix} a_{21} & \cdots & a_{2n-1} \\ \cdot & & \\ \cdot & & \\ \cdot & & \\ a_{n1} & \cdots & a_{nn-1} \end{vmatrix}$$

This definition is in terms of $(n - 1) \times (n - 1)$ determinants, the coefficient of a_{1j} being $(-1)^{j+1}$ times the determinant obtained from A by omitting row 1 and column j.

7.2.7 *Properties of determinants*

From the definition of an $n \times n$ determinant the following properties can be established. Proofs of these are omitted since they can be found in any suitable algebra text-book.

(1) $|A| = |A'|$ where A' denotes the transpose of matrix A. (This result means that any property of the rows of a determinant will be immediately applicable to the columns.)

(2) If B is obtained from A by interchanging two rows (or columns) then $|B| = -|A|$.

(3) If A has two identical rows or (columns) then $|A| = 0$. (This is a direct consequence of (2).)

(4) If B is obtained from A by multiplying all the elements in one row (or column) by a constant, c, then $|B| = c|A|$.

(5) If B is obtained from A by adding to one row (or column) k times another row (or column) then $|B| = |A|$.

(6) If A and B are any $n \times n$ matrices then $|AB| = |A| \cdot |B|$.

Evaluation of determinants. The $n \times n$ determinant $|A|$ has been defined in terms of the elements of the first row and certain smaller determinants. This is usually referred to as the expansion of the determinant in terms of its first row. In practice this full expansion can be very laborious and the above properties offer some useful short-cuts in this process. An immediate consequence of property (1) is that the expansion could just as well have been defined in terms of the first column (or, as will be seen later, of any row or column). Properties (4) and (5) are particularly useful since they enable constant factors to be removed and the rows and columns manipulated to obtain zero elements in the determinant. If this is done systematically the evaluation of the determinant is facilitated.

Example
Evaluate

$$\begin{vmatrix} 1 & 5 & 7 & -2 \\ 2 & 4 & 3 & 1 \\ -1 & 2 & 8 & 1 \\ 0 & 1 & 3 & 4 \end{vmatrix} = |A|$$

$$\begin{Bmatrix} R_2 - 2R_1 \\ R_3 + R_1 \end{Bmatrix} \text{ gives } |A| = \begin{vmatrix} 1 & 5 & 7 & -2 \\ 0 & -6 & -11 & 5 \\ 0 & 7 & 15 & -1 \\ 0 & 1 & 3 & 4 \end{vmatrix} = \{R_4 \leftrightarrow R_2\} - \begin{vmatrix} 1 & 5 & 7 & -2 \\ 0 & 1 & 3 & 4 \\ 0 & 7 & 15 & -1 \\ 0 & -6 & -11 & 5 \end{vmatrix}$$

$$= \begin{Bmatrix} R_3 - 7R_2 \\ R_4 + 6R_2 \end{Bmatrix} - \begin{vmatrix} 1 & 5 & 7 & -2 \\ 0 & 1 & -3 & -4 \\ 0 & 0 & -6 & -29 \\ 0 & 0 & 7 & 29 \end{vmatrix}$$

Expanding by the first column gives

$$|A| = - \begin{vmatrix} 1 & 3 & 4 \\ 0 & -6 & -29 \\ 0 & 7 & 29 \end{vmatrix} - \begin{vmatrix} -6 & -29 \\ 7 & 29 \end{vmatrix} = -29$$

7.2.8 *Minors and cofactors*

In the full expansion of an $n \times n$ determinant certain $(n-1) \times (n-1)$ determinants occur, and it is convenient to have a name and a notation for these. The $(n-1) \times (n-1)$ determinant obtained by removing the ith row and jth column from an $n \times n$ matrix A is called the *minor* of a_{ij}, usually denoted by M_{ij}.

The coefficient of a_{ij} in the full expansion of $|A|$ is called the *cofactor* of a_{ij} in $|A|$, denoted by A_{ij}.

The minors and cofactors are related by the rule $A_{ij} = (-1)^{i+j} M_{ij}$.

From the definition of the determinant this rule clearly holds for elements of the first row of A; it can be deduced for elements in the ith row, where $i \neq 1$, by repeated application of property (2) (interchange of rows). By a suitable interchange of rows any row can be brought into the first row position, and expanding in terms of this row gives

$$|A| = a_{i1}A_{i1} + a_{i2}A_{i2} + \cdots + a_{in}A_{in} \tag{1}$$

This is the formula for the expansion of A by the ith row. Application of this result to the jth row of A$'$ gives

$$|A| = |A'| = a_{1j}A_{1j} + a_{2j}A_{2j} + a_{3j}A_{3j} + \cdots + a_{nj}A_{nj} \qquad (2)$$

Suppose now that we replace the elements $a_{j1}, a_{j2}, \ldots, a_{jn}$ of the jth row of A by the corresponding elements $a_{i1}, a_{i2}, \ldots, a_{in}$ of the ith row, so that we now have a determinant with two equal rows. The co-factors of the elements of the jth row will be unaffected by this since the elements of this row do not appear in the co-factors. Hence, expanding in terms of the jth row gives

$$a_{i1}A_{j1} + a_{i2}A_{j2} + \cdots + a_{in}A_{jn} = \begin{vmatrix} a_{11} & \cdots & a_{1n} \\ \vdots & & \vdots \\ a_{i1} & & a_{in} \\ \vdots & & \vdots \\ a_{i1} & & a_{in} \\ \vdots & & \vdots \\ a_{n1} & & a_{nn} \end{vmatrix} \begin{matrix} \\ \\ (\text{row } i) \\ \\ (\text{row } j) \\ \\ \\ \end{matrix} = 0$$

Hence, in general,

$$a_{i1}A_{j1} + a_{i2}A_{j2} + \cdots + a_{in}A_{jn} = 0 \qquad (3)$$

when $i \neq j$. Applying this result to $|A'|$ gives a similar result for columns

$$a_{1i}A_{1j} + a_{2i}A_{2j} + \cdots + a_{ni}A_{nj} = 0, \quad \text{when } i \neq j \qquad (4)$$

Properties (1) and (3), (2) and (4) of cofactors may be summarised by the equations

$$\sum_{k=1}^{n} a_{ik}A_{jk} = \delta_{ij}|A| \qquad (5)$$

$$\sum_{k=1}^{n} a_{ki}A_{kj} = \delta_{ij}|A| \qquad (6)$$

Expressed verbally this is 'The sum of the products of the elements of one row (or column) with the corresponding cofactors of another row (or column) is zero. The sum of the products of the elements of one row (or column) with their own cofactors is equal to the determinant.

These properties will be useful in establishing Cramer's rule and also in inverting matrices.

7.2.9 *Cramer's rule*

The more general version of Cramer's rule for writing down the solution of n linear equations in n unknowns can now be derived.

Consider the equations

$$a_{11}x_1 + a_{12}x_2 + \cdots + a_{1n}x_n = c_1$$
$$a_{21}x_1 + a_{22}x_2 + \cdots + a_{2n}x_n = c_2$$

$$a_{n1}x_1 + a_{n2}x_2 + \cdots + a_{nn}x_n = c_n$$

Multiplying the first equation by A_{1i}, the second by A_{2i}, etc. and adding gives

$$\left(\sum_{k=1}^{n} a_{k1}A_{ki}\right)x_1 + \cdots + \left(\sum_{k=1}^{n} a_{ki}A_{ki}\right)x_i + \cdots + \left(\sum_{k=1}^{n} a_{kn}A_{ki}\right)x_n$$

$$= c_1 A_{1i} + c_2 A_{2i} + \cdots + c_n A_{ni}$$

Using the properties of cofactors this reduces to

$$|A| \cdot x_i = \begin{vmatrix} a_{1i} & \cdots & a_{1i-1} & c_1 & a_{1i+1} & \cdots & a_{1n} \\ \cdot & & \cdot & \cdot & \cdot & & \cdot \\ \cdot & & \cdot & \cdot & \cdot & & \cdot \\ \cdot & & \cdot & \cdot & \cdot & & \cdot \\ a_{n1} & \cdots & a_{ni-1} & c_n & a_{ni+1} & \cdots & a_{nn} \end{vmatrix}$$

or, provided $|A| \neq 0$, $x_i = \dfrac{|B_i|}{|A|}$

where B_i is the matrix obtained from A by replacing the ith column by the column vector C.

This result is usually expressed as

$$\frac{x_1}{|B_1|} = \frac{x_2}{|B_2|} = \cdots = \frac{x_n}{|B_n|} = \frac{1}{|A|}$$

Provided $|A| \neq 0$ and the equations have a unique solution, Cramer's rule provides a method of writing the solutions down immediately, but since these solutions involve $n \times n$ determinants they are not in a very convenient form. Also if $|A| = 0$ Cramer's rule provides no method of finding a solution if the equations are compatible. In practice it is usually preferable to use either the augmented matrix method, in the case of simple equations, or one of the numerical methods outlined in the next section.

7.2.10 *Numerical methods*

A large number of numerical methods have been developed for solving sets of linear equations where these equations have an exact solution. These methods are usually intended for use with either a calculating machine or a digital computer. They fall roughly into two types, direct methods, and iterative methods where a repetitive calculation is performed which, if the method converges, produces values nearer to the exact solution with each step. Examples of one method of each type are given below.

Gaussian elimination. This direct method is essentially the same as the augmented matrix method used earlier. However, where the computation is to be performed with a desk calculator or a computer (rather than by exact calculation as in the previous examples), a precaution must be taken to minimise the rounding errors. At each stage of the calculation the rows are rearranged so that the critical element or pivot a_{ii} used to obtain zeros in the lower positions in the ith column is the numerically largest eligible coefficient — this means that each row is multiplied by a factor less than 1. From each row below the ith, a_{ji}/a_{ii} times the ith row is subtracted. The method is illustrated in the example below.

Solve
$$3.41x_1 + 1.23x_2 - 1.09x_3 = 4.72$$
$$2.71x_1 + 2.14x_2 + 1.29x_3 = 3.10$$
$$1.89x_1 - 1.91x_2 - 1.89x_3 = 2.91$$

The largest coefficient in the first column is already in the first row and can be used as pivot without rearranging the equations. The first operations give

$$
\begin{pmatrix}
3.41 & 1.23 & -1.09 & | & 4.72 \\
2.71 & 2.14 & 1.29 & | & 3.10 \\
1.89 & -1.91 & -1.89 & | & 2.91
\end{pmatrix}
\begin{matrix} \\ R_2 - 2.71/3.41\,R_1 \\ R_3 - 1.89/3.41\,R_1 \end{matrix}
\begin{pmatrix}
3.41 & 1.23 & -1.09 & | & 4.72 \\
0 & 1.162 & 2.156 & | & -0.651 \\
0 & -2.592 & -1.286 & | & 0.294
\end{pmatrix}
$$

Interchanging $R_2 \leftrightarrow R_3$ and using coefficient -2.592 as pivot gives

$$
R_3 + \frac{1.162}{2.592}\,R_2
\begin{pmatrix}
3.41 & 1.23 & -1.09 & 4.72 \\
0 & -2.592 & -1.286 & 0.294 \\
0 & 0 & 1.579 & -0.519
\end{pmatrix}
$$

Hence

$$x_3 = \frac{-0.519}{1.579} = -0.329 \text{ or } -0.33 \text{ to 2 d.p.}$$

$$x_2 = \frac{0.294 + 1.286 \, x_3}{-2.592} = 0.050 \text{ or } 0.05 \text{ to 2 d.p.}$$

$$x_1 = \frac{4.72 + 1.09 \, x_3 - 1.23 \, x_2}{3.41} = 1.260 \text{ or } 1.26 \text{ to 2 d.p.}$$

From the above calculation we can deduce that the original matrix of coefficients has determinant $3.41 \times -2.592 \times 1.579 \times -1$, the sign being changed since the row operations involved one interchange of rows. It can be seen that the work involved in obtaining the solution by Gaussian elimination is very little more than that in calculating one determinant. Consequently this method is much quicker in practice than Cramer's rule.

Gauss-Seidel iterative method. Like all iterative methods the Gauss-Seidel method is more suitable for use with a computer than for hand calculation since the calculations are purely repetitive. Not all systems of equations are soluble by this method. It is most appropriate for solving systems of equations whose coefficient matrix has its elements of largest modulus along the diagonal, and as far as is possible the equations should be re-arranged so that this is the case. The method starts with an initial approximation to the solution and then successively calculates new values of the variable using the ith equation to calculate the value of x_i. It is illustrated in the example below.

Example

Solve:

$$0.9411x_1 - 0.0175x_2 + 0.1463x_3 = 0.631$$
$$-0.8641x_1 - 0.4243x_2 + 0.0711x_3 = 0.2501$$
$$0.2641x_1 + 0.1735x_2 + 0.8642x_3 = -0.7521$$

These equations already have two of the three coefficients of largest modulus along the diagonal. The situation cannot be improved by re-ordering the equations. The next stage is to re-write the equations to obtain iterative formulae for x_1, x_2, x_3. This gives

$$x_1 = \frac{1}{0.9411} \, (0.631 + 0.0175x_2 - 0.1463x_3)$$

$$x_2 = \frac{+1}{-0.4243} \, (0.2501 + 0.8641x_1 - 0.0711x_3)$$

$$x_3 = \frac{1}{0.8642} \, (-0.7521 - 0.2641x_1 - 0.1735x_2)$$

Any values of x_1, x_2, x_3 could be used as initial values but it is usually simplest to start with zero initial values, $x_1 = x_2 = x_3 = 0$. Using these gives $x_1 = 0.631/0.9411 = 0.67049$. This value, together with the value $x_3 = 0$, is then used to calculate x_2.

The calculated values of x_1, x_2 are then used to calculate x_3. A new estimated value of x_1 is then calculated from the values already obtained for x_2, x_3 and the whole process is repeated until the values of x_1, x_2, x_3 are apparently stabilising. The results (corrected to five decimal places) are given in the table below.

x_1	x_2	x_3
0.67049	−1.95492	−0.68271
0.74027	−2.21143	−0.65254
0.73081	−2.18711	−0.65453
0.73157	−2.18899	−0.65438
0.73151	−2.18885	−0.65439
0.73152	−2.18886	−0.65439

From this the solutions to four decimal places can be confidently quoted as

$$x_1 = 0.7315, \quad x_2 = -2.1889, \quad x_3 = -0.6544$$

The methods illustrated above are representative of two of the main types of numerical method used for the solution of linear equations. These can generally be classified as either elimination methods, similar to Gaussian elimination but differing mainly in the strategy for choosing pivot elements, and iterative methods similar to the Gauss-Seidel method but differing in their iteration formulae. In practice the elimination methods are usually preferred since the number of calculations to be performed in order to obtain a solution can be predetermined; the iterative methods will only give sufficiently rapid convergence to make them advantageous when the diagonal coefficients are considerably larger than the other coefficients or for large systems of sparse equations containing a high proportion of zero coefficients. Cramer's rule is never used as a numerical method since the amount of work involved is many times greater than in any of the elimination methods.

Exercises

1. Solve if possible the following systems of equations:

    (a) $x_1 + x_2 + x_3 = 1$
    $2x_1 + 4x_2 - 3x_3 = 9$
    $3x_1 + 5x_2 - 2x_3 = 11$

    (b) $2y_1 - y_2 + y_3 = 7$
    $3y_1 + y_2 - 5y_3 = 13$
    $y_1 + y_2 + y_3 = 5$

2. Find the most general form of solution of the equations

$$x_1 - x_2 + 2x_3 - x_4 = 1$$
$$2x_1 - x_2 + 3x_3 - 4x_4 = 2$$
$$-x_2 + 3x_2 - x_3 - x_4 = -1$$

3. Solve the equations

$$x_1 + 2x_2 - x_3 = 2$$
$$3x_1 + 6x_2 + x_3 = 1$$
$$3x_1 + 3x_2 + 2x_3 = 3$$

    (a)   By using Cramer's rule;
    (b)   By performing row operations on the augmented matrix.

4. Show that the equations

$$x_1 + 2x_2 - 3x_3 = 0$$
$$2x_1 - x_2 + 2x_3 = 0$$
$$x_1 + 7x_2 - 11x_3 = 0$$

    have a non-trivial solution. Find a solution which also satisfies

$$x_1^2 + x_2^2 + x_3^2 = 1.$$

5. Find the values of λ for which the equations

$$x_1 + 2x_2 + x_3 = \lambda x_1$$
$$2x_1 + x_2 + x_3 = \lambda x_2$$
$$x_1 + x_2 + 2x_3 = \lambda x_3$$

    have a non-trivial solution. For one of these values of λ give the most
    general solution.

6. (a)   Show that $\begin{vmatrix} 1 & 1 & 1 \\ a & b & c \\ a^2 & b^2 & c^2 \end{vmatrix} = (a-b)(b-c)(c-a)$

    (b)   Show that $x^2 + y^2 + z^2$ is a factor of

$$\begin{vmatrix} y^2 + z^2 & x^2 & yz \\ z^2 + x^2 & y^2 & zx \\ x^2 + y^2 & z^2 & xy \end{vmatrix}$$

    and hence factorise this determinant completely.

7. Find, by using Gaussian elimination, the solutions of the following
    equations correct to two decimal places

    $$2.1x_1 + 1.7x_2 - 1.1x_3 = 0.6$$
    $$1.4x_1 + 1.2x_2 - 2.1x_3 = -0.9$$
    $$0.8x_1 - 1.3x_2 + 1.8x_3 = 0.5$$

8. Use the Gauss-Seidel iterative method to find the solution of the following
    equations correct to three decimal places

    $$x_1 - 10x_2 + 2x_3 = 7$$
    $$10x_1 - x_2 + 3x_3 = 8$$
    $$2x_1 - 2x_2 + 5x_3 = 9$$

9. Solve the equations

    $$x_1 + 2x_2 + x_3 + x_4 = 2$$
    $$2x_1 + 3x_2 + 2x_3 + 3x_4 = 6$$
    $$-x_1 - x_2 + 2x_3 = 6$$
    $$3x_1 + 4x_2 + 2x_3 + x_4 = 4$$

10. Find, to three decimal places, the solution of the equations below,

    (a) using the Gauss-Seidel iterative method,
    (b) using the method of Gaussian elimination.

    $$10x_1 - x_2 + 2x_3 = 4$$
    $$x_1 + 10x_2 - x_3 = 3$$
    $$2x_1 + 3x_2 + 20x_3 = 7$$

7.3 The inverse of an n x n matrix

An $n \times n$ matrix A is said to be *regular* or *non-singular* if there is a matrix A^{-1}
such that $AA^{-1} = A^{-1}A = I$; A^{-1} is then called the *inverse* of A. It will be shown
that A is non-singular if and only if $|A| \neq 0$.

7.3.1 *Calculation of inverse using adjoint matrix*

Let A be any $n \times n$ matrix. Adj A, the *adjoint* of A is defined to be the transpose
of the $n \times n$ matrix whose elements are the cofactors of $|A|$, that is, if Adj A = B
then $b_{ij} = A_{ji}$ for all $i, j = 1, \ldots, n$. The matrix product A . Adj A has a
particularly simple form: Let C = A . Adj A.

Then, using the definitions of Adj A and of the matrix product we have

$$c_{ij} = \sum_{k=1}^{n} a_{ik} A_{jk} = \delta_{ij} |A| \text{ using equation (5), page 315}$$

Hence $A \cdot \text{Adj } A = |A| \cdot I$ (3)

Similarly by using equation (6, p. 315) we obtain

$$\text{Adj } A \cdot A = |A|I \qquad (4)$$

Equations (3) and (4) are valid whether or not $|A| = 0$. If however $|A| \neq 0$ the equations can be divided by the non-zero scalar $|A|$ to give

$$\left(\frac{1}{|A|} \cdot \text{Adj } A\right)A = I = A\left(\frac{1}{|A|} \text{Adj } A\right)$$

showing that in this case A is non-singular and has inverse $A^{-1} = (1/|A|) \text{Adj } A$.

If, on the other hand, $|A| = 0$ the assumption that A has an inverse leads to a contradiction since $|I| = 1 \neq 0 = |A| \, |A^{-1}|$.

Hence, A has no inverse if $|A| = 0$.

The formula $A^{-1} = (1/|A|) \text{Adj } A$ provides a method of calculating the inverse of A whenever A is non-singular. However, this is not usually the easiest method of performing the calculation since it becomes very laborious when A is larger than 3×3. For example, to find the inverse of a 4×4 matrix by this method would involve the evaluation of a 4×4 determinant and sixteen 3×3 determinants. An alternative method of calculating the inverse will be demonstrated in section 7.3.3.

7.3.2 *Properties of inverse matrices*

(1) The inverse of a non-singular $n \times n$ matrix is unique.

Proof. Suppose, if possible, that A has two distinct inverses A_1^{-1} and A_2^{-1}. Then

$$A_1^{-1}A = I = AA_1^{-1} \quad \text{and} \quad A_2^{-1}A = I = AA_2^{-1}$$

Hence

$$A_1^{-1} = A_1^{-1}I = A_1^{-1}(AA_2^{-1}) = (A_1^{-1}A)A_2^{-1} = IA_2^{-1} = A_2^{-1}$$

showing that A_1^{-1} and A_2^{-1} are identical.

From this proof we can further deduce that if A is non-singular and if A_1^{-1} is a matrix with the property (left inverse property) $A_1^{-1}A = I$ then, in fact, $A_1^{-1} = A^{-1}$ the unique inverse of A.

(2) If A and B are both non-singular $n \times n$ matrices then the product AB is also non-singular with inverse $B^{-1}A^{-1}$.

Proof. Since $|A| \neq 0$ and $|B| \neq 0$, $|AB| = |A|\,|B| \neq 0$ and hence AB is non-singular. Then

$$(B^{-1}A^{-1})AB = B^{-1}(A^{-1}A)B = B^{-1}IB = B^{-1}B = I$$

showing that AB has inverse $B^{-1}A^{-1}$.

(3) If A is non-singular then $AX = AY \Rightarrow X = Y$ (the cancellation law), where X and Y are $n \times m$ matrices.

Proof. Since A is non-singular A has inverse A^{-1}. Also $AX = AY$.
Pre-multiplying this equation by A^{-1} gives

$$A^{-1}(AX) = A^{-1}(AY)$$
$$\Rightarrow (A^{-1}A)X = (A^{-1}A)Y$$
$$\Rightarrow IX = IY$$
$$\Rightarrow X = Y$$

(4) If A is a non-singular matrix the matrix equation $AX = B$ has unique solution $X = A^{-1}B$, and the matrix equation $ZA = C$ has unique solution $Z = CA^{-1}$.

Proof. Consider $AX = B$; pre-multiplying by A^{-1} gives

$$A^{-1}(AX) = A^{-1}B \quad \text{or} \quad X = A^{-1}B$$

The uniqueness of this solution follows from property (3) above. Consider now $ZA = C$; post-multiplying by A^{-1} gives

$$(ZA)A^{-1} = CA^{-1} \quad \text{or} \quad Z = CA^{-1}$$

The uniqueness of this solution can be proved by an argument similar to that used in (3) above.

Note. Unless C and A^{-1} commute, $Z = A^{-1}C$ is not a solution of $ZA = C$.

Note. Property (4) shows that the inverse matrix A^{-1} provides a further method of calculating the solutions of a set of n linear equations $AX = C$. This method, although laborious for one set of equations (since the inverse requires a good deal of work to calculate), is very useful for obtaining solutions for a number of sets of related equations where the coefficients are unaltered but the constants C take different values. This situation is likely to arise when the matrix of coefficients represents a linear system and inputs have to be calculated for a number of different outputs.

7.3.3 *Calculation of inverse matrix using row operations*

For the solution of a system of n linear equations in n unknowns the use of elementary row operations on the augmented matrix provided an easier alternative to the use of Cramer's rule. A similar method can be applied to calculate the inverse of an $n \times n$ matrix as an alternative to first calculating the adjoint. This method is demonstrated in the example below, the theoretical justification being given later.

Example

Find the inverse of the matrix $A = \begin{pmatrix} 1 & 1 & 1 \\ 2 & 0 & 2 \\ 2 & -2 & 1 \end{pmatrix}$

The method begins by forming a 3×6 matrix consisting of A and I. The aim of the method is to perform row operations on this matrix until A is reduced to the unit matrix I; the matrix obtained by performing the same operations on I is then A^{-1}.

$$\begin{array}{cc} A & I \end{array}$$

$$\left(\begin{array}{ccc|ccc} 1 & 1 & 1 & 1 & 0 & 0 \\ 2 & 0 & 2 & 0 & 1 & 0 \\ 2 & -2 & 1 & 0 & 0 & 1 \end{array}\right)$$

$$\begin{array}{c} \\ R_2 - 2R_1 \\ R_3 - 2R_1 \end{array} \left(\begin{array}{ccc|ccc} 1 & 1 & 1 & 1 & 0 & 0 \\ 0 & -2 & 0 & -2 & 1 & 0 \\ 0 & -4 & -1 & -2 & 0 & 1 \end{array}\right)$$

$$\begin{array}{c} R_1 + \frac{1}{2}R_2 \\ -\frac{1}{2}R_2 \\ R_3 - 2R_2 \end{array} \left(\begin{array}{ccc|ccc} 1 & 0 & 1 & 0 & \frac{1}{2} & 0 \\ 0 & 1 & 0 & 1 & -\frac{1}{2} & 0 \\ 0 & 0 & -1 & 2 & -2 & 1 \end{array}\right)$$

$$\begin{array}{c} R_1 + R_3 \\ \\ -R_3 \end{array} \left(\begin{array}{ccc|ccc} 1 & 0 & 0 & 2 & -\frac{3}{2} & 1 \\ 0 & 1 & 0 & 1 & -\frac{1}{2} & 0 \\ 0 & 0 & 1 & -2 & 2 & -1 \end{array}\right)$$

$$I$$

A check shows that $\begin{pmatrix} 2 & -\frac{3}{2} & 1 \\ 1 & -\frac{1}{2} & 0 \\ -2 & 2 & -1 \end{pmatrix} \begin{pmatrix} 1 & 1 & 1 \\ 2 & 0 & 2 \\ 2 & -2 & 1 \end{pmatrix} = I$

verifying that the matrix obtained is indeed A^{-1}.

Theoretical justification. To justify the above method we introduce the so-called *elementary matrices* (or elementary row operation matrices).

An $n \times n$ elementary matrix E is a matrix obtained from the $n \times n$ identity matrix I by performing a single elementary row operation upon it. The elementary row operations and the corresponding elementary matrices E are connected by the property that if A is any $n \times n$ matrix then the product EA gives the matrix obtained by performing the corresponding operation on A. This property is proved by considering separately the three types of elementary row operation.

Type 1. Interchange the order of two rows.
Suppose rows r and s are interchanged.
Let the corresponding elementary matrix be E.
Then

$$e_{ij} = \delta_{ij} \text{ for } i \neq r \text{ or } s$$

$$e_{rj} = \delta_{sj} \text{ and } e_{sj} = \delta_{rj}$$

Let EA = B; then for $j = 1, \ldots, m,$ we have

$$b_{ij} = \sum_{k=1}^{n} \delta_{ik} a_{kj} = a_{ij} \text{ for } i \neq r \text{ or } s$$

$$b_{rj} = \sum_{k=1}^{n} \delta_{sk} a_{kj} = a_{sj} \qquad \text{and} \qquad b_{sj} = \sum_{k=1}^{n} \delta_{rk} a_{kj} = a_{rj}$$

Hence B is the matrix obtained by interchanging rows r and s of A.

Type 2. Multiply any row by a non-zero constant.
Suppose the rth row is multiplied by λ.
Let the corresponding elementary matrix be E and let EA = B.
Then

$$e_{ij} = \delta_{ij} \text{ for } i \neq r, \quad e_{rj} = \lambda \delta_{rj}$$

$$b_{ij} = \sum_{k=1}^{n} \delta_{ik} a_{kj} = a_{ij} \text{ for } i \neq r$$

$$b_{rj} = \sum_{k=1}^{n} \lambda \delta_{rk} a_{kj} = \lambda a_{rj}$$

Hence B is the matrix obtained from A by multiplying the rth row by λ.

Type 3. Add to any row a constant multiple of another row.

Suppose μ times row r is added to row s.

Then if E is the corresponding elementary matrix and EA = B

$$b_{ij} = \sum_{k=1}^{n} e_{ik}a_{kj}$$

$$= \sum_{k=1}^{n} \delta_{ik}a_{kj} = a_{ij}, \quad \text{for } i \neq s$$

$$b_{sj} = \sum_{k=1}^{n} e_{sk}a_{kj} = \sum_{k=1}^{n} (\delta_{sk} + \mu\delta_{rk}) a_{kj} = a_{sj} + \mu a_{rj}$$

Hence B is the matrix obtained from A by adding μ times row r to row s.

Suppose now that $E_1, E_2, \ldots, E_k$ are the elementary matrices which corresponds to a sequence of operations which will reduce an $n \times n$ matrix A to the identity I.

Since the application of these operations corresponds to pre-multiplying A in turn by the appropriate elementary row matrices we have

$$I = E_k E_{k-1} \ldots E_2 E_1 . A$$

hence

$$E_k E_{k-1} \ldots E_2 E_1 = A^{-1}$$

But the matrix $E_k E_{k-1} \ldots E_1 = E_k E_{k-1} \ldots E_1 . I$ is precisely the matrix obtained by applying the same sequence of elementary row operations to I. In the previous example this is the right-hand half of the final 3×6 matrix.

Notes. (i) Properties similar to the above can be proved for elementary column operations, but in this case the elementary matrices obtained must post-multiply the matrix being operated upon.

(ii) The properties of the elementary matrices provide a theoretical justification for the method of solving linear equations using the augmented matrix, or Gaussian elimination.

(iii) If A is singular the attempt to reduce A to the identity matrix by the use of elementary row operations will fail since a zero row will be produced at some stage of the calculation.

Exercises

1. Find the inverse of the matrices

$$A = \begin{pmatrix} 1 & 1 & 1 \\ 2 & 4 & 1 \\ 2 & 3 & 1 \end{pmatrix} \quad B = \begin{pmatrix} 2 & 3 \\ 3 & 4 \end{pmatrix}$$

Hence find a matrix X such that $BXA = \begin{pmatrix} 1 & 0 & 1 \\ 0 & 1 & 0 \end{pmatrix}$

2. A and B are two $n \times n$ matrices which commute. A is non-singular, prove that A^{-1} and B also commute. Prove also that $(A^{-1})' = (A')^{-1}$.

3. Find the inverse of the matrix

$$A = \begin{pmatrix} 1 & 2 & 0 & 1 \\ -1 & -1 & 1 & 0 \\ 2 & 3 & 0 & 0 \\ 1 & 4 & -1 & 5 \end{pmatrix}$$

Hence solve the equations:
$$\begin{aligned} x_1 + 2x_2 + x_4 &= 2 \\ -x_1 - x_2 + x_3 &= 1 \\ 2x_1 + 3x_2 &= 5 \\ x_1 + 4x_2 - x_3 + 5x_4 &= 0 \end{aligned}$$

4. Let $A = \begin{pmatrix} 1 & 1 & -2 \\ -1 & 2 & 1 \\ 0 & 1 & -1 \end{pmatrix}$ and $P = \begin{pmatrix} 1 & 1 & 3 \\ 0 & 3 & 2 \\ 1 & 1 & 1 \end{pmatrix}$

Show that $P^{-1} AP = \begin{pmatrix} -1 & 0 & 0 \\ 0 & 2 & 0 \\ 0 & 0 & 1 \end{pmatrix}$

Use this result to find the values of A^5 and A^{-1}.

5. Find the inverse of the matrix $A = \begin{pmatrix} 1 & 3 & 3 \\ 1 & 3 & 4 \\ 1 & 4 & 3 \end{pmatrix}$

by using row operations.

Find the inverse of the matrix $B = \begin{pmatrix} 2 & 3 & 4 \\ 4 & 3 & 1 \\ 1 & 2 & 4 \end{pmatrix}$

by first calculating Adj B.

Find X if $ABX = (1 \quad 0 \quad 1)'$.

6. Find the adjoint of the matrix $A = \begin{pmatrix} 2 & 3 & 5 \\ 1 & 4 & 7 \\ 3 & 2 & 3 \end{pmatrix}$

    Verify that $A(\text{Adj } A) = (\text{Adj } A)A = |A| . I$.

7. Find the inverses of each of the following matrices

$$A = \begin{pmatrix} 1 & 0 & 0 \\ 0 & 2 & 0 \\ 0 & 0 & 5 \end{pmatrix} \quad B = \begin{pmatrix} 1 & 3 & 4 \\ 0 & -1 & 1 \\ 0 & 0 & 2 \end{pmatrix} \quad C = \begin{pmatrix} 1 & 2 & 0 & 0 \\ 2 & 3 & 1 & 0 \\ 0 & 1 & -1 & 1 \\ 0 & 0 & -1 & 3 \end{pmatrix}$$

8. Find the maximum number of arithmetic operations which could be required in computing the inverse of a non-singular 5 x 5 matrix,

    (a)   using elementary row operations,

    or (b)   by first calculating the adjoint matrix (all determinants involved being evaluated directly, without any attempt at elimination.

    Note: an arithmetic operation is here understood to mean the addition, subtraction, multiplication, or division of two numbers.

9. The rotation of axes in cartesian coordinates is defined by the equation $x^* = Ax$, where

$$A = \begin{pmatrix} 1 & 0 & 0 \\ 0 & \cos\theta & \sin\theta \\ 0 & -\sin\theta & \cos\theta \end{pmatrix} \text{ and } x = \begin{pmatrix} x \\ y \\ z \end{pmatrix}$$

    Find the coordinates x of the point which has coordinates $x^* = \begin{pmatrix} 2 \\ 3 \\ 4 \end{pmatrix}$ after

    rotation.

10. By assuming the existence of an inverse of the form

$$A^{-1} = \begin{pmatrix} x & y & z \\ 0 & u & v \\ 0 & 0 & w \end{pmatrix}$$

    Find the inverse of $A = \begin{pmatrix} 1 & 3 & 4 \\ 0 & 2 & 1 \\ 0 & 0 & -1 \end{pmatrix}$

    [Hint: find, and solve, equations for x, y, z, v, u, w.]

NOTES ON CHAPTER 7

This chapter has provided an introduction to elementary matrix algebra; no attempt has been made to cover the entire subject nor to mention any of the many and varied applications.

From the point of view of the mathematician matrices have their most natural application to the theory of n dimensional vector spaces in which a matrix represents a transformation from one vector space into another. The problem then arises of finding the simplest form, whenever possible with zeros everywhere except on the diagonal, which the matrix can have and still fully represent the transformation. It can be shown that if A is an $m \times n$ matrix representing a linear transformation from an n dimensional vector space into an m dimensional vector space, then with a different choice of bases, or reference systems, in the vector spaces the same transformation is represented by a matrix $B = PAQ$ where P and Q are non-singular matrices. In a similar way if an $n \times n$ matrix C represents a linear transformation of an n dimensional vector space into itself then a different choice of basis will result in this transformation being represented by a matrix $D = R^{-1}CR$. Algebraically the problem is that of finding canonical forms (or simplified forms) of matrices after performing matrix transformations $B = PAQ$ where P and Q are non-singular matrices (the equivalence transformation) or $D = R^{-1}CR$ (the similarity transformation). The question of interest here is, given matrix A (or C), just how simple can the matrices B (or D) be made by a suitable choice of P and Q (or R).

As a particular instance of this, if Φ is the symmetric 3×3 inertia matrix of a rigid body and ω is the 3×1 angular velocity vector, then the product $H = \Phi\omega$ is the corresponding angular momentum vector; with a suitable choice of coordinate axes (chosen to coincide with the principal axes of inertia) the inertia matrix is reduced to a diagonal form. (See chapter 10.)

For further information on canonical forms and related subjects the reader is referred to L. Mirsky: *An Introduction to Linear Algebra*, O.U.P.

The most important topic in matrix algebra from the point of view of having widespread applications (a few of which are mentioned below) is the so-called *eigenvalue problem*. This is simply that of determining, for a given $n \times n$ matrix A, the values of scalars λ (the *characteristic values* or *eigenvalues*) and column vectors or $n \times 1$ matrices X (the *eigenvectors*) such that $AX = \lambda X$. A real matrix A does not always have real eigenvalues but it can be shown that if A is a real symmetric matrix then its eigenvalues, and consequently its eigenvectors are all real. In the field of mechanics the natural frequencies of a vibrating system can be expressed in terms of the eigenvalues of a matrix obtained from the equations of motion. As a further application the principal axes of inertia of a solid body are the eigenvectors of the symmetric matrix of moments and products of

inertia. In solid geometry the principal axes of a quadric surface are the eigenvectors of a symmetric matrix. Since eigenvectors are of such importance in
matrix applications it is not surprising that many numerical methods have been
developed for their determination. For a selection of these methods and also
for details of alternative numerical methods of solving linear equations and
calculating inverse matrices the reader is referred to L. Fox: *An Introduction to
Numerical Linear Algebra,* O.U.P. A really comprehensive, but advanced,
treatment of numerical methods of finding eigenvalues and eigenvectors can be
found in J. H. Wilkinson: *The Algebraic Eigenvalue Problem,* O.U.P.

Miscellaneous exercises

1. Solve the following system of equations

$$2x_1 + 3x_2 + 4x_3 = 5$$
$$4x_1 + 5x_2 + 6x_3 = 2$$
$$2x_1 + x_2 + x_3 = 6$$

(a)   By using Cramer's rule.
(b)   By finding the inverse of the matrix of coefficients.
(c)   By use of elementary row operations on the augmented matrix.

2. $A = \begin{pmatrix} 1 & 2 & 2 \\ 2 & 1 & 2 \\ 2 & 2 & 1 \end{pmatrix}$ Show that $A^2 - 4A - 5I = 0$
    Use this result to find A^{-1}

3. A square matrix S is said to be stochastic if all its elements are greater than
    or equal to 0 and if the sum of the elements in each row is 1. A $(1 \times n)$
    row vector V is called a fired point of S if VS = V. State which of the
    following matrices are stochastic and find their fixed points.

$$A = \begin{pmatrix} \frac{1}{3} & \frac{1}{3} & \frac{1}{3} \\ 0 & \frac{1}{2} & \frac{1}{2} \\ \frac{1}{4} & \frac{3}{4} & 0 \end{pmatrix} \quad B = \begin{pmatrix} \frac{1}{2} & 0 & \frac{1}{2} \\ \frac{2}{3} & \frac{2}{3} & -\frac{1}{3} \\ 0 & \frac{1}{2} & \frac{1}{2} \end{pmatrix} \quad C = \begin{pmatrix} \frac{1}{4} & \frac{1}{4} & \frac{1}{2} \\ \frac{1}{3} & \frac{1}{2} & \frac{1}{6} \\ \frac{1}{3} & \frac{1}{6} & \frac{1}{2} \end{pmatrix}$$

4. Find the value of λ if the equations below are consistent.

$$x_1 + 2x_2 - x_3 = \lambda$$
$$2x_1 + x_2 + 3x_3 = 2$$
$$4x_1 + 5x_2 + x_3 = 3$$

For this value of λ find a solution such that $x_1 + x_2 + x_3 = 1$.

5. $A = \begin{pmatrix} 2 & -4 & 1 \\ 3 & -2 & 5 \\ 1 & 6 & 1 \end{pmatrix} \quad B = \begin{pmatrix} -1 & 2 & 3 \\ 1 & 3 & -1 \\ 4 & 5 & 1 \end{pmatrix}$

verify that $|AB| = |BA| = |A||B|$.

6. Show that the equations
$$3x_1 + 4x_2 + 5x_3 = 2$$
$$2x_1 + 3x_2 + 4x_3 = 1$$
$$x_1 + x_2 + cx_3 = d$$

have a unique solution provided $c \neq 1$.

Find this solution and discuss the case $c = 1$.

7. $A = \begin{pmatrix} 1 & 3 & 1 \\ 1 & 4 & 2 \\ -1 & -2 & 3 \end{pmatrix}$

find lower and upper triangular matrices L and U such that $A = LU$ and

$$L = \begin{pmatrix} l_{11} & 0 & 0 \\ l_{21} & l_{22} & 0 \\ l_{31} & l_{32} & l_{33} \end{pmatrix} \quad U = \begin{pmatrix} 1 & u_{12} & u_{13} \\ 0 & 1 & u_{23} \\ 0 & 0 & 1 \end{pmatrix}$$

By letting $UX = Y$ with $LY = \begin{pmatrix} 3 \\ 3 \\ -6 \end{pmatrix}$ solve the equations

$$x_1 + 3x_2 + x_3 = 3$$
$$x_1 + 4x_2 + 2x_3 = 3$$
$$-x_1 - 2x_2 + 3x_3 = -6$$

Find also a matrix Z such that $LZU = A^2$.

8. Show that $\begin{vmatrix} 1 & \cos \omega & \cos 2\omega \\ \cos \omega & 1 & \cos \omega \\ \cos 2\omega & \cos \omega & 1 \end{vmatrix} = 0$

Show more generally that if Δ_n is the determinant of the $n \times n$ matrix D with $d_{ij} = \cos (i - j) \omega$ then $\Delta_n = 0$ for $n \geqslant 3$.

9. $f(x)$ is the real polynomial $f(x) = a_0 + a_1x + \cdots + a_nx^n$. For any $n \times n$ matrix $A, f(A)$ is defined as

$$f(A) = a_0 I + a_1 A + a_2 A^2 + \cdots A a_n A^n$$

If A is the matrix $A = \begin{pmatrix} 1 & 2 & 1 \\ 2 & 3 & 1 \\ 3 & 5 & 3 \end{pmatrix}$

and $f(x)$ is the polynomial $\begin{vmatrix} 1-x & 2 & 1 \\ 2 & 3-x & 1 \\ 3 & 5 & 2-x \end{vmatrix}$

show that $f(A) = 0$.

By using this result find an expression for A^5 in terms of I, A, A^2.

10. An $n \times n$ matrix A is said to be upper triangular if $a_{ij} = 0$ for all $i > j$
     (see exercise 7).

     An $n \times n$ matrix B is said to be a Hessenberg matrix if $b_{ij} = 0$ for all
     $i > j + 1$.

     Prove that:

     (i)   The sum of two upper triangular matrices is upper triangular;
     (ii) The product of two upper triangular matrices is upper triangular;
     (iii) The inverse of a non-singular upper triangular matrix is upper
           triangular;
     (iv) State which of the above statements remain true if the word
           Hessenberg is substitutes for upper triangular.

11. Show by counter-example that in general for non-singular matrices A and
     B we have

     $$(A + B)^{-1} \neq A^{-1} + B^{-1}$$

     Show that, if A and B commute, a necessary condition for $(A + B)^{-1} = A^{-1} + B$
     is that $A^2 + B^2 + AB = 0$. Hence find a 2×2 complex matrix A such that
     $(I + A)^{-1} = I + A^{-1}$.

12. A is an $n \times n$ matrix such that $a_{ij} = 0$ if $i \geqslant j$. Show that if $A^2 = B$ then
     $b_{ij} = 0$ if $i + 1 \geqslant j$. Prove by induction that $A^n = 0$.

13. (i)   A and B are skew-symmetric $n \times n$ matrices show that their product
           AB is a symmetric matrix if A and B commute. What conditions
           must A and B satisfy to ensure that AB is skew-symmetric?
     (ii) Show that for any matrix A (not necessarily square) the product
           $A'A$ is symmetric.

14. A square matrix A is said to be *nilpotent* of index r if $A^r = 0$ but $A^m \neq 0$

     for any positive integer $m < r$. Show that the matrix $A = \begin{pmatrix} 1 & 1 & 3 \\ 5 & 2 & 6 \\ -2 & -1 & -3 \end{pmatrix}$

     is nilpoint and find its index. Prove that for any nilpotent matrix A:

     (i) $|A| = 0$

     and   (ii) $(I + A)^n = I + nA + \dfrac{n(n - 1)}{2!} A^2 + \cdots + \dfrac{n(n - 1) \cdots (n - r + 2)}{(r - 1)!} A^{r-}$

     for any $n \geqslant r$.

15. If $A = \begin{pmatrix} 1 & 1 & -2 \\ -1 & 2 & 1 \\ 0 & 1 & -1 \end{pmatrix}$ show that $(A + I)(A - 2I)(A - I) = 0$

Use this result to find expressions for A^{-1} and $(2I + A)^{-1}$ in terms of I, A, and A^2.

16. Find the inverses of the matrices

$$A = \begin{pmatrix} 1 & 0 & 1 \\ 2 & 1 & 3 \\ -1 & 2 & 4 \end{pmatrix} \quad \text{and} \quad B = \begin{pmatrix} 0 & 1 & 0 \\ 0 & 0 & 1 \\ 1 & 2 & 3 \end{pmatrix}$$

Hence solve the equations

$$AXB = I \quad \text{and} \quad ABY = \begin{pmatrix} 1 \\ 0 \\ 1 \end{pmatrix}$$

17. The *trace* of an $n \times n$ matrix is defined to be the sum of the elements of the leading diagonal.

$$\text{Trace } A = \sum_{k=1}^{n} a_{kk}$$

State whether or not each of the statements below is true; if true, give a proof and if false give a numerical counter-example.

(a) Trace $(A + B)$ = trace A + trace B,
(b) Trace $(A - B)$ = trace A − trace B,
(c) Trace (A^{-1}) = $(\text{trace } A)^{-1}$,
(d) Trace (AB) = $(\text{trace } A)(\text{trace } B)$.

18. Determine the values of k for which the equations below are insoluble

$$x_1 + 3x_2 + x_3 = 1$$

$$2x_1 + 5x_2 + x_4 = 3$$

$$-x_1 + x_2 + 2x_3 + (k - 1)x_4 = 1$$

$$x_1 + 5x_2 + (k + 1)x_3 + x_4 = 17$$

19. Show that $\begin{vmatrix} 1 & \alpha & \alpha^2 & \cdot & \cdot & \cdot & \alpha^{n-1} \\ \alpha & 1 & \alpha & \cdot & \cdot & \cdot & \alpha^{n-2} \\ \alpha^2 & \alpha & 1 & \cdot & \cdot & \cdot & \alpha^{n-3} \\ \cdot & \cdot & \cdot & & & & \cdot \\ \cdot & \cdot & \cdot & & & & \cdot \\ \cdot & \cdot & \cdot & & & & \cdot \\ \alpha^{n-1} & \alpha^{n-2} & \alpha^{n-3} & \cdot & \cdot & \cdot & 1 \end{vmatrix} = (1 - \alpha^2)^{n-1}$

20. Find the values of λ for which the equations below have a non-trivial solution. For each such value of λ find the corresponding values of the ratio $x_1 : x_2 : x_3$.

$$(-2 - \lambda)x_1 + 6x_2 = 0$$
$$x_1 + (1 - \lambda)x_2 + x_2 = 0$$
$$2x_1 - 6x_2 - \lambda x_3 = 0.$$

8 ORDINARY DIFFERENTIAL EQUATIONS OF THE FIRST ORDER

8.0 Introduction

A differential equation is a relation between a function, its derivatives, and the variable or variables upon which they depend. In this chapter and the next we will be concerned with *ordinary differential equations*, in which the function involved depends upon a single variable, so that no partial derivatives arise. The most general form of an ordinary differential equation is

$$F(x, y, y', y'', \ldots, y^{(n)}) = 0 \tag{1}$$

where y and its derivatives are here functions of the single variable x.

The *order* of a differential equation is the order of the highest derivative it contains; the foregoing example is therefore an ordinary differential equation of order n. The *degree* of the equation is the power to which the derivative of highest order is raised, once fractional powers of derivatives (and of rational functions of derivatives) have been removed; for example

$$(1 + y'^2)^{3/2} = xy''$$

is an equation of the second order and second degree, since when both sides are squared in order to remove the fractional powers a term in y''^2 results.

A *solution* of an ordinary differential equation such as equation (1) is a relation between y and x which satisfies the equation, but which contains no derivatives. This solution may be an implicit relation of the form $w(x, y) = 0$, although it is sometimes possible to obtain y as an explicit function of x.

This chapter is chiefly concerned with equations of the first order and first degree, which may be expressed in either of the forms

$$P(x, y) + Q(x, y)y' = 0$$

or
$$y' = f(x, y)$$

where $f \equiv -P/Q$. The second of these two formulations permits a simple geometrical interpretation of the solution of a differential equation of this type. Let $f(x, y)$ be single-valued and defined in a domain D of the (x, y)-plane.

335

Then at every point (x, y) in D, the value of $f(x, y)$ specifies a direction, the gradient of y. The set of directions $\{f(x, y)\}$ is called a *direction field,* and the graph of a solution of $y' = f(x, y)$ is the locus of a point moving in the (x, y)-plane so that its direction of motion at any point (x, y) is aligned with the direction field at that point. In figure 8.1 part of the direction field of the equation $y' = x + y$ is shown diagrammatically, together with a sketch of the curve $y = e^x - x - 1$, which is a solution of the equation.

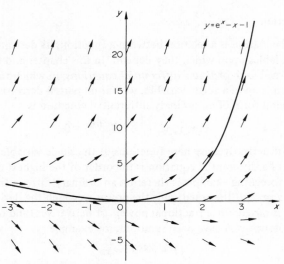

Fig. 8.1 The direction field of $y' = x + y$.

The most general solution of a first-order ordinary differential equation always contains an arbitrary constant. The simple equation $y' = x$, for example, has the solution $y = \frac{1}{2}x^2 + c$, which is obtained by integrating both sides of the equation. The constant c arises because the integrals evaluated are indefinite, and differentiation of the solution shows that it is valid whatever the value of c. The presence of an arbitrary constant in the general solution of $y' = f(x, y)$ stems from the freedom of choice of the starting-point of the motion referred to in the last paragraph. For each such equation there exists a family of solutions, one for each value of the arbitrary constant. In general, a given point (x, y) lies on only one curve of the family, and specification of a particular starting point is equivalent to the specification of a particular solution curve. If the analysis of some physical system leads to a first order differential equation, it is usually one particular solution which is required rather than the general solution; the problem is therefore not completely specified unless an *initial condition* (or *boundary condition*) $y_0 = y(x_0)$ is available. In any particular application, an initial condition can usually be obtained from physical considerations. In the case of the equation $y' = x + y$, the initial condition $y(0) = 0$ leads to the solution $y = e^x - x - 1$, passing through the point $(0, 0)$, which is shown in figure 8.1. The general solution of this equation is $y = ce^x - x - 1$, and the imposition of the initial condition has singled out that particular solution for which $c = 1$.

Methods for the analytical solution of ordinary differential equations of the first order and degree fall into two classes, comprising those based on the separation of the variables, and those based on rendering the equation exact. The standard analytical techniques are outlined in the following three sections; they are by no means invariably successful, and many equations can only be solved by the use of numerical methods such as those described later in this chapter.

Exercises

1. Use the given initial conditions to evaluate the constant c in the following relations:

   (i) $y = c\,e^x - x - 1$; $\ y(-1) = 0$,

   (ii) $(y - x + 1)^2 = c(y + x - 1)$; $\ y(6) = 7$,

   (iii) $x + y\,e^{x^3} = cy$; $\ y(1) = 1$,

   (iv) $x = y^3 + cy$; $\ y(0) = \frac{1}{2}$.

2. Differentiate the relations given in question 1, and in each case eliminate the constant c to obtain a first-order differential equation for y.

8.1 Analytical solution: Methods using separation of the variables

8.1.1 *Separable equations*
If, in the equation

$$P(x, y) + Q(x, y)y' = 0$$

P and Q take the form

$$P = g(x)s(y)$$

and

$$Q = h(x)r(y)$$

then division by $h(x)s(y)$ leads to

$$\frac{g(x)}{h(x)} + \frac{r(y)}{s(y)}\frac{dy}{dx} = 0$$

The equation may now be integrated with respect to x, the result being

$$\int \frac{g(x)}{h(x)} \, dx + \int \frac{r(y)}{s(y)} \frac{dy}{dx} \, dx = c$$

or

$$\int G(x) \, dx + \int R(y) \, dy = c$$

where $G \equiv g/h$ and $R \equiv r/s$.

Example.

$$(x + 1)y + x(y - 1)y' = 0; \quad y(1) = 1$$

Here $P(x, y) = (x + 1)y$ and $Q(x, y) = x(y - 1)$, both P and Q being products of a function of x with a function of y. Division by xy yields

$$\left(1 + \frac{1}{x}\right) + \left(1 - \frac{1}{y}\right)y' = 0$$

The variables are now separate, and integration leads to

$$x + \log x + y - \log y = c$$

or

$$y = Ax \, e^{x+y}$$

where $A \equiv e^{-c}$. This is the general solution of the original equation; use of the given initial condition shows that the required particular solution has $A = e^{-2}$, whence

$$y - x \, e^{x+y-2} = 0$$

In this example, y has been found as an implicit function of x; no explicit representation of the form $y = y(x)$ is possible.

In subsequent examples in this chapter we shall confine ourselves to finding general solutions, and initial conditions will no longer be specified.

8.1.2 *Homogeneous equations*

In order to discuss the next type of equation, we must introduce the concept of a homogeneous function of two variables:

Definition. A function of two variables $w(x, y)$ is said to be *homogeneous of degree n* if, for any constant λ, $w(\lambda x, \lambda y) = \lambda^n w(x, y)$.

For example,

$$2x^2 + 3xy + 4y^2 \qquad \text{is homogeneous of degree 2}$$

$$\frac{y}{x} \tan\left(\frac{y}{x}\right) \qquad \text{is homogeneous of degree 0}$$

$$\frac{2x + y}{x^2 y^2} \qquad \text{is homogeneous of degree } -3$$

A differential equation $P(x, y) + Q(x, y)y' = 0$ is said to be *homogeneous* if P and Q are homogeneous functions of the same degree n.

If this is the case, then

$$y' = -\frac{P(x, y)}{Q(x, y)} = -\frac{P(x, xy/x)}{Q(x, xy/x)} = -\frac{x^n P(1, y/x)}{x^n Q(1, y/x)} = g\left(\frac{y}{x}\right)$$

The substitutions $y = vx$, $y' = v + xv'$ therefore lead to $xv' = g(v) - v$, in which the variables are now separable.

Example. $x^2 - y^2 + xyy' = 0$ is homogeneous, since both $P(x, y) = x^2 - y^2$ and $Q(x, y) = xy$ are homogeneous functions of degree 2. Accordingly, we substitute $y = vx$, $y' = v + xv'$, to obtain

$$1 - v^2 + v(v + xv') = 0$$

or

$$1 + xvv' = 0$$

where a factor of x^2 has been cancelled. The variables may now be separated, with the result

$$\frac{1}{x} + vv' = 0$$

whence integration leads to

$$\log x + \tfrac{1}{2}v^2 = c$$

or

$$x = A\, e^{-\frac{1}{2}v^2}$$

where $A \equiv e^c$. Finally, since $v = y/x$, the solution in terms of the original variables is

$$x = A\, e^{-\frac{1}{2}(y/x)^2}$$

Clearly, this solution only exists provided $0 \leqslant x/A \leqslant 1$, when it may (unlike the solution of the last example) be expressed in an explicit form, $y = x\sqrt{\{-2\log(x/A)\}}$.

8.1.3 *Equations with linear coefficients*

An equation of the form

$$(a_1 x + b_1 y + c_1) + (a_2 x + b_2 y + c_2)y' = 0$$

in which the a's, b's and c's are constants, is said to have *linear coefficients.* Although such an equation is not homogeneous, it may be made so by means of a simple linear transformation, unless it so happens that $\begin{vmatrix} a_1 & b_1 \\ a_2 & b_2 \end{vmatrix} = 0$. If the system of linear equations

$$\left. \begin{array}{l} a_1 x + b_1 y + c_1 = 0 \\ a_2 x + b_2 y + c_2 = 0 \end{array} \right\} \tag{2}$$

possesses the solution $x = h$, $y = k$, then the substitutions $x = X + h$, $y = Y + k$ lead to the homogeneous equation

$$(a_1 X + b_1 Y) + (a_2 X + b_2 Y)\frac{dY}{dX} = 0$$

which may be solved by the method previously described. The substitutions have the effect of transferring the problem to a new co-ordinate system whose origin is at the intersection of the straight lines represented by equations (2).

Example

$$(2x + 9y - 20) - (6x + 2y - 10)y' = 0$$

The equations
$$\left. \begin{array}{l} 2x + 9y = 20 \\ 6x + 2y = 10 \end{array} \right\}$$

are satisfied by $x = 1$, $y = 2$. We therefore put $x = X + 1$, $y = Y + 2$ to obtain

$$(2X + 9Y) - (6Y + 2Y)\frac{dY}{dX} = 0$$

which is homogeneous. The substitution of $Y = vX$ and $Y' = v + Xv'$ now gives, after the cancellation of a factor X

$$(2 + 9v) - (6 + 2v)(v + Xv') = 0$$

or
$$2 + 3v - 2v^2 - (6 + 2v)Xv' = 0$$

The variables may here be separated, with the result

$$\frac{(6 + 2v)v'}{2 + 3v - 2v^2} = 2v' \left\{ \frac{1}{2 - v} + \frac{1}{1 + 2v} \right\} = \frac{1}{X}$$

where the left-hand side has been decomposed into partial fractions. Integration now gives

$$-2 \log (2 - v) + \log (1 + 2v) = \log X + c$$

or

$$1 + 2v = kX(2 - v)^2$$

where $c \equiv \log k$. But $v = Y/X$, whence

$$X + 2Y = k(2X - Y)^2$$

Finally we return to the original variables with the substitutions $X = x - 1$, $Y = y - 2$, which lead to

$$(x + 2y - 5) = k(2x - y)^2$$

If an equation with linear coefficients is encountered for which $\begin{vmatrix} a_1 & b_1 \\ a_2 & b_2 \end{vmatrix} = 0$, a different method is needed, since equations (2) now represent two parallel lines. These lines nowhere intersect, and the equations consequently have no solution. In this case the substitution $z = a_1 x + b_1 y$ leads to an equation in which the variables may be separated. The equation

$$(a_1 x + b_1 y + c_1) + (a_2 x + b_2 y + c_2)y' = 0$$

becomes

$$(z + c_1) + \left(\frac{z}{k} + c_2\right)\left(\frac{z' - a_1}{b_1}\right) = 0$$

whence

$$z' = \frac{(a_1 - kb_1)z + k(a_1 c_2 - b_1 c_1)}{z + kc_2}$$

and

$$x = \int \frac{z + kc_2}{(a_1 - kb_1)z + k(a_1 c_2 - b_1 c_1)} \, dz + \text{constant}$$

Example

$$(x + 2y - 3) + (2x + 4y + 5)y' = 0$$

Here we set $x + 2y = z$, $y' = \frac{1}{2}(z' - 1)$, with the result

$$2(z - 3) + (2z + 5)(z' - 1) = 0$$

or

$$z'(2z + 5) = 11$$

Integration of this equation yields

$$z^2 + 5z = 11x + c$$

which in terms of the original variables is

$$(x + 2y)^2 - 6x + 10y = c$$

We conclude this section by remarking that any equation which may be written in the form

$$y' = f\left(\frac{a_1 x + b_1 y + c_1}{a_2 x + b_2 y + c_2}\right)$$

can in principle be solved by one or other of the two techniques just outlined, according as to whether or not $a_1/a_2 = b_1/b_2$.

Exercises
Solve the following differential equations:

1. $y + y' \operatorname{cosec} x = 0$.
2. $(x^2 + y^2)y' = xy$.
3. $(2x + 3y - 3) + (3x + 2y - 7)y' = 0$.
4. $(x + y + 1) - (x + y - 1)y' = 0$.
5. $xy' = y + x \sin^2(y/x)$.
6. $xy' - y^2 = xy^2$.
7. $x + 2y + yy' = 1$.
8. $x^2 y' + (x + 2y - 2)^2 = 0$.
9. $y' = (x^2 + 3y^2)/(3x^2 + y^2)$.
10. $(2x + y - 1) - (4x + 2y + 3)y' = 0$.
11. $xyy' = y^2 + x\sqrt{(y^2 - x^2)}$.
12. $y' = 1 - y + x^2 - x^2 y$.

8.2 Analytical solutions: Exact equations and integrating factors

8.2.1 *Exact equations*

In chapter 4 it was shown that if $u(x, y)$ is a differentiable function of x and y, where y is in turn a differentiable function of x, then

$$\frac{du}{dx} = \frac{\partial u}{\partial x} + \frac{\partial u}{\partial y}\frac{dy}{dx}$$

Comparison with the equation

$$P(x, y) + Q(x, y)y' = 0 \tag{3}$$

suggests that there may exist a function $u(x, y)$ such that

$$\left.\begin{array}{r}\dfrac{\partial u}{\partial x} = P(x, y) \\[3mm] \dfrac{\partial u}{\partial y} = Q(x, y)\end{array}\right\} \tag{4}$$

and

If this is the case, equation (3) is said to be *exact*, and it may be written as

$$\frac{du}{dx} = 0$$

which has the solution $u = $ constant.

A *necessary* condition for equation (3) to be exact follows from equations (4); on differentiating the first equation partially with respect to y and the second with respect to x we obtain

$$\frac{\partial^2 u}{\partial y \partial x} = \frac{\partial P}{\partial y}$$

and

$$\frac{\partial^2 u}{\partial x \partial y} = \frac{\partial Q}{\partial x}$$

However, under certain mild restrictions upon u,

$$\frac{\partial^2 u}{\partial x \partial y} = \frac{\partial^2 u}{\partial y \partial x}$$

and we must therefore require the condition

$$\frac{\partial P}{\partial y} = \frac{\partial Q}{\partial x} \tag{5}$$

It may also be shown that this condition is *sufficient* for equation (3) to be exact.

Example

$$y\,e^{-xy} - x + x\,e^{-xy}y' = 0$$

In this equation we have $P = y\,e^{-xy} - x$ and $Q = x\,e^{-xy}$; then

$$\frac{\partial P}{\partial y} = \frac{\partial Q}{\partial x} = e^{-xy}(1 - xy)$$

and the equation is exact. We now determine the function $u(x, y)$, using equations (4). Since

$$\frac{\partial u}{\partial x} = P(x, y) = y\,e^{-xy} - x$$

integration with respect to x (keeping y constant) gives

$$u = -e^{-xy} - \tfrac{1}{2}x^2 + \phi(y) \tag{6}$$

Here the 'constant of integration' is constant only insofar as it is not a function of x; it is therefore written as $\phi(y)$ to allow for the possibility that it may, however, be a function of y. Partial differentiation of equation (6) with respect to y now leads to

$$\frac{\partial u}{\partial y} = x\,e^{-xy} + \phi'(y)$$

But the second of equations (4) shows that

$$\frac{\partial u}{\partial y} = Q(x, y) = x\,e^{-xy}$$

A comparison of these two equations for $\partial u/\partial y$ indicates that they are only compatible if $\phi'(y) = 0$, or $\phi = k$, a constant. Equation (6) now becomes

$$u = -e^{-xy} - \tfrac{1}{2}x^2 + k$$

and, since our original equation is equivalent to

$$\frac{du}{dx} = 0$$

its solution is therefore $u =$ constant, or

$$e^{-xy} + \tfrac{1}{2}x^2 = c$$

8.2.2 Integrating factors

If an equation

$$P(x, y) + Q(x, y)y' = 0 \tag{7}$$

is not exact, it may be shown (though the proof is outside the scope of this text) that there exists an *integrating factor* $\mu(x, y)$ such that

$$\mu\{P + Qy'\} = 0 \tag{8}$$

is exact. The condition which μ must fulfil is that

$$\frac{\partial}{\partial y}(\mu P) = \frac{\partial}{\partial x}(\mu Q)$$

or
$$P\frac{\partial u}{dx} - Q\frac{\partial \mu}{dy} = \mu\left\{\frac{\partial Q}{\partial x} - \frac{\partial P}{\partial y}\right\} \tag{9}$$

Although in most cases this *partial differential equation* for μ will be difficult to solve, it sometimes happens to possess a solution which is a function of x alone, or of y alone. In this event, the partial differential equation becomes an ordinary differential equation for μ in which the variables are separable.

Example
$$\sin 2x + -y' \sin^2 x = e^{-y}$$

This equation has $P = \sin 2x - e^{-y}$, $Q = \sin^2 x$; since $\partial P/\partial y \neq \partial Q/\partial x$, it is not exact. We therefore look for an integrating factor μ which must satisfy equation (9), or in this case

$$(\sin 2x - e^{-y})\frac{\partial \mu}{\partial y} - \sin^2 x \frac{\partial \mu}{\partial x} = \mu\{\sin 2x - e^{-y}\}$$

It is evident that if we attempt to find μ as a function of x alone, by setting $\partial\mu/\partial y = 0$, the resulting equation still contains a term in y. There is no solution $\mu = \mu(x)$, then. On the other hand, if we seek a solution $\mu = \mu(y)$, by setting $\partial\mu/\partial x = 0$, we are able to cancel a factor $\sin 2x - e^{-y}$, with the result

$$\frac{d\mu}{dy} = \mu$$

where, since μ is a function of y alone, the partial derivative has been replaced by an ordinary derivative. This simple equation has the general solution

$$\mu = \alpha e^y$$

and since μ will be an integrating factor whatever the value of α, we will take $\alpha = 1$ for the sake of simplicity. On multiplying the original equation by $\mu = e^y$, we obtain the exact equation

$$e^y \sin 2x + y' e^y \sin^2 x = 1$$

This equation is equivalent to $du/dx = 0$, where

$$\frac{\partial u}{\partial y} = Q = e^y \sin^2 x$$

or
$$u = e^y \sin^2 x + \phi(x)$$

Then
$$\frac{\partial u}{\partial x} = e^y \sin 2x + \phi'(x)$$

But also
$$\frac{\partial u}{\partial x} = P = e^y \sin 2x - 1$$

whence
$$\phi'(x) = -1$$

and
$$\phi(x) = -x + k$$

where k is a constant. The solution of the original equation is u = constant, or

$$e^y \sin^2 x - x = c$$

Exercises

Solve the following differential equations:

1. $2xy + 3y^2 + (x^2 + 6xy)y' = 0$.
2. $y^5 - 4xy^4 + (3xy^4 - 4x^2y^3 - 3)y' = 0$.
3. $y + (2y^3 e^{y^2} - x)y' = 0$.
4. $x - y^2 + 2xyy' = 0$.
5. $(\cos x + \sin x \cos y) - (\cos y - \cos x \sin y)y' = 0$.
6. $2xy^2 + (2x^2y + \log y)y' = 0$.
7. $(\tan x \tan y - e^x \cos x) + y' \sec^2 y = 0$.
8. $y' = (1 - x^2 - y)/(1 + x + y^2)$.

8.3 Analytical solution: Linear equations, and related types

8.3.1 *Linear equations*

Many first-order equations which arise in practical contexts are of the *linear* type

$$A(x)y' + B(x)y = C(x)$$

Such equations are linear in y and y', the coefficients being functions of x, in general. The standard form for a linear equation of the first order is

$$y' + p(x)y = q(x) \tag{10}$$

where $p \equiv B/A$ and $q \equiv C/A$. Discussion of a number of important properties possessed by linear equations in general is deferred until chapter 9.

A first-order linear equation always possesses an integrating factor which is a function of x alone. Any integrating factor $\mu(x, y)$ for equation (10) must satisfy the criterion given in section 8.2, and so we must require

$$\frac{\partial}{\partial y}\left\{\mu(x, y)[p(x)y - q(x)]\right\} = \frac{\partial}{\partial x}\,\mu(x, y)$$

If μ is to be a function of x alone, then $\partial\mu/\partial y = 0$, and this equation reduces to

$$\frac{d\mu}{dx} = \mu(x)p(x) \tag{11}$$

Separation of the variables now leads to

$$\log \mu(x) = \int p(x)dx + \text{const}$$

whence
$$\mu(x) = e^{\int p(x)dx} \tag{12}$$

Here, as in the previous example, an arbitrary multiplicative constant has been set equal to 1. In equation (12), then, we have a general expression for an integrating factor for a first-order linear equation.

On multiplying equation (10) by $\mu(x)$, we obtain the exact equation

$$\mu y' + \mu py = \mu q$$

and we may use equation (11) to rewrite this as

$$\mu y' + \mu' y = \mu q$$

or
$$\frac{d}{dx}(\mu y) = \mu q$$

Integration now leads to

$$\mu y = \int \mu q\,dx + c$$

$$y = \mu^{-1}\left\{\int \mu q\,dx + c\right\}$$

or, in terms of the functions involved in the original equation

$$y = e^{-\int p(x)dx}\left\{\int e^{\int p(x)dx}\,q(x)dx + c\right\} \tag{13}$$

This is the formal solution of a general first-order linear equation, and it consists of two terms. The term $\mu^{-1}c$ is called the *complementary function*; it is the solution of the *reduced equation* $y' + p(x)y = 0$, which is obtained by setting $q(x) = 0$ in the original equation, equation (10). The term dependent upon $q(x)$ is called the *particular integral,* and it satisfies the complete equation but contains no arbitrary constant. If the complementary function is denoted by u and the particular integral by v, we have

$$u' + pu = 0$$

and

$$v' + pv = q$$

so that, on addition,

$$(u' + v') + p(u + v) = q$$

and $u + v$ is the most general solution of the differential equation.

Cases sometimes arise in which, although $\int p(x)dx$ can be evaluated, the integral $\int \mu(x)q(x)dx$ cannot. If a boundary condition $y(x_0) = y_0$ is available, then substitution into equation (13) shows that $c = \mu(x_0)y_0$, so that

$$y(x) = \mu^{-1}(x) \left\{ \int_{x_0}^{x} \mu(x)q(x)dx + \mu(x_0)y_0 \right\}$$

Numerical evaluation of the integral for various values of x now provides a very satisfactory means of calculating an approximate solution.

Example

$$x^2 y' - 2xy = \frac{1}{x}$$

We first put the equation in the standard form where the coefficient of y' is unity:

$$y' - 2\frac{y}{x} = \frac{1}{x^3}$$

The integrating factor is given by equation (12) as

$$\mu(x) = e^{-\int 2dx/x} = e^{-\int 2dx/x} = e^{-2 \log x} = \frac{1}{x^2}$$

The standardised equation is therefore multiplied by $1/x^2$, with the result

$$\frac{y'}{x^2} - 2\frac{y}{x^3} = \frac{1}{x^5}$$

or

$$\frac{d}{dx}\left(\frac{y}{x^2}\right) = \frac{1}{x^5}$$

We may now integrate with respect to x, when we find

$$\frac{y}{x^2} = \int \frac{dx}{x^5} + c = -\frac{1}{4x^4} + c$$

or, finally,

$$y = cx^2 - \frac{1}{4x^2}$$

8.3.2 *Equations reducible to linear form*

There are several types of first-order equation which, although they are not linear, are easily converted into a linear form and thus solved. For example, an equation of the type

$$\{xs(y) + t(y)\}y' = u(y)$$

in which the coefficient of y' is a linear function of x and no other x's appear, may be expressed as a linear equation having x as the dependent and y as the independent variable. Multiplication by dx/dy leads to

$$u(y)\frac{dx}{dy} - s(y)x = t(y)$$

which may be solved as a linear equation for x as a function of y.

Example

$$(3x - 4y^3)y' + y = 0$$

Multiplication by dx/dy and division by y leads to the standardised linear equation

$$\frac{dx}{dy} + 3\frac{x}{y} = 4y^2$$

Since this equation is linear in x and dx/dy, the integrating factor is a function of y:

$$\mu(y) = e^{\int 3dy/y} = y^3$$

Accordingly, we multiply by y^3 to obtain the exact equation

$$y^3\frac{dx}{dy} + 3y^2 x = 4y^5$$

or

$$\frac{d}{dy}(xy^3) = 4y^5$$

which has the solution

$$3xy^3 - 2y^6 = c$$

Bernoulli's equation $y' + p(x)y = q(x)y^n$

differs from a linear equation in that the right-hand side is multiplied by y^n, where n ($\neq 0$ or 1) is a constant. Division by y^n and substitution of $v = y^{1-n}$ leads to the linear equation

$$v' + (1 - n)p(x)v = (1 - n)q(x)$$

which may be solved in the usual manner.

Example

$$xy' + y = x^4 y^3 e^{\frac{1}{2}x^2}$$

Division by x puts the equation into the standard form for a Bernoulli equation; a further division by y^3, followed by the substitutions $v = y^{-2}$, $v' = -2y^{-3}y'$, leads to the linear equation

$$v' - 2\frac{v}{x} = -2x^3 e^{\frac{1}{2}x^2}$$

Use of the integrating factor $\mu(x) = x^{-2}$ gives

$$\frac{v}{x^2} = -2e^{\frac{1}{2}x^2} + c$$

or, in terms of x and y

$$x^2 y^2 (2e^{\frac{1}{2}x^2} - c) + 1 = 0$$

Riccati's equation takes the form

$$y' = \alpha(x)y^2 + \beta(x)y + \gamma(x) \tag{14}$$

which reduces to a linear equation if $\alpha(x) = 0$ and to a Bernoulli equation if $\gamma(x) = 0$. Since it contains a term in y^2, Riccati's equation is non-linear although the substitution

$$y = -\frac{z'}{\alpha(x)z}$$

transforms it into a linear second-order equation, which may be tackled by methods explained in chapter 9. However, if a particular solution $y_1(x)$ is known, or can be found by inspection, the substitution $y = y_1 + 1/v$ reduces equation (14) to the linear first-order equation

$$v' + \{2\alpha(x)y_1(x) + \beta(x)\} v + \alpha(x) = 0$$

This new equation may be solved in the usual manner for v, to obtain the general solution of the original equation.

Example

$$xy' = y^2 - (2x + 1)y + x(x + 2)$$

Since the right-hand side is a quadratic expression in y, this is a Riccati equation. It possesses the particular solution $y_1 = x$, as is easily confirmed by substitution. Accordingly, we set

$$y = y_1 + \frac{1}{v} = x + \frac{1}{v}$$

and

$$y' = 1 - \frac{v'}{v^2}$$

to obtain, after some cancellations

$$-\frac{x}{v^2} v' = \frac{1}{v^2} - \frac{1}{v}$$

Multiplication by v^2/x puts this in the standard form for a linear equation; the integrating factor is x^{-1}, and the solution is

$$v = cx + 1$$

The general solution of the original Riccati equation is therefore

$$y = x + \frac{1}{cx + 1}$$

Exercises

Solve the following differential equations:

1. $xy' = 2y + x^3 e^x$.

2. $x^2 y' = xy + y^3$.

3. $(x - y^2 + 2)y' = 1$.

4. $(x + \beta)y' = 2(x + \beta)^4 + 2y$.

5. $(x + \cos y)y' = \cot y$.

6. $y' - 2y = \sqrt{(y)} \cos x$.

7. $y' + 2xy \cot(x^2) + 2x = 0$.

8. $(1 - x^2)y' - xy = x^2 y^2$.

9. $y' - 2xy = 2x(x^2 + 1)e^{2x^2}$.

10. $\cos y \sin y - (x + \cos y)y' = 0$.

11. $x^3 y' = 2x^4 y^2 - x^2 y - 3$, given a particular solution $y_1 = 1/x^2$.

12. $y' = x^2 y + x - y^2 + 2/x^2$, given a particular solution $y_1 = -1/x$.

8.4 First-order equations of other than the first degree

In dealing with differential equations of degree greater than one, it is customary to use the notation $p \equiv y'$.

An equation $F(x, y, p) = 0$ which is of the first-order but not of the first degree usually takes the form of a polynomial equation in p whose coefficients are functions of x and y. The cases which are easiest to deal with are those in which the equation may be solved algebraically for either p, x or y in the respective forms

$$p = f(x, y)$$
$$x = g(y, p)$$
or
$$y = h(x, p)$$

Examples will now be given to illustrate methods which may be used to solve these three types of equation respectively.

Example (Equation solvable for p)

$$xy(p^2 + 1) + (x^2 + y^2)p = 0$$

This second degree equation may be factorised as

$$(xp + y)(yp + x) = 0$$

from which we obtain the solutions for p in terms of x and y

$$p = -y/x$$
and
$$p = -x/y \tag{15}$$

These two relations are equations of the first-order and first degree; if we had started with an nth-degree equation which could be solved for p, we should, of course, have found n such relations, provided that no repeated factors arose.

Equations (15) have the solutions

$$xy = c_1$$
and
$$x^2 + y^2 = c_2 \tag{16}$$

respectively. As the original equation, regarded as a polynomial equation for p, is satisfied by either one of equations (15). Regarded as a differential equation for y, then, it is satisfied by either one of equations (16). This may readily be confirmed by substitution. Our two solutions can be combined into one in the form

$$(xy - c_1)(x^2 + y^2 - c_2) = 0 \tag{17}$$

since this equation will hold if and only if either of equations (16) holds.

At this point we encounter a difficulty in that, although the original differential equation was of the *first* order, equation (17) contains *two* arbitrary constants. This solution, in fact, represents the two families of curves obtained by letting c_1 and c_2 take all the values in the range $-\infty$ to $+\infty$ in the equations $xy = c_1$ and $x^2 + y^2 = c_2$. Now if we set $c_1 = c_2 = c$, and let c take all the values in the same range, we generate precisely the same two families of curves. Thus the presence of a single arbitrary constant in the solution is sufficient to ensure its complete generality, and the most general solution of the differential equation may be written as

$$(xy - c)(x^2 + y^2 - c) = 0$$

Example (Equation solvable for x)

$$2p^2 - 2px + y = 0 \tag{18}$$

We may solve this equation algebraically for x in the form

$$x = p + \frac{y}{2p}$$

We now differentiate with respect to y, replacing dx/dy by $1/p$

$$\frac{1}{p} = \frac{dp}{dy} + \frac{1}{2p} - \frac{y}{2p^2}\frac{dp}{dy}$$

or

$$p + (y - 2p^2)\frac{dp}{dy} = 0$$

The variable x has thus been removed from the problem, and we are left with a differential equation of the first order and first degree having p as the dependent and y as the independent variable. In this case, the equation which has arisen is exact, and its solution, which may be obtained by the method of section 8.2, is

$$py - \tfrac{2}{3}p^3 = c \tag{19}$$

The original equation, equation (18), is a relation connecting x, y and p; in equation (19) we have a further relation between y and p. If we can eliminate p between these two equations, then, we will obtain a relation between x and y involving an arbitrary constant — in other words, the general solution of equation (18). In this instance, equation (18) may be solved as a quadratic equation in p; substitution of the result into equation (19) gives, finally

$$3xy - x^3 \pm (x^2 - 2y)^{3/2} = c'$$

where $c' \equiv 6c$.

The next example deals with a case in which the elimination of p is not possible:

Example (Equation solvable for y)

$$p^3 + 2px^2 - 2xy = 0 \tag{20}$$

On solving this equation algebraically for y we find

$$y = \frac{p^3}{2x} + px$$

In order to remove the variable y from the problem, we differentiate with respect to x, to obtain

$$p = -\frac{p^3}{2x^2} + \frac{3p^2 p'}{2x} + xp' + p$$

or

$$p^3 - (3xp^2 + 2x^3)p' = 0$$

The original equation has thus been expressed as an equation of the first-order and first degree having p as the dependent and x as the independent variable. This latter equation happens to be homogeneous, and may therefore be solved by making the substitution $p = vx$, which leads to

$$v^3 - (3v^2 + 2)(v + xv') = 0$$

or

$$\frac{1}{x} = -\frac{3v^2 + 2}{2v(v^2 + 1)}\, v' = -\left\{\frac{1}{v} + \frac{v}{2(v^2 + 1)}\right\} v'$$

on separating the variables and using partial fractions. Integration yields

$$\log cx = -\log v - \tfrac{1}{4}\log (v^2 + 1)$$

or

$$x^4 v^4 (v^2 + 1) = c'$$

where $c' \equiv c^{-4}$. But $v = p/x$, and hence

$$p^4(p^2 + x^2) = c'x^2 \tag{21}$$

is the solution for p in terms of x. In principle, the general solution of equation (20) now follows on the elimination of p between equations (20) and (21). In the preceding example, we were able to accomplish this elimination, but here it involves the problem of solving either a cubic or a sextic equation for p, and we are unlikely to meet with success. We may nevertheless regard the general solution of equation (20) as being given by equations (20) and (21), in terms of p as a parameter. For a given constant c', we may choose any value for p; equation (21) then gives the corresponding values for x, whence the respective values for y are found from equation (20). Thus the assignment of a value to p specifies certain points in the (x, y)-plane, and by varying p we may trace out the graph of the solution of equation (20). To summarise, the general solution of our original equation of degree three is given parametrically by

$$\left. \begin{aligned} p^4(p^2 + x^2) &= c'x^2 \\ p^3 + 2px^2 - 2xy &= 0 \end{aligned} \right\}$$

and

8.5 Singular solutions, and Clairaut's equation

Consider the relation

$$y = cx + \frac{1}{c} \tag{22}$$

in which c is a constant. Differentiation with respect to x gives

$$y' = p = c$$

and we may accordingly substitute p for c in equation (22) to obtain

$$y = px + \frac{1}{p} \tag{23}$$

or

$$p^2x - py + 1 = 0 \tag{24}$$

This is a differential equation of the first order and second degree, whose general solution is given by equation (22).

If we adopt the method of section 8.4 we may differentiate equation (23) with respect to x, to obtain

$$p = p + xp' - \frac{1}{p^2}p'$$

or

$$\left(x - \frac{1}{p^2}\right)p' = 0 \tag{25}$$

This latter equation may be satisfied in either of two ways. If $p' = 0$, then $p = c$, and substitution of this result into equation (23) leads back, as we might expect, to the general solution, given by equation (22). On the other hand, we may take $p = x^{-1/2}$, which, when substituted into equation (23) leads to $y = 2x^{1/2}$, or

$$y^2 = 4x \tag{26}$$

Substitution confirms that this is also a solution of equation (24). However, it has the further properties that (a) it contains no arbitrary constant, and (b) it cannot be obtained from the general solution by a suitable choice of the arbitrary constant c. Any solution of a differential equation possessing both these properties is known as a *singular solution*.

At first sight there seems to be no connection between the singular solution we have found and the general solution from which we derived the differential equation, equation (24). There is, however, a connection which may be explained in geometric terms. The singular solution, $y^2 = 4x$, represents a parabola in the (x, y)-plane. Suppose that this parabola passes through the point $P(x_1, y_1)$. Now the tangent to the curve at P has the slope

$$m = (y')_{x=x_1} = x_1^{-\frac{1}{2}}$$

The equation for a straight line passing through a given point (x_1, y_1) and having a given slope m is (see Appendix)

$$(y - y_1) = m(x - x_1)$$

and hence the equation for the tangent to our parabola at $P(x_1, y_1)$ is

$$(y - y_1) = x_1^{-\frac{1}{2}}(x - x_1)$$

$$(y - 2x_1^{\frac{1}{2}}) = x_1^{-\frac{1}{2}}(x - x_1)$$

or
$$y = cx + \frac{1}{c}$$

where $c \equiv x_1^{-\frac{1}{2}}$. Thus the family of tangents to the graph of the singular solution $y^2 = 4x$ is the family of straight lines constituting the general solution, equation (22). In other words, the singular solution is the *envelope* of the family of straight lines $y = cx + 1/c$. This situation is illustrated in figure 8.2.

The foregoing example is a particular case of *Clairaut's equation*

$$y = px + f(p) \tag{27}$$

If we differentiate this equation with respect to x, we find

$$p = p + xp' + f'(p)p'$$

where $f'(p) = \mathrm{d}f/\mathrm{d}p$. Then

$$(x + f'(p))p' = 0 \tag{28}$$

and again two solutions arise. The first, $p' = 0$, gives $p = c$, and substitution for p in equation (27) then leads to

$$y = cx + f(c) \tag{29}$$

Thus the general solution of Clairaut's equation may be found simply on replacing p by c wherever it occurs. The second solution of equation (28) is

$$x + f'(p) = 0 \tag{30}$$

Elimination of p between equations (27) and (30), if it is possible, will give a relation between x and y, involving no arbitrary constant, which cannot in general be obtained from equation (29) by a suitable choice of c. This relation, then, is a singular solution. It may easily be shown (along lines similar to those employed in the last paragraph) that the singular solution is the envelope of the family of straight lines which comprise the general solution, equation (29).

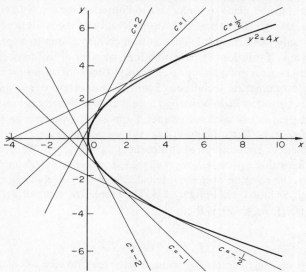

Fig. 8.2 Relation between general and singular solutions of $y = px + \dfrac{1}{p}$

Exercises

Solve the following differential equations, noting singular solutions where they occur:

1. $p^2 - p - 6 = 0$.
2. $2y = p^4/x^2$.
3. $y = p^2x + p$.
4. $4p^4 - 3px + 3 = 0$.
5. $y = p^3x + 1$.
6. $x = p \log p - p$.
7. $p^2 = x^3$.
8. $x = p^3y + 1$.
9. $p^2 - 2p \sinh x - 1 = 0$.

10. $y = px - 1/p^2.$ ·

11. $y = px - \sin p.$

12. $p = \log (px - y).$

8.6 The numerical solution of $y' = f(x, y)$: General considerations

Many first-order, first-degree differential equations cannot be solved analytically, and recourse must be made in such cases to numerical means. Numerous methods are available, though all of them lack the generality of the analytical approach, in that they only yield the particular solution corresponding to a specified initial condition. Thus, if solutions are required for a number of different initial conditions the numerical process must be repeated in its entirety for each new case.

The simplest numerical technique of general application to an equation $y' = f(x, y)$ is known as *Euler's method*, and it clearly illustrates most of the characteristic features of such techniques. Suppose that we have an initial condition $y(x_0) = y_0$. Then the point (x_0, y_0) lies on the desired solution curve, and the gradient of the solution at this point is $y_0' = f(x_0, y_0)$. We now choose a step length h, setting $x_1 = x_0 + h$, $x_2 = x_0 + 2h$, and so on. Euler's method approximates the solution over the interval $x_0 \leqslant x \leqslant x_1$ by its tangent at the point (x_0, y_0), as illustrated in figure 8.3. The computed value of y_1, where we define $y_1 = y(x_1)$ and so on, is then

$$y_1 = y_0 + hy_0'$$
or $$y_1 = y_0 + hf(x_0, y_0) \tag{31}$$

Taking (x_1, y_1) as the new starting point, a value may now be calculated for y_2 in a similar manner, and so on, the relation between successive computed values of y being

$$y_{n+1} = y_n + hf(x_n, y_n) \tag{32}$$

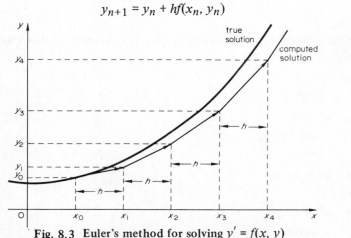

Fig. 8.3 Euler's method for solving $y' = f(x, y)$

It will be observed that the numerical process determines values of y only for certain discrete values of x; a continuous solution, such as would result if it were possible to solve the equation analytically, can only be obtained by interpolation between these values. Furthermore, the computed solution points do not fall exactly upon the true solution curve, due to errors arising in the course of the computation. These errors are of three types:

(i) *Round-off error.* If a computer can store numbers to an accuracy of, say, ten significant figures, then the result of multiplying together two such numbers will be stored, not as a twenty-figure result, but as the ten-figure result obtained by dropping the ten least significant figures of the product. Round-off is therefore inherent in almost any computer calculation which is not concerned solely with integer numbers.

(ii) *Truncation error.* This type of error is a result of the approximate nature of the formulae employed, which are generally based on truncated series. For example, equation (32) expresses y_{n+1} as the first two terms of a Taylor expansion of y about $x = x_n$. The second mean-value theorem (that is, Taylor's theorem with $n = 2$) tells us that for a given value of y_n the *true* value of y_{n+1} should be

$$\bar{y}_{n+1} = y_n + hy'_n + \tfrac{1}{2}h^2 y''(\xi)$$

where $x_n < \xi < x_{n+1}$. The error arising from the use of equation (32) is therefore

$$\epsilon_{n+1} = y_{n+1} - \bar{y}_{n+1} = -\tfrac{1}{2}h^2 y''(\xi)$$

It is clear that the use of a smaller step length should improve the accuracy attained, though this would, of course, necessitate more steps if a given range of x is to be covered.

(iii) *Propagated error.* This error results from the fact that each new step in the numerical solution (other than the first) starts from a point which is already off the true solution curve, due to errors in previous steps. In some cases, propagated error can have a disastrous effect, a phenomenon known as *instability.* Consider, for example, the equation

$$y' - 7y + 8 e^{-x} = 0$$

which has the general solution

$$y = e^{-x} + c e^{7x}$$

Suppose that we attempt to solve the equation numerically for the initial
condition $y(0) = 1$, so that we are seeking the particular solution $y = e^{-x}$,
for which $c = 0$. The first calculated solution point will not lie on the true
solution curve, due to rounding and truncation errors; it will, in fact, lie on
some other particular solution for which $c \neq 0$. In the next step, then,
we are effectively dealing with a different initial condition, and in
subsequent steps we will always have a contribution arising from the term
$c\,e^{7x}$ of the general solution. As x increases, this term will rapidly become
so large that it dominates the numerical solution, completely swamping
the desired e^{-x} term, which is meanwhile decreasing in magnitude.

The table below gives the results, to two decimal places, of a numerical
solution of $y' - 7y + 8\,e^{-x} = 0$ with $y(0) = 1$, using Euler's method with $h = 0.1$.
It is clear that after the first few steps the computed solution is deviating
markedly from the true solution $y = e^{-x}$ (which is included for comparison).

x	y(computed)	e^{-x}
0.0	1.00	1.00
0.1	0.90	0.90
0.2	0.81	0.82
0.3	0.72	0.74
0.4	0.62	0.67
0.5	0.52	0.61
0.6	0.41	0.55
0.7	0.25	0.50
0.8	0.03	0.45
0.9	−0.31	0.41
1.0	−0.86	0.37

Numerical solution of $y' - 7y + 8\,e^{-x} = 0$, exhibiting instability

Any numerical solution of a differential equation is subject to errors of the
types described, but the magnitudes of these errors can generally be kept within
acceptable bounds by a suitable choice of method and of step-length. If the
computation is well planned, it may be assumed with confidence that a smooth
curve passing through the computed set of solution points is a good approximation
to the true solution. It should be pointed out that the illustration just given was
deliberately ill-planned.

8.7 Predictor-corrector methods

8.7.1 *The modified Euler method*

Euler's method is crude, and rarely used in practice; a simple refinement, however, leads to the *modified Euler method* (sometimes known as *Heun's method*), which is the simplest of the class of *predictor-corrector methods* for the numerical solution of first-order equations. Let us assume that the solution has already been carried as far as $x = x_n$, so that the next value of y to be calculated is y_{n+1}. Integration of the equation $y' = f(x, y)$ between the limits x_n and x_{n+1} leads to

$$\left[y\right]_{x_n}^{x_{n+1}} = \int_{x_n}^{x_{n+1}} f(x, y)\mathrm{d}x$$

or
$$y_{n+1} = y_n + \int_{x_n}^{x_{n+1}} f(x, y)\mathrm{d}x \tag{33}$$

This relation is exact, though since we do not know the dependence of y upon x, we cannot evaluate the integral unless f happens to be a function of x alone. Instead, we approximate it, using the trapezium rule, to obtain

$$y_{n+1} = y_n + \tfrac{1}{2}(x_{n+1} - x_n)\{f(x_n, y_n) + f(x_{n+1}, y_{n+1})\}$$

or, since $x_{n+1} - x_n = h$, the step length,

$$y_{n+1} = y_n + \tfrac{1}{2}h\{f(x_n, y_n) + f(x_{n+1}, y_{n+1})\} \tag{34}$$

Occasionally, this equation can be solved explicitly for y_{n+1} (consider, for example, the case when the original differential equation is linear). Generally, however, this is not possible, and the crude value y_{n+1}^* given by Euler's method is substituted in the right-hand side of equation (34). The two equations used in the modified Euler method are then

$$y_{n+1}^* = y_n + hf_n \tag{35}$$

and
$$y_{n+1} = y_n + \tfrac{1}{2}h\{f_n + f_{n+1}^*\} \tag{36}$$

where $f_n \equiv f(x_n, y_n)$ and $f_{n+1}^* \equiv f(x_{n+1}, y_{n+1}^*)$.

Equations (35) and (36) are known respectively as the *predictor* and the *corrector*, since the first provides a rough estimate of y_{n+1}, which is improved upon by the second. In fact the application of the corrector amounts to a single application of a simple iterative process, and further iterations will usually improve the value of y_{n+1} still further. However, it is generally preferable, when using predictor-corrector methods, to achieve increased accuracy by using a smaller step-length rather than by multiple iteration of the corrector. This reduces the effects of truncation error. In the case of the modified Euler method the error in equation (36) is

$$\epsilon_{n+1} = -\frac{h^3}{12} f''(\xi) \qquad (37)$$

where $x_n < \xi < x_{n+1}$, resulting from the use of the trapezium rule to approximate the integral in equation (33).

Example. Find $y(1)$, if $y' = -x/y$ and $y(0) = -1$. We use the modified Euler method with step-length $h = 0.1$. The predictor gives

$$y*(0.1) = y(0) + 0 = -1$$

whence the corrector leads to

$$y(0.1) = y(0) + 0.05 \{0 + 0.1\} = -0.9950$$

Then
$$y*(0.2) = y(0.1) + 0.1 \frac{0.1}{0.9950} = -0.9849$$

and
$$y(0.2) = y(0.1) + 0.05 \left\{ \frac{0.1}{0.9950} + \frac{0.2}{0.9849} \right\} = -0.9798$$

where the results are rounded to four decimal places. Continuing in this manner, we build up the solution until we reach $x = 1$. The calculated values of y are given in the table below; for comparison, the results obtained using the basic Euler method are also given, together with the values found when the equation is solved analytically, as is possible in this instance.

x	y (Euler's Method)	y (modified Euler Method)	y (analytic solution)
0.0	−1.0000	−1.0000	−1.0000
0.1	−1.0000	−0.9950	−0.9950
0.2	−0.9900	−0.9798	−0.9798
0.3	−0.9698	−0.9540	−0.9539
0.4	−0.9389	−0.9166	−0.9165
0.5	−0.8963	−0.8661	−0.8660
0.6	−0.8405	−0.8001	−0.8000
0.7	−0.7691	−0.7144	−0.7141
0.8	−0.6781	−0.6005	−0.6000
0.9	−0.5601	−0.4376	−0.4359
1.0	−0.3994	−0.1191	−0.0000

Numerical solution of $y' = -x/y$ with $h = 0.1$

The general solution, $x^2 + y^2 = c^2$, represents a family of circles of radius c, centred at the origin. Our particular solution has $c = 1$, whence $y = \sqrt{(1 - x^2)}$ and $y(1) = 0$. The numerical solution starts at the point $(0, -1)$ and approximates that part of the circle of radius 1 which lies in the lower right-hand quadrant of the (x, y)-plane.

The accuracy of the modified Euler method is seen to be fairly good until x becomes close to 1. We must expect inaccuracy there, however, since

$$y' = f = -\frac{x}{y} \quad \text{gives} \quad y'' = f' = -\frac{1}{y} + \frac{x}{y^2} y' \quad \text{and} \quad f'' = \frac{2}{y^2} y' - \frac{2x}{y^3} (y')^2 + \frac{x}{y^2} y''$$

Substitution for y' and y'' leads to

$$f'' = -\frac{3x(x^2 + y^2)}{y^5}$$

and it is clear that as x approaches 1 and y approaches zero the truncation error, given by equation (37), increases very rapidly.

8.7.2 The Adams–Bashforth method

There are a number of predictor-corrector methods which use the values of $y_{n-1}, y_{n-2}, \ldots$, in addition to that of y_n, in calculating y_{n+1}. Typical of these is the *Adams–Bashforth method*. The basic equation is once again equation (33)

$$y_{n+1} = y_n + \int_{x_n}^{x_{n+1}} f(x, y)\mathrm{d}x \tag{38}$$

but we now approximate the integral by replacing f by the interpolating polynomial passing through the points $(x_{n+1}, f_{n+1}), (x_n, f_n), (x_{n-1}, f_{n-1}), \ldots$, and so on. Newton's backward-difference formula (see section 6.4) expresses f in the interval $x_n \leqslant x \leqslant x_{n+1}$ as

$$f(x_{n+1} + \theta h) = f_{n+1} + \theta \nabla f_{n+1} + \frac{1}{2!} \theta(\theta + 1)\nabla^2 f_{n+1}$$

$$+ \frac{1}{3!} \theta(\theta + 1)(\theta + 2)\nabla^3 f_{n+1} + \ldots \tag{39}$$

where $\theta h = x - x_{n+1}$, so that $-1 \leqslant \theta \leqslant 0$. On substituting equation (39) into equation (38) and transferring to θ as the variable of integration, we find

$$y_{n+1} = y_n + h \int_{-1}^{0} \left[f_{n+1} + \theta \nabla f_{n+1} + \frac{1}{2!} \theta(\theta + 1)\nabla^2 f_{n+1} \right.$$

$$\left. + \frac{1}{3!} \theta(\theta + 1)(\theta + 2)\nabla^3 f_{n+1} + \cdots \right] \mathrm{d}\theta$$

or $y_{n+1} = y_n + h \left[1 - \frac{1}{2} \nabla - \frac{1}{12} \nabla^2 - \frac{1}{24} \nabla^3 - \frac{19}{720} \nabla^4 - \cdots \right] f_{n+1}$

However, since we have not yet calculated y_{n+1}, we cannot determine f_{n+1}, whose value is needed for the formation of the table of differences. Accordingly, as in the modified Euler method, we use a less accurate predictor formula to find a first approximation to y_{n+1}. The predictor also results from equation (38), though this time we integrate the interpolating polynomial passing through the points $(x_n, f_n), (x_{n-1}, f_{n-1}), (x_{n-2}, f_{n-2}), \ldots$, all of which are known. The polynomial is used to *extrapolate* into the interval $x_n \leqslant x \leqslant x_{n+1}$. Newton's backward formula gives

$$f(x_n + \theta h) = f_n + \theta \nabla f_n + \frac{1}{2!} \theta(\theta + 1) \nabla^2 f_n + \frac{1}{3!} \theta(\theta + 1)(\theta + 2) \nabla^3 f_n + \cdots \quad (40)$$

where now $\theta h = x - x_n$, and $0 \leqslant \theta \leqslant 1$. Substitution of equation (40) into equation (38) leads to

$$y_{n+1}^* = y_n + h \int_0^1 \left[f_n + \theta \nabla f_n + \frac{1}{2!} \theta(\theta + 1) \nabla^2 f_n + \frac{1}{3!} \theta(\theta + 1)(\theta + 2) \nabla^3 f_n + \cdots \right] d\theta$$

or $\quad y_{n+1}^* = y_n + h \left[1 + \frac{1}{2} \nabla + \frac{5}{12} \nabla^2 + \frac{3}{8} \nabla^3 + \frac{251}{720} \nabla^4 + \cdots \right] f_n$

The Adams-Bashforth method thus uses for its predictor and corrector, respectively, the equations

$$y_{n+1}^* = y_n + h \left[1 + \frac{1}{2} \nabla + \frac{5}{12} \nabla^2 + \frac{3}{8} \nabla^3 + \frac{251}{720} \nabla^4 + \cdots \right] f_n \quad (41)$$

$$y_{n+1} = y_n + h \left[1 - \frac{1}{2} \nabla - \frac{1}{12} \nabla^2 - \frac{1}{24} \nabla^3 - \frac{19}{720} \nabla^4 + \cdots \right] f_{n+1}^* \quad (42)$$

where, as previously, $f_{n+1}^* \equiv f(x_{n+1}, y_{n+1}^*)$. It is worthy of note that the modified Euler method is in fact a special case of the Adams-Bashforth method in which only the first term in brackets in equation (41) is retained, and only the first two in equation (42). Equations (41) and (42) may alternatively be expressed in terms of function values if the first few differences are put in Lagrangean form (see section 6.4) and higher differences neglected.

Example. The table of figures below contains the results of the first three steps in the integration of the equation $y' + 2xy = 0$, with initial condition $y(0) = 1$. Obtain a value for $y(0.4)$, using the Adams-Bashforth method.

x	y	$f = -2xy$	∇f	$\nabla^2 f$	$\nabla^3 f$
0.0	1.0000	0.0000			
			-1980		
0.1	0.9900	-0.1980		117	
			-1863		106
0.2	0.9608	-0.3843		223	
			-1640		
0.3	0.9139	-0.5483			

The values of f have here been calculated from the given values of x and y, and the table of differences has been formed. The Adams-Bashforth predictor is

$$y^*(0.4) = y(0.3) + h\left\{1 + \frac{1}{2}\nabla + \frac{5}{12}\nabla^2 + \frac{3}{8}\nabla^3 + \cdots\right\}f(0.3)$$

and use of all the available differences gives

$$y^*(0.4) = 0.9139 + 0.1\left\{-0.5483 - \frac{1}{2}\cdot 0.1640 + \frac{5}{12}\cdot 0.0223 + \frac{3}{8}\cdot 0.0106\right\}$$

$$= 0.8522, \text{ to four decimal places.}$$

We now extend the difference table, using the predicted value of $y(0.4)$:

x	y	f	∇f	$\nabla^2 f$	$\nabla^3 f$	$\nabla^4 f$
0.0	1.0000	0.0000				
			-1980			
0.1	0.9900	-0.1980		117		
			-1863		106	
0.2	0.9608	-0.3843		223		-24
			-1640		82	
0.3	0.9139	-0.5483		305		
			-1335			
0.4*	0.8522	-0.6818				

We now have a fourth difference available; the corrector formula is

$$y(0.4) = y(0.3) + h\left\{1 - \frac{1}{2}\nabla - \frac{1}{12}\nabla^2 - \frac{1}{24}\nabla^3 - \frac{19}{721}\nabla^4 - \cdots\right\}f^*(0.4)$$

which leads to

$$y(0.4) = 0.9139 + 0.1\left\{-0.6818 + \frac{1}{2}\cdot 0.1335 - \frac{1}{12}\cdot 0.0305\right.$$

$$\left. - \frac{1}{24}\cdot 0.0082 + \frac{19}{720}\cdot 0.0024\right\}$$

$$= 0.8521, \text{ again to four decimal places.}$$

The predicted and corrected values differ only by one unit in the last decimal place and we may confidently assume that the truncation error in this step is no larger than 10^{-4}. The calculated value does, in fact, agree to four decimal places with that given by the analytical solution $y = e^{-x^2}$.

Clearly, we may expect the Adams-Bashforth method to give more accurate results than the modified Euler method with the same step-length, since it takes more information into account at each step. On the other hand, the method is not self-starting, since the required differences of f cannot be calculated until a number of steps have already been carried out. Initially, then, several steps of some other method are necessary; the modified Euler method may be used, but the more accurate fourth-order Runge-Kutta method, to be discussed in the next section, is generally preferable. A related problem arises if it is desired to change the step-length at some point in the solution, when it is necessary to form a fresh set of differences based on the new interval. Predictor-corrector methods do have the advantage, however, of permitting a check on the truncation error at each step by a comparison of the predicted and corrected values of y.

8.8 Runge-Kutta methods

Probably the most widely used methods for the numerical solution of first-order, first-degree equations are those known generically as *Runge-Kutta* techniques. They are self-starting, and are easy to program for a digital computer, which may account for some of their popularity.

The modified Euler method, which is the simplest of the predictor-corrector methods, may also be regarded as a simple Runge-Kutta procedure. Equations (35) and (36) can be rewritten as

$$y_{n+1} = y_n + \tfrac{1}{2}(k_0 + k_1) \tag{43}$$

where $\quad k_0 = hf(x_n, y_n) \quad$ and $\quad k_1 = hf(x_n + h, \; y_n + k_0)$

Now consider the following generalisation of equations (43):

$$y_{n+1} = y_n + \alpha k_0 + \beta k_1$$

where
$$k_0 = hf(x_n, y_n) \qquad (44)$$

and
$$k_1 = hf(x_n + \xi h, y_n + \eta k_0)$$

Both sides of the first of these equations may be expanded in Taylor series about the point (x_n, y_n). We have for the left-hand side

$$y_{n+1} = y_n + hy'_n + \tfrac{1}{2}h^2 y''_n + \cdots$$

$$= y_n + hf_n + \tfrac{1}{2}h^2 \left(\frac{\mathrm{d}f}{\mathrm{d}x}\right)_n + \cdots$$

$$= y_n + hf_n + \tfrac{1}{2}h^2 \left(\frac{\partial f}{\partial x} + f\frac{\partial f}{\partial y}\right)_n + \cdots \qquad (45)$$

where a subscript n denotes evaluation at $x = x_n$. For the expansion of the right-hand side we need the two-dimensional form of Taylor's series given in section 4.3. This gives

$$y_n + \alpha k_0 + \beta k_1 = y_n + \alpha hf_n + \beta hf(x_n + \xi h, y_n + \eta hf_n)$$

$$= y_n + \alpha hf_n + \beta h\left\{f_n + \left(\xi h \frac{\partial f}{\partial x} + \eta hf \frac{\partial f}{\partial y}\right)_n + \cdots\right\} \qquad (46)$$

If we now equate powers of h as far as h^2 in equations (45) and (46), we find

$$\alpha + \beta = 1, \qquad \beta\xi = \beta\eta = \tfrac{1}{2}$$

Then equations (44) may be rewritten, in terms of an arbitrary parameter α, as

$$y_{n+1} = y_n + \alpha k_0 + (1 - \alpha)k_1 \qquad (47)$$

where
$$k_0 = hf(x_n, y_n)$$

and
$$k_1 = hf(x_n + h/2(1 - \alpha), y_n + k_0/2(1 - \alpha))$$

This is the general second-order Runge-Kutta formula; the truncation error is of order h^3, since that is the first power of h neglected in comparing the foregoing expansions. If we choose $\alpha = \tfrac{1}{2}$, we rediscover the modified Euler formulae of equations (43); the choice of $\alpha = 0$ leads to

$$y_{n+1} = y_n + hf(x_n + \tfrac{1}{2}h, y_n + \tfrac{1}{2}hf_n)$$

There is, in fact, an infinite number of such formulae.

Runge-Kutta formulae of higher orders may be similarly derived, though much tedious algebra is involved. The general procedure is to set

$$y_{n+1} = y_n + \alpha k_0 + \beta k_1 + \gamma k_2 + \cdots$$

where
$$k_0 = hf(x_n, y_n)$$

$$k_1 = hf(x_n + \xi_1 h, y_n + \eta_{10} k_0)$$

$$k_2 = hf(x_n + \xi_2 h, y_n + \eta_{20} k_0 + \eta_{21} k_1)$$

and so on. As previously, all the terms are expanded about (x_n, y_n) and coefficients of powers of h equated to find the constants. These are not determined uniquely, since there are invariably more constants than equations. Particular Runge-Kutta formulae result from the arbitrary assignment of values to as many constants as may be necessary to determine the remainder.

The most frequently used Runge-Kutta process is one of the fourth order, based on the formulae

$$y_{n+1} = y_n + \tfrac{1}{6}(k_0 + 2k_1 + 2k_2 + k_3)$$

where
$$k_0 = hf(x_n, y_n)$$

$$k_1 = hf(x_n + \tfrac{1}{2}h, y_n + \tfrac{1}{2}k_0) \tag{48}$$

$$k_2 = hf(x_n + \tfrac{1}{2}h, y_n + \tfrac{1}{2}k_1)$$

$$k_3 = hf(x_n + h, y_n + k_2)$$

The truncation error is of order h^5.

Example. We will consider once more the equation of the example on p. 365, namely $y' + 2xy = 0$, with $y(0) = 1$, and we will assume that the integration has progressed as far as $x = 0.3$ in steps of length $h = 0.1$. The value found for $y(0.3)$ is 0.9139, and we now find $y(0.4)$ using equations (48).

We obtain
$$k_0 = 0.1(-2 \times 0.3 \times 0.9139) = -0.05483$$

$$k_1 = 0.1(-2 \times 0.35 \times 0.8865) = -0.06206$$

$$k_2 = 0.1(-2 \times 0.35 \times 0.8829) = -0.06180$$

and
$$k_3 = 0.1(-2 \times 0.4 \times 0.8521) = -0.06817$$

Here one more decimal place has been retained than we require in the final result. Now

$$\tfrac{1}{6}(k_0 + 2k_1 + 2k_2 + k_3) = -0.06179$$

and the first of equations (48) gives $y(0.4) = y(0.3) - 0.0618 = 0.8521$, to four decimal places, in agreement with both the Adams-Bashforth result and the analytic solution.

Runge-Kutta methods are easy to implement on a digital computer, and are probably preferable to predictor-corrector techniques for most purposes. Their main disadvantage is that it is difficult to keep a check on the truncation error; the simplest way of checking a solution is in fact to repeat it with a halved step-length, though more efficient means are suggested in specialist texts. A further point is that the widely used fourth-order Runge-Kutta method requires four evaluations per step of the function f, compared with at most two per step of a predictor-corrector solution of comparable accuracy. The latter method may therefore be more suitable in cases where f is very complicated, so that its evaluation is expensive of computing time.

Exercises

The use of a desk calculator, if available, is recommended when working these exercises, though they can all be tackled using only a standard set of four-figure tables. If the reader has some knowledge of programming, and access to a computer, he will find it instructive to repeat the calculations using various step lengths.

1. Continue the numerical solution of the example on p. 365, to $x = 0.5$ and $x = 0.6$, using (i) the modified Euler method, (ii) the Adams-Bashforth method, and (iii) the fourth-order Runge-Kutta method. Compare your results with the analytic solution.

2. Repeat the numerical solution of the example on p. 362 using the Runge-Kutta method with $h = 0.2$. Round the results to four decimal places, and compare them with those given in the table of solutions.

3. Given $y' = y + 1/x$, with $y(1) = 0$, calculate $y(2)$ to four decimal places, using the Adams-Bashforth method with $h = 0.2$. Three steps of the Runge-Kutta process should be used to start the solution.

4. Show that the previous exercise has the solution

$$y = e^x \int_1^x \frac{e^{-t}}{t} \, dt$$

and hence calculate an approximation to $y(2)$ using Simpson's rule with $h = 0.1$, rounding your result to four decimal places.

5. If the equation $y' = f(x, y)$ is such that higher derivatives of y are easily obtained, it may be solved numerically by a Taylor series method. For the equation of questions 3 and 4, for example, we have

$$y' = y + \frac{1}{x}$$

whence
$$y'' = y' - \frac{1}{x^2} = y + \frac{1}{x} - \frac{1}{x^2}$$

and so on.

Using this same equation, with $y(1) = 0$, expand $y(x)$ in a Taylor series about $x = 1$, and evaluate $y(2)$ approximately by setting $x = 2$ and summing the first ten terms of the series. [The series has alternating signs and converges slowly; a better approximation to its sum results from adding only half the last term rather than all of it.]

NOTES ON CHAPTER 8

1. The first half of this chapter covers most of the standard methods for the analytical solution of first-order equations. Cases may be encountered, however, where some modification is necessary before any of these techniques will prove successful; other cases do not possess solutions which are expressible in a closed form in terms of a finite number of elementary functions. For example

$$\sin^2(x + y) + y' = 0$$

cannot, as it stands, be solved by any of the standard methods, although the substitution $x + y = z$ immediately permits separation of the variables. Such a substitution is often suggested by the form of a particular equation. On the other hand, it has been proved that the apparently innocuous equation

$$y' = x^2 + y^2$$

has no solution in terms of the elementary functions.

2. In section 8.2 it is stated that any non-exact equation of the first order and first degree possesses an integrating factor $\mu(x, y)$ which will render it exact. In fact, any such equation has an infinite number of integrating factors, since if multiplication by μ gives the exact equation $du/dx = 0$, then multiplication by $\mu(df/du)$, where f is any *arbitrary* function of u, leads to $du/dx \cdot df/du = df/dx = 0$, which is also exact. Unfortunately, this in no way facilitates the finding of an integrating factor for a given equation. If all else fails, such a factor may sometime

be found by trial and error; the reader may like to confirm, for instance, that while

$$y' + \tan x \cot y + 2 \cos x \operatorname{cosec} y = 0$$

cannot be solved by any standard method, it becomes exact on multiplication by $\cos x \sin y$.

3. This book is concerned chiefly with applicable methods, and no theory relating to the existence or uniqueness of solutions has been included. For discussion of these matters the reader is referred to H. T. H. Piaggio: *Differential Equations*, Bell; E. L. Ince: *Ordinary Differential Equations*, Dover, or E. A. Coddington: *An Introduction to Ordinary Differential Equations*, Prentice-Hall. The first also treats partial differential equations, while the other two deal with differential equations in the complex domain. A more modern approach is adopted in the last-mentioned reference than in the others.

4. The fact that an equation can be solved analytically is often of no great advantage in a practical context. For instance, the solution of

$$y' - \frac{2y}{1 - x^4} = 0$$

is
$$y = c \left(\frac{1 + x}{1 - x} \right)^{\frac{1}{2}} e^{\tan^{-1} x}$$

and the problem of tabulating y for a series of values of x (in order that a graph may be drawn, for instance) involves the repeated computation of an inverse tangent, an exponential, and a square root, together with several arithmetic operations. It is quite possible, in fact, that a satisfactory tabulation may be made, with less computational labour, by solving the equation numerically from the outset. This is even more likely to be the case if the analytic solution cannot be expressed in an explicit form, since now we are faced with the additional task of solving a non-linear algebraic equation for y by some iterative method.

5. The discussion of numerical methods for the solution of $y' = f(x, y)$ in the second half of the chapter is necessarily only a brief introduction to this very large subject. The aim has been to outline the principles underlying the two main classes of methods; space has not permitted more than a superficial treatment of errors and stability, and further information on these topics may be found in (amongst many others) B. Noble: *Numerical Methods, Vol. II*, Oliver and Boyd, or R. W. Hamming: *Numerical Methods for Scientists and Engineers*, McGraw-Hill.

6. It is an easy matter to extend the numerical methods of this chapter to the solution of systems of simultaneous equations of the form

$$y'_1 = f_1(x, y_1, y_2, y_3, \ldots)$$
$$y'_2 = f_2(x, y_1, y_2, y_3, \ldots)$$
$$y'_3 = f_3(x, y_1, y_2, y_3, \ldots)$$

and so on. As will be shown in chapter 9, any ordinary differential equation of order greater than one may be written as such a system of first-order equations; the methods discussed in this chapter are therefore of very general application.

Miscellaneous exercises

Obtain the general solutions of the following differential equations:

1. $y' + 2y \tan x = x$.
2. $(3x^2 + 6xy^2) + (6x^2y - 2y)y' = 0$.
3. $x^2yy' - (x^2 + y^2)^{3/2} = xy^2$.
4. $y - (2x + y^3e^y)y' = 0$.
5. $(12x + 13y - 3) - (7x + 18y - 8)y' = 0$.
6. $y' + 2y = e^{-x} \cos x$.
7. $(x^2 + xy)y' + xy = 1$.
8. $(1 + x^2)y' + xy = x^2y^3$.
9. $(2x^4 - y^2)y' = xy(x^2 + 5y)$.

Solve the following equations subject to the given boundary conditions:

10. $y' \sin x + (1 + \cos x)y = \sin x$; $y(\pi/2) = \pi/2$.
11. $xy' = 3(y - x)^2 + (y - x) + x$; $y(1) = \frac{3}{4}$.
12. $x(1 + x^2y^2)y' + y(1 + xy) = 0$; $y(1) = \frac{1}{2}$.
13. $(y - x - \frac{1}{2})y' = x^2 - 2xy + y^2$; $y(0) = 0$.
14. $xy' = 1 - y - x^2$; $y(1) = 0$.
15. $2y' + y \log x = 2e^x(1 + \log x)/y$; $y(1) = 0$.
16. $2x^2y' = (x + y + 1)^2$; $y(1) = 0$.

Obtain general solutions and singular solutions (where they arise) of the following differential equations, in which $p \equiv y'$:

17. $4p^2 - 4p \cos 2y - \sin^2 2y = 0$.
18. $y = p(x - 1 + \log p)$.
19. $p^4 - 3pxy - x^4 = 0$.
20. $p^4 - p = e^{-x}$.

21. $y = xp^2 - p^3$.

22. $\sin px \cos y + p = \cos px \sin y$.

23. Show that an equation of the type $y = xf(p) + g(p)$ may have singular solutions $y = xf(p_i) + g(p_i)$, where p_i are the roots of the equation $p - f(p) = 0$. Obtain the general and singular solutions of $6y = x(p^3 - p^2 + 4p) + p$.

24. The table below contains the results of the first three steps in the integration of $x + y - xyy' = 0$, with $y(1) = 1$. Obtain values for $y(1.8)$ and $y(2.0)$ using

    (a) the Runge-Kutta fourth order formula, and
    (b) the Adams-Bashforth method.

x	y
1.0	1.0000
1.2	1.3526
1.4	1.6405
1.6	1.8874

25. Given the equation

$$y' = x^2 + y^2$$

with $y(0) = 0$, and working to four decimal places,

    (i)   find $y(1)$ using the fourth-order Runge-Kutta method with $h = 0.2$,
    (ii) repeat the last two steps of the solution using the Adams-Bashforth method with $h = 0.2$, and
    (iii) use the method of question 5 of the exercises on p. 370 to show that the first three terms in the Maclaurin series for y are

$$\frac{1}{3}x^3 + \frac{1}{63}x^7 + \frac{2}{2079}x^{11} + \cdots$$

and hence obtain a value for $y(1)$.

9 ORDINARY DIFFERENTIAL EQUATIONS OF ORDER > 1

9.0 Introduction: Linear equations

Many differential equations arising in engineering and the physical sciences, particularly in the study of vibratory or oscillatory phenomena, have the form

$$\alpha_n(x)y^{(n)} + \alpha_{n-1}(x)y^{(n-1)} + \cdots + \alpha_1(x)y'(x) + \alpha_0(x)y = f(x) \qquad (1)$$

in which $\alpha_n, \alpha_{n-1}, \ldots, \alpha_1, \alpha_0$ and f are given functions of x. Such an equation is known as a *linear ordinary differential equation* of order n. In this chapter it will sometimes be convenient to write a linear equation in the abbreviated form

$$L(y) = f(x) \qquad (2)$$

where L denotes a *linear differential operator*:

$$L \equiv \alpha_n(x)\frac{d^n}{dx^n} + \alpha_{n-1}(x)\frac{d^{n-1}}{dx^{n-1}} + \cdots + \alpha_1(x)\frac{d}{dx} + \alpha_0(x)$$

The linearity property of L is expressed by the easily confirmed result

$$L(c_1 y + c_2 z) = c_1 L(y) + c_2 L(z)$$

where c_1 and c_2 are any constants and y and z any functions of x possessing derivatives up to the nth order.

The general solution of a differential equation of order n always contains n arbitrary constants. This fact will not be proved, though it will later be shown that an ordinary differential equation of order n can always be expressed as a system of n simultaneous first-order equations, and it therefore seems reasonable to expect the presence in its general solution of n arbitrary constants. The evaluation of these in a specific application will normally require the availability of n boundary conditions. Let us suppose that we know any *particular integral* of equation (1) — that is, any function $y = v(x)$ which satisfies the equation but contains no arbitrary constants. Then, using the operator notation of equation (2) we have

$$L(v) = f(x) \qquad (3)$$

374

Let us now seek another solution, of the form $y = u(x) + v(x)$, which must satisfy

$$L(u + v) = L(u) + L(v) = f(x) \tag{4}$$

Subtraction of equation (3) from equation (4) gives

$$L(u) = 0$$

and $u(x)$ is therefore a solution of the *reduced equation* $L(y) = 0$ resulting from setting $f(x) = 0$ in equations (1) or (2); $u(x)$ is called the *complementary function*. In what follows, we shall find that the complementary function of a linear equation of order n always contains n arbitrary constants. Thus $u(x) + v(x)$, since it satisfies $L(y) = f(x)$ and contains n arbitrary constants, is the most general solution of that equation. Reference to section 8.3 of the last chapter will confirm this finding in the case of first-order linear equations.†

In the foregoing, the particular integral $v(x)$ is not unique, since the assignment of *any* specific values to the arbitrary constants in the general solution leads to a function which, since it satisfies the full equation and contains no arbitrary constants, is a particular integral. However, in a given application the choice of one particular integral rather than another simply leads to the attribution of different values to the arbitrary constants of the general solution when the boundary conditions are applied, the final result being the same for any choice of $v(x)$.

9.1 Linear equations with constant coefficients

Many practical problems give rise to linear equations in which the coefficients of y and its derivatives (the α's in equation (1)) are all constants. An equation of this type is rather easier to solve, in general, than an equation with variable coefficients. In the next section we shall outline a method of solution using Laplace transforms, but we shall first demonstrate some alternative techniques and discuss some of the properties of the solutions obtained. We consider first the problem of finding the complementary function.

9.1.1 *Solution of the reduced equation*
To illustrate the method, we will solve the second-order equation

$$L(y) = y'' + \alpha_1 y' + \alpha_0 y = 0 \tag{5}$$

---

† A parallel may be drawn here with the case of the matrix equation AY = B, where A is a square matrix, Y and B column vectors. It was proved in section 7.2.2 of chapter 7 that the most general solution of this equation is the sum of the general solution of AY = 0 and any particular solution of AY = B.

in which α_1 and α_0 are constants. There is no loss of generality in taking the coefficient of y'' to be unity, since this can always be arranged by multiplication by an appropriate constant. We will tentatively assume a solution of the form

$$y = e^{mx}$$

since it is clear that both y' and y'' are then simply multiples of y itself, and it therefore seems plausible that e^{mx} may be made to satisfy equation (5) by a suitable choice of the constant m. On substituting the assumed solution into that equation, we find

$$m^2 e^{mx} + \alpha_1 m e^{mx} + \alpha_0 e^{mx} = 0$$

or, since $e^{mx} \neq 0$ for any m,

$$m^2 + \alpha_1 m + \alpha_0 = 0$$

This algebraic equation is called the *auxiliary equation,* and its solutions are

$$m_1 = \tfrac{1}{2}\{-\alpha_1 + \sqrt{(\alpha_1^2 - 4\alpha_0)}\} \qquad \text{and} \qquad m_2 = \tfrac{1}{2}\{-\alpha_1 - \sqrt{(\alpha_1^2 - 4\alpha_0)}\} \quad (6)$$

Then
$$y_1 = e^{m_1 x}$$

and
$$y_2 = e^{m_2 x}$$

are both solutions of equation (5). Indeed, any linear combination of these functions is also evidently a solution, since, if c_1 and c_2 are arbitrary constants, we have

$$L(c_1 y_1 + c_2 y_2) = c_1 L(y_1) + c_2 L(y_2) = 0$$

Thus the function

$$y = c_1 e^{m_1 x} + c_2 e^{m_2 x} \tag{7}$$

is the general solution of equation (5), since it not only satisfies that equation but also contains two arbitrary constants (except, as we shall see shortly, when $m_1 = m_2$).

If, in equation (5), the coefficients are such that $\alpha_1^2 - 4\alpha_0 > 0$, then both m_1 and m_2 are real, and the solution of the equation is simply the sum of two exponential terms. On the other hand, if $\alpha_1^2 - 4\alpha_0 < 0$, then m_1 and m_2 are complex conjugates. If we set $m_1 = -\tfrac{1}{2}\alpha_1 + i\eta$, $m_2 = -\tfrac{1}{2}\alpha_1 - i\eta$, where $\eta \equiv \tfrac{1}{2}\sqrt{(4\alpha_0 - \alpha_1^2)}$, equation (7) becomes

$$y = e^{-\frac{1}{2}\alpha_1 x}\{c_1 e^{i\eta x} + c_2 e^{-i\eta x}\}$$
$$= e^{-\frac{1}{2}\alpha_1 x}\left\{(c_1 + c_2)\frac{e^{i\eta x} + e^{-i\eta x}}{2} + i(c_1 - c_2)\frac{e^{i\eta x} - e^{-i\eta x}}{2i}\right\}$$

or
$$y = e^{-\frac{1}{2}\alpha_1 x}\{c_1' \cos \eta x + c_2' \sin \eta x\} \tag{8}$$

on recalling from chapter 1 the relations between exponential and trigonometric functions. In equation (8) we have $c'_1 \equiv c_1 + c_2$ and $c'_2 \equiv i(c_1 - c_2)$; since they involve respectively the sum and difference of two arbitrary constants, c'_1 and c'_2 are themselves arbitrary. Equation (8) may be expressed in the alternative form

$$y = c'_3 e^{-\frac{1}{2}\alpha_1 x} \sin (\eta x + \phi) \tag{9}$$

expansion of the sine revealing that $c'_3 \sin = \phi = c'_1$ and $c'_3 \cos \phi = c'_2$, whence

$$\phi = \tan^{-1} c'_1/c'_2 \qquad \text{and} \qquad c'_3 = \sqrt{(c'^2_1 + c'^2_2)}$$

It remains to consider the situation when $\alpha_1^2 - 4\alpha_0 = 0$. This is the exceptional case mentioned earlier where equation (7) does not give the general solution of equation (5). We see from equation (6) that now $m_1 = m_2 = -\frac{1}{2}\alpha_1$; equation (7) therefore becomes $y = C e^{-\frac{1}{2}\alpha_1 x}$, where $C \equiv c_1 + c_2$. This is certainly a solution if $\alpha_1^2 - 4\alpha_0 = 0$, but not the general solution, since it contains only one arbitrary constant. However, we note that when $\alpha_1^2 - 4\alpha_0 = 0$ the equation may be written as

$$y'' + \alpha_1 y' + \tfrac{1}{4}\alpha_1^2 y = \left(\frac{d}{dx} + \tfrac{1}{2}\alpha_1\right)\left(\frac{dy}{dx} + \tfrac{1}{2}\alpha_1 y\right) = 0$$

If we define $z \equiv (dy/dx + \tfrac{1}{2}\alpha_1 y)$, this becomes

$$\frac{dz}{dx} + \tfrac{1}{2}\alpha_1 z = 0$$

which is a linear first-order equation in z whose solution is

$$z = c''_1 e^{-\frac{1}{2}\alpha_1 x}$$

Then
$$z = \frac{dy}{dx} + \tfrac{1}{2}\alpha_1 y = c''_1 e^{-\frac{1}{2}\alpha_1 x}$$

which is another linear first-order equation, this time in y, having the solution

$$y = (c''_1 x + c''_2) e^{-\frac{1}{2}\alpha_1 x} \tag{10}$$

Thus when $\alpha_1^2 - 4\alpha_0 = 0$ the general solution of equation (5) is given by equation (10), which contains the necessary two arbitrary constants. The reader may like to confirm for himself the details of the solution outlined above.

To summarise, then, the general solution of

$$y'' + \alpha_1 y' + \alpha_0 y = 0$$

takes one of three forms, depending on the values of α_1 and α_0:

(i) $\alpha_1^2 - 4\alpha_0 > 0$: the roots m_1 and m_2 of the auxiliary equation are real and distinct, and

$$y = c_1 e^{m_1 x} + c_2 e^{m_2 x}$$

(ii) $\alpha_1^2 - 4\alpha_0 < 0$: the auxiliary equation has complex conjugate roots $-\frac{1}{2}\alpha_1 \pm \eta i$, and

$$y = e^{-\frac{1}{2}\alpha_1 x}\left\{c_1' \cos \eta x + c_2' \sin \eta x\right\} = c_3' e^{-\frac{1}{2}\alpha_1 x} \sin(\eta x + \phi)$$

(iii) $\alpha_1^2 - 4\alpha_0 = 0$: the auxiliary equation has real coincident roots $m = -\frac{1}{2}\alpha_1$, and

$$y = (c_1'' x + c_2'') e^{-\frac{1}{2}\alpha_1 x}$$

The second-order equation we have been studying is of great importance in applied mathematics, and it is worth while committing the various forms of its solution to memory. For instance, if x is taken to represent time and y linear displacement from a reference position $y = 0$, the equation may be an expression of Newton's second law of motion, relating the acceleration y'' of a particle of mass M to a displacement-proportional force $-M\alpha_0 y$ and a velocity-proportional force $-M\alpha_1 y'$. Let us analyse the motion of the particle for the three cases above from the nature of the solution:

Case (*i*) ($\alpha_1^2 - 4\alpha_0 > 0$). Suppose that $c_1 \neq 0$ and $c_2 \neq 0$. If at least one of m_1 and m_2 is positive, the displacement y increases without limit as the time x increases; the system described by the equation is then said to be *unstable*. Only if m_1 and m_2 are both negative is the system *stable*, tending asymptotically to its equilibrium position $y = 0$ from some initial disturbed position. It is not difficult to see that $\alpha_1 > 0$ is a necessary and sufficient condition for stability.

Case (*ii*) ($\alpha_1^2 - 4\alpha_0 < 0$). The motion is now oscillatory. If α_1 is negative the exponential factor in the solution causes the amplitude of the oscillations to increase indefinitely as x increases, and the system is unstable. If α_1 is positive the system is said to be damped, and the amplitude of the oscillations decreases as the system returns to its equilibrium state.

Case (*iii*) ($\alpha_1^2 - 4\alpha_0 = 0$). Again, the system is stable if $\alpha_1 > 0$ and unstable if $\alpha_1 < 0$. For a given value of α_0, the choice of a positive α_1 such that $\alpha_1^2 - 4\alpha_0 = 0$ gives the maximum rate of return towards the equilibrium state consistent with no overshoot occurring; the system is then said to be *critically damped*.

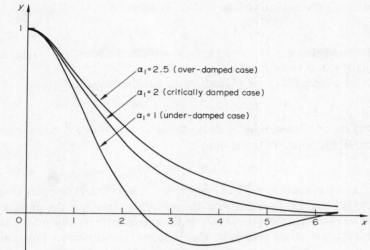

Fig. 9.1 Solutions of $y'' + \alpha_1 y' + y = 0$

Special mention should also be made of the behaviour of the system when $\alpha_1 = 0$, that is, when the equation contains no velocity-dependent term. The solutions of

$$y'' + \alpha_0 y = 0$$

are

$$y = c_1 e^{\sqrt{|\alpha_0|}x} + c_2 e^{-\sqrt{|\alpha_0|}x} \qquad (\alpha_0 < 0)$$

and

$$y = C \sin (\sqrt{(\alpha)_0}x + \phi) \qquad (\alpha_0 > 0)$$

In the former case the system is unstable, and in the latter case it performs the oscillatory motion with constant amplitude known as *simple harmonic motion*.

The extension of the method of this section to the determination of the complementary function of any linear equation with constant coefficients, whatever its order, is straightforward. The trial substitution $y = e^{mx}$ always leads to a polynomial equation in m, whose degree is equal to the order of the differential equation. Each distinct root m_i of this auxiliary equation gives rise to a term $c_i e^{m_i x}$ in the complementary function, where c_i is an arbitrary constant. If multiple roots occur, it is found that a root m_k of multiplicity p gives rise to a term $w(x) e^{m_k x}$, where $w(x)$ is a polynomial in x, of degree $p - 1$, having arbitrary coefficients. We have already observed an example of this latter behaviour in the solution of a second-order equation whose auxiliary equation has two equal roots. We conclude by working through a specific example.

Example. Find that solution of the fifth-order equation

$$y^{(v)} + 10y'' + 15y' + 6y = 0$$

which is bounded as $x \to +\infty$ and which also satisfies the boundary conditions $y(0) = y'(0) = 0; y(1) = e^{-1}$.

The trial substitution $y = e^{mx}$ leads to the auxiliary equation

$$m^5 + 10m^2 + 15m + 6 = 0$$

(note that the coefficient of m^i is always the same as that of $y^{(i)}$ in the original equation). Factorising this in the form

$$(m + 1)^3 (m^2 - 3m + 6) = 0$$

we see that it has a root $m = -1$ of multiplicity 3, and distinct complex conjugate roots $m = \frac{1}{2}(3 \pm i\sqrt{15}$. As indicated in the preceding paragraph, the triple root gives rise to a term $(c_0 + c_1 x + c_2 x^2)e^{-x}$ in the complementary function, where c_0, c_1 and c_2 are arbitrary constants. The complete complementary function is therefore

$$y = (c_0 + c_1 x + c_2 x^2)\, e^{-x} + e^{\frac{3}{2}x}(c_3\, e^{i\sqrt{(15)}x} + c_4\, e^{-i\sqrt{(15)}x})$$

$$= (c_0 + c_1 x + c_2 x^2)\, e^{-x} + \tfrac{1}{2} e^{\frac{3}{2}x}(\{c_3 + c_4\}\, \{e^{i\sqrt{(15)}x} + e^{-i\sqrt{(15)}x}\}$$

$$+ \{c_3 - c_4\}\, \{e^{i\sqrt{(15)}x} - e^{-i\sqrt{(15)}x}\})$$

or $\qquad y = (c_0 + c_1 x + c_2 x^2)\, e^{-x} + e^{\frac{3}{2}x}\{c_3' \cos\sqrt{(15)}x + c_4' \sin\sqrt{(15)}x\}$

where, since c_3 and c_4 are arbitrary, so are $c_3' \equiv c_3 + c_4$ and $c_4' \equiv i(c_3 - c_4)$. It will be observed that, since the original equation was of the fifth order, this general solution contains five arbitrary constants.

The particular solution required is to be bounded as $x \to +\infty$, and the presence of the factor $e^{\frac{3}{2}x}$ makes this impossible unless $c_3' = c_4' = 0$. Furthermore, if $y(0) = 0$, we must have $c_0 = 0$. We are left with

$$y = (c_1 x + c_2 x^2)\, e^{-x}$$

whence $\qquad\qquad y' = (c_1 + \{2c_2 - c_1\}x - c_2 x^2)\, e^{-x}$

If $y'(0) = 0$, it follows that $c_1 = 0$. There remains

$$y = c_2 x^2\, e^{-x}$$

whence $\qquad\qquad y(1) = c_2\, e^{-1}$

But we are given that $y(1) = e^{-1}$, and hence $c_2 = 1$. The final solution is therefore

$$y = x^2\, e^{-x}$$

9.1.2 *Determination of a particular integral*

Various methods exist for finding a particular integral of a linear equation with constant coefficients. In the next section we will demonstrate the use of Laplace transforms in this context,† but first we will illustrate a technique based on intelligent guesswork. Most linear differential equations arising in practice have the form

$$L(y) = f(x)$$

in which $f(x)$ is either a polynomial, an exponential function, a linear combination of a sine and a cosine, or a product of such functions. In such instances a particular integral may frequently be found by inspection, but otherwise one may usually be determined which is a function having the same characteristics as $f(x)$, but involving different numerical coefficients whose values may be established by means of a trial substitution. Some appropriate substitutions are listed below; in this table, known constants are denoted by small letters and undetermined coefficients by capital letters:

Form of $f(x)$	Trial substitution
$\displaystyle\sum_{r=0}^{n} a_r x^r$	$\displaystyle\sum_{r=0}^{n} A_r x^r$
e^{ax}	$A\,e^{ax}$
$p\cos ax + q\sin ax$	$A\cos ax + B\sin ax$
$\displaystyle e^{ax}\sum_{r=0}^{n} a_r x^r$	$\displaystyle e^{ax}\sum_{r=0}^{n} A_r x^r$
$\displaystyle(p\cos ax + q\sin ax)\sum_{r=0}^{n} a_r x^r$	$\displaystyle\cos ax\sum_{r=0}^{n} A_r x^r + \sin ax\sum_{r=0}^{n} B_r x^r$
$e^{ax}(p\cos bx + q\sin bx)$	$e^{ax}(A\cos bx + B\sin bx)$

Trial substitutions for finding particular integrals

---

† We have omitted the D-operator method because of its close similarity to the Laplace transform method, which is here preferred because of its wider application and more rigorous mathematical justification.

These trial substitutions may be used in conjunction with the following theorem, which is, in effect, simply a restatement of the linearity property of the operator L:

Theorem 1 (superposition theorem). If $y = y_1(x)$ satisfies $L(y) = g(x)$ and $y = y_2(x)$ satisfies $L(y) = h(x)$, where L is any linear ordinary differential operator, then $y = (y_1 + y_2)$ satisfies $L(y) = g(x) + h(x)$.

Proof.
We have $$L(y_1) = g(x)$$

and $$L(y_2) = h(x)$$

whence addition leads to

$$L(y_1) + L(y_2) = L(y_1 + y_2) = g(x) + h(x)$$

One implication of the superposition theorem is that, if a linear equation has a number of dissimilar terms on its right-hand side, a particular integral may be found by summing particular integrals of the equations resulting from taking each of these terms separately on the right-hand side.

Example. Find the general solution of the equation

$$y'' + 3y' + 2y = 1 + 4x + 2x^2 - 20e^{-3x} \cos 2x \tag{11}$$

The complementary function is the solution of the reduced equation $y'' + 3y' + 2y = 0$, and proves to be $c_1 e^{-x} + c_2 e^{-2x}$. In order to determine a particular integral we invoke the superposition theorem, and first find a particular integral of

$$y'' + 3y' + 2y = 1 + 4x + 2x^2 \tag{12}$$

Here, since the right-hand side is a second-degree polynomial, we substitute

$$y = A_0 + A_1 x + A_2 x^2$$

in accordance with the first entry in the table; this gives

$$y' = A_1 + 2A_2 x$$

and $$y'' = 2A_2$$

Substitution for y, y' and y'' into equation (12) leads to

$$(2A_2 + 3A_1 + 2A_0) + (6A_2 + 2A_1)x + 2A_2 x^2 = 1 + 4x + 2x^2$$

whence, by equating coefficients, we find $A_2 = 1$, $A_1 = -1$, and $A_0 = 1$. Therefore

$$y = 1 - x + x^2 \tag{13}$$

is a particular integral of equation (12), and it remains to find one of

$$y'' + 3y' + 2y = -20\, e^{-3x} \cos 2x \qquad (14)$$

Here the appropriate trial function is the last in the table, and we set

$$y = e^{-3x}(B_1 \cos 2x + B_2 \sin 2x)$$

Although equation (14) contains no $e^{-3x} \sin 2x$ term, it nonetheless is necessary to include one in the trial function, since differentiation of $e^{-3x} \cos 2x$ gives rise to terms of this type. We obtain

$$y' = e^{-3x}\, (\{2B_2 - 3B_1\} \cos 2x - \{2B_1 + 3B_2\} \sin 2x)$$

and $\qquad y'' = e^{-3x}\, (\{5B_1 - 12B_2\} \cos 2x + \{12B_1 + 5B_2\} \sin 2x)$

Substitution for y, y' and y'' into equation (14) gives, after cancellation of a factor e^{-3x}

$$-(2B_1 + 6B_2) \cos 2x + (6B_1 - 2B_2) \sin 2x = -20 \cos 2x$$

Then $\qquad\qquad\qquad\qquad 2B_1 + 6B_2 = 20$

and $\qquad\qquad\qquad\qquad 6B_1 - 2B_2 = 0$

whence $B_1 = 1$ and $B_2 = 3$. Hence a particular integral of equation (14) is

$$y = e^{-3x}\, (\cos 2x + 3 \sin 2x) \qquad (15)$$

Finally, by virtue of the superposition theorem

$$y = 1 - x + x^2 + e^{-3x}\, (\cos 2x + 3 \sin 2x)$$

is a particular integral of equation (11), from equations (13) and (15); addition of the complementary function yields the general solution

$$y = c_1 e^{-x} + c_2 e^{-2x} + (1 - x + x^2) + e^{-3x}\, (\cos 2x + 3 \sin 2x)$$

The process illustrated breaks down if one or more terms of the trial substitution are included in the complementary function; for this reason it is advisable to find the complementary function first. The remedy in such cases is simply to multiply the trial function by x before making the substitution; if one or more terms of the new trial function are contained in the complementary function, then multiply it by x yet again, and so on.

Example. Find a particular integral of the equation

$$y'' - 2y' + y = (1 + x)\, e^x$$

Since the auxiliary equation has equal roots $m = 1$, the complementary function is $(c_1 x + c_2)\, e^x$. At first sight, the appropriate trial substitution for finding a particular integral is $y = (A_0 + A_1 x)\, e^x$, but we note that both $A_0\, e^x$ and $A_1 x\, e^x$ are contained in the complementary function. Accordingly, we next consider $y = (A_0 x + A_1 x^2)\, e^x$ as our trial function. Even now, however, the term $A_0 x\, e^x$ is to be found in the complementary function. A further multiplication by x gives $y = (A_0 x^2 + A_1 x^3)\, e^x$; now neither term arises in the complementary function, and we therefore substitute this expression into the differential equation to obtain, after cancellation of e^x

$$(2A_0 + \{4A_0 + 6A_1\}x + \{A_0 + 6A_1\}x^2 + A_1 x^3) - 2(2A_0 x + \{A_0 + 3A_1\}\,x^2 + A_1 x^3)$$
$$+ (A_0 x^2 + A_1 x^3) = 1 + x$$

or $$2A_0 + 6A_1 x = 1 + x$$

the x^2 and x^3 terms having cancelled out. Then $A_0 = \tfrac{1}{2}$, $A_1 = \tfrac{1}{6}$, and the general solution is

$$y = (\tfrac{1}{6}x^3 + \tfrac{1}{2}x^2 + c_1 x + c_2)\, e^x$$

The reader may like to verify for himself that no values of A_0 and A_1 can be found such that the differential equation is satisfied by either of the two rejected trial functions.

Exercises

1. By differentiating the following relations twice and eliminating c_1 and c_2 between the resulting equations, show that in each case y satisfies a linear second-order differential equation with constant coefficients:

   (i) $y = c_1 e^x + c_2 e^{2x} + x + 3$,

   (ii) $y = c_1 \sin 3x + c_2 \cos 3x + e^{2x}$,

   (iii) $y = (c_1 x + c_2)\, e^{-x}$.

Determine the general solutions of the following equations. In the cases where boundary conditions are given, find also the solutions satisfying those conditions.

2. $y'' - y' - 2y = 4$; $y(0) = 1, y'(0) = 6$.

3. $y'' - 6y' + 9y = 0$; $y(0) = 0, y(1) = 1$.

4. $y'' + y' + y = x + e^{-x}$.

5. $y''' + 2y'' - 3y' = 130 \sin 2x$.

6. $y^{(iv)} - y = x^3$.

7. $y'' + 6y' + 8y = 4e^{-2x}$; $y(0) = 3, y'(0) = 2$.

8. $y'' + 9y = \cosh x$.

9. $y'' + 2y' + 10y = (25x^2 + 16x + 2)\, e^{3x}$; $y(0) = y'(0) = 0$.

10. $y''' - 3y' + 2y = 4x^2 - 6e^x$.

11. $y'' - 6y' + 13y = 8e^{3x} \sin 2x$; $y(0) = 1, y(\pi/4) = 0$.

12. $y^{(iv)} + 4y'' = 48x$; $y(0) = y'(0) = y''(0) = y'''(0) = 0$.

13. $2y'' + 3y' + y = (18 \sin x - \cos x) e^x$.

14. $y'' + 2y' + y = 6(2x^2 - x + 1) e^{-x}$; $y(0) = 1, y'(0) = 0$.

15. $y'' + 4y = 8 \cos^2 x$; $y(\pi) = 4, y'(0) = 4$.

16. $y''' - 6y'' + 12y' - 8y = 16x^3$.

17. $y'' + y' - y = 5e^{-x}(\sin x - 1)$.

18. $y'' - 3y' + 2y = 24 \sinh 2x$.

In the following systems of simultaneous equations, x and y are both functions of the independent variable t. By eliminating one of the unknown functions, express each system as a second-order linear equation in the other unknown, and hence solve it, subject to the given boundary conditions:

19. $\left.\begin{array}{l} x'(t) = x(t) + y(t) \\ y'(t) = 2x(t) + 4t \end{array}\right\}$ $x(0) = 0, y(0) = 2$.

20. $\left.\begin{array}{l} x'(t) = x(t) + y(t) - 5 \sin t \\ y'(t) = 3x(t) - y(t) \end{array}\right\}$ $x(0) = 1, y(0) = 0$.

9.2 Laplace transforms and their applications to the solution of linear equations with constant coefficients

9.2.1 *Definition and properties of the Laplace transform*

Definition. Let $f(t)$ be a function of the real variable t, defined for all $t \geqslant 0$. Then the *classical Laplace transform* of $f(t)$ is the function

$$F(s) \equiv \int_0^\infty e^{-st} f(t) \mathrm{d}t$$

provided that the improper integral exists for some finite value of s.

In this definition the usual convention has been adopted that a capital letter is used for the Laplace transform of the function denoted by the corresponding small letter. Another useful notation for expressing the relation between $f(t)$ and $F(s)$ is

$$F(s) = \mathcal{L}\{f(t)\}$$

where $\mathcal{L}$ is referred to as the Laplace operator. Conversely, we may write

$$f(t) = \mathcal{L}^{-1}\{\mathrm{F}(s)\}$$

Here $\mathcal{L}^{-1}$ is the inverse Laplace operator, and $f(t)$ is said to be the *inverse Laplace transform* of F(s). It may be shown that, for practical purposes, the inverse Laplace transform $f(t)$ of a given F(s) is unique.

For the purpose of this chapter, the parameter s will be regarded as real, although in more advanced applications it becomes necessary to treat it as complex.

Laplace transforms exist for a wide class of functions $f(t)$ having the property that $|f(t)|$ does not increase 'too rapidly' as $t \to \infty$. In particular, it may be shown that any function $f(t)$ which is sectionally continuous for $0 \leqslant t < \infty$ possesses a Laplace transform if, for some finite value of s, $e^{-st}f(t) \to 0$ as $t \to \infty$. A function is said to be sectionally continuous if, in any finite interval of its argument, it possesses at most a finite number of simple discontinuities (see section 2.1.5). The conditions given here are sufficient for the existence of F(s), though certain functions not fulfilling them do, nevertheless, possess transforms.

Example. Determine the range of values of s for which $f(t) = e^{at}$, (where a is a real constant) possesses a Laplace transform.

We have

$$\mathrm{F}(s) = \int_0^\infty e^{-st}\,e^{at}\,\mathrm{d}t = \lim_{\mathrm{T}\to\infty}\int_0^\mathrm{T} e^{-(s-a)t}\,\mathrm{d}t = \lim_{\mathrm{T}\to\infty}\left[-\frac{e^{-(s-a)t}}{s-a}\right]_0^\mathrm{T} = \frac{1}{s-a}$$

provided $s > a$. If $s < a$, the exponent of the indefinite integral in the square brackets becomes positive, and letting T$\to\infty$ then no longer gives a finite result. Note that the values of s for which the transform does exist are those for which $e^{-st}f(t) \to 0$ as $t \to \infty$.

Example. Show that $f(t) = e^{t^2}$ possesses no Laplace transform.

The transform, if it exists, is given by

$$\mathrm{F}(s) = \int_0^\infty e^{t^2-st}\,\mathrm{d}t$$

The integral defining the transform does not exist, since for any finite value of s the integrand $e^{-st}f(t) \to \infty$ as $t \to \infty$.

We shall now establish the two theorems which are the basis of the Laplace transform method for solving differential equations.

Theorem 2 (linearity of the Laplace operator $\mathcal{L}$). Let c_1 and c_2 be any constants. Then

$$\mathcal{L}\{c_1f_1(t) + c_2f_2(t)\} = c_1F_1(s) + c_2F_2(s)$$

Proof. $\mathcal{L}\{c_1f_1(t) + c_2f_2(t)\} = \int_0^\infty e^{-st}\{c_1f_1(t) + c_2f_2(t)\}\,dt$

$$= c_1\int_0^\infty e^{-st}f_1(t)\,dt + c_2\int_0^\infty e^{-st}f_2(t)\,dt$$

$$= c_1F_1(s) + c_2F_2(s)$$

The use of this linearity property is illustrated by the following examples.

Example. Find the Laplace transforms of cosh at and sinh at, where a is any real constant.

We have already seen that $\mathcal{L}\{e^{at}\} = 1/(s - a)$, provided $s > a$. The formal replacement of a by $-a$ gives $\mathcal{L}\{e^{-at}\} = 1/(s + a)$, $s > -a$. Then

$$\mathcal{L}\{\cosh at\} = \mathcal{L}\{\tfrac{1}{2}(e^{at} + e^{at})\} = \frac{1}{2}\left(\frac{1}{s - a} + \frac{1}{s + a}\right) = \frac{s}{s^2 - a^2}$$

and

$$\mathcal{L}\{\sinh at\} = \mathcal{L}\{\tfrac{1}{2}(e^{at} - e^{-at})\} = \frac{1}{2}\left(\frac{1}{s - a} - \frac{1}{s + a}\right) = \frac{a}{s^2 - a^2}$$

The domain of existence of these transforms is the region in which $\mathcal{L}\{e^{at}\}$ and $\mathcal{L}\{e^{-at}\}$ both exist, namely $s > |a|$.

Example. Find the Laplace transforms of cos at and sin at, where a is any real constant.

Consider $\mathcal{L}\{e^{iat}\}$. We have

$$\mathcal{L}\{e^{iat}\} = \int_0^\infty e^{-(s - ia)t}\,dt = \left[-\frac{e^{-(s - ia)t}}{s - ia}\right]_0^\infty = \frac{1}{s - ia}, \quad s > 0$$

Here we have used the fact that the numerator of the indefinite integral can be written as $e^{-st}(\cos at + i\sin at)$; both the real and imaginary parts of the bracketed expression are bounded as $t \to \infty$, and the factor e^{-st} therefore makes the numerator as a whole tend to zero as $t \to \infty$, provided $s > 0$.

Formally replacing a by $-a$ in the above result, we find

$$\mathcal{L}\{e^{-iat}\} = \frac{1}{s + ia}, \quad s > 0$$

Since

$$\cos at = \frac{1}{2}(e^{iat} + e^{-iat}) \qquad \text{and} \qquad \sin at = \frac{1}{2i}(e^{iat} - e^{-iat})$$

the linearity property permits us to write

$$\mathcal{L}\{\cos at\} = \frac{1}{2}\left(\frac{1}{s - ia} + \frac{1}{s + ia}\right) = \frac{s}{s^2 + a^2}, \qquad s > 0$$

and
$$\mathcal{L}\{\sin at\} = \frac{1}{2i}\left(\frac{1}{s - ia} - \frac{1}{s + ia}\right) = \frac{a}{s^2 + a^2}, \qquad s > 0$$

Theorem 3 (Laplace transform of a first derivative). Let $f(t)$ be a function, continuous for $t \geqslant 0$, having the Laplace transform $F(s)$. Then if $f'(t)$ possesses a transform, that transform is $\mathcal{L}\{f'(t)\} = sF(s) - f(0)$.

Proof. Integration by parts gives

$$\mathcal{L}\{f'(t)\} = \int_0^\infty e^{-st}f'(t)\mathrm{d}t = \left[e^{-st}f(t)\right]_0^\infty + \int_0^\infty s\, e^{-st}f(t)\mathrm{d}t$$

Since $f(t)$ is continuous, $F(s)$ cannot exist unless $\lim_{t \to \infty} e^{-st}f(t) = 0$. Then

$$\mathcal{L}\{f'(t)\} = -f(0) + s\int_0^\infty e^{-st}f(t)\mathrm{d}t = sF(s) - f(0)$$

If $f(t)$ and $f'(t)$ are both continuous for $t \geqslant 0$ then $\mathcal{L}\{f''(t)\}$, if it exists, is given by

$$\mathcal{L}\{f''(t)\} = s^2 F(s) - sf(0) - f'(0)$$

This result follows if we define $g(t) = f'(t)$, so that $G(s) = sF(s) - f(0)$, and apply theorem 3 once again. Repeated application of this procedure leads to the following generalisation:

Corollary (Laplace transform of a higher derivative). If $f(t)$ and its first $(n - 1)$ derivatives are continuous for $t \geqslant 0$ then $\mathcal{L}\{f^{(n)}(t)\}$, if it exists, is given by

$$\mathcal{L}\{f^{(n)}(t)\} = s^n F(s) - s^{n-1}f(0) - s^{n-2}f'(0) - \cdots - f^{(n-1)}(0) \qquad (16)$$

It is theorem 3 and its corollary which enable us to use Laplace transforms in the solution of differential equations.

Example. Solve the differential equation $y'' + 4y = 0$, subject to the boundary conditions $y(0) = 3, y'(0) = 2$.

The linearity property of the Laplace transform permits us to transform the differential equation term by term. Writing $Y(s)$ for $\mathcal{L}\{y(t)\}$, and using the corollary to theorem 3 to transform the derivative, we obtain

$$s^2 Y(s) - 3s - 2 + 4Y(s) = 0$$

or
$$Y(s) = \frac{3s}{s^2 + 4} + \frac{2}{s^2 + 4}$$

The terms on the right-hand side are recognisable as the transforms of $3 \cos 2t$ and $\sin 2t$ respectively (see the last example). Taking inverse transforms term by term, we therefore find

$$y(t) = 3 \cos 2t + \sin 2t$$

This is the solution of the differential equation which satisfies the prescribed boundary conditions.

In this example, we see that the virtue of Laplace transformation is that it turns the original differential equation in $y(t)$ into an algebraic equation in $Y(s)$ whose solution is very easy to obtain. The process is examined in more detail in section 9.2.3; meanwhile, we shall prove a number of additional useful properties of Laplace transforms and illustrate them by deriving the transforms of some further simple functions.

Theorem 4 (first translation property). If $\mathcal{L}\{f(t)\} = F(s)$, then, where a is any real constant, $\mathcal{L}\{e^{at} f(t)\} = F(s - a)$.

Proof.

$$\mathcal{L}\{e^{at} f(t)\} = \int_0^\infty e^{-(s-a)t} f(t) \mathrm{d}t = F(s - a)$$

from the definition of the transform.

Example. Derive $\mathcal{L}\{e^{at} \cos bt\}$ and $\mathcal{L}\{e^{at} \sin bt\}$, where a and b are real constants.
    Since we have already found that

$$\mathcal{L}\{\cos bt\} = \int_0^\infty e^{-st} \cos bt \, \mathrm{d}t = \frac{s}{s^2 + b^2}, \qquad s > 0$$

it follows that

$$\mathcal{L}\{e^{at} \cos bt\} = \int_0^\infty e^{-(s-a)t} \cos bt \, \mathrm{d}t = \frac{(s - a)}{(s - a)^2 + b^2}, \qquad s > a$$

in accordance with the theorem. Similarly,

$$\mathcal{L}\{e^{at} \sin bt\} = \frac{b}{(s-a)^2 + b^2}, \qquad s > a$$

Theorem 5 (multiplication by t). If $\mathcal{L}\{f(t)\} = F(s)$, then $\mathcal{L}\{tf(t)\} = -(d/ds)F(s)$.

Proof. Using Leibniz' rule for differentiating the integral,

$$-\frac{d}{ds} F(s) = -\frac{d}{ds} \int_0^\infty e^{-st}f(t)dt = \int_0^\infty e^{-st} tf(t)dt = \mathcal{L}\{tf(t)\}$$

Repeated application of this theorem leads to

Corollary (multiplication by t^n).

$$\mathcal{L}\{t^n f(t)\} = (-1)^n \frac{d^n}{ds^n} F(s)$$

Example. Find the Laplace transform of $t^n e^{at}$, and hence derive $\mathcal{L}\{t^n\}$.

We commence with the result of an earlier example, namely $\mathcal{L}\{e^{at}\} = 1/(s-a)$, provided that $s > a$. Then

$$\mathcal{L}\{t \, e^{at}\} = -\frac{d}{ds} \left(\frac{1}{s-a}\right) = \frac{1}{(s-a)^2}, \qquad s > a$$

$$\mathcal{L}\{t^2 \, e^{at}\} = \frac{d^2}{ds^2} \left(\frac{1}{s-a}\right) = \frac{2}{(s-a)^3}, \qquad s > a$$

and in general

$$\mathcal{L}\{t^n e^{at}\} = (-1)^n \frac{d^n}{ds^n} \left(\frac{1}{s-a}\right) = \frac{n!}{(s-a)^{n+1}}, \qquad s > a$$

In particular, putting $a = 0$ in these results leads to

$$\mathcal{L}\{1\}^\dagger = \frac{1}{s}, \qquad \mathcal{L}\{t\} = \frac{1}{s^2}, \qquad \mathcal{L}\{t^2\} = \frac{2}{s^3}$$

and in general, $\qquad \mathcal{L}\{t^n\} = \dfrac{n!}{s^{n+1}}, \qquad s > 0$

---

† In this context, 1 is used to denote not the number 1 but the function of t whose value is unity for all t.

Theorem 6 (second translation property). If $\mathcal{L}\{f(t)\} = F(s)$, and if $g(t)$ is the function defined by

$$g(t) = \begin{cases} 0 & t < a \\ f(t - a) & t > a \end{cases}$$

where a is any real constant, then $\mathcal{L}\{g(t)\} = e^{-as}F(s)$.

Proof. $\mathcal{L}\{g(t)\} = \int_0^a e^{-st} \cdot 0 \, dt + \int_a^\infty e^{-st} f(t - a) \, dt$

The first integral is zero, and putting $t - a = \tau$ in the second leads to

$$\mathcal{L}\{g(t)\} = e^{-as} \int_0^\infty e^{-s\tau} f(\tau) d\tau = e^{-as} F(s)$$

The significance of this theorem may seem at first sight a little obscure, but, as shown in figure 9.2, $g(t)$ is the function obtained by shifting $f(t)$ bodily along the t-axis through a distance a.

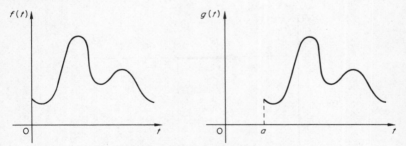

Fig. 9.2. Relation between $f(t)$ and $g(t)$.

Example. The *unit step function* $u(t)$ has the value 0 when $t < 0$ and the value 1 when $t > 0$, its value at $t = 0$ being undefined.† Find $\mathcal{L}\{u(t)\}$ and $\mathcal{L}\{u(t - a)\}$, where a is a real constant.

† In some texts the *two-sided* Laplace transform of a function $f(t)$ is defined by the integral $\int_{-\infty}^\infty e^{-st} f(t) dt$, and in certain respects this type of transform has advantages over the classical, or *one-sided,* transform used in this chapter. The two types of transform may be simply related by the use of the unit step function, since

$$F(s) = \int_0^\infty e^{-st} f(t) dt = \int_{-\infty}^\infty e^{-st} \{u(t)f(t)\} \, dt$$

Since the integral defining the transform takes no account of the behaviour of $f(t)$ for negative values of t we see that $\mathcal{L}\{u(t)\} = \mathcal{L}\{1\} = 1/s$, the functions $u(t)$ and 1 being identical for $t > 0$.

The function $u(t - a)$ has the value 0 when $t - a < 0$ (or $t < a$) and the value 1 when $t - a > 0$ (or $t > a$); this is clearly the function obtained by shifting $u(t)$ a distance a along the positive t-axis. We may therefore use the second translation property to write

$$\mathcal{L}\{u(t - a)\} = e^{-as} \cdot \frac{1}{s}, \qquad s > 0$$

The unit step function may be used to define many discontinuous functions which, like $u(t)$ itself, possess Laplace transforms. We are thereby enabled to solve problems involving such functions quickly and simply. Furthermore, the use of $u(t)$ permits the following concise restatement of theorem 6:

If $\mathcal{L}\{f(t)\} = F(s)$, then $\mathcal{L}\{u(t - a)f(t - a)\} = e^{-as}F(s)$.

Example. Find the Laplace transform of the rectangular pulse function $p(t)$ shown in figure 9.3.

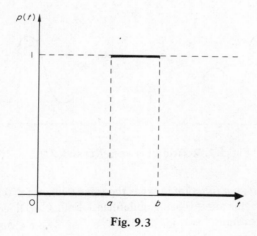

Fig. 9.3

The pulse can be expressed as $p(t) = u(t - a) - u(t - b)$; its transform $P(s)$ is therefore

$$e^{-as} \frac{1}{s} - e^{-bs} \frac{1}{s}, \qquad s > 0$$

or

$$P(s) = \frac{1}{s}(e^{-as} - e^{-bs}), \qquad s > 0$$

9.2.2 *Inversion of Laplace transforms*

In the present context the problem of inversion is that of finding the inverse function $f(t)$ corresponding to a given Laplace transform $F(s)$. For practical purposes, as already mentioned, any transform $F(s)$ possesses a unique inverse. A short table of Laplace transforms is given on p. 395; this table may be used both for finding the transforms of commonly occurring functions and for finding the inverses of commonly occurring transforms. The three following examples illustrate procedures which will be found to enhance the usefulness of the table for finding inverse transforms.

Example. Find the inverse Laplace transform of $F(s) = (7s - 6)/(s^2 - s - 6)$.

Since $s^2 - s - 6 = (s + 2)(s - 3)$, $F(s)$ may be expressed in partial fractions as

$$F(s) = \frac{4}{s + 2} + \frac{3}{s - 3}$$

Each term is now recognisable as the transform of an exponential function, and hence the inverse transform is

$$f(t) = 4\,e^{-2t} + 3\,e^{3t}$$

Example. Find the inverse Laplace transform of $F(s) = (2s + 1)/(s^2 + 4s + 13)$.

Since the denominator has no real factors, the partial fraction method will now involve the use of complex algebra. In this case it is more convenient to write

$$f(t) = \mathcal{L}^{-1}\left\{\frac{2s + 1}{s^2 + 4s + 13}\right\} = \mathcal{L}^{-1}\left\{\frac{2s + 1}{(s + 2)^2 + 9}\right\} = \mathcal{L}^{-1}\left\{\frac{2(s + 2) - 3}{(s + 2)^2 + 3^2}\right\}$$

$$= e^{-2t}\mathcal{L}^{-1}\left\{\frac{2s}{s^2 + 3^2} - \frac{3}{s^2 + 3^2}\right\}$$

Hence
$$f(t) = e^{-2t}(2\cos 3t - \sin 3t)$$

from results previously obtained. Note that the denominator of the transform is first written as the sum (or difference) of two squares; the numerator is then expressed in terms of the same linear function of s, in this case $s + 2$, as has arisen in the denominator. Theorem 4 now enables us to remove an exponential factor, what remains being recognisable as a linear combination of $\mathcal{L}\{\cos 3t\}$ and $\mathcal{L}\{\sin 3t\}$.

Example. Find the inverse transform of $F(s) = 1/(s^2 + 1)^2$.

We see from the table that $\mathcal{L}\{t \cos t\} = (s^2 - 1)/(s^2 + 1)^2$ and also that $\mathcal{L}\{\sin t\} = 1/(s^2 + 1) = (s^2 + 1)/(s^2 + 1)^2$. Thus $\mathcal{L}\{\sin t - t \cos t\} = 2/[(s^2 + 1)^2]$, and it follows that

$$\mathcal{L}^{-1}\left\{\frac{1}{(s^2 + 1)^2}\right\} = \tfrac{1}{2}(\sin t - t \cos t)$$

9.2.3 *The use of Laplace transforms in solving linear differential equations with constant coefficients*

This section is devoted entirely to worked examples which illustrate some of the finer points of the Laplace transform approach to the solution of linear differential equations.

Example. Solve the differential equation

$$y'' + y = t$$

for $y(t)$, subject to the boundary conditions $y(0) = 1, y'(0) = -2$.

If we set $\mathcal{L}\{y(t)\} = Y(s)$ and use equation (9.16) in transforming the differential equation, we obtain

$$s^2 Y(s) - sy(0) - y'(0) + Y(s) = \frac{1}{s^2}$$

where $\mathcal{L}\{t\}$ has been obtained from the table of transforms on p. 395. On putting in the given boundary conditions we obtain

$$(s^2 + 1)Y(s) - s + 2 = \frac{1}{s^2}$$

which may be solved for $Y(s)$:

$$Y(s) = \frac{1}{s^2(s^2 + 1)} + \frac{s}{s^2 + 1} - \frac{2}{s^2 + 1}$$

or

$$Y(s) = \frac{1}{s^2} + \frac{s}{s^2 + 1} - \frac{3}{s^2 + 1}$$

Each expression here is recognisable as the Laplace transform of a specific function of t, and reference to the table of transforms enables us to write down the inverse equation

$$y(t) = t + \cos t - 3 \sin t$$

which is the required solution.

Table of elementary Laplace transforms and their properties

$f(t)$	$F(s) = \int_0^\infty e^{-st} f(t)\,dt$
1. $af_1(t) + bf_2(t)$	$aF_1(s) + bF_2(s)$
2. $e^{at}f(t)$	$F(s-a)$
3. $t^n f(t) \quad (n \geqslant 0)$	$(-1)^n F^{(n)}(s)$
4. $f(at) \quad (a > 0)$	$\dfrac{1}{a} F\left(\dfrac{s}{a}\right)$
5. $g(t) = \begin{cases} 0, & 0 < t < a \\ f(t-a) & t > a \end{cases}$	$e^{-as}F(s)$
6. $f^{(n)}(t)$	$s^n F(s) - s^{n-1}f(0) - s^{n-2}f'(0) - \cdots - f^{(n-1)}(0)$
7. $u(t)$	$1/s$
8. $t^n \quad (n \geqslant 0)$	$n!/s^{n+1}$
9. e^{at}	$1/(s-a)$
10. $t^n e^{at} \quad (n \geqslant 0)$	$n!/(s-a)^{n+1}$
11. $\sin at$	$a/(s^2 + a^2)$
12. $\cos at$	$s/(s^2 + a^2)$
13. $\sinh at$	$a/(s^2 - a^2)$
14. $\cosh at$	$s/(s^2 - a^2)$
15. $t \sin at$	$2as/(s^2 + a^2)^2$
16. $t \cos at$	$(s^2 - a^2)/(s^2 + a^2)^2$
17. $t \sinh at$	$2as/(s^2 - a^2)^2$
18. $t \cosh at$	$(s^2 + a^2)/(s^2 - a^2)^2$
19. $e^{at} \sin bt$	$b/\{(s-a)^2 + b^2\}$
20. $e^{at} \cos bt$	$(s-a)/\{(s-a)^2 + b^2\}$

The following observations are relevant:

(i) The effect of taking the Laplace transform of the original differential equation in $y(t)$ has been to give an algebraic equation in $Y(s)$ which is easily solved. This new equation is valid provided there exists some domain of s in which the transforms of the separate terms all exist. Beyond this, we need not concern ourselves with the details of s, since it disappears from the problem when inverse transforms are taken in the last step.

(ii) Since all the boundary conditions were specified at $t = 0$ the method has led directly to the desired particular integral, and it has not been necessary first to find the general solution. The procedure to adopt when some or all of the boundary conditions are not specified at $t = 0$, or when the general solution is sought, will be shown in the next example.

(iii) The chief difficulty arising is usually the algebraic one of expressing $Y(s)$ in such a form that all its terms can be inverted. When, as is often the case, $Y(s)$ proves to be a rational function of s, it must be decomposed into partial fractions, and a good working knowledge of the methods of achieving this (see Appendix) is therefore essential.

Example. Solve the differential equation

$$y'' + 2y' + 5y = 2 \cos t + 14 \sin t$$

for $y(t)$, subject to the boundary conditions $y(0) = 0$, $y(\pi/4) = \sqrt{2}$.

On taking Laplace transforms, we obtain

$$s^2 Y(s) - s y(0) - y'(0) + 2s Y(s) - 2y(0) + 5Y(s) = \frac{2s}{s^2 + 1} + \frac{14}{s^2 + 1}$$

We are not given the value of $y'(0)$, and for the time being must leave this as an arbitrary parameter. On putting in the other boundary condition and solving for $Y(s)$ we find

$$Y(s) = \frac{2s + 14}{(s^2 + 1)(s^2 + 2s + 5)} + \frac{y'(0)}{s^2 + 2s + 5}$$

or

$$Y(s) = \frac{3 - s}{s^2 + 1} + \frac{s - 1 + y'(0)}{s^2 + 2s + 5}$$

where the first term has been split into partial fractions.

Then

$$y(t) = 3 \sin t - \cos t + \mathcal{L}^{-1} \left\{ \frac{s - 1 + y'(0)}{s^2 + 2s + 5} \right\}$$

Since the denominator of the remaining transform has no real factors, we use the first translation property for its inversion:

$$\mathcal{L}^{-1}\left\{\frac{s-1+y'(0)}{s^2+2s+5}\right\} = \mathcal{L}^{-1}\left\{\frac{s-1+y'(0)}{(s+1)^2+4}\right\} = \mathcal{L}^{-1}\left\{\frac{(s+1)}{(s+1)^2+4} + \frac{y'(0)-2}{(s+1)^2+4}\right\}$$

$$= e^{-t}\mathcal{L}^{-1}\left\{\frac{s}{s^2+4} + (\tfrac{1}{2}y'(0)-1)\frac{2}{s^2+4}\right\}$$

$$= e^{-t}(\cos 2t + (\tfrac{1}{2}y'(0)-1)\sin 2t)$$

Then $\qquad y(t) = 3\sin t - \cos t + e^{-t}\cos 2t + (\tfrac{1}{2}y'(0)-1)e^{-t}\sin 2t$

Now, finally, we may use the other boundary condition, which leads to

$$y(\pi/4) = \frac{3}{\sqrt{2}} - \frac{1}{\sqrt{2}} + e^{-\pi/4}(\tfrac{1}{2}y'(0)-1) = \sqrt{2} + e^{-\pi/4}(\tfrac{1}{2}y'(0)-1)$$

Since we are given that $y(\pi/4) = \sqrt{2}$, it follows that $y'(0) = 2$ and that the required particular integral is

$$y(t) = 3\sin t - \cos t + e^{-t}\cos 2t$$

If we had been seeking the general solution of the differential equation, we would have left both $y(0)$ and $y'(0)$ unspecified at the outset, so that they would have appeared as the two necessary arbitrary constants in the solution.

In the next example it is demonstrated how the unit step function $u(t)$, defined on p. 391, can be used in problems involving discontinuous functions:

Example. Solve the equation

$$y'' + y' = f(t)$$

for $y(t)$ if

$$f(t) = \begin{cases} t, & 0 \leqslant t < 1 \\ 0, & t > 1 \end{cases}$$

and $y(0) = 0$, $y'(0) = -1$.

We may write $f(t)$ in terms of the unit step function as $t\{1 - u(t-1)\}$, since $u(t-1)$ is zero for $0 \leqslant t < 1$ and 1 for $t > 1$. Taking Laplace transforms, we find

$$s^2 Y(s) - sy(0) - y'(0) + sY(s) - y(0) = \frac{1}{s^2} + \frac{d}{ds}\left(\frac{e^{-s}}{s}\right) = \frac{1}{s^2} - \frac{e^{-s}(1+s)}{s^2}$$

where the t-multiplication theorem has been used in transforming the right-hand side. Substitution of the boundary conditions and solution for $Y(s)$ now gives

$$Y(s) = \frac{1}{s^3(s+1)} - \frac{1}{s(s+1)} - \frac{e^{-s}}{s^3}$$

$$= \left(\frac{1}{s^3} - \frac{1}{s^2} + \frac{1}{s} - \frac{1}{s+1}\right) - \left(\frac{1}{s} - \frac{1}{s+1}\right) - \frac{e^{-s}}{s^3}$$

$$= \frac{1}{s^3} - \frac{1}{s^2} - \frac{e^{-s}}{s^3}$$

The inverse of the third term is found with the aid of the second translation theorem, and the solution is

$$y(t) = \tfrac{1}{2}t^2 - t - \begin{cases} 0, & 0 \leqslant t < 1 \\ \tfrac{1}{2}(t-1)^2, & t > 1 \end{cases}$$

or

$$y(t) = \begin{cases} \tfrac{1}{2}t^2 - t, & 0 \leqslant t < 1 \\ -\tfrac{1}{2} & t > 1 \end{cases}$$

We see that the solution changes its nature at the occurrence of the discontinuity in $f(t)$; note, however, that if we define $y(1) = -\tfrac{1}{2}$ both $y(t)$ and $y'(t)$ are continuous at $t = 1$.

Finally, it will be shown how systems of linear equations with constant coefficients may be solved by this method.

Example. Solve the system of equations

$$\left.\begin{array}{c} y' + 2z - 7e^{-t} = 0 \\ 2z' + y + 3e^{-t} = 0 \end{array}\right\}$$

for $y(t)$ and $z(t)$, subject to the boundary conditions $y(0) = -1$, $z(0) = 2$.

The transformed equations are linear algebraic simultaneous equations in $Y(s)$ and $Z(s)$ whose coefficients are functions of s:

$$sY(s) + 2Z(s) = \frac{7}{s+1} - 1$$

$$2sZ(s) + Y(s) = -\frac{3}{s+1} + 4$$

Eliminating $Z(s)$ and solving for $Y(s)$, we obtain

$$Y(s) = \frac{2}{(s+1)^2} - \frac{1}{s+1}$$

whence

$$y(t) = 2t\,e^{-t} - e^{-t}$$

Similarly, $$Z(s) = \frac{1}{(s+1)^2} + \frac{2}{(s+1)}$$

whence $$z(t) = t\,e^{-t} + 2\,e^{-t}$$

Larger systems of equations may be similarly dealt with, though the algebra usually becomes rather tedious.

Exercises

1. Using the table of transforms on p. 395, find the Laplace transforms of:

   (i) $3\cosh 4t - 2\sinh 4t$,   (ii) $(t^2+1)^2$,

   (iii) $e^{-3t}\cos t$,   (iv) $e^{-2t}\cos^2 t$,

   (v) $(1 - t\,e^{-t})^3$,   (vi) $(\sin t - \cos t)^2$,

   (vii) $\frac{1}{6}t^3\sin 2t$,   (viii) $\cos\alpha t\cosh\alpha t$,

   (ix) $f(t) \equiv \begin{cases} 0, & 0 < t < 1 \\ \sin(t-1), & t > 1, \end{cases}$ (x) $f(t) \equiv \begin{cases} 1, & 0 < t < 2 \\ 0, & t > 2, \end{cases}$

   (xi) $f(t) \equiv \begin{cases} e^{2t}, & 0 < t < 3 \\ 0, & t > 3, \end{cases}$ (xii) $f(t) \equiv \begin{cases} t, & 0 < t < 1 \\ e^{1-t}, & t > 1. \end{cases}$

2. Find the inverse Laplace transforms of:

   (i) $\dfrac{1}{s^2+3}$,   (ii) $\dfrac{s+4}{s^2+5s+6}$,   (iii) $\dfrac{3s-2}{s^2-4s+8}$,

   (iv) $\dfrac{3s+4}{4s^2+12s+9}$,   (v) $\dfrac{2s+1}{(s+1)(s^2+1)}$,   (vi) $\dfrac{2s^2+9s+16}{(s-2)^2(s+1)}$,

   (vii) $\dfrac{s+3}{s^2(s-1)^3}$,   (viii) $\dfrac{s^2+2s+3}{(s^2+2s+2)(s^2+2s+5)}$,   (ix) $\dfrac{3s^2}{s^3-\alpha^3}$,

   (x) $\dfrac{3e^{-2s}}{s^2+2s+10}$,   (xi) $\dfrac{1}{s^2}(1-e^{-s})$,   (xii) $\dfrac{1}{s^2}(1-e^{-s})^2$.

3. If $\mathcal{L}\{f''(t)\} = \tan^{-1}(1/s)$, $f(0) = 3$ and $f'(0) = -2$, find $\mathcal{L}\{f(t)\}$.

4. If a is positive, prove that if $\mathcal{L}\{f(t)\} = F(s)$ then $\mathcal{L}\{f(at)\} = (1/a)F(s/a)$.
   Hence, if $\mathcal{L}\{g(t)\} = s^{-1/2}e^{-1/s}$, find $\mathcal{L}\{t\,e^{-3t}g(4t)\}$.

5. Using the table of Laplace transforms, prove that (i) $\displaystyle\int_0^\infty t\,e^{-3t}\cos t\,dt = \frac{2}{25}$,

   (ii) $\displaystyle\int_0^\infty t^3 e^{-t}\sin t\,dt = 0$, and (iii) $\displaystyle\int_0^\infty t^2 e^{-4t}\cosh 2t\,dt = \frac{7}{54}$.

6. Use Laplace transforms to solve the following differential equations, subject to the given boundary conditions:

  (i) $y'' + y = t$; $y(0) = 2, y'(0) = 1$,

  (ii) $y'' + 2y' + 5y = 10 \cos t$; $y(0) = 0, y'(0) = 3$,

  (iii) $y'' + 4y' + 4y = t^2 e^{-2t}$; $y(0) = 0, y'(0) = 0$,

  (iv) $y'' - 9y = 6 \sinh 3t$; $y(0) = 0, y'(0) = 4$,

  (v) $y''' - y = e^{-t}$; $y(0) = y''(0) = 1, y'(0) = 2$.

7. Use the Laplace transform method to solve exercises 2, 3, 7, 9, 11, 12, 14, 15, 19 and 20 on pages 384 and 385.

8. Solve the following systems of equations by the method of Laplace transforms:

  (i) $\left.\begin{aligned} y' + z' - 3z &= 0 \\ y'' + z' &= 0 \end{aligned}\right\}$ $y(0) = y'(0) = 0, z(0) = 4/3$,

  (ii) $\left.\begin{aligned} y' + z &= 2 \cos t \\ z' - y &= 1 \end{aligned}\right\}$ $y(0) = -1, z(0) = 1$,

  (iii) $\left.\begin{aligned} y' + z' - 2y &= 1 \\ z - y' &= t \end{aligned}\right\}$ $y(0) = z(0) = 1$,

  (iv) $\left.\begin{aligned} y' + 2z &= 1 \\ 2y - z' &= 2t \end{aligned}\right\}$ $y(0) = 0, z(0) = 1$.

9. Solve the equation $y'' + 4y = f(t)$ with $y(0) = 1, y'(0) = 2$, when $f(t)$ is given by

  (i) $\begin{cases} 8t, & 0 < t < \pi \\ 0, & t > \pi, \end{cases}$ (ii) $\begin{cases} 4(\pi - t), & 0 < t < 2\pi \\ 0, & t > 2\pi, \end{cases}$

  (iii) $\begin{cases} 4, & 0 < t < \pi \\ -4, & \pi < t < 2\pi \\ 0, & t > 2\pi, \end{cases}$ (iv) $\begin{cases} 10\, e^t, & 0 < t < \pi \\ 10\, e^{2\pi - t}, & t > \pi. \end{cases}$

9.3 Linear equations with variable coefficients

Many of the important differential equations of physics and applied mathematics are second-order linear equations with variable coefficients. In this section three methods for the solution of such equations are outlined.

9.3.1 *Variation of parameters*
Suppose that it is wished to find a particular integral of the equation

$$L(y) = \alpha_2(x)y'' + \alpha_1(x)y' + \alpha_0(x)y = f(x) \tag{17}$$

and that the complementary function has already been found to be $c_1 u_1(x) + c_2 u_2(x)$, c_1 and c_2 being arbitrary constants. The method of variation of parameters determines functions $w_1(x)$ and $w_2(x)$ such that

$$v(x) = u_1(x)w_1(x) + u_2(x)w_2(x) \tag{18}$$

is the desired particular integral. Differentiation of equation (18) gives

$$v' = u_1' w_1 + u_1 w_1' + u_2' w_2 + u_2 w_2'$$

We now impose (apparently rather arbitrarily, but see Note 5 at the end of this chapter) the requirement that

$$u_1 w_1' + u_2 w_2' = 0 \tag{19}$$

whence

$$v' = u_1' w_1 + u_2' w_2 \tag{20}$$

and

$$v'' = u_1'' w_1 + u_1' w_1' + u_2'' w_2 + u_2' w_2' \tag{21}$$

Substitution of equations (21), (20) and (18) into $L(y) = f(x)$ now leads to

$$\alpha_2(u_1'' w_1 + u_1' w_1' + u_2'' w_2 + u_2' w_2') + \alpha_1(u_1' w_1 + u_2' w_2) + \alpha_0(u_1 w_1 + u_2 w_2) = f \tag{22}$$

However, since u_1 and u_2 are both particular solutions of the reduced equation $L(y) = 0$, we have

$$w_1(\alpha_2 u_1'' + \alpha_1 u_1' + \alpha_0 u_1) = 0$$

and

$$w_2(\alpha_2 u_2'' + \alpha_1 u_2' + \alpha_0 u_2) = 0$$

and removal of these terms from equation (22) leaves

$$\alpha_2(u_1' w_1' + u_2' w_2') = f \tag{23}$$

The functions w_1' and w_2' are now obtained as the solution of the linear algebraic equations (23) and (19):

$$w_1' = \frac{fu_2}{\alpha_2(u_1' u_2 - u_1 u_2')} \qquad w_2' = \frac{-fu_1}{\alpha_2(u_1' u_2 - u_1 u_2')}$$

The required particular integral of $L(y) = f(x)$ is therefore, from equation (18)

$$v = u_1 \int \frac{fu_2 \, dx}{\alpha_2 U} - u_2 \int \frac{fu_1 \, dx}{\alpha_2 U}$$

where $U \equiv u_1' u_2 - u_1 u_2'$.

Example. Find the general solution of

$$(1 + x)y'' + xy' - y = (1 + x)^2$$

given that the complementary function is $c_1 x + c_2 e^{-x}$.

We seek the particular integral $v(x)$ in the form

$$v = xw_1 + e^{-x}w_2 \tag{24}$$

Then $v' = w_1 + xw_1' - e^{-x}w_2 + e^{-x}w_2'$

and the requirement that

$$xw_1' + e^{-x}w_2' = 0 \tag{25}$$

leaves $v' = w_1 - e^{-x}w_2$

whence $v'' = w_1' + e^{-x}w_2 - e^{-x}w_2'$

Substitution of v'', v' and v into the original equation leads to

$$(1 + x)(w_1' + e^{-x}w_2 - e^{-x}w_2') + x(w_1 - e^{-x}w_2) - (xw_1 + e^{-x}w_2) = (1 + x)^2$$

or $w_1' - e^{-x}w_2' = (1 + x) \tag{26}$

On solving equations (25) and (26) for w_1' and w_2', we find

$$w_1' = 1, \qquad w_2' = -x\,e^x$$

Integration then yields

$$w_1 = x, \qquad w_2 = e^x(1 - x)$$

where the constants of integration have been taken as zero, since otherwise they merely give rise to terms which are already present in the complementary function. Finally, equation (24) gives the particular integral as

$$v = x^2 - x + 1$$

and the general solution is therefore

$$y = c_1 x + c_2\,e^{-x} + (x^2 - x + 1)$$

It may be noted that this method provides an alternative to those discussed earlier for finding a particular integral of an equation with constant coefficients. The extension to equations of other orders is straightforward.

9.3.2 *Solution in series*
The essence of this method, in its simplest version, lies in the assumption that an equation

$$\alpha_2(x)y'' + \alpha_1(x)y' + \alpha_0(x)y = 0$$

possesses a solution which can be expressed as a power series in x, $\displaystyle\sum_{r=0}^{\infty} \beta_r x^r$,

this solution being valid for values of x lying within the interval of convergence of the series. The series is substituted into the differential equation, and like powers of x are equated in order to determine the coefficients β_r in the power series. In some cases the sum of the series solution may then be found, but, more often, equations with variable coefficients have solutions which are not expressible in terms of a finite number of elementary functions.

Example. Consider *Legendre's equation*, which arises in connection with many physical problems:

$$(1 - x^2)y'' - 2xy' + n(n + 1)y = 0$$

where n is a positive integer.

Substitution of the assumed solution

$$y = \sum_{r=0}^{\infty} \beta_r x^r$$

into the differential equation gives

$$(1 - x^2) \sum_{r=0}^{\infty} r(r - 1)\beta_r x^{r-2} - 2x \sum_{r=0}^{\infty} r\beta_r x^{r-1} + n(n + 1) \sum_{r=0}^{\infty} \beta_r x^r = 0$$

or

$$\sum_{r=0}^{\infty} r(r - 1)\beta_r x^{r-2} - \sum_{r=0}^{\infty} \left\{ r(r - 1) + 2r - n(n + 1) \right\} \beta_r x^r = 0$$

Since, in the first summation, the terms corresponding to $r = 0$ and $r = 1$ are both zero, we may write

$$\sum_{r=0}^{\infty} r(r - 1)\beta_r x^{r-2} = \sum_{r=0}^{\infty} (r + 2)(r + 1)\beta_{r+2} \, x^r$$

our equation then becomes

$$\sum_{r=0}^{\infty} \{(r + 2)(r + 1)\beta_{r+2} - r(r + 1)\beta_r + n(n + 1)\beta_r\}x^r = 0$$

or, finally,

$$\sum_{r=0}^{\infty} \{(r + 2)(r + 1)\beta_{r+2} + (n - r)(n + r + 1)\beta_r\}x^r = 0$$

If y is a solution of Legendre's equation, then the coefficient of every power of x on the left-hand side of this equation must be zero. Taking $r = 0, 1, 2, \ldots$, and so on, we find successively

$$\beta_2 = -\frac{(n+1)n}{2}\beta_0$$

$$\beta_3 = -\frac{(n+2)(n-1)}{3.2}\beta_1$$

$$\beta_4 = -\frac{(n+3)(n-2)}{4.3}\beta_2 = \frac{(n+3)(n+1)n(n-2)}{4.3.2}\beta_0$$

$$\beta_5 = -\frac{(n+4)(n-3)}{5.4}\beta_3 = \frac{(n+4)(n+2)(n-1)(n-3)}{5.4.3.2}\beta_1$$

A pattern is now beginning to emerge, and we find that in general, where m is any integer

$$\beta_{2m} = (-1)^m \frac{(n+2m-1)(n+2m-3)\cdots(n+1)n(n-2)\cdots(n-2m+2)}{(2m)!}\beta_0$$

$$\beta_{2m+1} = (-1)^m \frac{(n+2m)(n+2m-2)\cdots(n+2)(n-1)(n-3)\cdots(n-2m+1)}{(2m+1)!}\beta_1$$

We note that the coefficients are determined alternately in terms of β_0 and β_1, the solution therefore taking the form

$$y(x) = \beta_0 y_1(x) + \beta_1 y_2(x)$$

where β_0 and β_1 are arbitrary constants,

$$y_1(x) = 1 - \frac{(n+1)n}{2!}x^2 + \frac{(n+3)(n+1)n(n-2)}{4!}x^4 - \cdots \tag{27}$$

and $\quad y_2(x) = x - \frac{(n+2)(n-1)}{3!}x^3 + \frac{(n+4)(n+2)(n-1)(n-3)}{5!}x^5 - \cdots \tag{28}$

Both y_1 and y_2 are particular solutions of Legendre's equation, corresponding to the choices $\beta_0 = 1$, $\beta_1 = 0$ and $\beta_0 = 0$, $\beta_1 = 1$ respectively. It is interesting to note that $y_1(x)$ terminates as a polynomial whenever n is a positive even integer, as does $y_2(x)$ when n is a positive odd integer. The following observations apply:

(i) It may be shown that any equation of the form

$$\alpha_2(x)y'' + \alpha_1(x)y' + \alpha_0(x)y = 0$$

possesses a solution of the form $y = c_1 u_1(x) + c_2 u_2(x)$, where $u_1(x)$ and $u_2(x)$ are power series in x, provided that $\alpha_2(0) \neq 0$ and that $\alpha_1(x)/\alpha_2(x)$ and $\alpha_0(x)/\alpha_2(x)$ can both be expanded in convergent Maclaurin series of powers of x. The radii of convergence of u_1 and u_2 are at least as large as the lesser of the radii of convergence of the series for α_1/α_2 and α_0/α_2. For the Legendre equation we have $\alpha_2(0) = 1 \neq 0$,

$$\frac{\alpha_1(x)}{\alpha_2(x)} = -\frac{2x}{1 - x^2} = -2(x + x^3 + x^5 + \cdots)$$

and

$$\frac{\alpha_0(x)}{\alpha_2(x)} = \frac{n(n + 1)}{1 - x^2} = n(n + 1)(1 + x^2 + x^4 + \cdots)$$

Both series converge for $|x| < 1$, and we may therefore anticipate that both $y_1(x)$ and $y_2(x)$, given by equations (27) and (28), also converge for $|x| < 1$. Use of the ratio test readily confirms this.

(ii) If the differential equation is such that $\alpha_2(0) = 0$, a slightly different procedure is necessary. In this case, the equation will possess a power series solution provided that $x\alpha_1(x)/\alpha_2(x)$ and $x^2\alpha_0(x)/\alpha_2(x)$ can both be expanded in convergent power series. The series substitution is now of the form

$$y = x^s \sum_{r=0}^{\infty} \beta_r x^r$$

where it is assumed that $\beta_0 \neq 0$, and when the coefficient of the lowest power of x arising is equated to zero there results a quadratic *indicial equation* for s. The two roots of this equation lead, in general, to two independent series of powers of x, which are combined in the usual way to give the general solution. Unfortunately, in many cases of interest the roots of the indicial equation are equal (in which instance only one series is obtained) or they differ by an integer. In this latter instance an attempt to find the series corresponding to the smaller value of s may fail because certain of the coefficients prove to be infinite. In either case, if $y_1(x)$ is the one solution already found, a second particular integral of the form $y_1(x)z(x)$ exists, where $z(x)$ is some function which may be determined by substitution of this second solution into the original equation.

Example. Consider *Bessel's equation*

$$x^2 y'' + xy' + (x^2 - n^2)y = 0$$

in which n is a positive integer.

The equation has $\alpha_2(0) = 0$, but we see that $x\alpha_1(x)/\alpha_2(x) = 1$, $x^2\alpha_0(x)/\alpha_2(x) = x^2 - n^2$; these power series expansions terminate after one term and two terms respectively, and are clearly convergent for all x. Bessel's equation therefore has a solution involving two power series which are convergent for all x. Making the substitution

$$y = x^s \sum_{r=0}^{\infty} \beta_r x^r$$

we obtain

$$\sum_{r=0}^{\infty} (s + r)(s + r - 1)\beta_r x^{s+r} + \sum_{r=0}^{\infty} (s + r)\beta_r x^{s+r} + \sum_{r=0}^{\infty} \beta_r x^{s+r+2} - n^2 \sum_{r=0}^{\infty} \beta_r x^{s+r} = 0$$

whence

$$\sum_{r=0}^{\infty} \left\{ (s + r)^2 - n^2 \right\} \beta_r x^{s+r} + \sum_{r=0}^{\infty} \beta_r x^{s+r+2} = 0$$

or

$$\sum_{r=0}^{\infty} \left\{ \left((s + r)^2 - n^2 \right) \beta_r + \beta_{r-2} \right\} x^{s+r} = 0 \qquad (29)$$

In this last step, we have written $\displaystyle\sum_{r=0}^{\infty} \beta_r x^{s+r+2} = \sum_{r=0}^{\infty} \beta_{r-2} x^{s+r}$, defining $\beta_{-1} = \beta_{-2} = 0$. The lowest power of x which arises is that for which $r = 0$, namely x^s. Equating its coefficient to zero, we obtain the indicial equation

$$(s^2 - n^2)\beta_0 + \beta_{-2} = (s^2 - n^2)\beta_0 = 0$$

which has the solutions $s = \pm n$, since, by hypothesis, $\beta_0 \neq 0$.

For $s = n$, equation (29) becomes

$$\sum_{r=0}^{\infty} \left\{ (r^2 + 2nr)\beta_r + \beta_{r-2} \right\} x^{n+r} = 0$$

We have already arranged for the coefficient of x^n to be zero, and taking $r = 1, 2, 3, \ldots$, we obtain

$$(1^2 + 2n)\beta_1 + \beta_{-1} = 0, \quad \text{or } \beta_1 = 0 \text{ (since } \beta_{-1} = 0)$$

$$(2^2 + 2.2n)\beta_2 + \beta_0 = 0, \quad \text{or } \beta_2 = -\frac{\beta_0}{(n+1)} \left(\frac{1}{2}\right)^2$$

$$(3^2 + 2.3n)\beta_3 + \beta_1 = 0, \quad \text{or } \beta_3 = 0$$

$$(4^2 + 2.4n)\beta_4 + \beta_2 = 0, \quad \text{or } \beta_4 = \frac{\beta_0}{(n+1)(n+2) \cdot 2!} \left(\frac{1}{2}\right)^4$$

and so on. All the coefficients with odd suffixes are zero, and the resulting series is $\beta_0 y_1(x)$, where

$$y_1(x) = x^n \left\{ 1 - \frac{1}{(n+1)} \left(\frac{x}{2}\right)^2 + \frac{1}{(n+1)(n+2) \cdot 2!} \left(\frac{x}{2}\right)^4 \right.$$
$$\left. - \frac{1}{(n+1)(n+2)(n+3) \cdot 3!} \left(\frac{x}{2}\right)^6 + \cdots \right\} \tag{30}$$

This series converges for all x, by the ratio test, and it is therefore a particular integral of Bessel's equation.

For $s = -n$, equation (29) becomes

$$\sum_{r=0}^{\infty} \left\{ (r^2 - 2nr)\beta_r + \beta_{r-2} \right\} x^{-n+r} = 0$$

Proceeding as before, we obtain the expression

$$x^{-n} \left\{ 1 - \frac{1}{(-n+1)} \left(\frac{x}{2}\right)^2 + \frac{1}{(-n+1)(-n+2) \cdot 2!} \left(\frac{x}{2}\right)^4 \right.$$
$$\left. - \frac{1}{(-n+1)(-n+2)(-n+3) \cdot 3!} \left(\frac{x}{2}\right)^6 + \cdots \right\}$$

Now it is clear that the $(n-1)$th and subsequent coefficients in this expression will have in their denominators the factor $(-n+n)$; these coefficients are therefore infinite, and the process has not given the second particular integral of Bessel's equation which is needed to complete the general solution.

As previously indicated, in cases such as this the second particular integral may be sought by substituting $y_1(x)z(x)$ into the differential equation, y_1 being the one particular integral which has already been found. For Bessel's equation y_1 is given by equation (30). The substitution gives

$$x^2(y_1''z + 2y_1'z' + y_1z'') + x(y_1'z + y_1z') + (x^2 - n^2)y_1z = 0$$

Since y_1 is a solution, we have

$$z(x^2y_1'' + xy_1' + (x^2 - n^2)y_1) = 0$$

and the deletion of these terms from the previous equation leaves

$$x^2(2y_1'z' + y_1z'') + xy_1z' = 0$$

which, when expressed in the form

$$z'' + \left(\frac{1}{x} + 2\frac{y_1'}{y_1}\right)z' = 0$$

is recognisable as a linear first-order equation in z', having an integrating factor

$$\exp\left[\int\left(\frac{1}{x}+2\frac{y_1'}{y_1}\right)dx\right] = \exp\left(\log x + 2\log y_1\right) = xy_1^2$$

Hence
$$xy_1^2 z'' + (y_1^2 + 2xy_1 y_1')z' = 0$$

gives
$$\frac{d}{dx}(xy_1^2 z') = 0$$

or
$$xy_1^2 z' = c$$

where c is a constant. Then

$$z' = \frac{c}{xy_1^2} = \frac{c}{x^{2n+1}\left\{1 - \frac{1}{(n+1)}\left(\frac{x}{2}\right)^2 + \cdots\right\}^2}$$

or
$$z' = cx^{-(2n+1)}\left\{1 + \frac{2}{(n+1)}\left(\frac{x}{2}\right)^2 + \cdots\right\}$$

Thus $z'(x)$ consists of a series of increasing powers of x, commencing with $x^{-(2n+1)}$, and containing only odd powers of x including, in particular, x^{-1}. A term-by-term integration gives the further series[†]

$$z(x) = \gamma_0 x^{-2n} + \gamma_1 x^{-(2n-2)} + \cdots + \gamma_{n-1}x^{-2}$$
$$+ \gamma_n \log x + \gamma_{n+1}x^2 + \cdots + \gamma_{n+m}x^{2m} + \cdots$$

which contains only even powers of x, excluding x^0, but also includes a term in $\log x$. The determination of the coefficients γ_r from what has gone before is difficult, but we have at least established the general form of the second solution of Bessel's equation as

$$y_2(x) = y_1(x)z(x)$$
$$= x^n\left\{1 - \frac{1}{(n+1)}\left(\frac{x}{2}\right)^2 + \cdots\right\}$$
$$\left\{\gamma_0 x^{-2n} + \cdots + \gamma_n \log x + \cdots + \gamma_{n+m}x^{2m} + \cdots\right\}$$

or
$$y_2(x) = \gamma_n y_1(x)\log x + \sum_{r=0}^{\infty}\delta_r x^{-n+2r} \tag{31}$$

[†] Note that the retention of a constant of integration in this step simply gives rise to a constant multiple of the first solution, $y_1(x)$.

The coefficients δ_r may now be found by substituting equation (31) into the original differential equation in the usual way. The result for the case $n = 0$ is

$$y_2(x) = y_1(x)\log x + \sum_{r=1}^{\infty} \frac{(-1)^{r+1}}{(r!)^2} \left(\frac{x}{2}\right)^{2r} \left(1 + \frac{1}{2} + \frac{1}{3} + \cdots + \frac{1}{r}\right) \qquad (32)$$

For other values of n the solutions are more complicated, and we will not go into details. For present purposes it is sufficient that a method for obtaining these second solutions has been illustrated.

9.3.3 *Laplace transform method*

When the coefficients of a linear differential equation are of polynomial form, Laplace transformation may occasionally simplify the equation. The method makes use of the t-multiplication theorem, and its effect is that, if the degree of every polynomial coefficient is less than the order of the differential equation, the transformed equation is another differential equation, of lower order than the original. For second-order equations, therefore, this technique is only likely to be helpful if the coefficients are linear functions of the independent variable, as they are in the following example.

Example. Consider Bessel's equation with $n = 0$:

$$xy'' + y' + xy = 0$$

The transformed equation is

$$-\frac{\mathrm{d}}{\mathrm{d}s}(s^2 Y(x) - sy(0) - y'(0)) + sY(s) - y(0) - \frac{\mathrm{d}}{\mathrm{d}s}(Y(s)) = 0$$

or
$$(s^2 + 1)Y'(s) + sY(s) = 0$$

Our original second-order equation has been transformed into a first-order equation, in which the variables are separable, having the solution

$$Y(s) = \frac{c}{\sqrt{(s^2 + 1)}}$$

where c is a constant. Thus

$$Y(s) = \frac{c}{s}\left(1 + \frac{1}{s^2}\right)^{-\frac{1}{2}} = c\left\{\frac{1}{s} - \frac{1}{2} \cdot \frac{1}{s^3} + \frac{3}{8} \cdot \frac{1}{s^5} - \cdots\right\}$$

the general term in this series being

$$\frac{(-1)^r \left(\frac{1}{2} \cdot \frac{3}{2} \cdot \frac{5}{2} \cdots \frac{2r-1}{2}\right)}{r!} \cdot \frac{1}{s^{2r+1}} = \frac{(-1)^r}{2^r r!} \left(1 \cdot 3 \cdot 5 \ldots (2r-1)\right) \cdot \frac{1}{s^{2r+1}}$$

$$= \frac{(-1)^r}{2^r r!} \cdot \frac{(2r-1)!}{2^{r-1}(r-1)!} \cdot \frac{1}{s^{2r+1}} = \frac{(-1)^r (2r)!}{2^{2r}(r!)^2} \cdot \frac{1}{s^{2r+1}}$$

Then
$$y(x) = c\mathcal{L}^{-1}\left\{\sum_{r=0}^{\infty} \frac{(-1)^r (2r)!}{2^{2r}(r!)^2} \cdot \frac{1}{s^{2r+1}}\right\} = c \sum_{r=0}^{\infty} \frac{(-1)^r}{(r!)^2} \left(\frac{x}{2}\right)^{2r}$$

If we impose the boundary condition $y(0) = 1$, we find that $c = 1$, and the resulting solution is the previously found first solution of Bessel's equation (see equation (30)), with $n = 0$. In fact, the choice of any boundary condition of the form $y(x_0) = y_0$ simply gives this solution multiplied by a constant. Differentiation then shows that $y'(0) = 0$, and it is evident that the initial choice of any non-zero value for $y'(0)$ would have led to an impasse. This sort of situation arises because, in using the Laplace transform method, we make the tacit assumptions that (a) the solution $y(x)$ possesses a Laplace transform, and (b) $y(x)$ and $y'(x)$ exist at $x = 0$. The method will only find those parts of the solution for which both these conditions hold — hence the non-appearance of the second solution of Bessel's equation, equation (32), which is not defined at $x = 0$. The absence of the second solution leaves us with the problem of adjusting one arbitrary constant so as to fulfil two boundary conditions, which is clearly impossible for any non-zero choice of $y'(0)$. The fact that many linear differential equations with polynomial coefficients have general solutions which do not comply with conditions (a) and (b) above severely limits the usefulness of the Laplace transform approach to their solution.

Exercises.
Use the method of variation of parameters to obtain particular integrals of the following equations:

1. $y'' + y = \operatorname{cosec} x$.

2. $y'' + 9y = 9 \cot 3x$.

3. $y'' + y' - 2y = \dfrac{3}{(1 - e^{-x})}$.

4. $y'' - 4y = \dfrac{1 - e^{2x}}{1 + e^{2x}}$.

5. $y'' - 2y' + y = \dfrac{e^x}{x}$.

6. Show that the series solution of the equation $y'' + y = 0$ is the sum of arbitrary multiples of the sine and cosine series.

7. Find the two series which satisfy the equation $(1 - x^2)y'' + 2y = 0$. Show that one of the series terminates and that the other is convergent for $|x| < 1$.

8. Obtain the two series which satisfy the equation $y'' + xy' + 2y = 0$, and show that they are both convergent for all values of x.

Exercises 9–12 exhibit the four main variations of behaviour of second-order equations with polynomial coefficients such that the coefficient of y'' is zero when $x = 0$. In each case the substitution $y = x^s \displaystyle\sum_{r=0}^{\infty} a_r x^r$ should be made.

9. Show that the indicial equation of $2xy'' + (2x - 1)y' + 2y = 0$ has two distinct roots, differing by a non-integral number, each giving rise to a series which is a solution of the differential equation, valid for all values of x.

10. Show that the indicial equation of $x(x + 1)y'' + (3x + 1)y' + y = 0$ has a repeated root. Obtain the series solution $u_1(x)$ corresponding to this root, determine its interval of convergence and find its sum to infinity. By finding $z(x)$ such that $u_1(x)z(x)$ satisfies the differential equation, find a second solution, $u_2(x)$.

11. Show that the indicial equation of $2xy'' + (x + 6)y' + 3y = 0$ has two roots differing by an integer. Find the series solution corresponding to the greater root, and sum it to infinity. Show that there is no solution corresponding to the other root, and obtain a second solution (expressed in terms of an integral) by the method of question 10.

12. Show that the indicial equation of $(x^2 - x)y'' + 3(2x - 1)y' + 6y = 0$ has two roots differing by an integer. Find the solution $u_1(x)$ corresponding to the larger root, and show that the series solution $u_2(x)$ corresponding to the smaller root contains an arbitrary multiple of $u_1(x)$ because of the occurrence of an indeterminate coefficient in the series.

Find the general solutions of the following equations:

13. $x(1 - x)y'' - 3xy' - y = 0$.

14. $x(x - 1)y'' + 2y' - 2y = 0$.

15. $4xy'' + 2y' + y = 0$.

16. $x^2(x + 1)y'' + 3x(x + 1)y' + y = 0$.

17. Use the Laplace transform method to find the general solution of
$$xy'' + (x - 1)y' - y = 0.$$

18. Use the Laplace transform method to solve $xy'' - (x + 2)y' + 3y = x - 1$, given that $y(0) = 0$, $y(2) = 9$.

9.4 Miscellaneous analytical methods

9.4.1 *Euler equations*
A linear equation of the form

$$\alpha_n x^n y^{(n)} + \alpha_{n-1} x^{n-1} y^{(n-1)} + \cdots + \alpha_1 xy' + \alpha_0 y = f(x)$$

in which the α's are all constants, is called an Euler equation of the nth order. The substitution $x = e^t$ transforms such an equation into an nth-order equation with constant coefficients.

Example. Find the general solution of
$$x^2 \frac{d^2 y}{dx^2} + 4x \frac{dy}{dx} + 2y = 4 \log x$$

The substitution $x = e^t$ leads to
$$\frac{dy}{dx} = \frac{dy}{dt} \cdot \frac{dt}{dx} = e^{-t} \frac{dy}{dt}$$

whence
$$\frac{d^2 y}{dx^2} = \frac{d}{dx}\left(\frac{dy}{dx}\right) = e^{-t} \frac{d}{dt}\left(e^{-t} \frac{dy}{dt}\right) = e^{-2t}\left(\frac{d^2 y}{dt^2} - \frac{dy}{dt}\right)$$

The resulting differential equation has constant coefficients
$$\frac{d^2 y}{dt^2} + 3\frac{dy}{dt} + 2y = 4t$$

and its general solution is quickly found to be

$$y(t) = c_1 e^{-t} + c_2 e^{-2t} + 2t - 3$$

The solution of the original equation, in terms of x, is therefore

$$y(x) = \frac{c_1}{x} + \frac{c_2}{x^2} + 2 \log x - 3$$

9.4.2 Three special types of nonlinear second-order equations

A general second-order ordinary differential equation has the form

$$f(x, y, y', y'') = 0$$

Here we briefly consider three special cases of this equation in which the general solution may be obtained by means of two successive integrations. The methods given are applicable both to linear and to non-linear equations.

(i)   The dependent variable y is absent. The equation then has the form $f(x, y', y'') = 0$, and the substitution $y' = p$ results in the first-order equation $f(x, p, p') = 0$, which may be solved for $p(x)$ using the methods of the previous chapter. A single further integration then gives the solution $y(x)$.

(ii) The independent variable x is absent. The form of the equation is now $f(y, y', y'') = 0$. Again, we substitute $y' = p$, whence

$$y'' = \frac{dp}{dx} = \frac{dp}{dy} \cdot \frac{dy}{dx} = p \frac{dp}{dy}$$

This leads to the first-order equation

$$g\left(y, p, \frac{dp}{dy}\right) = 0$$

which may be solved for $p(y)$. Then $y(x)$ follows as the solution of $y' = p(y)$.

(iii) The equation has the form $y'' + g(y) = 0$. This type of equation is of frequent occurrence in problems in dynamics. Multiplication by $2y'$

gives $2y'y'' + g(y)y' = 0$; integration then leads to $(y')^2 + \int g(y) \, dy = c$,

a constant. This latter equation is solved for y' in terms of y, the result being a first-order separable equation from which $y(x)$ is obtained.

Example. We will apply the last method to the equation of simple harmonic motion,

$$y'' + k^2 y = 0$$

which, being linear, can also be solved by the techniques given in sections 9.1 and 9.2.

Multiplication by $2y'$ leads to

$$2y'y'' + 2k^2 yy' = 0$$

which gives, on integration

$$(y')^2 + k^2 y^2 = k^2 c_1^2$$

Here we have written the constant of integration as $k^2 c_1^2$, where c_1 is arbitrary. Then

$$y' = k\sqrt{(c_1^2 - y^2)}$$

Separation of the variables, followed by a further integration, gives

$$\sin^{-1}(y/c_1) = kx + c_2$$

or

$$y = c_1 \sin(kx + c_2)$$

in which c_1 and c_2 are both arbitrary; c_1 represents the amplitude of the oscillatory motion and c_2 its phase. Both these characteristics therefore depend upon the initial conditions. The frequency of the oscillations, on the other hand, is governed by the constant k which occurs in the original equation, and this characteristic is therefore an inherent property of the system described by that equation.

Exercises

Find the general solutions of the following differential equations:

1. $4x^2 y'' + 4xy' - y = 3x$.
2. $4x^2 y'' + 8xy' + y = 0$.
3. $x^2 y'' + xy' + y = \log x$.
4. $x^2 y'' - xy' + y = 2x$.
5. $xy'' = y'$.
6. $y'' + 3y' = 3e^{-3x}$.
7. $yy'' = (y')^2$.
8. $yy'' = (y')^2 - y'$.
9. $2y'' = \{1 + (y')^2\}^{3/2}$.

Solve the following differential equations, subject to the given boundary conditions:

10. $y'' - 4 e^{2y} = 0$; $y(0) = 0, y'(0) = 2$.
11. $y'' \sin x + \cos xy' = \cos 2x$; $y(0) = 1, y'(0) = 1$.
12. $(1 + x^2)y'' = 1 + (y')^2$; $y(0) = 1, y'(0) = 1$.
13. $(2 + y)y'' - 3(y')^2 = 0$; $y(0) = -1, y'(0) = -2$.
14. $x^2 y'' + xy' - y = 2/x$; $y(1) = 3, y'(1) = 0$.
15. $y'' = \sec^2 y \tan y$; $y(0) = 0, y'(0) = 1$.
16. $y'' = 2y(1 + y^2)$; $y(0) = 0, y'(0) = 1$.

9.5 Numerical methods for initial-value problems

In chapter 8 a number of methods for the numerical solution of first-order differential equations were described. Amongst these was the popular fourth-order Runge-Kutta process, which uses the relations

$$y_{n+1} = y_n + \tfrac{1}{6}(k_0 + 2k_1 + 2k_2 + k_3)$$

where
$$k_0 = hf(x_n, y_n)$$
$$k_1 = hf(x_n + \tfrac{1}{2}h, y_n + \tfrac{1}{2}k_0)$$
$$k_2 = hf(x_n + \tfrac{1}{2}h, y_n + \tfrac{1}{2}k_1)$$
$$k_3 = hf(x_n + h, y_n + k_2)$$

in order to extend the solution of an equation $y' = f(x, y)$ by a step of length $x_{n+1} - x_n = h$. This method is easily adapted to the solution of two simultaneous first-order equations of the form

$$y'(x) = F(x, y, z)$$
$$z'(x) = G(x, y, z)$$

provided that the boundary conditions on y and z are both specified for the same value of x, say $x = x_0$. The relations used are now

$$y_{n+1} = y_n + \tfrac{1}{6}(k_0 + 2k_1 + 2k_2 + k_3)$$
$$z_{n+1} = z_n + \tfrac{1}{6}(m_0 + 2m_1 + 2m_2 + m_3)$$

where

$$
\left.\begin{aligned}
k_0 &= hF(x_n, y_n, z_n) \\
m_0 &= hG(x_n, y_n, z_n) \\
k_1 &= hF(x_n + \tfrac{1}{2}h, y_n + \tfrac{1}{2}k_0, z_n + \tfrac{1}{2}m_0) \\
m_1 &= hG(x_n + \tfrac{1}{2}h, y_n + \tfrac{1}{2}k_0, z_n + \tfrac{1}{2}m_0) \\
k_2 &= hF(x_n + \tfrac{1}{2}h, y_n + \tfrac{1}{2}k_1, z_n + \tfrac{1}{2}m_1) \\
m_2 &= hG(x_n + \tfrac{1}{2}h, y_n + \tfrac{1}{2}k_1, z_n + \tfrac{1}{2}m_1) \\
k_3 &= hF(x_n + h, y_n + k_2, z_n + m_2) \\
m_3 &= hG(x_n + h, y_n + k_2, z_n + m_2)
\end{aligned}\right\} \tag{33}
$$

If the equations for the k's and m's are used in the order given, the right-hand side of each relation contains only quantities which have already been evaluated. Clearly, this Runge-Kutta method can be extended in a similar manner to the numerical solution of three or more simultaneous first-order equations.

Now, suppose we wish to calculate a numerical solution to the second-order differential equation

$$
y'' = g(x, y, y') \tag{34}
$$

By making the definition $z \equiv y'$ we may express this equation as a system of two simultaneous first-order equations:

$$
y' = z
$$
$$
z' = g(x, y, z)
$$

Provided, then, that the boundary conditions on y and y' (that is, y and z) are both specified for the same value of x, equation (34) may be solved numerically using the process outlined above. The calculation of k_0, k_1, k_2 and k_3 in equations (33) is simplified in this case since $F(x, y, z) = z$; thus

$$
k_0 = hz_n, \quad k_1 = h(z_n + \tfrac{1}{2}m_0), \quad k_2 = h(z_n + \tfrac{1}{2}m_1), \quad k_3 = h(z_n + m_2)
$$

The equations for m_0, m_1, m_2 and m_3 are as written above, with $g(x, y, z)$ substituted for $G(x, y, z)$. It is evident that equations (33) will be still further simplified if g is independent of y'. In the case of a linear differential equation

$$
\alpha_2(x)y'' + \alpha_1(x)y' + \alpha_0(x)y = f(x)
$$

it is in principle always possible to take advantage of this simplification, since the change of variable

$$
y(x) = e^{-\frac{1}{2}\int(\alpha_1/\alpha_2)\mathrm{d}x} Y(x)
$$

results in an equation of the form

$$\beta_2(x)Y'' + \beta_0(x)Y = f(x)$$

containing no first derivative term.

If it is desired to solve numerically an equation of order $n > 2$, say

$$y^{(n)} = \phi(x, y, y', \ldots, y^{(n-1)}) \tag{35}$$

then a system of n first-order equations results if we write

$$y' = z_1, \quad y'' = z_2, \quad y''' = z_3, \ldots, y^{(n-1)} = z_{n-1}$$

This system has the form

$$y' = z_1$$
$$z_1' = z_2$$
$$\ldots\ldots\ldots$$
$$z_{n-2}' = z_{n-1}$$
$$z_{n-1}' = \phi(x, y, z_1, z_2, \ldots, z_{n-1})$$

In order for the corresponding Runge-Kutta process to be applicable, boundary conditions on $y, y', \ldots, y^{(n-1)}$ must all be specified at $x = x_0$; the problem of solving equation (35) is then called an *initial-value problem*. It should be noted that all the other numerical methods given in chapter 8 are, like the Runge-Kutta process, adaptable to the numerical solution of nth-order initial-value problems. It is only necessary first to express the equation to be solved as n simultaneous first-order equations, the foregoing method being perhaps the most straightforward of many possible ways of achieving this end.

Example. Consider the non-linear second-order equation

$$y'' - (y')^2 + 4y = 6$$

with initial conditions $y(0) = 1, y'(0) = 0$.

Denoting y' by z, we obtain the system of two first-order equations

$$y' = z$$
$$z' = z^2 - 4y + 6$$

From equations (33), the corresponding Runge-Kutta relations are

$$y_{n+1} = y_n + \tfrac{1}{6}(k_0 + 2k_1 + 2k_2 + k_3)$$

and
$$z_{n+1} = z_n + \tfrac{1}{6}(m_0 + 2m_1 + 2m_2 + m_3)$$

where

$$k_0 = hz_n \qquad\qquad m_0 = h\{z_n^2 - 4y_n + 6\}$$

$$k_1 = h(z_n + \tfrac{1}{2}m_0) \qquad m_1 = h\{(z_n + \tfrac{1}{2}m_0)^2 - 4(y_n + \tfrac{1}{2}k_0) + 6\}$$

$$k_2 = h(z_n + \tfrac{1}{2}m_1) \qquad m_2 = h\{(z_n + \tfrac{1}{2}m_1)^2 - 4(y_n + \tfrac{1}{2}k_1) + 6\}$$

$$k_3 = h(z_n + m_2) \qquad m_3 = h\{(z_n + m_2)^2 - 4(y_n + k_2) + 6\}$$

If we take $y_0 = y(0) = 1$, $z_0 = y'(0) = 0$, and integrate from $x = 0$ to $x = 1$ using a step-length $h = 0.2$, the following results are obtained, to four decimal places:

x	y(computed)	y(exact)
0.0	1.0000	1.00
0.2	1.0400	1.04
0.4	1.1600	1.16
0.6	1.3600	1.36
0.8	1.6399	1.64
1.0	1.9997	2.00

The values of the exact solution, $y = x^2 + 1$, are included in the table above for comparison.

9.6 Numerical methods for boundary-value problems

If the boundary conditions of a differential equation are not all specified for the same value of the independent variable, we are confronted with a *boundary-value problem*. Such problems present many more difficulties to the numerical analyst than do the initial-value problems of the last section. Here we will briefly outline three methods which may be applied to second-order boundary-value problems.

Firstly, suppose that we are concerned with a second-order linear equation $L(y) = f(x)$, subject to the boundary conditions $y(a) = A$, $y(b) = B$. In this case, we may proceed as follows:

(i) Taking $u(a) = 0$ and an arbitrary non-zero value for $u'(a)$, compute a solution of $L(u) = 0$ as far as $x = b$, using some method appropriate for an initial-value problem.

(ii) Taking $v(a) = A$ and an arbitrary value for $v'(a)$, compute similarly a solution of $L(v) = f(x)$.

(iii)   The linear combination $y(x) = v(x) + cu(x)$ is clearly a solution of
$L(y) = f(x)$, since $L(y) = L(v) + cL(u) = f(x)$; furthermore, $y(x)$ as thus
defined satisfies the boundary condition $y(a) = A$. In order to satisfy the
other boundary condition, we require $y(b) = v(b) + cu(b) = B$; the appropriate
value of c is therefore

$$c = \frac{B - v(b)}{u(b)}$$

Provided $f(x)$ and the coefficients arising in $L(y)$ are continuous, the required
solution is uniquely determined by this method, except when $u(b) = 0$. In this
case, if $v(b) = B$ then c is arbitrary and there are infinitely many solutions, or if
$v(b) \neq B$ then c does not exist and there is no solution.

The method of the last paragraph succeeds only by virtue of the properties of
the linear differential operator L, and it is therefore not applicable to non-linear
equations. If a non-linear equation

$$y'' = G(x, y, y')$$

is to be solved numerically subject to the boundary conditions $y(a) = A$,
$y(b) = B$, one fairly straightforward approach is to define $w(x, \alpha)$ as the solution
of the initial-value problem

$$w'' = G(x, w, w')$$

with $w(a) = A$, $w'(a) = \alpha$, and to look for a value of α such that $w(b, \alpha) = B$. For
instance, if α_1 and α_2 were first found such that $w(b, \alpha_1) > B$, $w(b, \alpha_2) < B$, then
the required value of α might be found to any desired accuracy using the interval
bisection method outlined in section 6.3. The reader should be warned that this
process, even if it works satisfactorily, (which is by no means guaranteed), is very
time-consuming.

Finally, we will illustrate the application to a second-order linear boundary-
value problem of a simple method based on finite differences. As shown in the
last section, a linear second-order equation can always be expressed in the form

$$y'' + p(x)y = f(x) \tag{36}$$

Let us take the boundary conditions to be $y(a) = A$, $y(b) = B$. Now suppose the
interval $a \leqslant x \leqslant b$ to be divided into n equal subintervals of length $h = (b - a)/n$,
and set $x_0 = a$, $x_1 = a + h$, $x_2 = a + 2h, \ldots, x_n = a + nh = b$. If we define
$y_r \equiv y(x_r)$, we may write down the Taylor series

$$y_{r+1} = y_r + hy_r' + \frac{h^2}{2!}y_r'' + \frac{h^3}{3!}y_r''' + O(h^4)$$

and

$$y_{r-1} = y_r - hy_r' + \frac{h^2}{2!}y_r'' - \frac{h^3}{3!}y_r''' + O(h^4)$$

Adding, and solving for y_r'', we find

$$y_r'' \simeq \frac{y_{r-1} - 2y_r + y_{r+1}}{h^2} \tag{37}$$

with an error which is of order h^2. The numerator of the right-hand side is in fact the second difference $\delta^2 y_r$, and reference to section 6.5.1 shows that we are neglecting fourth and higher differences of y in using this approximation. On substituting equation (37) into equation (36), multiplying by h^2, and setting r successively equal to $1, 2, \ldots, n - 1$, we obtain the system of $n - 1$ linear algebraic equations

$$y_0 + y_1\{h^2 p_1 - 2\} + y_2 \qquad\qquad\qquad\qquad = h^2 f_1$$

$$y_1 + y_2\{h^2 p_2 - 2\} + y_3 \qquad\qquad\qquad = h^2 f_2$$

$$y_2 + y_3\{h^2 p_3 - 2\} + y_4 \qquad\qquad = h^2 f_3$$

$$\cdots\cdots\cdots\cdots\cdots\cdots\cdots\cdots\cdots\cdots\cdots\cdots\cdots$$

$$y_{n-2} + y_{n-1}\{h^2 p_{n-1} - 2\} + y_n = h^2 f_{n-1}$$

Here $p_r \equiv p(x_r)$ and $f_r \equiv f(x_r)$. Since $y_0 = a$ and $y_n = b$ are prescribed by the boundary conditions, these equations may be solved for the $n - 1$ unknowns $y_1, y_2, \ldots, y_{n-1}$. The methods of chapter 7 may be used in their solution, though more specialised methods such as successive over-relaxation are often preferred in this context.

Many refinements of this basic technique exist, but the foregoing should suffice to illustrate the general principle involved. Such methods have an advantage over the step-by-step methods used for solving initial-value problems in that they are not subject to propagated error (see section 8.6).

Example. Given the differential equation

$$y'' - 25y = 50x \tag{38}$$

and the boundary conditions $y(0) = 1$, $y(1) = -1$, calculate approximate values for y at $x = 0.2, 0.4, 0.6$ and 0.8.

Substitution of equation (37) into equation (38) with $h = 0.2$ and $r = 1, 2, 3, 4$ respectively gives the system of equations

$$y_0 - 3y_1 + y_2 \qquad\qquad\quad = 0.4$$

$$y_1 - 3y_2 + y_3 \qquad\quad = 0.8$$

$$y_2 - 3y_3 + y_4 \quad = 1.2$$

$$y_3 - 3y_4 + y_5 = 1.6$$

We may put in the boundary conditions by setting $y_0 = y(0) = 1$,
$y_5 = y(1) = -1$; elimination of y_1 between the first pair of equations and y_4
between the second pair then leads to

$$-8y_2 + 3y_3 = 1.8$$

$$3y_2 - 8y_3 = 6.2$$

and the solution follows. The results are tabulated below, together with the
corresponding values of y given by the analytic solution

$$y = \frac{\sinh 5(1 - x) + \sinh 5x}{\sinh 5} - 2x$$

for comparison. In view of the crudeness of our approximation, good accuracy
could hardly have been expected, but the results are clearly of the right order.

x	y(computed)	y(analytic) to 3 d.p.
0.0	1.0	1.000
0.2	0.0	−0.016
0.4	−0.6	−0.616
0.6	−1.0	−1.016
0.8	−1.2	−1.216
1.0	−1.0	−1.000

Exercises

Use the Runge-Kutta method with $h = 0.2$ to obtain numerical solutions to the
following initial-value problems as far as $x = 1$ (work to 4 decimal places):

1. $y'' - y = x$; $y(0) = 1, y'(0) = 2$.

2. $y'' - y' - y = 0$; $y(0) = 0, y'(0) = 1$.

3. $y'' - xy' - xy = 0$; $y(0) = 0, y'(0) = 1$.

Use the first method of section 9.6 with $h = 0.2$ to calculate numerical
solutions to the following linear boundary-value problems (work to 4 decimal
places):

4. $y'' + 2xy' = 0$; $y(0) = 0, y(1) = 1$.

5. $y'' - y + x = 0$; $y(0) = 1, y(1) = 1$.

Use a difference method with $h = 0.25$ to solve the following boundary-value
problems numerically:

6. $y'' - 16y = 0$; $y(0) = 0, y(1) = 1$.

7. $y'' - 16xy = 32x$; $y(0) = 0, y(1) = 3$.

NOTES ON CHAPTER 9

1. This chapter has been chiefly concerned with linear equations. Such an emphasis is appropriate, since such equations describe the behaviour of many physical systems, and since a large body of theory is available concerning the existence and stability of their solutions. These latter considerations often pose severe problems in the treatment of nonlinear equations.

2. We have seen that the general solution of an nth-order linear equation $L(y) = f(x)$ has the form

$$y = c_1 u_1(x) + c_2 u_2(x) + \cdots + c_n u_n(x) + v(x)$$

where the c's are arbitrary constants, v is a particular integral of the equation, and $u_1, u_2, \ldots, u_n$ are independent solutions of $L(y) = 0$. We have so far avoided stating precisely what is meant by the word 'independent', though it has been implied that a solution is not independent if it is a linear combination of other solutions; in other words, it is linear independence as defined below, which is the criterion. If the solutions $u_1, u_2, \ldots, u_n$ are *linearly dependent*, then a set of constants $k_1, k_2, \ldots, k_n$ *which are not all zero*, may be found such that

$$k_1 u_1 + k_2 u_2 + \cdots + k_n u_n = 0$$

Otherwise, they are said to be *linearly independent*. If they are linearly dependent it follows that

$$k_1 u_1' + k_2 u_2' + \cdots + k_n u_n' = 0$$

$$\cdots\cdots\cdots\cdots\cdots\cdots\cdots\cdots\cdots\cdots\cdots\cdots\cdots\cdots\cdots$$

$$k_1 u_1^{(n-1)} + k_2 u_2^{(n-1)} + \cdots + k_n u_n^{(n-1)} = 0$$

Thus for any particular value of x we have a homogeneous system of n linear algebraic equations in the unknowns $k_1, k_2, \ldots, k_n$. But this system only possesses the trivial solution $k_1 = k_2 = \cdots = k_n = 0$ unless the determinant of the matrix of coefficients is zero. Thus the criterion for linear independence of the solutions of $L(y) = 0$ is

$$W(x) \equiv \begin{vmatrix} u_1 & u_2 & \cdots & u_n \\ u_1' & u_2' & \cdots & u_n' \\ \cdots\cdots\cdots\cdots\cdots\cdots\cdots\cdots \\ u_1^{(n-1)} & u_2^{(n-1)} & \cdots & u_n^{(n-1)} \end{vmatrix} \neq 0$$

This determinant is called the *Wronskian*.

3. A section on Laplace transforms has been included in this chapter, not because their use necessarily saves time and effort in the solution of linear differential equations (which is by no means always the case), but by way of an introduction to the simpler properties and applications of these transforms. More advanced results in particular, the convolution theorem and the complex inversion theorem, allow Laplace transforms to be used in a wide variety of problems other than differential equations.

4. The treatment given to the method of solution in series is necessarily rather condensed, though the basic principle should be clear enough. We have confined ourselves to finding series solutions in powers of x, though it is equally possible to find solutions about points other than $x = 0$ by assuming trial series of the form

$$\sum_{r=0}^{\infty} \alpha_r (x - x_0)^{r+s}$$

where $x_0 \neq 0$. Perhaps the simplest way of doing this is to make a change of the independent variable. For example, we have found the series solution of Legendre's equation

$$(1 - x^2)y'' - 2xy' + n(n + 1)y = 0$$

in powers of x; we may find the solution about $x = 1$ by defining $x - 1 = \xi$, when the equation becomes

$$\xi(\xi + 2) \frac{d^2 y}{d\xi^2} - 2(\xi + 1) \frac{dy}{d\xi} + n(n + 1)y = 0$$

and the required solution may be sought in a series of powers of ξ.

Some equations of this type do not possess series solutions in ascending powers of x, but do have solutions in series of descending powers of x (see question 28 of the miscellaneous exercises following these notes). In other cases, a solution may exist in ascending powers of x, for, say, $|x| < R$ and another solution in descending powers of x for $|x| > R$; Legendre's equation, whose general solution when expressed in terms of ascending powers of x is only valid for $|x| < 1$, is of this type.

The method illustrated in the determination of the second solution of a second-order equation, when this is not directly given by the substitution of the trial series, is not the only one available. An alternative approach, due to Frobenius, gives the second solution as $\{(\partial/\partial s)u_1(x, s)\}_{s=s_0}$, where $u_1(x, s)$ is the first solution written with s, the exponent of x in the first term of the series, left general and not replaced by the appropriate root, s_0, of the indicial equation. While this result appears attractive at first sight, its application in practice is usually rather complicated.

5. The fact that an nth-order ordinary differential equation may be expressed as a system of n first-order equations is more fundamental than it may have appeared in this chapter. One important consequence is that an nth-order equation may be written in the form

$$\mathbf{y}' = \mathbf{f}(\mathbf{x}, \mathbf{y})$$

which is entirely analogous to a general first-order equation, except that y is now a column vector (of the type met with in chapter 7), and f is now a vector-valued function. For example, the second-order linear equation

$$y'' + \alpha_1(x)y' + \alpha_0(x)y = 0$$

may be expressed as the system

$$\left. \begin{array}{l} y' = z \\ z' = -\alpha_1(x)z - \alpha_0(x)y \end{array} \right\}$$

which, in matrix notation, becomes

$$\mathbf{y}' = A\mathbf{y}$$

where

$$\mathbf{y} = \begin{pmatrix} y \\ z \end{pmatrix} \quad \text{and} \quad A = \begin{pmatrix} 0 & 1 \\ -\alpha_0(x) & -\alpha_1(x) \end{pmatrix}$$

The use of such a formulation for a linear differential equation enables us to employ matrix methods to good effect; in particular, the method of variation of parameters, which at first acquaintance seems rather an arbitrary procedure, results quite naturally from a matrix analysis.

6. Further information on the subject matter of this chapter is to be found in the references cited at the end of chapter 8. Comprehensive treatments at a rather more advanced level are given on the analytical side by E. A. Coddington and N. Levinson: *Theory of Ordinary Differential Equations*, McGraw-Hill, and on the numerical side by P. Henrici: *Discrete Variable Methods in Ordinary Differential Equations*, John Wiley & Sons.

Miscellaneous exercises

Find the solutions of the following differential equations which satisfy the given boundary conditions, using (a) the method of undetermined coefficients, and (b) the Laplace transform method:

1. $y'' + y = x^2$; $y(0) = -2, y'(0) = 3$.
2. $y'' + 2y' + 17y = 8(5x - 1) e^{-3x}$; $y(0) = 2, y'(0) = 0$.
3. $y'' + 2y' + y = 12x^2 e^{-x}$; $y(0) = 3, y'(0) = -2$.
4. $y''' - y = 3 e^x$; $y(0) = 0, y'(0) = 2, y''(0) = 1$.
5. $y'' + 2y' + 5y = e^{-x} \sin x$; $y(0) = 0, y'(0) = 1$.
6. $y^{(iv)} - y = 30 \cos 2x$; $y(0) = y'(\pi) = y'''(0) = 0, y''(\pi) = -10$.

Find the general solutions of the following differential equations:

7. $xy'' - (1 + x)y' = 0$.
8. $y'' + y = 16 \sin^2 x \cos x$.
9. $y'' = y^{-3}$.
10. $x^2 y'' + xy' - y = x^2 e^{-x}$.
11. $y'' = (1 + (y')^2)^{1/2}$.
12. $2x^2 y'' + 3xy' - 6y = 7x^{-2}$.
13. $x^3 y''' + 2x^2 y'' - xy' + y = 0$.
14. $y'' = (x + y')^2$.
15. $y'' - 4y' + 3y = e^{3x}/(1 + e^{2x})$.

Use the Laplace transform method to solve the following systems of equations:

16. $\left. \begin{array}{l} y' = 2y - 3z \\ z' = z - 2y \end{array} \right\}$ $y(0) = -2, y'(0) = 3$.

17. $\left. \begin{array}{l} y' + z' = e^t \\ y'' - z = t \end{array} \right\}$ $y(0) = z(0) = \frac{1}{2}, y'(0) = \frac{3}{2}$.

18. $\left. \begin{array}{l} y'' + 2z' + y = 2 \sin t \\ 2z'' + y' + 2z = 2 \end{array} \right\}$ $y(0) = y'(0) = z'(0) = 0, z(0) = 1$.

19. $\left. \begin{array}{l} x' = y + z \\ y' = z + x \\ z' = x + y \end{array} \right\}$ $x(0) = \alpha, y(0) = \beta, z(0) = \gamma$.

20. Solve the equation $y'' + 2y' + y = f(t)$, with $y(0) = y'(0) = 0$, when $f(t)$ is given by

(i) $\begin{cases} t, & 0 < t < 1 \\ 0, & t > 1, \end{cases}$ (ii) $\begin{cases} 2 \sin t & 0 < t < \pi \\ 0 & t > \pi, \end{cases}$ (iii) $\begin{cases} 0 & 0 < t < a \\ 1 & a < t < b \\ 0 & t > b. \end{cases}$

21. Obtain the general solution, in series, of *Hermite's equation*

$$y'' - 2xy' + 2ny = 0$$

Show that when n is a positive integer or zero the equation is satisfied by a polynomial of degree n in x.

22. Obtain the general solution, in series, of *Chebyshev's equation*

$$(1 - x^2)y'' - xy' + n^2 y = 0$$

Show that when n is an integer or zero the equation is satisfied by a polynomial of degree n in x. Obtain the general solution in closed form by making the substitution $x = \cos \theta$, and hence prove that

$$\cos 3\theta = 4 \cos^3 \theta - 3 \cos \theta$$

and $\cos 4\theta = 8 \cos^4 \theta - 8 \cos^2 \theta + 1$

23. Obtain a series solution $L_n(x)$ of *Laguerre's equation*

$$xy'' + (1 - x)y' + ny = 0$$

and show that it becomes a polynomial in x when n is a positive integer or zero. Show that there is a second solution, having the form

$$y = L_n(x) \int \frac{e^x \, dx}{x L_n^2(x)}$$

24. Show that, if c is neither an integer nor zero, the *hypergeometric equation*

$$x(1 - x)y'' + \{c - (a + b + 1)x\}y' - aby = 0$$

has the solutions, convergent for $|x| < 1$,

$F(a, b, c; x)$ and $x^{1-c}F(a - c + 1, b - c + 1, 2 - c; x)$

where $F(a, b, c; x)$ denotes the *hypergeometric series*

$$1 + \frac{ab}{1!c} x + \frac{a(a + 1)b(b + 1)}{2!c(c + 1)} x^2 + \frac{a(a + 1)(a + 2)b(b + 1)(b + 2)}{3!c(c + 1)(c + 2)} x^3 + \cdots$$

25. Show that an attempt to solve Laguerre's equation (see question 23) by the Laplace transform method only gives the first solution, $L_n(x)$. Explain.

26. The method of variation of parameters enables the general solution of an equation

$$L(y) = \alpha_2(x)y'' + \alpha_1(x)y' + \alpha_0(x)y = f(x)$$

to be found if two independent solutions of $L(y) = 0$ are known. Show that, even if only one solution of $L(y) = 0$ (say $u_1(x)$) is known, the substitution of $y = u_1(x)z(x)$ into $L(y) = f(x)$ leads to a linear first-order equation in z' from which the general solution may (at least in principle) be obtained.

Find, by inspection, a particular solution of the reduced equation of

$$(x + 1)(x + 2)y'' + xy' - y = 2\frac{(x + 1)^2}{(x + 2)}$$

and hence derive the general solution by the foregoing method.

27. If, for any $\epsilon > 0$ we define

$$\delta_\epsilon(t) \equiv \begin{cases} 1/\epsilon, & 0 \leqslant t \leqslant \epsilon \\ 0, & \text{elsewhere} \end{cases}$$

show that $\lim_{\epsilon \to 0} \mathcal{L}\{\delta_\epsilon(t)\} = 1$.

The *Dirac delta function* $\delta(t)$ is often defined as $\lim_{\epsilon \to 0} \delta_\epsilon(t)$. The above result makes plausible the statement that $\mathcal{L}\{\delta(t)\} = 1$, though a rigorous derivation of this result is outside the scope of this book (but see Note 1 following chapter 5).

The ends of a horizontal beam are rigidly clamped, the unsupported length of the beam being a. A concentrated load p acts vertically downwards at $x = \frac{1}{3}a$. Show that this loading may be represented by $w(x) = p\delta(x - \frac{1}{3}a)$, where $w(x)$ is the distribution of load per unit length of the beam. Hence, given that the equation for the deflection $y(x)$ of the beam under loading $w(x)$ is $y^{(iv)} = 27w(x)$, where $y(0) = y(a) = 0$, $y'(0) = y'(a) = 0$, calculate $y(x)$, assuming that the weight of the beam itself may be neglected.

28. Show that the equation

$$x^4y'' + 2x^3y' - y = 0$$

has no series solution in positive powers of x. Use the Runge-Kutta method with $h = 0.2$ to calculate between $x = 1$ and $x = 2$ the solution which satisfies $y(1) = 0, y'(1) = 3$. Deduce the values of y at $x = 1.2, 1.4, 1.6$ and 1.8 for the boundary-value problem with $y(1) = 0, y(2) = 1$.

Show that the equation has a series solution, in positive powers of $1/x$, which is expressible in a closed form. Hence check your numerical solutions.

29. Two possible formulations of Legendre's equation

$$(1 - x^2)y'' - 2xy' + n(n + 1)y = 0$$

as first-order systems are

$$\left.\begin{array}{l} y' = z \\[2mm] z' = \dfrac{2xz - n(n + 1)y}{1 - x^2} \end{array}\right\} \quad \text{and} \quad \left.\begin{array}{l} y' = \dfrac{w}{1 - x^2} \\[2mm] w' = -n(n + 1)y \end{array}\right\}$$

Take $n = 2$, and for both formulations use the Runge-Kutta method with $h = 0.1$ to calculate as far as $x = 0.5$ the solution which satisfies the initial conditions $y(0) = 0$, $y'(0) = 1$.

30. Given the differential equation

$$y'' + 50y = 25x$$

use the finite difference method to calculate values at $x = 0.2, 0.4, 0.6$ and 0.8 of the solution satisfying the boundary conditions $y(0) = y(1) = 0$. Compare your results with the exact solution.

10 VECTOR ALGEBRA WITH APPLICATIONS TO MECHANICS

10.0 Introduction

The physical quantities with which the science of mechanics is concerned can be loosely classified as *scalars,* which can be completely specified by single real numbers, and *vectors*, which require both magnitude and direction for their complete specification. Typical scalar quantities are mass, density, time, whereas vectors are typified by velocity, force, moment and acceleration. In this chapter an algebra is developed which can be applied to these vector quantities and which leads to a more concise and more comprehensible method of expressing some of the basic equations of mechanics. Once vector algebra has been developed a vector quantity can more properly be defined as a quantity with magnitude and direction which obeys the laws of vector algebra; not all quantities specified by a magnitude and a direction are vectors (see exercise 5, page 438).

10.1 Addition and subtraction of vectors

10.1.1 *Notation and basic definitions*
A vector quantity can be represented in magnitude and direction by a directed line segment, the length of the line corresponding to the magnitude of the vector. In this chapter, vector algebra will be developed as the algebra of directed line segments. Vector quantities will be denoted by $\mathbf{v}$, or, if they are of unit length, $\hat{\mathbf{v}}$; scalar quantities will be denoted by small letters, Greek or Roman. With each vector $\mathbf{v}$ there is associated a positive scalar quantity, the *magnitude* or *modulus* of $\mathbf{v}$; this is denoted $|\mathbf{v}|$ or, occasionally, v. Also associated with $\mathbf{v}$ is a unit vector $\hat{\mathbf{v}}$, with $|\hat{\mathbf{v}}| = 1$, which defines the direction of $\mathbf{v}$.

Equality. Two vectors $\mathbf{v}$ and $\mathbf{w}$ are said to be equal if they have the same magnitude and direction. Note that for equality of $\mathbf{v}$ and $\mathbf{w}$ it is not necessary for them to act at the same point or even have a common line of action. If $\mathbf{v} = \mathbf{w}$ then it follows from the definition that $|\mathbf{v}| = |\mathbf{w}|$ and $\hat{\mathbf{v}} = \hat{\mathbf{w}}$. (See figure 10.1.)

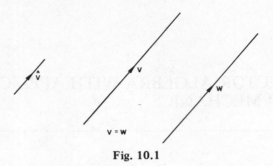

Fig. 10.1

10.1.2 *Addition of vectors*

Two vectors are added according to the parallelogram or triangle law of addition. This is illustrated in figure 10.2. The result is, of course, only directly applicable to vectors which can be considered as acting at the same point, the combination of a vector **a** and a vector **b** acting at P being a vector **a** + **b** acting at P.

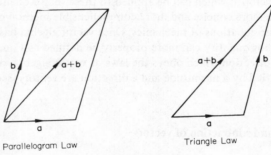

Fig. 10.2

Properties

   (i) **a** + **b** = **b** + **a** (the commutative law) [See figure 10.3.]
  (ii) (**a** + **b**) + **c** = **a** + (**b** + **c**) (The associative law) [See figure 10.4.]
 (iii) **a** + **0** = **a**, where **0** is the *null* or *zero vector*, a vector of zero magnitude and unspecified direction.

10.1.3 *Subtraction of vectors*

For any vector **v**, a vector −**v** is defined as the vector having the same magnitude as **v** but acting in the opposite direction. Thus −**v** is the vector obtained by rotating **v** through an angle of π about a perpendicular axis. **a** − **b** is then

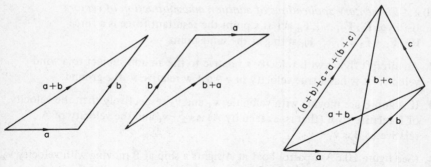

Fig. 10.3

[Note: a,b,c are not necessarily coplanar]

Fig. 10.4

defined as $a + (-b)$, and so depends upon the definition of vector addition [see figure 10.5].

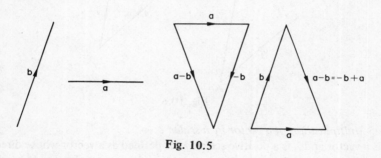

Fig. 10.5

Properties. From the definition of $-v$ it follows that

(i) $-(-v) = v$,

(ii) $v + (-v) = 0$.

Using the associative law of addition and property (ii) above we can deduce that

(iii) $a + b = a + c \Rightarrow b = c$ (the cancellation rule).

This is proved by adding $-a$ to each side of the above equation to give

$$-a + (a + b) = -a + (a + c)$$
$$\Rightarrow (-a + a) + b = (-a + a) + c \quad \text{(using associative law)}$$
$$\Rightarrow 0 + b = 0 + c$$
$$\Rightarrow b = c$$

10.1.4 *Elementary applications of addition and subtraction of vectors*

1. If forces $F_1, F_2, \ldots, F_n$ act at a point the resultant force is a force
   $R = F_1 + F_2 + \cdots + F_n$ acting at the same point.

2. An aircraft flying with velocity **a** relative to the air and subject to a wind
   velocity of **w** has a true velocity of $v = a + w$ relative to the ground.

3. If A and B are moving with velocities v_1 and v_2 respectively then the velocity
   of B relative to A (that is, as seen by A) is $v_2 - v_1$ and the velocity of A
   relative to B is $v_1 - v_2$.

4. (See figure 10.6.) A patrol boat at A sights a ship at B moving with velocity v_2.
   If the ship is to be intercepted the patrol boat must sail with velocity v_1
   such that $v_1 - v_2$ (the velocity of the patrol boat relative to the ship) is in
   direction AB.

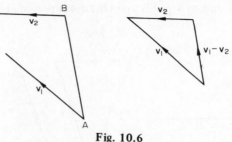

Fig. 10.6

10.1.5 *Multiplication of a vector by a scalar*

If **v** is a vector and λ is a positive scalar, λv is defined as a vector whose direction
is the same as **v** and whose magnitude is λ times the magnitude of **v**. If λ is
negative λv is defined as $|\lambda| (-v)$, that is, a vector in the opposite direction to **v**
and of $|\lambda|$ times the magnitude of **v**.

Properties

(i) $\lambda(a + b) = \lambda a + \lambda b$,

(ii) $(\lambda + \mu)a = \lambda a + \mu a$,

(iii) $1 \cdot a = a$,

(iv) $\lambda(\mu a) = (\lambda\mu)a$,

(v) $\hat{v} = \dfrac{1}{|v|} v$ or $v = |v| \hat{v}$.

These properties, with the exception of (i), can be deduced directly from the
definition given above and from the properties of real numbers. Property (i) is
proved by using the fact that the triangles with sides **a**, **b**, **a + b** and λa, λb, and
$\lambda a + \lambda b$ are similar.

10.1.6 *Resolution of a vector into components*

General definition. If **v** is any vector and if **a**, **b**, **c** are any 3 non-coplanar directions, (that is, **a**, **b**, **c** are not all in the same plane), then **v** can be expressed uniquely as the sum $\mathbf{v} = v_a\hat{\mathbf{a}} + v_b\hat{\mathbf{b}} + v_c\hat{\mathbf{c}}$ of three vectors in the directions of **a**, **b** and **c** respectively. v_a, v_b and v_c are called the *components,* or *resolved parts,* of **v** in these directions.

The fact that this resolution is possible is demonstrated by the fact that, given **v** and the directions **a**, **b**, **c** which are not all in the same plane, it is possible to construct a parallelepiped with edges parallel to **a**, **b** and **c** and with **v** as a diagonal (figure 10.7). The uniqueness of this resolution is proved below.

Proof of uniqueness

Suppose $\mathbf{v} = v_a\hat{\mathbf{a}} + v_b\hat{\mathbf{b}} + v_c\hat{\mathbf{c}}$

and $\mathbf{v} = v_a'\hat{\mathbf{a}} + v_b'\hat{\mathbf{b}} + v_c'\hat{\mathbf{c}}$

are two such expressions for **v**.

Then

$$v_a\hat{\mathbf{a}} - v_a'\hat{\mathbf{a}} = v_b'\hat{\mathbf{b}} + v_c'\hat{\mathbf{c}} - (v_b\hat{\mathbf{b}} + v_c\hat{\mathbf{c}})$$

$$\Rightarrow (v_a - v_a')\,\hat{\mathbf{a}} = (v_b' - v_b)\,\hat{\mathbf{b}} + (v_c' - v_c)\,\hat{\mathbf{c}}$$

but the vector on the right of this equation must lie in the plane of $\hat{\mathbf{b}}$ and $\hat{\mathbf{c}}$ whereas the vector on the left is in the direction of $\hat{\mathbf{a}}$ which is, by assumption, not in the plane of $\hat{\mathbf{b}}$ and $\hat{\mathbf{c}}$. This leads to a contradiction unless $v_a - v_a' = 0$; hence $v_a = v_a'$.

Similarly $v_b = v_b'$ and $v_c = v_c'$, showing that this resolution is unique.

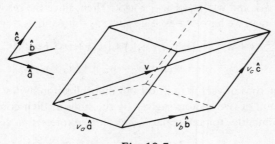

Fig. 10.7

Rectangular cartesian components. The most frequent application of the above resolution occurs when the directions chosen are those of a set of mutually perpendicular cartesian axes. It is conventional to choose the axes OX, OY, OZ so that they form a right-handed set (that is, OZ is in the sense of a right-handed rotation from OX to OY). The unit vectors in the directions of OX, OY and OZ respectively are denoted $\hat{i}, \hat{j}$ and $\hat{k}$. Any vector $\mathbf{v}$ then has a unique expression $\mathbf{v} = v_1\hat{i} + v_2\hat{j} + v_3\hat{k}$, with fixed axes; $\mathbf{v}$ is then completely defined by the set (v_1, v_2, v_3).

Once the origin and axes have been fixed any position P in space can be specified by its position vector, that is the vector from O to P. If P has cartesian components (x, y, z) its position vector is $\mathbf{r} = x\hat{i} + y\hat{j} + z\hat{k}$. (See figure 10.8.)

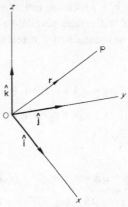

Fig. 10.8

10.1.7 *Vector algebra in component form*

The unique resolution of a vector into components provides a method of performing simple algebraic calculations with vectors using the properties established in 10.1.2 and 10.1.3. Suppose $\mathbf{v}$ and $\mathbf{w}$ are vectors with $\mathbf{v} = v_1\hat{j} + v_2\hat{j} + v_3\hat{k}$ and $\mathbf{w} = w_1\hat{i} + w_2\hat{j} + w_3\hat{k}$. Then, since the resolved parts of a vector are unique, we have: $\mathbf{v} = \mathbf{w} \Leftrightarrow v_1 = w_1$, $v_2 = w_2$ and $v_3 = w_3$. Also

$$\mathbf{v} + \mathbf{w} = (v_1\hat{i} + v_2\hat{j} + v_3\hat{k}) + (w_1\hat{i} + w_2\hat{j} + w_3\hat{k})$$
$$= (v_1 + w_1)\hat{i} + (v_2 + w_2)\hat{j} + (v_3 + w_3)\hat{k}$$

(using the properties of vector addition and multiplication by a scalar).

Hence the sum of two vectors is given by the sums of their corresponding components. Similarly, for any scalar λ, $\lambda\mathbf{v}$ can be expressed in component form as

$$\lambda\mathbf{v} = \lambda(v_1\hat{i} + v_2\hat{j} + v_3\hat{k})$$
$$= \lambda v_1\hat{i} + \lambda v_2\hat{j} + \lambda v_3\hat{k}$$

showing that the effect of multiplying $\mathbf{v}$ by λ is to multiply each of its components by λ.

Note. The above expressions for equality, addition and multiplication by a scalar would remain valid if the unit vectors $\hat{i}, \hat{j}, \hat{k}$ were replaced by the more general unit vectors $\hat{a}, \hat{b}, \hat{c}$ in any three specified non-coplanar directions.

10.1.8 *Worked examples on elementary vector algebra*

1. A particle at O is subject to the following forces:

   A force of 5 units acting along OX
   A force of 3 units acting along ZO
   A force of 2 units acting along OY
   A force of $2\sqrt{2}$ units acting towards O at an angle of $\pi/4$ to the axes OX, OY and in the plane OXY

   Find the resultant force on the particle.

Solution. Let $\hat{i}, \hat{j}, \hat{k}$ be unit vectors along OX, OY, OZ respectively.
Let the forces be $\mathbf{F}_1, \mathbf{F}_2, \mathbf{F}_3, \mathbf{F}_4$ respectively.
Then if $\mathbf{R}$ is the resultant force $\mathbf{R} = \mathbf{F}_1 + \mathbf{F}_2 + \mathbf{F}_3 + \mathbf{F}_4$
$\mathbf{F}_1 = 5\hat{i}$
$\mathbf{F}_2 = -3\hat{k}$ (negative since its direction is along ZO)
$\mathbf{F}_3 = 2\hat{j}$
$\mathbf{F}_4$ must be resolved to obtain its expression in component form.

From the diagram (figure 10.9) $\mathbf{F}_4$ can be expressed as the sum of 2 forces each of 2 units acting along XO and YO respectively.

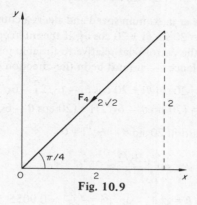

Fig. 10.9

Thus $\qquad\qquad\qquad\qquad \mathbf{F}_4 = -2\hat{i} - 2\hat{j}$

Hence $\qquad \mathbf{R} = \mathbf{F}_1 + \mathbf{F}_2 + \mathbf{F}_3 + \mathbf{F}_4 = 5\hat{i} - 3k + 2\hat{j} - 2\hat{i} - 2\hat{j}$
$\qquad\qquad\qquad = 3\hat{i} - 3\hat{k}.$

2. A ship is sighted 10 nautical miles North of a patrol boat, the ship is
    travelling N.E. at 12 knots. The patrol boat has a maximum speed of
    20 knots; find the minimum time taken to intercept the ship and the
    course the patrol boat must sail to achieve this. (See figure 10.10.)

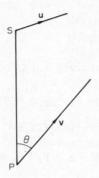

Fig. 10.10

Solution. Let $\mathbf{u}$ = velocity of ship, $\mathbf{v}$ = velocity of patrol boat. Then if $\hat{\mathbf{i}}, \hat{\mathbf{j}}$
are unit vectors in E and N directions respectively

$$\mathbf{u} = 6\sqrt{2}\,\hat{\mathbf{i}} + 6\sqrt{2}\,\hat{\mathbf{j}}$$

If the patrol boat sails at maximum speed and steers a course at an angle θ
East of North then $\mathbf{v} = 20 \sin \theta \hat{\mathbf{i}} + 20 \cos \theta \hat{\mathbf{j}}$. If the interception is to take
place the velocity of the patrol boat relative to the ship must be in a
northerly direction. Hence $\mathbf{v} - \mathbf{u}$ must be in the direction of $\hat{\mathbf{j}}$. But

$$\mathbf{v} - \mathbf{u} = 20 \sin \theta \hat{\mathbf{i}} + 20 \cos \theta \hat{\mathbf{j}} - 6\sqrt{2}\,\hat{\mathbf{i}} - 6\sqrt{2}\,\hat{\mathbf{j}}$$
$$= (20 \sin \theta - 6\sqrt{2})\hat{\mathbf{i}} + (20 \cos \theta - 6\sqrt{2})\hat{\mathbf{j}}$$

θ is given by the condition $20 \sin \theta - 6\sqrt{2} = 0$

Hence $\theta = \sin^{-1} \dfrac{3\sqrt{2}}{10} \simeq 25°6'$

$$\cos \theta = \sqrt{(1 - \sin^2 \theta)} = \frac{\sqrt{82}}{10} \simeq 0.9055$$

Hence $\mathbf{v} - \mathbf{u} = (20 \cos \theta - 6\sqrt{2})\hat{\mathbf{j}} \simeq 9.63\hat{\mathbf{j}}.$

Since the patrol boat was initially 10 nautical miles South of the ship the
interception will take place after $10/9.63 = 1.038$ hrs or approx. $62\frac{1}{2}$ minutes.

3. Prove that the lines joining the mid-points of the opposite edges of a tetrahedron bisect each other.

Solution. Let one vertex of the tetrahedron be at O, and let the other vertices A, B, C have position vectors **a**, **b**, **c** respectively (see figure 10.11). If L is the mid-point of AB it has position vector

$$1 = OL = \mathbf{a} + \tfrac{1}{2}(AB)$$
$$= \mathbf{a} + \tfrac{1}{2}(\mathbf{b} - \mathbf{a})$$
$$= \tfrac{1}{2}(\mathbf{a} + \mathbf{b})$$

(Showing that the position vector of the mid-point of a line is the mean of the position vectors of the ends.)

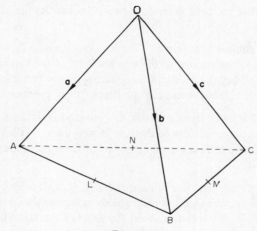

Fig. 10.11

Similarly, the mid-points of BC and CA have position vectors $\tfrac{1}{2}(\mathbf{b} + \mathbf{c})$ and $\tfrac{1}{2}(\mathbf{c} + \mathbf{a})$ respectively.

The mid-point of OC, the edge opposite to AB, has position vector $\tfrac{1}{2}\mathbf{c}$. Hence the mid-points of the line joining this point to L has position vector

$$\mathbf{r} = \tfrac{1}{2}(\tfrac{1}{2}(\mathbf{a} + \mathbf{b}) + \tfrac{1}{2}\mathbf{c}) = \tfrac{1}{4}(\mathbf{a} + \mathbf{b} + \mathbf{c})$$

Similarly, the mid-points of the lines joining M and N to the mid-points of the opposite edges will also have position vectors

$$\mathbf{r} = \tfrac{1}{4}(\mathbf{a} + \mathbf{b} + \mathbf{c})$$

Hence the three lines joining the mid points of opposite edges bisect each other at the point with position vector

$$\tfrac{1}{4}(\mathbf{a} + \mathbf{b} + \mathbf{c})$$

Note. The above example illustrates the application of vector algebra to problems in solid geometry. Vector algebra provides a convenient notation for these problems and in simple cases the computations can be even simpler than those for corresponding two-dimensional problems using coordinate geometry.

Exercises

1. Prove by vector methods that the diagonals of a parallelogram bisect one another.

2. An aircraft has a cruising speed, as indicated by its instruments, of 300 knots. Find the direction in which the pilot must fly the plane in order to travel due East when there is a wind of 50 knots blowing from the North. Find the time taken to travel 1200 nautical miles in this direction.

3. A particle is subject to forces of 3 lb wt, 4 lb wt, and 5 lb wt respectively acting in directions parallel to the edges AB, BC, CA of an equilateral triangle ABC. Find the resultant force acting on the particle. Find the resultant force if the direction of the first of these forces is reversed.

4. A bird is 100 ft away from a man with a gun and is flying at 50 m.p.h. in a direction perpendicular to the line joining them. If the gun fires its bullet at 500 m.p.h. find how far in front of the bird he must aim in order to hit it.

5. A cube of unit side has four of its vertices A, B, C, D initially at points with position vectors $\mathbf{O}, \hat{\mathbf{i}}, \hat{\mathbf{j}}, \hat{\mathbf{k}}$ respectively referred to a fixed set of axes OX, OY, OZ. R_1 is a rotation about the axis OX through $90°$, R_2 is a rotation about OY through $90°$. Find the position vectors of A, B, C, D after performing the following rotations:

    (i) R_1,
    (ii) R_2,
    (iii) $R_1 + R_2$ (that is, R_1 followed by R_2),
    (iv) $R_2 + R_1$.

    Deduce that finite rotations, although completely specified by a magnitude and a direction, are not vector quantities.

6. Show by vector methods that the points A, B, C, with rectangular coordinates (1, 3, 2), (7, 0, 8), (5, 1, 6) respectively are collinear. Find the coordinates of the mid-point of the line AC.

7. If A and B have position vectors **a** and **b** respectively, find the position vector of the point P which divides the line AB in the ratio $\alpha : \beta$.

8.   ABCD is a quadrilateral (not necessarily plane). If P, Q, R, S denote respectively the mid-points of AB, BC, CD and DA, prove that PQRS is a parallelogram.

9.   A and B are two points in the same horizontal plane, 4 ft apart. A weight of 50 lb is suspended from the mid-point of a 6 ft long rope whose ends are attached to A and B. Find the tension in the rope.

10.   A particle situated at the corner of a cube is acted upon by unit forces directed along the three edges and three diagonals of faces of the cube which meet at that vertex. Find the magnitude of the resultant force acting upon the particle.

10.2 Products of vectors

10.2.1 *Introduction*

A consideration of the manner in which two vector quantities may be combined in elementary mechanics shows that there are two distinct methods of combination each of which have properties similar to a product. The calculation of the work done by a force depends upon two vector quantities, the force $\mathbf{F}$ and the distance $\mathbf{d}$ moved by the point of application. The final result is a scalar quantity W which is such that if either $\mathbf{F}$ or $\mathbf{d}$ is increased by a factor K then W is increased by the same factor. In a similar manner the calculation of the moment of a force $\mathbf{F}$ about a point O involves the vector quantities $\mathbf{F}$ and the position vector $\mathbf{r}$ of the point of application of $\mathbf{F}$. Once more if $\mathbf{F}$ or $\mathbf{r}$ is increased the result is a corresponding proportional increase in the moment but, unlike work, moment is a vector quantity requiring an axis as well as a magnitude for its complete specification (in the simple case of coplanar forces all moments have the same direction for their axis, namely the direction perpendicular to the plane, and the fact that moments are vector quantities can be overlooked). The above examples provide the motivation for the two forms of product, namely scalar products and vector products which will be defined in the following paragraphs.

10.2.2 *The scalar product*

Definition 1. If $\mathbf{a}$ and $\mathbf{b}$ are two vectors such that the angle from $\mathbf{a}$ to $\mathbf{b}$ is θ and their moduli are a and b respectively the *scalar* or '*dot*' *product* is defined as $\mathbf{a} . \mathbf{b} = ab \cos \theta$.

Properties

(i) $\mathbf{a} . \mathbf{b} = \mathbf{b} . \mathbf{a}$ (the commutative law),

(ii) $\mathbf{a} . \mathbf{a} = a^2 = |\mathbf{a}|^2$,

(iii) $\mathbf{a} . (\lambda\mathbf{b}) = \lambda(\mathbf{a} . \mathbf{b}) = (\lambda\mathbf{a}) . \mathbf{b}$,

(iv) $\mathbf{a} . \mathbf{b} = 0$ if $\mathbf{a} = 0$, or if $\mathbf{b} = 0$, or if $\mathbf{a}$ and $\mathbf{b}$ are perpendicular,

(v) $\mathbf{a} . (\mathbf{b} + \mathbf{c}) = \mathbf{a} . \mathbf{b} + \mathbf{a} . \mathbf{c}$ (the distributive law).

Properties (i)–(iv) above are immediate consequences of the definition of a scalar product; the distributive law is established below by a simple geometrical argument.

Let $\mathbf{a}, \mathbf{b}, \mathbf{c}$ be three vectors, not necessarily in the same plane, such that the angle between $\mathbf{a}$ and $\mathbf{b}$ is θ, the angle between $\mathbf{a}$ and $\mathbf{c}$ is ϕ, and the angle between $\mathbf{a}$ and $\mathbf{b} + \mathbf{c}$ is ψ. (See figure 10.12.)

Then $\mathbf{a} . \mathbf{b} = ab \cos \theta = a(b \cos \theta) = a(\text{OB}')$ where OB$'$ is the projected length of $\mathbf{b}$ in the direction of $\mathbf{a}$. Similarly $\mathbf{a} . \mathbf{c} = a(\text{B}'\text{C}')$ where B$'$C$'$ is the projected length of $\mathbf{c}$ in the direction of $\mathbf{a}$.

From figure 10.12, the projected length of $\mathbf{b} + \mathbf{c}$ in direction of $\mathbf{a}$ is OC$'$ = OB$'$ + B$'$C$'$.

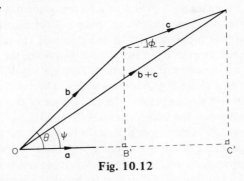

Fig. 10.12

Hence $\quad a(\text{OB}' + \text{B}'\text{C}') = a(\text{OC}')$

$\Rightarrow a(\text{OB}') + a(\text{B}'\text{C}') = a(\text{OC}')$ (distributive law for numbers)

$\Rightarrow \mathbf{a} . \mathbf{b} + \mathbf{a} . \mathbf{c} = \mathbf{a} . (\mathbf{b} + \mathbf{c})$

Scalar product in component form. Suppose $\mathbf{a}$ and $\mathbf{b}$ are expressed in rectangular Cartesian component form as $\mathbf{a} = a_1\hat{\mathbf{i}} + a_2\hat{\mathbf{j}} + a_3\hat{\mathbf{k}}$ and $\mathbf{b} = b_1\hat{\mathbf{i}} + b_2\hat{\mathbf{j}} + b_3\hat{\mathbf{k}}$. The properties (iii)–(v) above then provide a method of expressing $\mathbf{a} . \mathbf{b}$ in terms of these components

$$\begin{aligned}
\mathbf{a} . \mathbf{b} &= \mathbf{a} . (b_1\hat{\mathbf{i}} + b_2\hat{\mathbf{j}} + b_3\hat{\mathbf{k}}) \\
&= b_1\mathbf{a} . \hat{\mathbf{i}} + b_2\mathbf{a} . \hat{\mathbf{j}} + b_3\mathbf{a} . \hat{\mathbf{k}} \\
&= b_1(a_1\hat{\mathbf{i}} . \hat{\mathbf{i}} + a_2\hat{\mathbf{i}} . \hat{\mathbf{j}} + a_3\hat{\mathbf{i}} . \hat{\mathbf{k}}) + b_2(a_1\hat{\mathbf{i}} . \hat{\mathbf{j}} + a_2\hat{\mathbf{j}} . \hat{\mathbf{j}} + a_3\hat{\mathbf{k}} . \hat{\mathbf{j}}) \\
&\quad + b_3(a_1\hat{\mathbf{i}} . \hat{\mathbf{k}} + a_2\hat{\mathbf{j}} . \hat{\mathbf{k}} + a_3\hat{\mathbf{k}} . \hat{\mathbf{k}})
\end{aligned}$$

but since $\hat{i}, \hat{j}, \hat{k}$ are mutually perpendicular vectors of unit length

$$\hat{i} \cdot \hat{i} = \hat{j} \cdot \hat{j} = \hat{k} \cdot \hat{k} = 1 \qquad \text{and} \qquad \hat{i} \cdot \hat{j} = \hat{j} \cdot \hat{k} = \hat{k} \cdot \hat{i} = 0$$

hence

$$\mathbf{a} \cdot \mathbf{b} = a_1 b_1 + a_2 b_2 + a_3 b_3$$

As a particular case of the above $\mathbf{a} \cdot \mathbf{a} = |\mathbf{a}|^2 = a_1^2 + a_2^2 + a_3^2$.

Note. Unlike the expressions for summation and multiplication by a scalar in component form, the above expression for $\mathbf{a} \cdot \mathbf{b}$ is only valid for the special case of resolution into three mutually perpendicular directions.

10.2.3 *Elementary applications of the scalar product*

1. The resolved part of a given force $\mathbf{F}$ in a given direction $\mathbf{d}$ is $\mathbf{F} \cdot \hat{\mathbf{d}}$.

   If $\mathbf{F}$ acts at an angle θ to $\mathbf{d}$ and has magnitude F, the resolved part is $F \cos \theta$. But $\mathbf{F} \cdot \mathbf{d} = Fd \cos \theta$ and hence, if we replace $\mathbf{d}$ by a unit vector $\hat{\mathbf{d}}$ in the same direction, we obtain $\mathbf{F} \cdot \hat{\mathbf{d}} = F \cos \theta =$ resolved part of $\mathbf{F}$. (See figure 10.13.)

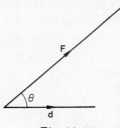

Fig. 10.13

2. The work done by a force $\mathbf{F}$ in moving in a straight line from A to B is $\mathbf{F} \cdot (\mathbf{b} - \mathbf{a})$ where $\mathbf{a}$ and $\mathbf{b}$ are the position vectors of A and B referred to any fixed origin O. (See figure 10.14.)

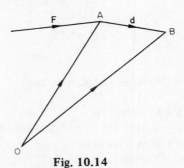

Fig. 10.14

In elementary terms the work done by a force in moving its points of application a distance d is given as (resolved part of force) $\times$ (distance moved). Using the result above, this becomes work = $(\mathbf{F} \cdot \hat{\mathbf{d}})/d = \mathbf{F} \cdot \mathbf{d}$, where $\mathbf{d}$ is the vector distance moved. But from figure 10.14, $\mathbf{d} = \mathbf{b} - \mathbf{a}$ so that work = $\mathbf{F} \cdot (\mathbf{b} - \mathbf{a})$.

3. The direction cosines of a vector in direction $\hat{\mathbf{d}}$ are (d_1, d_2, d_3).

In solid geometry the direction of a line is usually specified by its 'direction cosines'. If the line makes angles of $\theta_1, \theta_2, \theta_3$ with the three coordinate axes, its direction cosines are $\cos \theta_1$, $\cos \theta_2$ and $\cos \theta_3$. But, if $\hat{\mathbf{d}}$ is a unit vector in the direction of the line, from the definition of the scalar product we have $\hat{\mathbf{d}} \cdot \hat{\mathbf{i}} = \cos \theta_1$, $\hat{\mathbf{d}} \cdot \hat{\mathbf{j}} = \cos \theta_2$ and $\hat{\mathbf{d}} \cdot \hat{\mathbf{k}} = \cos \theta_3$. Hence $(\cos \theta_1, \cos \theta_2, \cos \theta_3) = (d_1, d_2, d_3)$.

10.2.4 *The vector product*

Definition 2. If $\mathbf{a}$ and $\mathbf{b}$ are two vectors, such that the angle from $\mathbf{a}$ to $\mathbf{b}$ is θ and their moduli are a and b respectively, the *vector* or '*cross*' *product* is defined as $\mathbf{a} \times \mathbf{b} = ab \sin \theta \hat{\mathbf{n}}$, where $\hat{\mathbf{n}}$ is a unit vector in a direction perpendicular to the plane of $\mathbf{a}$ and $\mathbf{b}$ and in the sense of a right-handed rotation from $\mathbf{a}$ to $\mathbf{b}$. (See figure 10.15.)

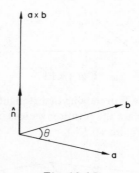

Fig. 10.15

Properties
- (i) $\mathbf{a} \times \mathbf{b} = -\mathbf{b} \times \mathbf{a}$ (the anti-commutative law),
- (ii) $\mathbf{a} \times \mathbf{a} = 0$,
- (iii) $\mathbf{a} \times (\lambda \mathbf{b}) = \lambda(\mathbf{a} \times \mathbf{b}) = (\lambda \mathbf{a}) \times \mathbf{b}$,
- (iv) $\mathbf{a} \times \mathbf{b} = 0$ if $\mathbf{a} = 0$ or if $\mathbf{b} = 0$ or if $\mathbf{a}$ and $\mathbf{b}$ are parallel,
- (v) $\mathbf{a} \times (\mathbf{b} + \mathbf{c}) = \mathbf{a} \times \mathbf{b} + \mathbf{a} \times \mathbf{c}$ and $(\mathbf{b} + \mathbf{c}) \times \mathbf{a} = \mathbf{b} \times \mathbf{a} + \mathbf{c} \times \mathbf{a}$.
    (The distributive laws.)

Property (i) is a direct consequence of the definition of the sense of $\hat{n}$ in the definition of $\mathbf{a} \times \mathbf{b}$. Because the vector product is not commutative, care must be taken not to interchange the order of terms in a vector product. Properties (ii), (iii) and (iv) can be easily deduced from the definition. Property (v) can be proved by first resolving $\mathbf{b}$ and $\mathbf{c}$ into their components parallel and perpendicular to $\mathbf{a}$. (See exercise 10, p. 449.)

Vector product in component form. Using properties (i), (iii) and (v) above, the vector product $\mathbf{a} \times \mathbf{b}$ can be expanded in component form; this gives

$$\mathbf{a} \times \mathbf{b} = (a_1\hat{\mathbf{i}} + a_2\hat{\mathbf{j}} + a_3\hat{\mathbf{k}}) \times (b_1\hat{\mathbf{i}} + b_2\hat{\mathbf{j}} + b_3\hat{\mathbf{k}})$$
$$= a_1b_1\hat{\mathbf{i}} \times \hat{\mathbf{i}} + a_1b_2\hat{\mathbf{i}} \times \hat{\mathbf{j}} + a_1b_3\hat{\mathbf{i}} \times \hat{\mathbf{k}} + a_2b_1\hat{\mathbf{j}} \times \hat{\mathbf{i}} + a_2b_2\hat{\mathbf{j}} \times \hat{\mathbf{j}}$$
$$+ a_2b_3\hat{\mathbf{j}} \times \hat{\mathbf{k}} + a_3b_1\hat{\mathbf{k}} \times \hat{\mathbf{i}} + a_3b_2\hat{\mathbf{k}} \times \hat{\mathbf{j}} + a_3b_3\hat{\mathbf{k}} \times \hat{\mathbf{k}}$$

But the vectors $\hat{\mathbf{i}}, \hat{\mathbf{j}}, \hat{\mathbf{k}}$ are mutually perpendicular and form a right-handed set in the sense that a right-handed rotation from $\hat{\mathbf{i}}$ to $\hat{\mathbf{j}}$ gives the sense of $\hat{\mathbf{k}}$. From the definition of the vector product we thus obtain

$$\hat{\mathbf{i}} \times \hat{\mathbf{i}} = \hat{\mathbf{j}} \times \hat{\mathbf{j}} = \hat{\mathbf{k}} \times \hat{\mathbf{k}} = 0, \quad \hat{\mathbf{i}} \times \hat{\mathbf{j}} = -\hat{\mathbf{j}} \times \hat{\mathbf{i}} = \hat{\mathbf{k}}, \quad \hat{\mathbf{j}} \times \hat{\mathbf{k}} = -\hat{\mathbf{k}} \times \hat{\mathbf{j}} = \hat{\mathbf{i}},$$
$$\hat{\mathbf{k}} \times \hat{\mathbf{i}} = -\hat{\mathbf{i}} \times \hat{\mathbf{k}} = \hat{\mathbf{j}}$$

[As an aid to memory, the vector product of any two of these unit vectors is the third, the sign being + if the shortest route between them in figure 10.16 follows the arrows, the sign being − otherwise.]

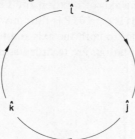

Fig. 10.16

Substituting these values into the expression for $\mathbf{a} \times \mathbf{b}$ gives

$$\mathbf{a} \times \mathbf{b} = (a_2b_3 - a_3b_2)\hat{\mathbf{i}} + (a_3b_1 - a_1b_3)\hat{\mathbf{j}} + (a_1b_2 - a_2b_1)\hat{\mathbf{k}}$$

$\mathbf{a} \times \mathbf{b}$ can also be expressed as a 3×3 determinant:

$$\mathbf{a} \times \mathbf{b} = \begin{vmatrix} \hat{\mathbf{i}} & \hat{\mathbf{j}} & \hat{\mathbf{k}} \\ a_1 & a_2 & a_3 \\ b_1 & b_2 & b_3 \end{vmatrix}$$

10.2.5 *Elementary applications of the vector product*

1. The moment about O of a force **F** acting at a point **P** with position vector **r** is **r** × **F**. (See figure 10.17.)

    The moment has a magnitude equal to force times perpendicular distance from **F** to O, and is associated with an axis perpendicular to the plane of **r** and **F**. If θ is the angle between **r** and **F** the perpendicular distance from O to the line of action of **F** is $r \sin \theta$; hence the moment has magnitude $Fr \sin \theta$ and direction $\hat{n}$ or **M** = **r** × **F**.

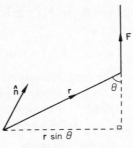

Fig. 10.17

2. The velocity **v** of a particle at P, with position vector **r**, on a rigid body rotating about O with angular velocity **ω** is **v** = **ω** × **r**. (See figure 10.18.)

    If the angle between the axis of rotation and **r** is θ then the perpendicular distance from P to the axis is $r \sin \theta$. P is thus moving with a velocity $\omega r \sin \theta$ in a direction perpendicular to both the axis and to **r**. With the usual convention that anti-clockwise rotations are regarded as positive we obtain **v** = **ω** × **r**.

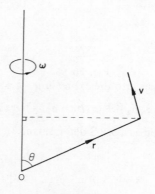

Fig. 10.18

3. The area of the parallelogram whose edges are **a** and **b** is $|(\mathbf{a} \times \mathbf{b})|$. (See figure 10.19.)

By elementary geometry the area of a parallelogram is given by the formula area = base × perpendicular height. From figure 10.19, area = $\mathbf{OA}.\mathbf{BB'}$; but $BB' = b \sin \theta$, and so area = $ab \sin \theta = |\mathbf{a} \times \mathbf{b}|$. $\mathbf{a} \times \mathbf{b}$ is usually referred to as the vector area of the parallelogram, that is a vector whose magnitude is equal to the area and whose direction is perpendicular or normal to the plane of the parallelogram.

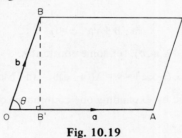

Fig. 10.19

10.2.6 *Triple products of vectors*

The triple scalar product. If **a**, **b**, **c** are any three vectors the triple scalar product of **a**, **b** and **c** is denoted $(\mathbf{a}, \mathbf{b}, \mathbf{c})$ and is defined as $(\mathbf{a}, \mathbf{b}, \mathbf{c}) = \mathbf{a} . (\mathbf{b} \times \mathbf{c})$.

In component form this becomes

$$\mathbf{a} . (\mathbf{b} \times \mathbf{c}) = (a_1\hat{\mathbf{i}} + a_2\hat{\mathbf{j}} + a_3\hat{\mathbf{k}}) . \begin{vmatrix} \hat{\mathbf{i}} & \hat{\mathbf{j}} & \hat{\mathbf{k}} \\ b_1 & b_2 & b_3 \\ c_1 & c_2 & c_3 \end{vmatrix} = \begin{vmatrix} a_1 & a_2 & a_3 \\ b_1 & b_2 & b_3 \\ c_1 & c_2 & c_3 \end{vmatrix} = \Delta$$

by using the properties of determinants we obtain

$$\Delta = \begin{vmatrix} c_1 & c_2 & c_3 \\ a_1 & a_2 & a_3 \\ b_1 & b_2 & b_3 \end{vmatrix} = \mathbf{c} . (\mathbf{a} \times \mathbf{b}) = (\mathbf{a} \times \mathbf{b}) . \mathbf{c}$$

showing that the exact positions of the . and the × in the expression for the triple scalar product are not critical. If **a**, **b**, **c** are non-zero vectors the condition $(\mathbf{a}, \mathbf{b}, \mathbf{c}) = 0$ implies that **a** is perpendicular to the normal to the plane of **b** and **c** (since $\mathbf{a} . (\mathbf{b} \times \mathbf{c}) = 0$) or, more simply, that the vectors **a**, **b**, **c** are coplanar.

Since $\mathbf{b} \times \mathbf{c}$ gives the vector area of the parallelogram whose edges are **b** and **c**, then $\mathbf{a} . (\mathbf{b} \times \mathbf{c})$ gives the volume of the parallelepiped whose edges are **a**, **b** and **c**.

The triple vector product. The expression $a \times (b \times c)$ defines a vector quantity whose direction is perpendicular to a and to $\hat{n}$, where $\hat{n}$ is the normal to the plane of b and c.

If $v = a \times (b \times c)$ then the fact that v is perpendicular to $\hat{n}$ means that v must lie in the plane of b and c; hence v must be of the form

$$v = xb + yc$$

Also v is perpendicular to a so that $v \cdot a = 0$.

Thus

$$xa \cdot b + ya \cdot c = 0$$

Thus $x = \lambda a \cdot c$ and $y = -\lambda(a \cdot b)$, for some constant λ.

Hence $\qquad a \times (b \times c) = v = \lambda((a \cdot c)b - (a \cdot b)c)$

λ can now be determined by expanding one component of $a \times (b \times c)$:

$$a \times (b \times c) = (a_1\hat{i} + a_2\hat{j} + a_3\hat{k}) \times \begin{vmatrix} \hat{i} & \hat{j} & \hat{k} \\ b_1 & b_2 & b_3 \\ c_1 & c_2 & c_3 \end{vmatrix}$$

Expanding the first component shows that $\lambda = 1$, whence

$$a \times (b \times c) = (a \cdot c)b - (a \cdot b)c$$

Note: $\qquad (a \times b) \times c = -c \times (a \times b) = -((c \cdot b)a - (c \cdot a)b)$

$$= (c \cdot a)b - (c \cdot b)a$$

These equations show that in general $a \times (b \times c) \neq (a \times b) \times c$; the associative law is thus not valid for the vector product and expressions such as $a \times b \times c$ are ambiguous, their value depending upon the order of calculating the products.

10.2.7 *Worked examples on products of vectors*

1. Find the work done by the force $F = 2\hat{i} + \hat{j} + \hat{k}$ if its point of application moves in a straight line from $A(1, 1, 1)$ to $B(2, 1, 3)$.

   Solution. Referred to an origin O, A has position vector $a = \hat{i} + \hat{j} + \hat{k}$ and B has position vector $b = 2\hat{i} + \hat{j} + 3\hat{k}$.
   The distance moved by the force is $d = b - a = \hat{i} + 2\hat{k}$; the work done is
   $W = F \cdot d = (2\hat{i} + \hat{j} + \hat{k}) \cdot (\hat{i} + 2\hat{k}) = 4$ units.

2. Show that the points $A(1, 2, 1)$, $B(2, 3, 2)$, $C(3, 3, -2)$ are the vertices of a right-angled triangle, and find the other angles of the triangle and its area.

Solution. Referred to an origin O, the position vectors of A, B and C are

$$a = \hat{i} + 2\hat{j} + \hat{k}, \quad b = 2\hat{i} + 3\hat{j} + 2\hat{k}$$

and

$$c = 3\hat{i} + 3\hat{j} - 2\hat{k}$$

The edges of the triangle have vectors (see figure 10.20):

$$b - a = \hat{i} + \hat{j} + \hat{k}$$
$$c - a = 2\hat{i} + \hat{j} - 3\hat{k}$$
$$c - b = \hat{i} - 4\hat{k}$$

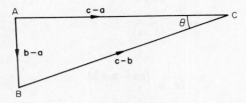

Fig. 10.20

Since $(b - a) \cdot (c - a) = 0$ the triangle is right-angled at A. If $\angle ACB = \theta$ then θ is given by the equation

$$(c - a) \cdot (c - b) = |(c - a)| \cdot |(c - b)| \cos \theta$$
$$\Rightarrow 14 = \sqrt{14} \cdot \sqrt{17} \cos \theta$$
$$\Rightarrow \theta = \cos^{-1}\left(\frac{\sqrt{14}}{\sqrt{17}} \right)$$

Since the triangle is right-angled its area is

$$\tfrac{1}{2}|(c - a)| \cdot |(b - a)| = \tfrac{1}{2} \sqrt{14} \cdot \sqrt{3} = \tfrac{1}{2} \sqrt{42}$$

Alternatively the area could have been calculated as

$$\tfrac{1}{2} |(c - a) \times (c - b)| \quad \text{or} \quad \tfrac{1}{2} |(b - a) \times (c - a)|$$

3. Find a vector x such that $a \times x = b$ and $a \cdot x = c$ where a and b are given vectors and c is a constant.

Solution. From the equation $a \times x = b$ we can deduce that b is perpendicular (or orthogonal) to a and to x.
Thus the vectors a, b and $a \times b$ form a set of mutually orthogonal vectors and x can be expressed in the form $x = \alpha a + \beta b + \gamma a + b$. Since x is orthogonal to b, $\beta = 0$.

Also

$$\mathbf{a} \times \mathbf{x} = \mathbf{a} \times (\alpha \mathbf{a} + \gamma \mathbf{a} \times \mathbf{b})$$

$$\Rightarrow \mathbf{b} = \alpha \mathbf{a} \times \mathbf{a} + \gamma \mathbf{a} \times (\mathbf{a} \times \mathbf{b})$$

$$\Rightarrow \mathbf{b} = \gamma((\mathbf{a} . \mathbf{b})\mathbf{a} - (\mathbf{a} . \mathbf{a})\mathbf{b})$$

$$\Rightarrow \mathbf{b} = -\gamma(\mathbf{a} . \mathbf{a})\mathbf{b} \quad (\text{since } \mathbf{a} . \mathbf{b} = 0)$$

$$\Rightarrow \gamma = \frac{-1}{(\mathbf{a} . \mathbf{a})}$$

α is determined from the condition $\mathbf{a} . \mathbf{x} = c$.

$$\mathbf{a} . \mathbf{x} = \mathbf{a} . (\alpha \mathbf{a} + \gamma \mathbf{a} \times \mathbf{b})$$

$$\Rightarrow c = \alpha \mathbf{a} . \mathbf{a}$$

$$\Rightarrow \alpha = \frac{c}{(\mathbf{a} . \mathbf{a})}$$

Hence

$$\mathbf{x} = \frac{1}{(\mathbf{a} . \mathbf{a})} \{ c\mathbf{a} - \mathbf{a} \times \mathbf{b} \}$$

Exercises

1. Find a unit vector perpendicular to $\mathbf{v} = \hat{\mathbf{i}} - 2\hat{\mathbf{j}} + \hat{\mathbf{k}}$ and $\mathbf{w} = 2\hat{\mathbf{i}} + \hat{\mathbf{j}} + \hat{\mathbf{k}}$; find also the angle between the directions of $\mathbf{v}$ and $\mathbf{w}$.

2. The points A, B and C have rectangular cartesian coordinates $(1, 0, -1)$ $(1, 2, 0)$ and $(0, 1, 2)$. Find the area of triangle ABC (a scalar quantity); find also a unit vector perpendicular to the plane of A, B and C.

3. If $\mathbf{a}$, $\mathbf{b}$ and $\mathbf{c}$ are three non-zero vectors, find the conditions under which $\mathbf{a} \times (\mathbf{b} \times \mathbf{c}) = (\mathbf{a} \times \mathbf{b}) \times \mathbf{c}$. If $\mathbf{a} = \hat{\mathbf{i}} + 2\hat{\mathbf{j}}$, $\mathbf{b} = -4\hat{\mathbf{i}} + 2\hat{\mathbf{j}} + 4\hat{\mathbf{k}}$, and $\mathbf{c} = \hat{\mathbf{i}} + \hat{\mathbf{k}}$, verify that $\mathbf{a} \times (\mathbf{b} \times \mathbf{c}) = (\mathbf{a} \times \mathbf{b}) \times \mathbf{c}$.

4. Assuming the formula for the vector triple product show that

$$(\mathbf{a} \times \mathbf{b}) \times (\mathbf{c} \times \mathbf{d}) = (\mathbf{a}, \mathbf{c}, \mathbf{d})\mathbf{b} - (\mathbf{b}, \mathbf{c}, \mathbf{d})\mathbf{a}$$

$$= (\mathbf{a}, \mathbf{b}, \mathbf{d})\mathbf{c} - (\mathbf{a}, \mathbf{b}, \mathbf{c})\mathbf{d}$$

Hence if $\mathbf{a} = \hat{\mathbf{i}} + \hat{\mathbf{j}}$, $\mathbf{b} = \hat{\mathbf{j}} + \hat{\mathbf{k}}$, $\mathbf{c} = \hat{\mathbf{i}} + \hat{\mathbf{k}}$, find an expression for $\mathbf{d} = x\hat{\mathbf{i}} + y\hat{\mathbf{j}} + z\hat{\mathbf{k}}$ in terms of $\mathbf{a}$, $\mathbf{b}$ and $\mathbf{c}$.

5. The points A, B, C, D, with position vectors $\mathbf{a}$, $\mathbf{b}$, $\mathbf{c}$, $\mathbf{d}$, form the vertices of a tetrahedron. Find expressions for the vector areas of each of the four faces of the tetrahedron and show that if these areas are taken in the sense of the outward normals from the tetrahedron their vector sum is zero.

6. Show that, if $\mathbf{u}$ and $\mathbf{v}$ are constant vectors such that $\mathbf{u} \cdot \mathbf{v} = 0$, the simultaneous equations

$$x + y = \mathbf{u}$$
$$x \times y = \mathbf{v}$$

have a solution involving one arbitrary scalar.

7. A top is rotating about an axis through O in the direction of $\mathbf{OZ}$ with an angular velocity of ω radians/sec. Find the velocity of the point P of the top with cartesian coordinates (x, y, z). If the top continues to revolve with the same angular velocity but the point of contact 0 has in addition a linear velocity v in the direction of OX, find the cartesian coordinates of those points of the top which are instantaneously at rest.

8. A rigid body is acted upon by forces $\mathbf{F}_1 = \hat{\mathbf{i}} + \hat{\mathbf{j}} - \hat{\mathbf{k}}$ acting at $(1, 1, 0)$, $\mathbf{F}_2 = \hat{\mathbf{i}} - \hat{\mathbf{j}} + \hat{\mathbf{k}}$ acting at $(1, 0, 1)$, and $\mathbf{F}_3 = 2\hat{\mathbf{i}}$ acting at $(1, 1, 1)$. Find the moment $\mathbf{M}$ about O of this system of forces. Show that $\mathbf{M}$ can be reduced to O by the introduction of a suitable additional force $\mathbf{F}_4$ acting at $(1, 0, 0)$ but that $\mathbf{F}_4$ is not uniquely determined by this condition.

9. The points A, B, C, P, have position vectors $\mathbf{a}, \mathbf{b}, \mathbf{c}, \mathbf{r}$, referred to the origin O. What is the geometrical relationship between A, B, C and P if $(\mathbf{r} - \mathbf{a}) \cdot (\mathbf{b} - \mathbf{a}) \times (\mathbf{c} - \mathbf{a}) = 0$?
    Find the equation of the plane passing through the points $(1, 1, 0)$, $(0, 1, -1)$ and $(1, 2, 1)$.

10. (i) $\mathbf{b} = \mathbf{b}_1 + \mathbf{b}_2$ where $\mathbf{b}_1$ is perpendicular to $\mathbf{a}$ and $\mathbf{b}_2$ is parallel to $\mathbf{a}$; prove from the definition of a vector product that $\mathbf{a} \times \mathbf{b} = \mathbf{a} \times \mathbf{b}_1$.
     (ii) The vectors $\mathbf{b}_1$ and $\mathbf{c}_1$ are in the plane perpendicular to the vector $\mathbf{a}$; prove from the definition of a vector product that $\mathbf{a} \times \mathbf{b}_1 + \mathbf{a} \times \mathbf{c}_1 = \mathbf{a} \times (\mathbf{b}_1 + \mathbf{c}_1)$.
     (iii) From (i) and (ii) deduce the general distributive law for vector products.

10.3 Differentiation of vectors

10.3.1 *Definition and properties*

Definition 3. Suppose $\mathbf{v} = \mathbf{v}(t)$ is a vector function of a scalar parameter t. (For example, the velocity of a moving particle where t represents time.) Then, since the subtraction of vectors has already been defined, $\mathbf{v}(t + \delta t) - \mathbf{v}(t)$ can be calculated for any values of t and $t + \delta t$ at which the velocity exists.

The derivative is then defined as

$$\frac{d\mathbf{v}}{dt} = \lim_{\delta t \to 0} \frac{\mathbf{v}(t + \delta t) - \mathbf{v}(t)}{\delta t}$$

If this limit exists the function $\mathbf{v}$ is said to be differentiable at the point t, and the derivative, $d\mathbf{v}/dt$, will itself be a vector function of t.

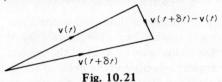

Fig. 10.21

Properties. If $\mathbf{a}$ and $\mathbf{b}$ are vector functions of t, and if λ is a scalar function of t, the following properties are valid whenever the derivatives concerned exist.

(i) $\dfrac{d}{dt} (\mathbf{a} + \mathbf{b}) = \dfrac{d\mathbf{a}}{dt} + \dfrac{d\mathbf{b}}{dt}$,

(ii) $\dfrac{d}{dt} (\mathbf{a} \cdot \mathbf{b}) = \left(\dfrac{d\mathbf{a}}{dt}\right) \cdot \mathbf{b} + \mathbf{a} \cdot \left(\dfrac{d\mathbf{b}}{dt}\right)$,

(iii) $\dfrac{d}{dt} (\lambda \mathbf{a}) = \left(\dfrac{d\lambda}{dt}\right) \mathbf{a} + \lambda \dfrac{d\mathbf{a}}{dt}$,

(iv) $\dfrac{d}{dt} (\mathbf{a} \times \mathbf{b}) = \left(\dfrac{d\mathbf{a}}{dt}\right) \times \mathbf{b} + \mathbf{a} \times \left(\dfrac{d\mathbf{b}}{dt}\right)$.

All the above properties can be deduced from the definition of differentiation and the algebraic properties of sums and products of vectors. Property (iv) is proved below as an example of the type of argument involved.

Suppose $\mathbf{a}$, $\mathbf{b}$ and $\mathbf{a} \times \mathbf{b}$ are differentiable vector functions of t.

Then, from the definition of differentiation

$$\frac{d}{dt} (\mathbf{a} \times \mathbf{b}) =$$

$$= \lim_{\delta t \to 0} \frac{\mathbf{a}(t + \delta t) \times \mathbf{b}(t + \delta t) - \mathbf{a}(t) \times \mathbf{b}(t)}{\delta t}$$

$$= \lim_{\delta t \to 0} \frac{\mathbf{a}(t + \delta t) \times \mathbf{b}(t + \delta t) - \mathbf{a}(t) \times \mathbf{b}(t + \delta t) + \mathbf{a}(t) \times \mathbf{b}(t + \delta t) - \mathbf{a}(t) \times \mathbf{b}(t)}{\delta t}$$

$$= \lim_{\delta t \to 0} \frac{(\mathbf{a}(t + \delta t) - \mathbf{a}(t)) \times \mathbf{b}(t + \delta t)}{\delta t} + \lim_{\delta t \to 0} \frac{\mathbf{a}(t) \times (\mathbf{b}(t + \delta t) - \mathbf{b}(t))}{\delta t}$$

$$= \left(\frac{d\mathbf{a}}{dt}\right) \times \mathbf{b}(t) + \mathbf{a}(t) \times \left(\frac{d\mathbf{b}}{dt}\right)$$

since $\mathbf{a}$ and $\mathbf{b}$ are differentiable and, by implication, continuous functions of t.

Note. Since the vector product is not commutative, care must be taken when differentiating vector products to keep the factors in the correct order

$$\frac{d}{dt}(a \times b) \neq \left(\frac{da}{dt}\right) \times b + \left(\frac{db}{dt}\right) \times a$$

Differentiation of a vector in component form. Properties (i) and (iii) above may be used to obtain an expression in component form for the derivative of a vector function.

Suppose $\mathbf{v}(t)$ is a vector function of t. Then for fixed axes the expression $\mathbf{v}(t) = v_1(t)\hat{\mathbf{i}} + v_2(t)\hat{\mathbf{j}} + v_3(t)\hat{\mathbf{k}}$ defines three scalar functions v_1, v_2, v_3.

Now, $\quad \dfrac{d\mathbf{v}}{dt} = \dfrac{d}{dt}(v_1(t)\hat{\mathbf{i}} + v_2(t)\hat{\mathbf{j}} + v_3(t)\hat{\mathbf{k}})$

$$= \frac{d}{dt}(v_1\hat{\mathbf{i}}) + \frac{d}{dt}(v_2\hat{\mathbf{j}}) + \frac{d}{dt}(v_3\hat{\mathbf{k}}) \quad \text{(Using (i))}$$

$$= \frac{dv_1}{dt}\hat{\mathbf{i}} + v_1\frac{d\hat{\mathbf{i}}}{dt} + \frac{dv_2}{dt}\hat{\mathbf{j}} + v_2\frac{d\hat{\mathbf{j}}}{dt} + \frac{dv_3}{dt}\hat{\mathbf{k}} + v_3\frac{d\hat{\mathbf{k}}}{dt} \quad \text{(Using (iii))}$$

Hence

$$\frac{d\mathbf{v}}{dt} = \frac{dv_1}{dt}\hat{\mathbf{i}} + \frac{dv_2}{dt}\hat{\mathbf{j}} + \frac{dv_3}{dt}\hat{\mathbf{k}}$$

since $\hat{\mathbf{i}}, \hat{\mathbf{j}}, \hat{\mathbf{k}}$ are constant.

10.3.2 *Applications of differentiation*

1. If $\mathbf{r}(t)$ is the position vector of a moving particle referred to a fixed origin O then its velocity is $\mathbf{v} = d\mathbf{r}/dt$ and its acceleration is $\mathbf{f} = d\mathbf{v}/dt = d^2\mathbf{r}/dt^2$.

2. To find the acceleration of a point on a body moving with uniform angular velocity about a fixed axis.

   Let the body be rotating about O with constant angular velocity $\boldsymbol{\omega}$, and let point P have position vector $\mathbf{r}$ relative to O. (See figure 10.22.) Then P has velocity $\mathbf{v} = \boldsymbol{\omega} \times \mathbf{r}$, and $\mathbf{f} = $ acceleration of $P = d\mathbf{v}/dt = d/dt(\boldsymbol{\omega} \times \mathbf{r})$.

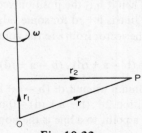

Fig. 10.22

Hence
$$f = \frac{d\boldsymbol{\omega}}{dt} \times \mathbf{r} + \boldsymbol{\omega} \times \frac{d\mathbf{r}}{dt}$$

But $\boldsymbol{\omega}$ is constant and $d\mathbf{r}/dt = \mathbf{v} = \boldsymbol{\omega} \times \mathbf{r}$.

Hence
$$\mathbf{f} = \boldsymbol{\omega} \times (\boldsymbol{\omega} \times \mathbf{r})$$
$$= (\boldsymbol{\omega} . \mathbf{r})\boldsymbol{\omega} - \omega^2 \mathbf{r}$$

If, in particular, $\mathbf{r}$ is perpendicular to the axis of rotation, $\boldsymbol{\omega} . \mathbf{r} = 0$ and the acceleration is simply $-\boldsymbol{\omega}^2 \mathbf{r}$ and is directed towards O. More generally $\mathbf{r}$ can be expressed as $\mathbf{r} = \mathbf{r}_1 + \mathbf{r}_2$ where $\mathbf{r}_1$ is parallel to $\boldsymbol{\omega}$ and $\mathbf{r}_2$ is perpendicular to $\boldsymbol{\omega}$.

Then
$$\mathbf{f} = (\boldsymbol{\omega} . (\mathbf{r}_1 + \mathbf{r}_2))\boldsymbol{\omega} - \omega^2 (\mathbf{r}_1 + \mathbf{r}_2)$$
$$= r_1 \omega \boldsymbol{\omega} - \omega^2 \mathbf{r}_1 - \omega^2 \mathbf{r}_2$$
$$= -\omega^2 \mathbf{r}_2 \text{ since } \mathbf{r}_1 \text{ and } \boldsymbol{\omega} \text{ are parallel.}$$

This shows that once more the acceleration of P is equal to ω^2 times the perpendicular distance from the axis and is directed towards the axis.

3. To find the minimum distance from a given point to a given line.

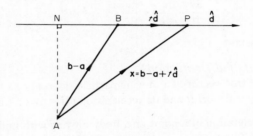

Fig. 10.23

Let the given point be A with position vector $\mathbf{a}$, and let the line pass through B in direction $\hat{\mathbf{d}}$. Then if $\mathbf{b}$ is the position vector of B, the position vector of any point on the line is $\mathbf{b} + t\hat{\mathbf{d}}$ for some value of the parameter t. (See figure 10.23.) If $\mathbf{x}$ is the vector from $\mathbf{a}$ to the point $\mathbf{r} = \mathbf{b} + t\hat{\mathbf{d}}$ on the line then

$$x^2 = (\mathbf{b} - \mathbf{a} + t\hat{\mathbf{d}}) . (\mathbf{b} - \mathbf{a} + t\hat{\mathbf{d}})$$

x^2, and hence $|x|$, is a minimum when $d/dt (\mathbf{b} - \mathbf{a} + t\hat{\mathbf{d}})^2 = 0$; t is thus given by the condition $2\hat{\mathbf{d}} . (\mathbf{b} - \mathbf{a} + t\hat{\mathbf{d}}) = 0$ or $\hat{\mathbf{d}} . \mathbf{x} = 0$, confirming that the shortest distance from a point to a line is the normal to the line through that point.

Since $\hat{\mathbf{d}}$ is a unit vector the condition $\hat{\mathbf{d}} \, (\mathbf{b} - \mathbf{a} + t\hat{\mathbf{d}}) = 0$ gives $t = -\hat{\mathbf{d}} \,.\, (\mathbf{b} - \mathbf{a})$. Substituting this value of t into the expression for x^2 gives

$$x^2 = (\mathbf{b} - \mathbf{a} - [\hat{\mathbf{d}} \,.\, (\mathbf{b} - \mathbf{a})]\,\hat{\mathbf{d}})^2$$
$$= (\mathbf{b} - \mathbf{a})^2 - (\hat{\mathbf{d}} \,.\, (\mathbf{b} - \mathbf{a}))^2$$

This result can also be obtained geometrically by using Pythagoras' Theorem to calculate the length of the side AN of triangle ABN in figure 10.23.

* 10.4 Vector mechanics

In this section we shall show how some of the basic equations of mechanics can be expressed in vector form. This is not intended as an introduction to mechanics for those unfamiliar with the subject but it will show how the use of vector notation leads to a more concise form for the equations, enabling the fundamental principles to be more easily understood.

10.4.1 *Motion of a particle*

Suppose the particle P has position vector $\mathbf{OP} = \mathbf{r}$ relative to some fixed origin O. Then its velocity is given as $\mathbf{v} = d\mathbf{r}/dt$, and its acceleration is $d\mathbf{v}/dt = d^2\mathbf{r}/dt^2 = \mathbf{a}$, where t is time.

Constant acceleration. If in particular the acceleration is constant and has the value $\mathbf{a}_0$, the equation of motion becomes

$$\frac{d\mathbf{v}}{dt} = \mathbf{a}_0$$

This equation can be integrated to give

$$\mathbf{v} = \mathbf{a}_0 t + \mathbf{k}$$

where $\mathbf{k}$ is an arbitrary vector constant. If the initial velocity, when $t = 0$, is $\mathbf{v}_0$, then $\mathbf{k} = \mathbf{v}_0$ and $\mathbf{v} = \mathbf{a}_0 t + \mathbf{v}_0$. Since $\mathbf{v} = d\mathbf{r}/dt$ we can integrate again to obtain

$$\mathbf{r} = \tfrac{1}{2}\,\mathbf{a}_0 t^2 + \mathbf{v}_0 t + \mathbf{r}_0$$

where $\mathbf{r}_0$ is the initial value of $\mathbf{r}$.

Newton's laws of motion. Newton's first two laws of motion state (i) that a particle will continue in a state of rest or uniform motion in a straight line unless it is acted upon by external forces, and (ii) that when a force is applied to the particle the rate of change of momentum is proportional to the applied force and in the same direction. Momentum is defined as the product of the mass and the velocity; hence for the particle the above laws can be expressed by the single vector equation

$$k \frac{\mathrm{d}}{\mathrm{d}t} (m\mathbf{v}) = \mathbf{F} \tag{1}$$

where m is the mass, $\mathbf{F}$ the applied force, and k a constant of proportionality. With a suitable choice of units (for example, mass in kilograms, velocity in metres/sec and force in newtons (the SI units)) the constant of proportionality becomes $k = 1$ and equation (1) simplifies to

$$\frac{\mathrm{d}}{\mathrm{d}t} (m\mathbf{v}) = \mathbf{F} \tag{2}$$

If the mass remains constant this simplifies further to

$$m \frac{\mathrm{d}\mathbf{v}}{\mathrm{d}t} = m \frac{\mathrm{d}^2\mathbf{r}}{\mathrm{d}t^2} = \mathbf{F} \tag{3}$$

Taking the scalar product of equation (3) with $\mathbf{v}$ gives

$$m \frac{\mathrm{d}\mathbf{v}}{\mathrm{d}t} \cdot \mathbf{v} = \mathbf{F} \cdot \mathbf{v}$$

Since m is assumed constant this can be rewritten as

$$\frac{\mathrm{d}}{\mathrm{d}t} (\tfrac{1}{2} m\mathbf{v} \cdot \mathbf{v}) = \mathbf{F} \cdot \frac{\mathrm{d}\mathbf{r}}{\mathrm{d}t}$$

Integration with respect to t gives

$$\left[\tfrac{1}{2} m\mathbf{v}^2\right]_{t_0}^{t_1} = \int_{t_0}^{t_1} \mathbf{F} \cdot \frac{\mathrm{d}\mathbf{r}}{\mathrm{d}t} \, \mathrm{d}t = \int_{t_0}^{t_1} \mathbf{F} \cdot \mathrm{d}\mathbf{r} \tag{4}$$

This is the vector form of the well-known equation relating the change in the kinetic energy to the work done by the external force.

The solution of equation (2) depends essentially on the nature of the force $\mathbf{F}$; particularly simple cases arise (a) when the only force acting is gravity, or (b) when $\mathbf{F}$ consists of an external force independent of the motion together with a resisting force related to the velocity.

(a) $\mathbf{F} = -mg\hat{\mathbf{k}}$ with a suitable choice of axes. Equation (2) becomes

$$\frac{\mathrm{d}}{\mathrm{d}t} (m\mathbf{v}) = -mg\hat{\mathbf{k}}$$

or

$$\frac{\mathrm{d}\mathbf{v}}{\mathrm{d}t} = -g\hat{\mathbf{k}}$$

which is the equation of motion of a projectile.

(b) $\mathbf{F} = \mathbf{F_0} - f(v)\mathbf{v}$, where $\mathbf{F_0}$ is an external force independent of the motion and $f(v)$ is a function of the magnitude of the velocity (in simple cases the resistance may be proportional to the square of the velocity). In this case equation (2) becomes the equation of motion

$$\frac{d}{dv}(m\mathbf{v}) = \mathbf{F_0} - f(v)\mathbf{v}$$

10.4.2 Dynamics of a system of particles

Suppose the particles are of masses $m_1, m_2, \ldots, m_n$, and, referred to a fixed origin O, have position vectors $\mathbf{r_1}, \mathbf{r_2}, \ldots, \mathbf{r_n}$.

Let m denote the total mass of the system then

$$m = \sum_{i=1}^{n} m_i$$

The centre of mass of the system has position vector $\bar{\mathbf{r}}$ given by the equation:

$$m\bar{\mathbf{r}} = \sum_{i=1}^{n} m_i \mathbf{r_i} \tag{5}$$

If $\mathbf{M}$ is the momentum of the system then $\mathbf{M}$ is the sum of the momenta of the individual particles; thus

$$\mathbf{M} = \sum_{i=1}^{n} m_i \frac{d\mathbf{r_i}}{dt}$$

But if the masses m_i of the system remain constant

$$\mathbf{M} = \sum_{i=1}^{n} \frac{d}{dt}(m_i \mathbf{r_i}) = \frac{d}{dt} \sum_{i=1}^{n} m_i \mathbf{r_i} = \frac{d}{dt}(m\bar{\mathbf{r}}) = m\frac{d\bar{\mathbf{r}}}{dt}$$

Showing that the momentum of the system is equivalent to that of a single particle of mass m moving with the velocity of the centre of mass.

If forces $\mathbf{F_1}, \mathbf{F_2}, \ldots, \mathbf{F_n}$ act upon the system we can deduce from Newton's Laws that

$$\sum_{i=1}^{n} \mathbf{F_i} = \frac{d}{dt}(\mathbf{M}) = \frac{d}{dt}(m\bar{\mathbf{v}}) \tag{6}$$

where $\bar{\mathbf{v}}$ is the velocity of the centre of mass.

Equation (6) should be compared with equation (2) which gives the equation of motion for a single particle. Note that in summing the forces $\mathbf{F_i}$ in equation (6) the internal forces between the particles can be ignored since these are equal and opposite and have the same line of action, by *Newton's third law*. To obtain the equation for the angular momentum of the system we once more consider the system as a set of individual particles. Each particle is subject to the equation $F_i = d/dt\,(m_i v_i)$, where F_i is the total force (internal and external) acting on the particle and v_i is its velocity.

Taking moments about O and summing over all particles of the system gives

$$\sum_{i=1}^{n} r_i \times F_i = \sum_{i=1}^{n} r_i \times m_i \frac{d}{dt} v_i$$

$$= \frac{d}{dt} \left(\sum_{i=1}^{n} r_i \times m_i v_i \right),$$

using 10.3.1 (iv), since $d/dt\,r_i = v_i$ and $v_i \times v_i = 0$. In this summation internal forces can again be ignored; thus if G denotes the total moment about O of all the external forces the equation becomes

$$G = \frac{d}{dt} \left(\sum_{i=1}^{n} r_i \times m_i v_i \right) = \frac{dH}{dt} \tag{7}$$

where $H = \sum_{i=1}^{n} r_i \times m_i v_i$ is the total angular momentum of the system about O.

10.4.3 *Statics of a rigid body*

Suppose a rigid body of mass M is acted on by a system of forces $F_1, F_2, \ldots, F_n$ acting at points with position vectors $r_1, r_2, \ldots, r_n$. Then it will be in equilibrium provided the momentum of the body and the angular momentum about O are both identically zero.

Conditions for this are that the body should be initially at rest and that there should be no resultant force F acting on the body and no couple G acting about O. In vector terms these conditions for equilibrium are

$$F = \sum_{i=1}^{n} F_i = 0 \tag{8}$$

and

$$G = \sum_{i=1}^{n} r_i \times F_i = 0 \tag{9}$$

If these conditions are fulfilled then there is no moment about any point since the moment about the point A with position vector **a** is (see figure 10.24).

$$\sum_{i=1}^{n} (\mathbf{r}_i - \mathbf{a}) \times \mathbf{F}_i = \sum_{i=1}^{n} \mathbf{r}_i \times \mathbf{F}_i - \mathbf{a} \times \sum_{i=1}^{n} \mathbf{F}_i$$

$$= 0 \text{ (using equations (8) and (9))}$$

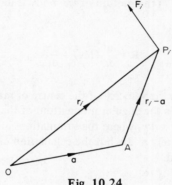

Fig. 10.24

Equivalent systems of forces. Two systems of forces acting upon a rigid body are said to be *equivalent* if they have the same dynamical effect on the body. If this is the case the body would clearly be in equilibrium if it were acted upon by both systems of forces with one of them reversed in direction. From the conditions for equilibrium, equation (8) and (9), we can deduce that two systems of forces are equivalent if they have the same resultant $\mathbf{R} = \sum_{i=1}^{n} \mathbf{F}_i$ and the same moment about O (or about any fixed point A). Any system of forces, however complex, can thus be replaced by a single force **R** acting at O together with a couple $\mathbf{G} = \sum_{i=1}^{n} \mathbf{r}_i \times \mathbf{F}_i$. The system could also be replaced by a single force acting at A together with a couple but, although the single force would in each case be **R**, the couple would generally have a different value. (See exercise 11, p. 465.)

10.4.4 *Dynamics of a rigid body*

The rigid body can be considered as a limiting case of a collection of a number of particles, with the distances between the particles invariant, as their number tends to infinity. The results of section 10.4.2 can then be applied to a rigid body; in this application Σ will be used to denote summation over the whole body. (In practice these summations will normally be evaluated as integrals.)

If the rigid body is acted upon by a system of forces $F_1, F_2, \ldots, F_n$, acting at points with position vectors $r_1, r_2, \ldots, r_n$, then this system is equivalent to a resultant $R = \sum\limits_{i=1}^{n} F_i$ acting at O together with a couple $G = \sum\limits_{i=1}^{n} r_i \times F_i$ about O. From equations (6) and (7) the motion of the body is determined by the conditions

$$R = \frac{d}{dt} (Mv) = \frac{dM}{dt}$$

and $G = dH/dt$, where v is the velocity of the centre of mass, M the total mass, M the momentum and H is the angular momentum of the system about O. M is given as Σmv and H as $\Sigma r \times mv$, where the summations are taken throughout the body. M is given immediately at Mv but the calculation of the angular momentum is less straightforward.

Calculation of angular momentum and kinetic energy
Case 1. Simple rotational motion. Suppose the body is rotating about the fixed point O with angular velocity ω. The velocity of any particle P of the body is then $v = \omega \times r$, where r is its position vector.

Then the angular momentum H is given by

$$H = \Sigma r \times mv = \Sigma r \times m(\omega \times r)$$
$$= \Sigma m(r \cdot r)\omega - \Sigma m(r \cdot \omega)r \qquad (10)$$

Let $r = x\hat{i} + y\hat{j} + z\hat{k}$ and $\omega = \omega_1\hat{i} + \omega_2\hat{j} + \omega_3\hat{k}$, referred to a set of rectangular cartesian axes-through 0. Then the above equation can be expressed as

$$H = \{ \Sigma m(y^2 + z^2)\omega_1 - \Sigma mxy\omega_2 - \Sigma mxz\omega_3 \}\hat{i}$$
$$+ \{ \Sigma m(z^2 + x^2)\omega_2 - \Sigma myz\omega_3 - \Sigma mxy\omega_1 \}\hat{j}$$
$$+ \{ \Sigma m(x^2 + y^2)\omega_3 - \Sigma mzx\omega_1 - \Sigma myz\omega_2 \}\hat{k}$$

In this expression the coefficients $A = \Sigma m(y^2 + z^2)$, $B = \Sigma m(z^2 + x^2)$, $C = \Sigma m(x^2 + y^2)$, $D = \Sigma myz$, $E = \Sigma mzx$, $F = \Sigma mxy$ depend upon the distribution of mass in the body; the first three are called the moments of inertia and the second three the products of inertia. The equation for the angular momentum can also be written in matrix form as

$$\mathbf{H} = \begin{pmatrix} A & -F & -E \\ -F & B & -D \\ -E & -D & C \end{pmatrix} \begin{pmatrix} \omega_1 \\ \omega_2 \\ \omega_3 \end{pmatrix} \text{ or } \mathbf{H} = \Phi\,\boldsymbol{\omega}$$

where Φ is a symmetric matrix called the *inertia matrix*.

Note that in general **H** is not parallel to $\boldsymbol{\omega}$.

The kinetic energy of a particle of mass m is $\frac{1}{2}mv^2$ hence the kinetic energy of the body is

$$\Sigma\tfrac{1}{2}mv^2 = \tfrac{1}{2}\Sigma m\mathbf{v}\cdot\mathbf{v} = \tfrac{1}{2}\Sigma m(\boldsymbol{\omega}\times\mathbf{r})\cdot(\boldsymbol{\omega}\times\mathbf{r}) = \tfrac{1}{2}\Sigma m\{\boldsymbol{\omega}\times\mathbf{r}\cdot(\boldsymbol{\omega}\times\mathbf{r})\}$$

$$= \tfrac{1}{2}\Sigma m\boldsymbol{\omega}\cdot(\mathbf{r}\times(\boldsymbol{\omega}\times\mathbf{r})) \text{ (interchanging . and x in the scalar triple product)}$$

$$= \tfrac{1}{2}\boldsymbol{\omega}\cdot\Sigma m\mathbf{r}\times(\boldsymbol{\omega}\times\mathbf{r})$$

$$= \tfrac{1}{2}\boldsymbol{\omega}\cdot\mathbf{H} \tag{11}$$

This expression for the kinetic energy can also be written as the matrix product $\frac{1}{2}\boldsymbol{\omega}'\Phi\boldsymbol{\omega}$ where Φ is the inertia matrix and

$$\boldsymbol{\omega} = \begin{pmatrix} \omega_1 \\ \omega_2 \\ \omega_3 \end{pmatrix}$$

Case 2. More general motion. If the motion of the body is not a simple rotation then it can be described by giving the linear velocity $\bar{\mathbf{v}}$ of the centre of mass together with the angular velocity $\boldsymbol{\omega}$ of the body about the centre of mass. If we choose O to coincide with the centre of mass then the velocity of any point P of the body is $\mathbf{v} = \bar{\mathbf{v}} + \boldsymbol{\omega}\times\mathbf{r}$.

The angular momentum **H** is then given as

$$\mathbf{H} = \Sigma\mathbf{r}\times m\mathbf{v} = \Sigma\mathbf{r}\times m(\bar{\mathbf{v}} + \boldsymbol{\omega}\times\mathbf{r})$$

$$= \Sigma m\mathbf{r}\times\bar{\mathbf{v}} + \Sigma\mathbf{r} + m(\boldsymbol{\omega}\times\mathbf{r})$$

but, since the centre of mass is at O, $\Sigma m\mathbf{r} = 0$; hence $\mathbf{H} = \Sigma\mathbf{r}\times m(\boldsymbol{\omega}\times\mathbf{r})$, an expression identical to that of equation (10).

H is again expressible as $\Phi\boldsymbol{\omega}$ where Φ is the inertia matrix with the centre of mass as origin.

Note. The expression $\mathbf{H} = \Phi\boldsymbol{\omega}$ is only valid when O is either a fixed point on the axis of rotation or coincides with the centre of mass.

The kinetic energy is defined to be

$$\Sigma\tfrac{1}{2}mv^2 = \tfrac{1}{2}\Sigma m(\bar{\mathbf{v}} + \boldsymbol{\omega}\times\mathbf{r}).(\bar{\mathbf{v}} + \boldsymbol{\omega}\times\mathbf{r})$$

$$= \tfrac{1}{2}\Sigma m\bar{\mathbf{v}}^2 + \tfrac{1}{2}\Sigma m(\boldsymbol{\omega}\times\mathbf{r}).(\boldsymbol{\omega}\times\mathbf{r}) + \Sigma m\bar{\mathbf{v}}.(\boldsymbol{\omega}\times\mathbf{r})$$

$$= \tfrac{1}{2}M\bar{\mathbf{v}}^2 + \tfrac{1}{2}\Sigma m\,\boldsymbol{\omega}.(\mathbf{r}\times(\boldsymbol{\omega}\times\mathbf{r})) + \bar{\mathbf{v}}\times\boldsymbol{\omega}\,.\,\Sigma m\mathbf{r}$$

$$= \tfrac{1}{2}M\bar{\mathbf{v}}^2 + \tfrac{1}{2}\,\boldsymbol{\omega}.\mathbf{H},\text{ since }\Sigma m\mathbf{r} = 0$$

The kinetic energy thus has two distinct terms, the first corresponding to the linear kinetic energy of the centre of mass and the second to the energy of the rotational motion about the centre of mass.

10.4.5 *Worked examples on vector mechanics*

1. A particle P of constant mass m moves under the influence of a force which is always directed towards a fixed point O. Show that the angular momentum about O is constant. Deduce that the particle moves in a fixed plane through O and that the component of its velocity perpendicular to OP is inversely proportional to OP.

Fig. 10.25

Solution. Suppose the force is **F** and the velocity of the particle is **v**. Then the equation of motion is $d/dt\,(m\mathbf{v}) = \mathbf{F}$. But m is a constant and since **F** is always directed towards O, $\mathbf{F} = -F\hat{\mathbf{r}}$ where F is in the most general case a function of r, θ and t. (See figure 10.24.)

Hence
$$m\frac{d\mathbf{v}}{dt} = -F\hat{\mathbf{r}}$$

The angular momentum about O is $\mathbf{h} = \mathbf{r}\times m\mathbf{v}$

and
$$\frac{d\mathbf{h}}{dt} = \frac{d}{dt}(\mathbf{r}\times m\mathbf{v}) = \frac{d\mathbf{r}}{dt}\times m\mathbf{v} + \mathbf{r}\times m\frac{d\mathbf{v}}{dt}$$

$$= \mathbf{r}\times m\frac{d\mathbf{v}}{dt}\text{ since }\frac{d\mathbf{r}}{dt} = \mathbf{v}$$

Hence
$$\frac{d\mathbf{h}}{dt} = \mathbf{r} \times (-F\hat{\mathbf{r}}) = 0$$

$\Rightarrow \mathbf{h} = \text{const.} = \mathbf{h}_0 = \mathbf{r}_0 \times m\mathbf{v}_0$ where $\mathbf{r}_0$, $\mathbf{v}_0$ are the initial values of $\mathbf{r}$ and $\mathbf{v}$ respectively.

Also,
$$\mathbf{r} \cdot \mathbf{h}_0 = \mathbf{r} \cdot \mathbf{h} = \mathbf{r} \cdot (\mathbf{v} \times m\mathbf{v}) = 0$$

$\Rightarrow \mathbf{r}$ is always perpendicular to the constant vector $\mathbf{h}_0$ showing that the particle always remains in the plane through O perpendicular to $\mathbf{h}_0$, that is the plane of 0 and the initial velocity.

Suppose now that $\mathbf{v}$ is resolved as $\mathbf{v} = v_1 \hat{\mathbf{r}} + v_2 \hat{\mathbf{s}}$ where $\hat{\mathbf{s}}$ is a unit vector normal to $\mathbf{r}$ in the plane of the motion. Then

$$\mathbf{h} = m\mathbf{r} \times \mathbf{v} = mr\hat{\mathbf{r}} \times (v_1 \hat{\mathbf{r}} + v_2 \hat{\mathbf{s}})$$
$$= mrv_2 \hat{\mathbf{h}}$$

Since $\mathbf{h}$ is a constant, mrv_2 is constant, showing that v_2, the component of $\mathbf{v}$ perpendicular to $\mathbf{r}$, is inversely proportional to r.

Note. The above is an example of a central orbit; the exact nature of the orbit will depend upon the nature of F. In simple cases $F = F(r)$, and in the case of gravitational motion the force is inversely proportional to r^2 and the orbits are conic sections with focus at O. A second case of a central orbit is illustrated in example 2 below.

2. A particle of mass m is executing simple harmonic motion under the influence of a central force $-m\omega^2 \mathbf{r}$. Find its position at time t in terms of its initial position and velocity.

Solution. From the previous example, the particle will remain in a fixed plane; suppose the plane of motion is the XY plane. Let the initial position be $(x_0, 0)$ and the initial velocity be $\mathbf{u} = u_1 \hat{\mathbf{i}} + u_2 \hat{\mathbf{j}}$.
The equation of motion is $m(d^2\mathbf{r}/dt^2) = -m\omega^2 \mathbf{r}$. But $\mathbf{r} = x\hat{\mathbf{i}} + y\hat{\mathbf{j}}$, and hence

$$\hat{\mathbf{i}}\frac{d^2x}{dt^2} + \hat{\mathbf{j}}\frac{d^2y}{dt^2} = -\omega^2(x\hat{\mathbf{i}} + y\hat{\mathbf{j}})$$

with $\mathbf{r} = x_0\hat{\mathbf{i}}$ at $t = 0$ and $d\mathbf{r}/dt = u_1\hat{\mathbf{i}} + u_2\hat{\mathbf{j}}$ at $t = 0$.

This vector equation is equivalent to a pair of ordinary differential equations

$$\frac{d^2x}{dt^2} + \omega^2 x = 0 \quad \text{with} \quad x(0) = x_0 \quad \text{and} \quad \frac{dx}{dt} = u_1 \quad \text{at} \quad t = 0$$

$$\frac{d^2y}{dt^2} + \omega^2 y = 0 \quad \text{with} \quad y(0) = 0 \quad \text{and} \quad \frac{dy}{dt} = u_2 \quad \text{at} \quad t = 0$$

The solutions of these equations are of the form

$$x = A_1 \cos \omega t + B_1 \sin \omega t$$
$$y = A_2 \cos \omega t + B_2 \sin \omega t$$

From the boundary conditions we obtain

$$A_1 = x_0, B_1 = u_1/\omega$$
$$A_2 = 0, \quad B_2 = u_2/\omega$$

The solution is thus

$$x = x_0 \cos \omega t + u_1/\omega \sin \omega t$$
$$y = u_2/\omega \sin \omega t$$

or $\qquad \mathbf{r} = (x_0 \cos \omega t + u_1/\omega \sin \omega t)\hat{\mathbf{i}} + (u_2/\omega \sin \omega t)\hat{\mathbf{j}}$

Note. If $u_2 = 0$ this solution reduces to 1 dimensional simple harmonic motion.

3. The moment of inertia of a particle of mass m about an axis is defined to be $\Sigma m s^2$, where s is the distance of the particle from the axis. Show that the moment of inertia of a body, regarded as the limiting case of a collection of particles, about an axis in direction $\hat{\mathbf{d}}$ is $I = \hat{\mathbf{d}}'\Phi\hat{\mathbf{d}}$ where Φ is the inertia matrix of the body about 0. Show that if the angular velocity of the body about this axis is ω then its kinetic energy is $\frac{1}{2}I\omega^2$.

Solution. From figure 10.26, $s = r \sin \theta = |\mathbf{r} \times \mathbf{d}|$

Hence $\qquad I = \Sigma m s^2 = \Sigma m (\mathbf{r} \times \hat{\mathbf{d}})^2$

$$= -\hat{\mathbf{d}} \cdot \Sigma (m\mathbf{r} \times (\mathbf{r} \times \hat{\mathbf{d}}))$$
$$= \hat{\mathbf{d}} \cdot \Phi\hat{\mathbf{d}} \quad \text{or} \quad \hat{\mathbf{d}}'\Phi\hat{\mathbf{d}}$$

(since $\Sigma(m\mathbf{r} \times (\mathbf{r} \times \hat{\mathbf{d}})) = -\Phi\hat{\mathbf{d}}$ by comparison with $\Sigma m\mathbf{r} \times (\boldsymbol{\omega} \times \mathbf{r}) = \Phi\boldsymbol{\omega}$ (equation (10)).

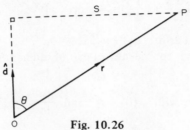

Fig. 10.26

If the axis has direction cosines d_1, d_2, d_3 then $\hat{\mathbf{d}} = d_1 \hat{\mathbf{i}} + d_2 \hat{\mathbf{j}} + d_3 \hat{\mathbf{k}}$ and

$$I = (d_1, d_2, d_3) \Phi \begin{pmatrix} d_1 \\ d_2 \\ d_3 \end{pmatrix}$$

Also when the body is rotating about this axis with angular velocity ω the kinetic energy is, by equation (11), $\frac{1}{2}\boldsymbol{\omega}'\Phi\boldsymbol{\omega}$ where $\boldsymbol{\omega} = \omega\mathbf{d}$. Hence, the kinetic energy is $\frac{1}{2}\omega\hat{\mathbf{d}}'\Phi\omega\hat{\mathbf{d}} = \frac{1}{2}I\omega^2$.

NOTES ON CHAPTER 10

1. This chapter has been mainly concerned with the development of vector algebra. This algebra can be applied to the vector quantities which occur in mechanical problems and it also has widespread application to three-dimensional geometry, particularly the geometry of lines and planes.

2. The vector quantities which occur in physical problems can be classified into three distinct types, namely, free vectors, line-bound vectors and bound vectors. Free vectors are those which have a magnitude and direction associated with them but no particular point or line of action; examples of free vectors are the acceleration due to gravity near the earth's surface and the velocity of a rigid body moving in a straight line. Line-bound vectors are those which have a specified line of action; forces are typical examples of these. Bound vectors are vectors which have a specified point of action; an example is the velocity of a fluid which can vary from point to point within the fluid, since not all particles of fluid along a line of flow need have the same velocity. Vector algebra is applicable to free vectors anywhere, to line-bound vectors at a point of intersection of their lines of action, or to bound vectors acting at the same point.

3. Section 10.3 was concerned with the differentiation of a vector function of a real parameter and particularly with the applications of this to the motion of a particle. A further application of this theory is to the geometry of a twisted curve, full details of which can be found in chapter V of *Elementary Vector Analysis* by C. E. Weatherburn. A logical step from vector functions of a single variable is to consider vector functions of several real variables. For example, the velocity of a point in a moving fluid can be considered as a vector function of the variables x, y, z and t where x, y, z are cartesian coordinates and t represents time. This leads to the study of vector analysis which has widespread applications to problems in fluid mechanics, electromagnetic theory and gravitational theory. Vector analysis is also closely related to the theory of integration of functions

of several variables. A comprehensive treatment of vector analysis and its
applications can be found in *Advanced Vector Analysis* by C. E. Weatherburn
(Bell & Sons, London).

Miscellaneous Exercises

1. A circular disc, centre O, is rotating with constant angular velocity ω
    about an axis through O perpendicular to the plane of the disc. Show that
    the point P on the disc with position vector $\mathbf{r}$ has acceleration $-\omega^2\mathbf{r}$. Find
    also an expression for the acceleration of P if ω·is not constant.

2. A system of forces acting on a rigid body consists of: a force of $2\hat{\mathbf{i}} + 2\hat{\mathbf{j}}$ lb
    acting at $(0, 0, 0)$, a force of $-3\hat{\mathbf{i}} + \hat{\mathbf{j}}$ lb acting at $(1, 0, 1)$ and a force of
    $p\hat{\mathbf{k}}$ lb acting at $(1, 1, 1)$. Find the equivalent resultant force $\mathbf{R}$ acting at O
    and couple $\mathbf{G}$. Find p if the system can be replaced by a single force. [Hint:
    if the system is equivalent to a single force $\mathbf{R}$ acting at A then $\mathbf{a} \times \mathbf{R} = \mathbf{G}$.]

3. Show that any point P on the line joining the points B and C with position
    vectors $\mathbf{b}$ and $\mathbf{c}$ has position vector $\mathbf{r}$ given by the equation $\mathbf{r} = \mathbf{b} + \lambda(\mathbf{c} - \mathbf{b})$,
    where λ is an arbitrary constant. Find the point on the line joining
    $(1, 0, -1)$ and $(2, 3, 4)$ which is nearest to the point $(0, 1, 0)$.

4. The centre of mass of a rigid body, instantaneously at O, has linear
    velocity $\mathbf{v}$. The body is rotating with angular velocity ω about the centre
    of mass. Show that if $\mathbf{v} \cdot \omega = 0$ one point of the body is instantaneously at
    rest. Find this point if $\mathbf{v} = \hat{\mathbf{i}} + \hat{\mathbf{j}} + 2\hat{\mathbf{k}}$ and $\omega = \hat{\mathbf{i}} - \hat{\mathbf{j}}$.

5. A particle P of mass m moves in space; its position vector at time t is

    $$\mathbf{r} = \hat{\mathbf{i}} \cos \omega t + \hat{\mathbf{j}} \sin \omega t + \hat{\mathbf{k}} t$$

    Find the velocity and acceleration of P. If this motion is due to the action
    of a single force $\mathbf{F}$ find $\mathbf{F}$ and the position and velocity of the particle at
    $t = 0$. Sketch the path of the particle.

6. A system is made up of particles of unit mass at $(1, 0, -1)$, $(2, 1, 2)$,
    $(-3, 1, 1)$ and $(0, -2, -2)$. Show that the centre of mass of the system is
    at O. Find the inertia matrix of the system about O. If the system is
    rotating about O with angular velocity $\omega = \hat{\mathbf{i}} + \hat{\mathbf{j}} + \hat{\mathbf{k}}$ find the angular
    momentum and kinetic energy of the system. Verify the expression for
    the kinetic energy by calculating the kinetic energies of the individual
    particles.

7. ABCD is a skew quadrilateral. A rigid body has simultaneous angular
    velocities about AB, BC, CD, DA which are proportional to the lengths
    of these sides. Show that all points of the body have the same velocity.

8. A rigid body is acted upon by a system of forces which are equivalent to a resultant $\mathbf{R}$ acting at O and couple $\mathbf{G}$. Show that this system of forces can only be replaced by a single force $\mathbf{F}$ if $\mathbf{R} \cdot \mathbf{G} = 0$. Show that if $\mathbf{R} \cdot \mathbf{G} \neq 0$ the system is equivalent to a wrench (that is a single force $\mathbf{F}$ together with a couple whose axis is in the direction of $\mathbf{F}$). If $\mathbf{R} = \hat{\mathbf{i}} + \hat{\mathbf{j}}$ and $\mathbf{G} = 2\hat{\mathbf{i}} + \hat{\mathbf{j}} + \hat{\mathbf{k}}$ find the line of action of the equivalent wrench.

9. A particle of mass m is projected from a horizontal plane with velocity $\mathbf{v} = v_1\hat{\mathbf{i}} + v_2\hat{\mathbf{j}} + v_3\hat{\mathbf{k}}$. If the only force acting upon the particle is the gravitational force $-mg\hat{\mathbf{k}}$ find the time the particle is in the air and the distance travelled.

10. A particle of mass m is acted upon by a central force $-mk^2\mathbf{r}$. At $t = 0$ the particle is at $(a, 0, 0)$ and has velocity $v_0\mathbf{j}$. Find the position vector $\mathbf{r}$ of the particle in terms of t and show that the particle moves in an ellipse. Assuming $v_0 < ak$ find the maximum and minimum speeds of the particle in the subsequent motion.

11. A system of forces acting on a rigid body consists of: a force of $\hat{\mathbf{i}} - \hat{\mathbf{j}}$ units acting at $(1, 1, -1)$, a force of $2\hat{\mathbf{i}} + \hat{\mathbf{j}} + \mathbf{k}$ units acting at $(0, 1, 2)$ and a force of $\hat{\mathbf{j}} + 2\hat{\mathbf{k}}$ units acting at $(1, 0, 1)$. Find the equivalent resultant force $\mathbf{R}_1$ acting at O and couple $\mathbf{G}_1$. Find also the equivalent resultant force $\mathbf{R}_2$ acting at $(1, 2, 3)$ and couple $\mathbf{G}_2$. Show that $\mathbf{G}_1 \neq \mathbf{G}_2$ but $\mathbf{R}_1 \cdot \mathbf{G}_1 = \mathbf{R}_2 \cdot \mathbf{G}_2$.

12. Show that, for any vectors $\mathbf{a}, \mathbf{b}, \mathbf{c}$, we have

$$\mathbf{a} \times (\mathbf{b} \times \mathbf{c}) + \mathbf{c} \times (\mathbf{a} \times \mathbf{b}) + \mathbf{b} \times (\mathbf{c} \times \mathbf{a}) = 0$$

13. A dynamical system consists of unit masses placed at the eight vertices of a unit cube. The system is rotating about one vertex which is at the origin and initially the edges are aligned with the coordinate axes. Find the inertia matrix of the system. Find the angular momentum and kinetic energy of the system if it is rotating with unit angular velocity

    (a) about OX,
    (b) about an axis through O and the centre of the cube.

14. A tetrahedron ABCD has its vertices at points with coordinates $(1, 2, 3)$, $(-1, 4, 7)$, $(2, 3, -1)$, and $(0, 3, 2)$. Find its volume.

15. Three vectors $\mathbf{a}, \mathbf{b}, \mathbf{c}$, are said to be *linearly dependent* if scalars α, β, γ, not all zero, can be found such that

$$\alpha\mathbf{a} + \beta\mathbf{b} + \gamma\mathbf{c} = 0$$

Show that, if **a**, **b** and **c** are linearly dependent then

$$\begin{vmatrix} a_1 & a_2 & a_3 \\ b_1 & b_2 & b_3 \\ c_1 & c_2 & c_3 \end{vmatrix} = 0$$

[Hint: consider the scalar product of $\alpha\mathbf{a} + \beta\mathbf{b} + \gamma\mathbf{c}$ with another vector. Compare this result with the definition of a determinant given in section 7.2.6.]

16. Given three vectors **a**, **b** and **c**, such that

$$\mathbf{a} + \mathbf{b} + \mathbf{c} = 0$$

prove the sine rule for a triangle.
[Hint: consider **a** x **a** and **b** x **b**.]

17. A moving particle has position vector

$$\mathbf{r} = \hat{\mathbf{i}} \sin t + \hat{\mathbf{j}} \cos 2t + \hat{\mathbf{k}}(t^2 + 2t)$$

at time t. Find the components of the acceleration in directions parallel and perpendicular to the velocity at time $t = 0$.

18. $\mathbf{F}_1$ and $\mathbf{F}_2$ are two forces which vary with position. OABC is a square with vertices at $(0, 0, 0)$, $(0, 1, 0)$, $(1, 1, 0)$, $(1, 0, 0)$. Find the work done by each force if its point of application moves from O to B
    (a) along OAB,
    (b) along OCB.

19. A man travelling north at 5 m.p.h. finds that the wind appears to come from the south-west. He doubles his speed and finds that the wind now appears to come from the north-west. Find the true wind velocity.

20. Prove that in general any system of forces is equivalent to a single force together with a parallel couple. This resultant force and couple constitute what is called a *wrench* equivalent to the original system. Find the equivalent wrench and line of action in the case of the following system of forces:

$$\mathbf{F}_1 = \hat{\mathbf{i}} + 2\hat{\mathbf{j}} \text{ acting at } (1, 0, 1),$$
$$\mathbf{F}_2 = 2\hat{\mathbf{i}} + \hat{\mathbf{j}} - \hat{\mathbf{k}} \text{ acting at } (1, 2, 3),$$
$$\mathbf{F}_3 = \hat{\mathbf{i}} - \hat{\mathbf{j}} \text{ acting at } (2, 2, 0),$$
$$\mathbf{F}_4 = -\hat{\mathbf{i}} + \hat{\mathbf{k}} \text{ acting at } (0, 0, 0).$$

APPENDIX : USEFUL RESULTS AND FORMULAE

Algebra

Binomial theorem. For any positive integer n

$$(a + b)^n = a^n + na^{n-1}b + {}^nC_2 a^{n-2}b^2 + \cdots + {}^nC_r a^{n-r}b^r + \cdots + b^n$$

where

$$ {}^nC_r = \frac{n!}{r!(n-r)!} $$

For $|x| < 1$ and any n

$$(1 + x)^n = 1 + nx + \frac{n(n-1)}{2!}x^2 + \cdots + \frac{n(n-1)\cdots(n-r+1)}{r!}x^r + \cdots$$

Geometric progression

$$a + ar + ar^2 + \cdots + ar^{n-1}$$

has sum to n terms

$$S_n = \frac{a(1 - r^n)}{1 - r}$$

Provided $|r| < 1$:

$$S = \lim_{n \to \infty} S_n = \frac{a}{1 - r}$$

Partial fractions: Any rational function, that is a function of the form $f(x)/g(x)$ where $f(x)$ and $g(x)$ are polynomials in x, can be expressed as a quotient polynomial plus a sum of partial fractions. If the degree of $f(x)$ is greater than or equal to the degree of $g(x)$, $f(x)$ is first divided by $g(x)$ to give the quotient polynomial and remainder $r(x)$; the problem remaining is that of expressing $r(x)/g(x)$ in partial fractions.

The form of these partial fractions depends upon the nature of the factors of $g(x)$. By the results of chapter 6 any real polynomial $g(x)$ can be expressed

467

as a product of real linear and quadratic factors, some of which may be repeated (corresponding to multiple roots of $g(x)$). Suppose that

$$g(x) = (x - \alpha_1)^{r_1}(x - \alpha_2)^{r_2} \cdots (x - \alpha_m)^{r_m}(a_1x^2 + b_1x + c_1)^{s_1} \cdots$$

$$(a_kx^2 + b_k^2 + c_k)^{s_k}$$

Then $r(x)/g(x)$ has a unique expression as the sum of $r_1 + r_2 + \cdots + r_m + s_1 + \cdots + s_k$ partial fractions. The partial fractions related to the factor $(x - \alpha_i)^{r_i}$ are of the form

$$\frac{A_{r_i}}{(x - \alpha_i)}\, r_i + \frac{A_{r_{i-1}}}{(x - \alpha_i)}\, r_i - 1 + \cdots + \frac{A_1}{x - \alpha_i}$$

The partial fractions related to the factor $(a_jx^2 + b_jx + c_j)^{s_j}$ are of the form

$$\frac{B_{s_j}x + C_{s_j}}{(a_jx^2 + b_jx + c_j)}\, s_j + \cdots + \frac{B_1x + C_1}{a_jx^2 + b_jx + c_j}$$

The constant coefficients A, B, C which occur in these expressions could be found by 'simplifying' the expression in partial fractions to have common denominator $g(x)$; the numerator will then be identical to $r(x)$. Coefficients of corresponding powers of x can then be compared or appropriate numerical values of x substituted into the two expressions. In practice the coefficients A_{r_i} of the highest power of each linear factor are given by the so-called 'cover-up rule'

$$A_{r_i} = \frac{r(\alpha_i)}{h(\alpha_i)} \quad \text{where} \quad h(x) = g(x)/(x - \alpha_i)^{r_i}$$

[*Notes.* $h(x) =$ polynomial obtained by 'covering-up' the term $(x - \alpha_i)^{r_i}$ in the factorised form of $g(r)$; the cover-up rule is equivalent to making the substitution $x = \alpha_i$ in the 'simplified' expression.]

Coordinate geometry

Two dimensions. Any point P is uniquely identified by its rectangular cartesian coordinates (x, y) giving the distances of P from the perpendicular axes OY and OX respectively. If $P_1(x_1, y_1)$ and $P_2(x_2, y_2)$ are two points the distance $P_1 P_2$ is $((x_2 - x_1)^2 + (y_2 - y_1)^2)^{\frac{1}{2}}$.

Any straight line has an equation of the form $ax + by + c = 0$. A line of slope m has equation:

$$y = mx + c$$

The line through P_1 and P_2 has equation:

$$\frac{y - y_1}{x - x_1} = \frac{y_2 - y_1}{x_2 - x_1}$$

$x/a + y/b = 1$ is the line which intersects axes at $(a, 0)$, $(0, b)$.

A circle at centre O and radius r has equation:

$$x^2 + y^2 = r^2$$

A circle centre (a, b) and radius r has equation:

$$(x - a)^2 + (y - b)^2 = r^2$$

In general any equation of the second degree, $ax^2 + by^2 + 2fx + 2gy + 2hyx + c = 0$, represents a conic section. With a suitable choice of origin and, if necessary, by rotating the axes it can be expressed as one of the standard forms:

$$\frac{x^2}{a^2} + \frac{y^2}{b^2} = 1 \quad \text{(an ellipse)}$$

$$\frac{x^2}{a^2} - \frac{y^2}{b^2} = 1 \quad \text{(a hyperbola)}$$

$$xy = c^2 \quad \text{(a rectangular hyperbola)}$$

or
$$y^2 = 4ax \quad \text{(a parabola)}$$

Three-dimensional coordinate geometry. Any point P is uniquely identified by its rectangular cartesian coordinates (x, y, z) giving the perpendicular distances from P to the planes OYZ, OXZ and OXY respectively.

If $P_1(x_1, y_1, z_1)$ and $P_2(x_2, y_2, z_2)$ are two points the distance $P_1 P_2$ is $((x_2 - x_1)^2 + (y_2 - y_1)^2 + (z_2 - z_1)^2)^{\frac{1}{2}}$.

The direction of a line is specified by giving its 'direction cosines'; these are the cosines of the angles which the line makes with the coordinate axes OX, OY and OZ. (See 10.2.3.) The equations of the line through (x_0, y_0, z_0) with direction cosines (l, m, n) are

$$\frac{x - x_0}{l} = \frac{y - y_0}{m} = \frac{z - z_0}{n}$$

Any equation of the form $ax + by + cz + d = 0$ represents a plane, whose normal has direction cosines $(a/r, b/r, c/r)$, where $r^2 = a^2 + b^2 + c^2$.

$x/a + y/b + z/c = 1$ is the equation of a plane meeting the coordinates axes at $(a, 0, 0)$, $(0, b, 0)$, $(0, 0, c)$.

The equation $(x - a)^2 + (y - b)^2 + (z - c)^2 = r^2$ is the equation of a sphere centre (a, b, c) and of radius r.

Trigonometric identities

$$\sin^2 x + \cos^2 x = 1$$

$$\sin (x \pm y) = \sin x \cos y \pm \cos x \sin y$$

$$\cos (x \pm y) = \cos x \cos y \mp \sin x \sin y$$

From the above identities and the definitions of $\tan x$, $\cot x$, $\sec x$, $\operatorname{cosec} x$ the following identities can be deduced

$$1 + \tan^2 x = \sec^2 x, \ 1 + \cot^2 x = \operatorname{cosec}^2 x$$

$$\tan (x \pm y) = \frac{\tan x \pm \tan y}{1 \mp \tan x \tan y}$$

$$\tan 2x = \frac{2 \tan x}{1 - \tan^2 x}$$

$$\sin 2x = 2 \sin x \cos x$$

$$\cos 2x = \cos^2 x - \sin^2 x = 2 \cos^2 x - 1 = 1 - 2 \sin^2 x$$

$$\sin x \cos y = \tfrac{1}{2} (\sin (x + y) + \sin (x - y))$$

$$\cos x \cos y = \tfrac{1}{2} (\cos (x + y) + \cos (x - y))$$

$$\sin x \sin y = \tfrac{1}{2} (\cos (x + y) - \cos (x - y))$$

SOLUTIONS TO EXERCISES

CHAPTER 1

Exercises, p. 8: **1.** Each of the numbers concerned satisfies an algebraic equation with integral coefficients: (a) $x^2 - 3 = 0$, (b) $x^3 - 3 = 0$, (c) $x^2 - 2x - 1 = 0$, (d) $x^4 - 16x^2 + 4 = 0$. **2.** (a) $\sqrt{3}$ and $\sqrt{5}$, (b) $\sqrt{2}$ and $1 - \sqrt{2}$. **3.** Use the fact that $0 = (-1) \times \{(+1) + (-1)\} = (-1) \times (+1) + (-1) \times (-1)$.

Exercises, p. 16: **1.** (a) $10 + 5i$, (b) $-\frac{1}{2} + i\frac{5}{2}$, (c) $3 + 4i$, (d) $1 - 2i$, (e) $\frac{21}{2} + \frac{i}{2}$.
2. (a) $\sqrt{34} \approx 5.83$, $\tan^{-1}\left(\frac{-5}{3}\right) \approx -59°2'$, (b) $1, -\frac{\pi}{2}$, (c) $1, 0$, (d) $4, \frac{\pi}{3}$.

Exercises, p. 21: **2.** (a) $3 - 2i, -3 + 2i$, (b) $1 + 2i, \frac{1}{2} - \sqrt{3} + (1 + \frac{1}{2}\sqrt{3})i$, $-\frac{1}{2} - \sqrt{3} + (\frac{1}{2}\sqrt{3} - 1)i$. **3.** (a) $\frac{1}{2}(\sqrt{3} + i), i, \frac{1}{2}(-\sqrt{3} + i), \frac{1}{2}(-\sqrt{3} - i), \frac{1}{2}(\sqrt{3} - i)$, (b) $x^6 + 1 = (x^2 + 1)(x^2 - x\sqrt{3} + 1)(x^2 + x\sqrt{3} + 1)$. **4.** $-2 + i, 1 + i(1 \pm \sqrt{3})$.
5. $1, -3 - i$. **6.** Use the fact that $1 + \omega + \omega^2 = 0$.

Exercises, p. 26: **1.** Line given by $2y = 16x - 1$. **3.** (a) circle, centre the origin and radius 2, described three times anti-clockwise, (b) segment of real axis, $-1 \leqslant x \leqslant +1$, (c) circle, centre $z = 1$ and radius 1, described once anti-clockwise, (d) circle, centre the origin and radius 1, described twice anti-clockwise.
4. $p = -5 \pm \sqrt{21}$. **5.** Put $z = r(\cos\theta + i\sin\theta)$ so that $z^n = r^n \cos n\theta + ir^n \sin n\theta$.

Exercises, p. 31: **1.** Due to rounding errors the computer will never reach the precise value of 2.0. **2.** (a) Error $= 0.1$, % error $= 0.0388$, (b) error $= 0.0375$, % error $= 0.117$, (c) error $= 0.00625$, % error $= 6.25$, (d) error $= 83$, % error $= 6.479$. **3.** (a) $224\frac{1}{4}$, (b) $224\frac{1}{2}$.

Miscellaneous Exercises, p. 34: **4.** Put $\alpha = a + b, \beta = a - b$, and use previous exercise. **5.** Show first that $(1 \pm a_1)(1 \pm a_2) \cdots (1 \pm a_n) > 1 \pm s_n$, and use the fact that if $0 < a < 1$, then $0 < (1 - a)(1 + a) < 1$. **8.** The numbers each satisfy algebraic equations with integral coefficients: (a) $x^4 - 4x^3 - 4x^2 + 16x - 8 = 0$, (b) $x^4 - 14x^2 + 42 = 0$, (c) $x^2 - 10x + 1 = 0$, (d) $x^9 - 15x^6 - 87x^3 - 125 = 0$.

10. Put $z_1 = \alpha + \sqrt{(\alpha^2 - \beta^2)}$, $z_2 = \alpha - \sqrt{(\alpha^2 - \beta^2)}$. **14.** $\displaystyle\int_0^{\pi/4} \sin^4 \theta \, d\theta = \frac{3\pi}{32} - \frac{1}{4}$.

16. Circle, centre $z = a$, radius r. **17.** R.H. half-plane, imaginary axis, L.H. half-plane. **18.** $4|z|^2 - 2(a + b)z - 2(\bar{a} + \bar{b})\bar{z} + |a + b|^2 - |b - a|^2 = 0$.

19. $2z\bar{z} = (1 + i)(z + \bar{z})$, or $x^2 + y^2 = x + y$; centre $z = \frac{1}{2}(1 + i)$, radius $\frac{1}{\sqrt{2}}$.

22. (a) single root $x = 2$, double root $x = -1$, (b) single roots $x = \pm 2$, double roots $x = \pm i\sqrt{2}$.

CHAPTER 2

Exercises, p. 46: **1.** (i) $x \neq 0$, (ii) $x \neq 0$, (iii) all x, (iv) $x = n\pi$ (n an integer $\neq 1$), (v) all x, (vi) $x > 0$, (vii) all x.

Exercises, p. 49: **2.** (i) 0, (ii) 0.

Exercises, p. 52: **2.** (i) differentiable for all $x \neq 0$, (ii) differentiable for no x. **3.** 0.

Exercises, p. 54: **1.** (i) $\dfrac{1 + (\sin x)^2}{(\cos x)^2}$, (ii) $\dfrac{x - \sin x \cos x}{(x \cos x)^2}$,
(iii) $1 + 4x + 9x^2 + 16x^3 + 35x^4 + 12x^5$, (iv) $10(2 \cos x - \sin x)(\cos x + 2 \sin x)^9$,
(v) $\dfrac{2}{1 + \cos x} + \dfrac{x \sin x}{(1 + \cos x)^2}$.

Exercises, p. 60: **1.** (i) tends to zero as $x \to \infty$, (ii) tends to ∞ as $x \to 0+$, tends to $-\infty$ as $x \to 0-$, (iii) tends to ∞ as $x \to \infty$, tends to $-\infty$ as $x \to 0+$, (iv) tends to ∞ as $x \to \infty$, tends to 0 as $x \to 0$.

Exercises, p. 67: **1.** (i) $\pi^n \sin\left[\pi\left(\xi + \dfrac{n}{2}\right)\right](x - 1)^n/n!$, (ii) $e^\xi(x - 1)^n/n!$,
(iii) $(-1)^{n+1} \xi^{-n}(x - 1)^n/n$, $[1 \leqslant \xi \leqslant x]$. **2.** (i) 2.012, (ii) 1.221, (iii) 0.061, (iv) 0.182.

Exercises, p. 70: **1.** (i) minima at $x = (n + \frac{1}{3})\pi$ for all odd n, and maxima for all even n, (ii) minimum at $x = 0$ and maxima at $x = \pm 1$, (iii) minimum at $x = -\frac{1}{3}a$ and maximum at $x = \frac{1}{3}a$.

Exercises, p. 74: **1.** (i) $\frac{1}{2}\pi^2$, (ii) 0, (iii) $-\frac{3}{2}$, (iv) 0, (v) 3. **2.** $3f''(0)$. **3.** $x \sin(1/x) \to 0$ and $x/\sin x \to 1$ as $x \to 0$.

Miscellaneous Exercises, p. 80: **1.** (i) $\dfrac{-1}{(x+1)\sqrt{(x(x-1))}}$, (ii) $\dfrac{1}{\cos x}$,

(iii) $e^{-x}\left[\dfrac{6x^2}{2x^3-1} - \log(1-2x^3)\right]$, (iv) $\dfrac{x^2}{2y-y^2}$, (v) $-\dfrac{3x^2+y^2}{2xy+3y^2}$,

(vi) $\left(1+\dfrac{1}{x}\right)^x\left[\log\left(1+\dfrac{1}{x}\right) - \dfrac{1}{1+x}\right]$. **3.** (i) tends to +1 as $x \to 0+$, tends to -1 as

$x \to 0-$, (ii) tends to 1, (iii) tends to 0 as $x \to 0+$, tends to ∞ as $x \to 0-$,
(iv) tends to 0 as $x \to 0+$, (v) tends to $-\infty$ as $x \to 0+$, $+\infty$ as $x \to 0-$,
(vi) tends to $-3/2$. **7.** (i) min. at $1/e$, (ii) max. at e, (iii) max. at $\sqrt{(ab)}$,
min. at $-\sqrt{(ab)}$, (iv) minima at 0 and π, maxima at $126°52'$ and $233°8'$,
(v) point of inflexion at $x = -1$ and minimum at $x = +1$.

CHAPTER 3

Exercises, p. 86: **1.** (a) 325, (b) 3250, (c) 32,500. **3.** (a) 0, (b) 6, (c) 0,
(d) $-\frac{1}{2}$, (e) $\sqrt{(3)}/2$, (f) $-\dfrac{50}{3}$, (g) $\frac{1}{2}$.

Exercises, p. 93: **1.** (a) 0, (b) 0, (c) 0, (d) 1, (e) 3. **2.** (a) limit is (positive)
root of $x^2 - 2x = 0$, (b) limit is (positive) root of $x^2 - x - 2 = 0$. **3.** $\sqrt{3}$.

Exercises, p. 103: **1.** (a) $S_n = \dfrac{1+x-(2n+1)x^n+(2n-1)x^{n+1}}{(1-x)^2}$,

(b) $S_n = 1 - \dfrac{1}{n+1}$, (c) $S_n = \dfrac{1}{4} - \dfrac{1}{2(n+1)(n+2)}$, (d) $1 - \dfrac{1}{(n+1)!}$,

(e) $S_n = \dfrac{1}{2} - \dfrac{1}{2(2n+1)}$. **2.** (a) Absolutely convgt., (b) conditionally convgt.,
(c) divergent.

Exercises, p. 109: **1.** (a) convgt., (b) convgt., (c) divgt., (d) divgt., (e) convgt.,
(f) convgt., (g) convgt. **2.** (a) convgt., (b) divgt., (c) convgt., (d) divgt.

Exercises, p. 117: **1.** (a) Radius infinite, (b) 4, (c) 1, (d) 0, (e) 1.
2. (a) $1 + 2x + 3x^2 + 4x^3 + \cdots$, $|x| < 1$, (b) $\dfrac{1}{2} + \dfrac{x^2}{4} + \dfrac{x^4}{8} + \dfrac{x^6}{16} + \cdots$, $|x| < \sqrt{2}$,

(c) $1 + 2x + 2x^2 + 2x^3 + \cdots$, $|x| < 1$, (d) $\dfrac{1}{4} + \dfrac{x^2}{8} + \dfrac{x^4}{16} + \dfrac{x^6}{32} + \cdots$, $|x| < \sqrt{2}$.

Exercises, p. 125: **2.** (d) $\tanh^{-1}x = \log\sqrt{\left(\dfrac{1+x}{1-x}\right)}$, $x^2 < 1$,

$\coth^{-1}x = \log\sqrt{\left(\dfrac{x+1}{x-1}\right)}$, $x^2 > 1$. **5.** $\sec x = 1 + \dfrac{x^2}{2!} + \dfrac{5x^4}{4!} + \dfrac{61x^6}{6!} + \cdots$.

Miscellaneous Exercises, p. 130: **1.** (a) $1/2^7$, (b) $\sqrt{2}$, (c) a, if $|a| > 1$, and $1/3$ if $|a| \leqslant 1$. **3.** $1 + 2\sqrt{2}$. **6.** (a) $S_n = \dfrac{1}{60} - \dfrac{1}{6(3n + 2)(3n + 5)}$,

(b) $S_n = \dfrac{3}{4} - \dfrac{4n + 3}{2(n + 1)(n + 2)}$, (c) $\dfrac{1}{3} - \dfrac{n + 1}{(2n + 1)(2n + 3)}$,

(d) $\dfrac{29}{36} - \dfrac{6n^2 + 27n + 29}{6(n + 1)(n + 2)(n + 3)}$. **7.** (a) convgt., (b) convgt., (c) divgt.,

(d) divgt., (e) convgt., (f) divgt., (g) convgt., (h) convgt., (j) convgt.
8. (a) $\frac{1}{2}$, (b) radius infinite, (c) $e/2$, (d) 27, (e) 1. **9.** First use the given

integral inequality to show $A_n - 1 < \log n < A_n - 1/n$, where $A_n = \displaystyle\sum_{k=1}^{n} 1/k$.

10. (a) Show first that, if $S_n = 1 - \frac{1}{2} + \frac{1}{3} - \frac{1}{4} + \cdots$, to n terms and $A_n = \displaystyle\sum_{k=1}^{n} 1/k$,

then $S_{2n} = A_{2n} - A_n$. (The remaining examples can be treated similarly.)
15. If $e = p/q$ then, for any $n > q$, the number $n!e$ is an integer. But,

$n!e = n! \left(1 + 1 + \dfrac{1}{2!} + \cdots + \dfrac{1}{n!}\right) + n!\epsilon_n$, where $0 < n!\epsilon_n < \dfrac{1}{n}$.

16. (a) $x + \dfrac{x^3}{3} - \dfrac{x^5}{30} - \dfrac{x^7}{630} + \cdots$, (b) $1 + x - \dfrac{x^3}{3} - \dfrac{x^4}{6} - \dfrac{x^5}{30} + \dfrac{x^7}{630} + \cdots$,

(c) $1 + x + \dfrac{x^2}{2} + \dfrac{x^3}{2} + \dfrac{3x^4}{8} + \cdots$, (d) $\dfrac{x^2}{2} + \dfrac{x^4}{12} + \dfrac{x^6}{45} + \dfrac{17x^8}{2520} + \cdots$,

(e) $x - \dfrac{x^3}{3} + \dfrac{2x^5}{15} - \dfrac{17x^7}{315} + \cdots$, (f) $\dfrac{x^2}{2} - \dfrac{x^4}{12} + \dfrac{x^6}{45} - \dfrac{17x^8}{2520} + \cdots$.

CHAPTER 4

Exercises, p. 138: **1.** (i) continuous, (ii) not continuous, (iii) not continuous, (iv) not continuous.

Exercises, p. 142: **1.** (i) $f_x = -y^2 \sin(xy^2)$, $f_y = -2xy \sin(xy^2)$,

(ii) $f_x = (2x + x^2)e^{(x+y)}$, $f_y = x^2 e^{(x+y)}$ 1, (iii) $f_x = \dfrac{1}{x}, f_y = \dfrac{1}{y}$,

(iv) $f_x = \dfrac{-y}{(x^2 + y^2)}$, $f_y = \dfrac{-x}{(x^2 + y^2)}$. **2.** f is continuous but its partial derivatives are not; $\sin 2\theta$ in a direction making angle θ with x-axis.

Exercises, p. 143: **1.** (i) $z = ax + by$, (ii) $4z = x + y + 8$, (iii) $z = 2x + y + 2$, (iv) $z = x + 2y + 1$. **2.** (i) $3z = 3x + 2y - 6$, $(3/\sqrt{22}, 2/\sqrt{22}, -3/\sqrt{22})$, (ii) $2z = x + y$, $(1/\sqrt{6}, 1/\sqrt{6}, -2/\sqrt{6})$, (iii) $z = y - 2x + 2$, $(-2/\sqrt{6}, 1/\sqrt{6}, -1/\sqrt{6})$.

Exercises, p. 146: **1.** (i) $\dfrac{\partial z}{\partial x} = 1, \dfrac{\partial z}{\partial y} = 0$, (ii) $\dfrac{\partial z}{\partial x} = 4, \dfrac{\partial z}{\partial y} = 2$, (iii) $\dfrac{\partial z}{\partial x} = \dfrac{2}{15}, \dfrac{\partial z}{\partial y} = \dfrac{6}{5}$,

(iv) $\dfrac{\partial z}{\partial x} = 0, \dfrac{\partial z}{\partial y} = 1$. **2.** $\dfrac{1}{4}$.

Exercises, p. 149: **1.** $\dfrac{\partial z}{\partial x} = \dfrac{1}{y} \cos \dfrac{x}{y}, \dfrac{\partial z}{\partial y} = -\dfrac{x}{y^2} \cos \dfrac{x}{y}, \dfrac{\partial z}{\partial r} = 0, \dfrac{\partial z}{\partial \theta} = \dfrac{-\cos(\cot \theta)}{\sin^2 \theta}$.

2. $\dfrac{\partial z}{\partial u} = \left(y \dfrac{\partial z}{\partial x} + x \dfrac{\partial z}{\partial y} \right)/(x^2 + y^2), \dfrac{\partial z}{\partial v} = \dfrac{1}{2} \left(x \dfrac{\partial z}{\partial x} - y \dfrac{\partial z}{\partial y} \right)/(x^2 + y^2),$

$\dfrac{\partial z}{\partial x} = y \dfrac{\partial z}{\partial u} + 2x \dfrac{\partial z}{\partial v}, \dfrac{\partial z}{\partial y} = x \dfrac{\partial z}{\partial u} - 2y \dfrac{\partial z}{\partial v}.$

Exercises, p. 153: **1.** (i) $f_{xx} = (2y + xy^2)e^{xy}$, $f_{xy} = (2x + x^2 y)e^{xy}$, $f_{yy} = x^3 e^{xy}$,

(ii) $f_{xx} = 0$, $f_{xy} = \dfrac{-1}{y^2}$, $f_{yy} = \dfrac{2x}{y^3}$, (iii) $f_{xx} = \dfrac{-y}{x^2}$, $f_{xy} = \dfrac{1}{x}$, $f_{yy} = 0$,

(iv) $f_{xx} = y \sin x$, $f_{xy} = -\sin y - \cos x$, $f_{yy} = -x \cos y$. **3.** $\dfrac{\partial z}{\partial u} = \dfrac{1}{2x} \dfrac{\partial z}{\partial x} + \dfrac{1}{2y} \dfrac{\partial z}{\partial y}$,

$\dfrac{\partial z}{\partial v} = \dfrac{1}{2x} \dfrac{\partial z}{\partial x} - \dfrac{1}{2y} \dfrac{\partial z}{\partial y}, \dfrac{\partial^2 z}{\partial u^2} = \dfrac{3}{2y} - \dfrac{3x^2}{4y^3}, \dfrac{\partial^2 z}{\partial u \partial v} = \dfrac{3}{2y} + \dfrac{3x^2}{4y^3}, \dfrac{\partial^2 z}{\partial v^2} = -\dfrac{9}{2y} - \dfrac{3x^2}{4y^3}.$

Exercises, p. 165: **1.** Local maximum at $(0, 0)$ and a saddle-point at $(2, 0)$.
2. Saddle-point at $(0, 0)$ and local minima at $(a, 0)$ and $(-a, 0)$.

Miscellaneous Exercises, p. 170: **3.** (i) $f_r = 3 \cos \theta + 4 \sin \theta$, maximum value is

5 when $\theta = 53°$, (ii) $f_r = \frac{1}{4}(\cos \theta + \sin \theta)$, maximum value is $\dfrac{1}{2\sqrt{2}}$ when $\theta = \dfrac{\pi}{4}$,

(iii) $f_r = 2 \cos \theta$, maximum value is 2 when $\theta = 0$, (iv) $f_r = (\cos \theta + 2 \sin \theta) e^2$,

maximum value is $\sqrt{5}\, e^2$ when $\theta = 63\frac{1}{2}°$. **6.** The parametric equation of the

normal at (x_0, y_0, z_0) is $x = x_0 + \alpha f^{\,\prime}$, $y = y_0 - \alpha y_0, z = z_0 - \alpha z_0$, which

intersects the x-axis (when $\alpha = 1$). **9.** $\dfrac{dy}{dx} = -\dfrac{f_x}{f_y}, \dfrac{d^2 y}{dx^2} = \dfrac{2 f_x f_y f_{xy} - f_y^2 f_{xx} - f_x^2 f_{yy}}{f_y^3}$,

$\dfrac{dy}{dx} = \dfrac{-y}{2y + x}, \dfrac{d^2 y}{dx^2} = \dfrac{2y(y + x)}{(2y + x)^3}.$

CHAPTER 5

Exercises, p. 187: **3.** (a) $\dfrac{a + b}{2}$, (b) $\dfrac{a^2 + ab + b^2}{3}$, (c) $\dfrac{1}{ab}$, **6.** (a) $\frac{1}{2}$,

(b) $\dfrac{2(2\sqrt{(2)} - 1)}{3}$.

Exercises, p. 196: **1.** (i) $t + \left(1 + \dfrac{3}{\sqrt{5}}\right) \log\left(2t - \sqrt{(5)} - 1\right)$

$$+ \left(1 - \frac{3}{\sqrt{5}}\right) \log\left(2t + \sqrt{5} - 1\right),$$

(ii) $\log(t - 1) - \dfrac{2}{t - 1}$,   (iii) $\frac{1}{2}\log(t - 1) - 4\log(t - 2) + \frac{9}{2}\log(t - 3)$,

(iv) $\dfrac{1}{\sqrt{2}}\tan^{-1}\dfrac{t}{\sqrt{2}} - \dfrac{1}{\sqrt{3}}\tan^{-1}\dfrac{t}{\sqrt{3}}$,   (v) $\sqrt{3}\tan^{-1}\dfrac{t}{\sqrt{3}} - \sqrt{2}\tan^{-1}\dfrac{t}{\sqrt{2}}$,

(vi) $\dfrac{1}{4\sqrt{2}}\log\dfrac{1 + t\sqrt{(2)} + t^2}{1 - t\sqrt{(2)} + t^2} + \dfrac{1}{2\sqrt{2}}\tan^{-1}\dfrac{t\sqrt{2}}{1 - t^2}$,

(vii) $\dfrac{1}{4\sqrt{2}}\log\dfrac{1 - t\sqrt{(2)} + t^2}{1 + t\sqrt{(2)} + t^2} + \dfrac{1}{2\sqrt{2}}\tan^{-1}\dfrac{t\sqrt{2}}{1 - t^2}$,   (viii) $\dfrac{1}{\sqrt{3}}\sin^{-1}\dfrac{3t - 1}{2}$,

(ix) $\log\dfrac{1 + \sqrt{t}}{1 - \sqrt{t}}$,   (x) $\dfrac{1}{2\sqrt{2}}\log\dfrac{t\sqrt{2} + \sqrt{(1 + t^2)}}{t\sqrt{2} - \sqrt{(1 + t^2)}}$,   (xi) $\frac{1}{2}\sec^2 t + \log\tan t$,

(xii) $\frac{1}{2}(1 + t^2)\tan^{-1}t - t/2$,   (xiii) $(4t^3 - 24t)\sin t - (t^4 - 12t^2 + 24)\cos t$,

(xiv) $\dfrac{1}{ab}\tan^{-1}\left(\dfrac{a}{b}\tan t\right)$,   (xv) $t\tan\dfrac{t}{2}$,   (xvi) $\frac{1}{2}(\cosh t . \cos t + \sinh t . \sin t)$.

3. (i) $\dfrac{m!n!}{(m + n + 1)!}$.

4. $I = \displaystyle\int_0^{\pi/4} \log(1 + \tan\theta)\,d\theta = \int_0^{\pi/4} \log\left\{1 + \tan\left(\dfrac{\pi}{4} - \theta\right)\right\}\,d\theta = \int_0^{\pi/4} \log\dfrac{2}{1 + \tan\theta}\,d\theta.$

Hence, $2I = \displaystyle\int_0^{\pi/4} \log 2\,d\theta$, and so $I = \dfrac{\pi}{8}\log 2$.

Exercises, p. 205: **3.** (i) Convgt. (first kind), (ii) divgt. (first kind), (iii) convgt. (third kind), (iv) convgt. (first kind), (v) convgt. (second kind), (vi) convgt. (first kind), (vii) convgt. (second kind).

Exercises, p. 213: **3.** (a) All x, (b) $-1 \leqslant x \leqslant +1$, (c) all $x > 0$.

Exercises, p. 229: **1.** (a) 1, (b) $\frac{9}{2}$, (c) $\frac{1}{3}\log(1 + \sqrt{2})$, (d) $\dfrac{\pi}{4}(1 - e^{-a^2})$.
2. (a) $\frac{1}{2}(e - 1)$, (b) $4\{\log(1 + \sqrt{2}) + (1 - \sqrt{2})\}$.   **3.** $\frac{3}{4}$.   **5.** $4\pi\log 3$.

Exercises, p. 232: **3.** $\dfrac{2\pi}{3\sqrt{3}}$.   **4.** $\dfrac{2}{(\alpha + 1)^3}$.   **5.** (a) $2x + 1$, (b) $\dfrac{2}{e^x} - \dfrac{1}{e}$

Miscellaneous Exercises, p. 236: **2.** (a) 1, (b) $\frac{\pi}{4}$, (c) $\frac{1}{e}$. **6.** $\frac{1}{16}$. **11.** Use the fact

that $\displaystyle\int_0^a f(a-t)\,dt = \int_0^a f(t)\,dt$. **12.** Note that, for all real k,

$$0 \leqslant \int_a^b \{kf(t) + g(t)\}^2\,dt = k^2 \int_a^b f^2(t)\,dt + 2k \int_a^b f(t)g(t)\,dt + \int_a^b g^2(t)\,dt.$$

13. $\tan^{-1} x = x - \dfrac{x^3}{3} + \dfrac{x^5}{5} - \dfrac{x^7}{7} + \cdots, \ (-1 \leqslant x \leqslant +1)$,

$\log(1+x) = x - \dfrac{x^2}{2} + \dfrac{x^3}{3} - \dfrac{x^4}{4} + \cdots, \ (-1 < x \leqslant +1)$.

14. (i) $I_1 = \displaystyle\lim_{\epsilon_1 \to 0} \int_{-1}^{-\epsilon_1} \frac{dx}{x^2} + \lim_{\epsilon_2 \to 0} \int_{\epsilon_2}^{1} \frac{dx}{x^2} = \lim_{\epsilon_1 \to 0}\left(\frac{1}{\epsilon_1} - 1\right) + \lim_{\epsilon_2 \to 0}\left(\frac{1}{\epsilon_2} - 1\right)$.

(ii) If $x = \dfrac{1}{y}$ then as x goes from -1 through 0 to $+1$, so y goes from -1 to $-\infty$
and then from $+\infty$ to $+1$:

$I_2 = \displaystyle\int_{-1}^{+1} \frac{dx}{1+x^2} = \int_{-\infty}^{-1} \frac{dy}{1+y^2} + \int_{1}^{\infty} \frac{dy}{1+y^2} = \frac{\pi}{2}$. **15.** (a) $-1 < \alpha < +1$,

(b) $-1 < \alpha < 2$. **16.** (a) Convgt. (first kind), (b) convgt. (first kind), (c) convgt.
(first kind; note that $\displaystyle\lim_{x \to 0} \frac{1 - \cos^2 x}{x^2} = 1$), (d) divgt. (second kind).
18. (a) $\log 4$, (b) $\log\sqrt{2}$, (c) $\frac{1}{2}\log 3 - 2$. **20.** $\frac{3}{8}$.

CHAPTER 6

Exercises, p. 247: **1.** (i) 45, (ii) 0, (iii) 313/32. **2.** $1, 2, -\frac{1}{4}\{5 \pm \sqrt{33}\}$.
3. $x = 2, 2, -3$. **4.** $x = (1 \pm 2i), \frac{1}{2}(-1 \pm i\sqrt{3})$. **5.** $x = -\frac{1}{2}, -\frac{1}{3}, -3$. **7.** $x = \frac{5}{2}, \frac{3}{2}, -4$.
9. $x = 3, -(1 \pm i\sqrt{3})$; $k = -12$.

Exercises, p. 258: **1.** (i) $x = i, -2i$, (ii) $x = \frac{1}{2}(1 - i), -\frac{1}{2}(3 + i)$. **2.** (i) $\dfrac{3}{2}, \pm \dfrac{3\sqrt{3}}{2}i$,

(ii) $-\dfrac{4}{3}, \dfrac{5}{3} \pm \dfrac{\sqrt{2}}{3}i$, (iii) $\dfrac{5}{3}, \dfrac{-4}{3} \pm \sqrt{3}$, (iv) $i, \frac{1}{2}(-i \pm 3\sqrt{3})$. **3.** (i) one real root, > 0,

(ii) one real root, > 0, (iii) one real root, < 0, (iv) two real roots, one > 0,
one < 0. **4.** (i) $0.1001, -3.2111, 3.1110$, (ii) $0.7626, 1.5597, -1.1612 \pm 1.6898i$,
(iii) 2.0665, (iv) $0.5373, -1.3160$, (v) $-0.7549, 0.8774 \pm 0.7449i$, (vi) 0.7391.
5. $x = \frac{1}{2}, \frac{3}{2}, -4$. **6.** $x_1 = \dfrac{1}{3} + \dfrac{2}{3}i$, $x_2 = \dfrac{131}{225} + \dfrac{208}{225}i$; converging to $\dfrac{1}{2} + \dfrac{\sqrt{3}}{2}i$.

7. (i) 232, (ii) 19, (iii) −6, (iv) −17 − 4i.   **8.** Coefficients of quotient: $c_{n-2} = a_n$, $c_{n-3} = a_{n-1} - \beta c_{n-2}$, $c_{k-2} = a_k - \beta c_{k-1} - \gamma c_k$, $k = (n-2), (n-3), \ldots, 0$; remainder $px + q$, where $p = c_{-1}$, $q - \beta p = c_{-2}$; $x^3 + 4x^2 + 2x - 8, -12x + 17$. **19.** 0.1133.   **10.** Modified formula is of second order.

Exercises, p. 273: **1.** $\frac{1}{2}x^3 - 2x^2 - \frac{1}{2}x + 4$; 1.384.   **2.** 0.4200.   **3.** 11.65625, 12.24336, 13.04901, 14.10416, 15.44241, 17.10000.   **4.** $x(57) = 3.7619$. **5.** $f(1.7) = 8.4012$; 1.2744, 9.4325, 29.0951.   **7.** approximate root 1.409; exact root 1.355.   **10.** approximate sum 0.6911 (about 500 terms of the original series needed to achieve this accuracy).

Exercises, p. 280: **4.** $n = 3$.

Exercises, p. 284: **1.** (i) $2x + 1$, (ii) $\frac{1}{8}x^3 + x^2 + \frac{63}{40}x - 1$.   **3.** (i) $\frac{13}{5}x + \frac{4}{3}$,

(ii) $-\frac{19}{5}x + \frac{34}{3}$, (iii) $\frac{19}{35}x + \frac{17}{21}$.   **4.** (i) $\frac{1}{2}x^2 - \frac{7}{2}x + 4$, (ii) $-\frac{1}{2}x^2 - \frac{1}{2}x + 10$,

(iii) $\frac{9}{14}x^2 - \frac{89}{70}x + \frac{66}{35}$ (the polynomials fit the data exactly in cases (i) and (ii)).
5. $2\cos x + \sin x$.

Miscellaneous Exercises, p. 287: **1.** $\pm \left(q + \dfrac{ib}{2q}\right)$, where $q^2 = \frac{1}{2}\{a + |(a^2 + b^2)^{1/2}|\}$;
(i) $z = 1 - i, -3 + 2i$, (ii) $z = 1 + 2i, 3 - i$.   **3.** $a = 45, b = -9$; $x = \frac{1}{3}, \frac{1}{2}(-1 \pm i\sqrt{11})$.
4. $x = \pm\frac{3}{2}, \frac{1}{2}(-3 \pm i\sqrt{3})$; $k = -27$.   **5.** $x = 2(1 \pm i\sqrt{3}), (1 \pm i)$; $k = -40$.
7. $x = 2, 2, \frac{1}{32}(-15 \pm \sqrt{481})$.   **8.** (a) (i) 2.8553, (ii) 0.6309; (b) 0.9477.
9. (a) $x_{n+1} = \frac{1}{2}(x_n + a/x_n)$, (i) 2.4495, (ii) 8.4853; (b) 1.2599.   **10.** $x = 1.7335$, $-3.7335, -1 \pm 1.2133i$.   **11.** $3x^3 - 8x^2 - 2x + 8$.   **12.** estimated sum 0.7861.
13. $y(1.2) = -1.6558$; $y(0.06) = -3.3062$, $y(1.32) = -0.8909$, $y(2.82) = 24.8787$, $y'(2.80) \approx 29.2251$, $y'(1.3) \approx 6.7845$, $y''(2) \approx 14.6625$, integral ≈ 18.1411, approximate solution of $y(x) = 0$ is 1.4373.
14. $(2y_0 - 2y_1 + y_0' + y_1')x^3 + (3y_1 - 3y_0 - 2y_0' - y_1')x^2 + y_0'x + y_0$;

$\displaystyle\int_0^1 y(x)\,dx \approx \frac{1}{2}(y_0 + y_1) + \frac{1}{12}(y_0' - y_1')$; 0.435 (exact value 0.441, to 3 d.p.; the

formula is not a very good one).   **17.** $T(\frac{1}{2}) = 0.6190$, $T(\frac{1}{4}) = 0.6081$, $S(\frac{1}{2}) = 0.6032$, $S(\frac{1}{4}) = 0.6045$; $T^*(\frac{1}{4}) = 0.6045$, $S^*(\frac{1}{4}) = 0.6046$.   **18.** $\frac{1}{9}, \frac{8}{9}, \frac{8}{9}, \frac{1}{9}$.
19. (a) $-0.371x + 2.845$, $0.038x^2 - 0.562x + 2.973$, (b) $2.971e^{-0.198x}$.
20. $-4.1225x^2 + 4.1225x - 0.0505$.

CHAPTER 7

Exercises, p. 301: **1.** $AB = \begin{pmatrix} 0 & -3 \\ 10 & 8 \\ 8 & 3 \end{pmatrix}$, $BC = \begin{pmatrix} 11 & 7 \\ 0 & 10 \\ -5 & -5 \end{pmatrix}$.

3. (i) $A^2 + AB - BA - B^2$, (ii) $A^3 - A^2B - ABA - BA^2 + AB^2 + BAB + B^2A - B^3$, (iii) $A^3 + 3A^2 + 3A + I$.

8. $A^2 = \begin{pmatrix} -5 & -6 & -6 \\ 9 & 10 & 9 \\ -4 & -4 & -3 \end{pmatrix}$. $A^3 = A = A^{17} = A^{123}$. **9.** $X = \pm \begin{pmatrix} 1/\sqrt{2} & -1/\sqrt{2} \\ 1/\sqrt{2} & 1/\sqrt{2} \end{pmatrix}$.

Exercises, p. 319: **1.** (a) Equations insoluble, (b) $y_1 = 4, y_2 = 1, y_3 = 0$.

2. $x_1 = 1 + 11\lambda/3, x_2 = 4\lambda/3, x_3 = -2\lambda/3, x_4 = \lambda$. **3.** $x_1 = \frac{35}{4}, x_2 = -4, x_3 = -\frac{5}{4}$.

4. $x_1 = \pm 1/3\sqrt{10}, x_2 = \mp 4\sqrt{2}/(3\sqrt{5}), x_3 = \mp \sqrt{5}/(3\sqrt{2})$. **5.** $\lambda = -1, 1, 4$;
$x_1 : x_2 : x_3 = 1:1:-2$ for $\lambda = 1, = 1:-1:0$ for $\lambda = -1, = 1:1:1$ for $\lambda = 4$.
6. (b) $(x^2 + y^2 + z^2)(x - y)(z - x)(y - z)(x + y + z)$. **7.** $x_1 = 0.00$,

$x_2 = 1.00 = x_3$. **8.** $x_1 = 0.304, x_2 = -0.363, x_3 = 1.533$. **9.** $x_1 = \frac{4}{5}, x_2 = \frac{-6}{5}$,

$x_3 = \frac{14}{5}, x_4 = \frac{4}{5}$. **10.** $x_1 = 0.375, x_2 = 0.289, x_3 = 0.269$.

Exercises, p. 327: **1.** $A^{-1} = \begin{pmatrix} -1 & -2 & 3 \\ 0 & 1 & -1 \\ 2 & 1 & -2 \end{pmatrix}$, $B^{-1} = \begin{pmatrix} -4 & 3 \\ 3 & -2 \end{pmatrix}$,

$X = \begin{pmatrix} -4 & 7 & -7 \\ 3 & -5 & 5 \end{pmatrix}$.

3. $A^{-1} = \begin{pmatrix} 15 & -3 & -7 & -3 \\ -10 & 2 & 5 & 2 \\ 5 & 0 & -2 & -1 \\ 6 & -1 & -3 & -1 \end{pmatrix}$, $\begin{pmatrix} x_1 \\ x_2 \\ x_3 \\ x_4 \end{pmatrix} = \begin{pmatrix} -8 \\ 7 \\ 0 \\ -4 \end{pmatrix}$.

4. $A^5 = \begin{pmatrix} 9 & 11 & 8 \\ -31 & 32 & 31 \\ -10 & 11 & 9 \end{pmatrix}$, $A^{-1} = \frac{1}{2} \begin{pmatrix} 3 & 1 & -5 \\ 1 & 1 & -1 \\ 1 & 1 & -3 \end{pmatrix}$.

5. $A^{-1} = \begin{pmatrix} 7 & -3 & -3 \\ -1 & 0 & 1 \\ -1 & 1 & 0 \end{pmatrix}$, $B^{-1} = \frac{1}{5} \begin{pmatrix} -10 & 4 & 9 \\ 15 & -4 & -14 \\ -5 & 1 & 6 \end{pmatrix}$, $X = \frac{1}{5} \begin{pmatrix} -49 \\ 74 \\ -26 \end{pmatrix}$.

6. $AdjA = \begin{pmatrix} -2 & 1 & 1 \\ 18 & -9 & -9 \\ -10 & 5 & 5 \end{pmatrix}$.

7. $A^{-1} = \begin{pmatrix} 1 & 0 & 0 \\ 0 & 1/2 & 0 \\ 0 & 0 & 1/5 \end{pmatrix}$, $B^{-1} = \begin{pmatrix} 1 & 3 & -7/2 \\ 0 & -1 & 1/2 \\ 0 & 0 & 1/2 \end{pmatrix}$, $C^{-1} = \begin{pmatrix} 9 & -4 & -6 & 2 \\ -4 & 2 & 3 & -1 \\ -6 & 3 & 3 & -1 \\ -2 & 1 & 1 & 0 \end{pmatrix}$

8. (a) Approx. 250. (b) Approx. 1900.

9. $\begin{pmatrix} 2 \\ 3\cos\theta - 4\sin\theta \\ 3\sin\theta + 4\cos\theta \end{pmatrix}$ **10.** $A^{-1} = \begin{pmatrix} 1 & -3/2 & 5/2 \\ 0 & 1/2 & 1/2 \\ 0 & 0 & -1 \end{pmatrix}$.

Miscellaneous Exercises, p. 330: **1.** $x_1 = 15/2, x_2 = -26, x_3 = 17$.

2. $A^{-1} = \frac{1}{5}(A - 4I) = \begin{pmatrix} -3/5 & 2/5 & 2/5 \\ 2/5 & -3/5 & 2/5 \\ 2/5 & 2/5 & -3/5 \end{pmatrix}$.

3. A, fixed point $(3/25, 14/25, 8/25)$; C, fixed point $(4/13, 15/52, 21/52)$.

4. $\lambda = \frac{1}{2}, x_1 = 0, x_2 = \frac{1}{2}, x_3 = \frac{1}{2}$. **6.** $x_1 = \frac{3 - 2c - d}{1 - c}$, $x_2 = \frac{-3 + c + 2d}{1 - c}$, $x_3 = \frac{1 - d}{1 - c}$; when $c = 1$ the equations are consistent only if $d = 1$ also.

7. $L = \begin{pmatrix} 1 & 0 & 0 \\ 1 & 1 & 0 \\ -1 & 1 & 3 \end{pmatrix}$, $U = \begin{pmatrix} 1 & 3 & 1 \\ 0 & 1 & 1 \\ 0 & 0 & 1 \end{pmatrix}$, $X = \begin{pmatrix} 1 \\ 1 \\ -1 \end{pmatrix}$, $Z = UL = \begin{pmatrix} 3 & 4 & 3 \\ 0 & 2 & 3 \\ -1 & 1 & 3 \end{pmatrix}$

9. $A^5 = 228A^2 + 37A$. **10.** (iv) only (i) remains true.

11. One solution is $A = \begin{pmatrix} \omega & 0 \\ 0 & \omega \end{pmatrix}$, where $\omega^3 = 1$. **13.** (i) $AB = -BA$.

14. Index $= 3$. **15.** $A^{-1} = -\frac{1}{2}A^2 + A + \frac{1}{2}I$, $(2I + A)^{-1} = \frac{1}{12}(A^2 - 4A - 7I)$.

16. $A^{-1} = \frac{1}{3}\begin{pmatrix} -2 & 2 & -1 \\ -11 & 5 & -1 \\ 5 & -2 & 1 \end{pmatrix}$, $B^{-1} = \begin{pmatrix} -2 & -3 & 1 \\ 1 & 0 & 0 \\ 0 & 1 & 0 \end{pmatrix}$,

$X = \frac{1}{3}\begin{pmatrix} 6 & 5 & -2 \\ 27 & 32 & -11 \\ -12 & -14 & 5 \end{pmatrix}$, $Y = \begin{pmatrix} 16 \\ -1 \\ -4 \end{pmatrix}$.

17. (a) True, (b) true, (c) false, (d) false. **18.** $k = 0, 1$. **20.** $\lambda = 0, 3:1:0$; $\lambda = 1, 2:1:-2; \lambda = -2, 1:0:-1$.

CHAPTER 8

Exercises, p. 337: **1.** (i) 0, (ii) $\frac{1}{3}$, (iii) $1 + e$, (iv) $-\frac{1}{4}$. **2.** (i) $y' = x + y$,
(ii) $(x + 3y - 1) = (3x + y - 3)y'$, (iii) $xy' = y + 3x^2y^2e^{x^3}$, (iv) $y = (x + 2y^3)y'$.

Exercises, p. 342: **1.** $y = ce^{\cos x}$. **2.** $x^2 = 2y^2 \log cy$.
3. $x^2 + 3xy + y^2 - 3x - 7y = c$. **4.** $x + y = ce^{y-x}$. **5.** $y = x \cot^{-1}(-\log cx)$.
6. $y = (c - x - \log x)^{-1}$. **7.** $1 - x = (x + y - 1) \log c (x + y - 1)$.
8. $cx^3(x + 4y - 4) = x + y - 1$. **9.** $2xy = (y - x)^2 \log c (y - x)$.
10. $2x + y + 1 = ce^{x-2y}$. **11.** $(y^2 - x^2)^{1/2} = x \log cx$. **12.** $y = 1 - ce^{-x-x^3/3}$.

Exercises, p. 346: **1.** $x^2y + 3xy^2 = c$. **2.** $xy^4 - 2x^2y^3 + cy + 3 = 0$.
3. $x + ye^{y^*} = cy$. **4.** $y^2 = x(c - \log x)$. **5.** $\sin x - \sin y - \cos x \cos y = c$.
6. $x^2y^3 + cy + 1 = 0$. **7.** $\sec x \tan y - e^x = c$. **8.** $3(x - xy - y) - (x^3 + y^3) = c$.

Exercises, p. 351: **1.** $y = x^2(e^x + c)$. **2.** $x^2 = y^2(c - 2x)$. **3.** $x = y^2 + 2y + ce^y$.
4. $y = (x + \beta)^4 + c(x + \beta)^2$. **5.** $4x \cos y + \cos 2y = c$.
6. $4y^{1/2} = (\sin x - \cos x) + ce^x$. **7.** $y \sin (x^2) = \cos (x^2) + c$.
8. $1 + xy = y(1 - x^2)^{1/2} (\sin^{-1}x + c)$. **9.** $y = x^2e^{2x^2} + ce^{x^2}$. **10.** $x = c \tan y - \sec y$.
11. $x^2y(c - 2x^5) = c + 3x^5$. **12.** $xy = x^3(1 + ce^{-x^3/3})^{-1} - 1$.

Exercises, p. 357: **1.** $(y - 3x + c)(y + 2x + c) = 0$. **2.** $y = \frac{1}{2}(x^{3/2} - c)^{4/3}$; singular
solution $y = 0$. **3.** $(p - 1)^2x = \log p - p + c$, $(p - 1)^2y = p^2(\log p - 2 + c) + p$.
4. $x = \frac{4}{3}p^3 + \frac{1}{p}$, $y = p^4 - \log p + c$. **5.** $(y - 1)^{2/3} = x^{2/3} - c$; singular solution $y = 1$.
6. $x = p \log p - p$, $y = \frac{1}{2}p^2 \log p - \frac{1}{4}p^2$. **7.** $25(y + c)^2 = 4x^5$.
8. $y = \{(x - 1)^{4/3} + c\}^{3/4}$. **9.** $(y - e^x + c)(y - e^{-x} + c) = 0$. **10.** $y = cx - c^{-2}$;
singular solution $4y^3 + 27x^2 = 0$. **11.** $y = cx - \sin c$; singular solution
$y = x \cos^{-1}x - (1 - x^2)^{1/2}$. **12.** $y = cx - e^c$; singular solution $y = x \log x - x$.

Exercises, p. 369: **1.** Analytic values are 0.7788, 0.6977. **2.** $y(0.8) = -0.5999$,
$y(1.0) = -0.0679$; otherwise, results agree with analytic values. **3.** 1.2597.
4. 1.2597. **5.** 1.2573.

Miscellaneous Exercises, p. 372: **1.** $y = \frac{1}{2} x \sin 2x + \cos^2x (\log \cos x + c)$.
2. $x^3 + 3x^2y^2 - y^2 = c$. **3.** $(x^2 + y^2)^{1/2} \log cx + x = 0$. **4.** $x = y^2(e^y + c)$.
5. $(x - y + 1)^5(2x + 3y - 1) = c$. **6.** $y = \frac{1}{2} e^{-x}(\cos x + \sin x) + ce^{-2x}$.
7. $\frac{1}{2}y^2 + xy - \log x = c$. **8.** $y = \{x - (1 + x^2)(\tan^{-1} x + c)\}^{-1/2}$.
9. $(2y - x^2)^3 = cy^4(y + 3x^2)^2$. **10.** $y(1 - \cos x) = x - \sin x + 1$.
11. $(1 + 3x)y = 3x^2$. **12.** $2 - (xy)^{-1} = \log \{2(xy - 1)^2/x^2y\}$.
13. $e^{2x} = 2(y - x)^2 - 2(y - x) + 1$. **14.** $x^3 + 3xy - 3x + 2 = 0$.
15. $y^2 = 2e^x(1 - x^{-x})$. **16.** $\frac{\pi}{2} + \log x - 2 \tan^{-1} \left(\frac{y + 1}{x} \right) = 0$.

17. $(x - \tan y + c)(x - \cot y + c) = 0$.   **18.** $y = c(x + \log c - 1)$; singular solution
$y = -e^{-x}$.   **19.** $(x^2 + 2p^2)^7(2x^2 - p^2)^{13} = cp^{10}x^{10}$, $3pxy = p^4 - x^4$.
20. $x = -\log(p^4 - p)$,

$$y = \sqrt{3} \tan^{-1} \frac{1}{\sqrt{3}} (2p + 1) - 4p - \log\{(p - 1)/(p^2 + p + 1)^{1/2}\} + c.$$

21. $x = p + \frac{1}{2}\{1 - c/(p - 1)^2\}$, $y = \frac{1}{2}p^2\{1 - c/(p - 1)^2\}$; singular solution $y = 0$.
22. $y = cx + \sin^{-1}c$; singular solution $\pm y = (x^2 - 1)^{1/2} - \tan^{-1}(x^2 - 1)^{1/2}$.

23. $x = (cp^2 - p^3 - 3p - 1)/(p - 2)^2(p + 1)^3$,

$$y = \frac{\{cp^3(p^2 - p + 4) - 3p^2(4p^2 - p + 1)\}}{6(p - 2)^2(p + 1)^3};$$

singular solutions $y = 0, y = -x - \frac{1}{6}, y = 2x + \frac{1}{3}$.   **24.** (a) 2.1054, 2.3015,
(b) 2.1052, 2.3012.   **25.** (i) $y(1) = 0.3503$, (ii) $y(1) = 0.3504$,
(iii) $y(1) = 0.3502$ (this is the correct value, to 4 d.p.).

CHAPTER 9

Exercises, p. 384: **1.** (i) $y'' - 3y' + 2y = 2x + 3$, (ii) $y'' + 9y = 13e^{2x}$,
(iii) $y'' + 2y' + y = 0$. **2.** $y = 3e^{2x} - 2$. **3.** $y = xe^{3(x - 1)}$.

4. $y = e^{-1/2\,x}\left\{c_1 \cos \frac{\sqrt{3}}{2}x + c_2 \sin \frac{\sqrt{3}}{2}x\right\} + x - 1 + e^{-x}$.

5. $y = c_1 + c_2e^x + c_3e^{-3x} + 7 \cos 2x - 4 \sin 2x$.

6. $y = c_1e^x + c_2e^{-x} + c_3 \cos x + c_4 \sin x - x^3$. **7.** $y = (6 + 2x)e^{-2x} - 3e^{-4x}$.
8. $y = c_1 \cos 3x + c_2 \sin 3x + \frac{1}{10} \cosh x$. **9.** $y = x^2e^{3x}$.
10. $y = (c_1 + c_2x - x^2)e^x + 2x^2 + 6x + 9$. **11.** $y = e^{3x}(1 - 2x) \cos 2x$.
12. $y = \frac{3}{2} \sin 2x - 3x + 2x^3$. **13.** $y = c_1e^{-x} + c_2e^{-x/2} + e^x (\sin x - 2 \cos x)$.
14. $y = e^{-x}(1 + x + 3x^2 - x^3 + x^4)$. **15.** $y = (x + 2) \sin 2x + 3 \cos 2x + 1$.
16. $y = (c_1 + c_2x + c_3x^2)e^{2x} - (15 + 18x + 9x^2 + 2x^3)$.

17. $y = e^{-x/2}\left(c_1 \cosh \frac{\sqrt{5}}{2}x + c_2 \sinh \frac{\sqrt{5}}{2}x\right) + e^{-x}(5 + \cos x - 2 \sin x)$.

18. $y = c_1e^x + (c_2 + 12x)e^{2x} - e^{-2x}$. **19.** $x = e^{2t} - 2e^{-t} - 2t + 1$,
$y = e^{2t} + 4e^{-t} + 2t - 3$. **20.** $x = \cos t + \sin t$, $y = 3 \sin t$.

Exercises, p. 399: **1.** (i) $\dfrac{3s - 8}{s^2 - 16}$, (ii) $\dfrac{24}{s^5} + \dfrac{4}{s^3} + \dfrac{1}{s}$, (iii) $\dfrac{s + 3}{s^2 + 6s + 10}$,

(iv) $\dfrac{1}{2}\left(\dfrac{1}{s + 2} + \dfrac{s + 2}{s^2 + 4s + 8}\right)$, (v) $\dfrac{1}{s} - \dfrac{3}{(s + 1)^2} + \dfrac{6}{(s + 2)^3} - \dfrac{6}{(s + 3)^4}$, (vi) $\dfrac{1}{s} - \dfrac{2}{s^2 + 4}$,

(vii) $\dfrac{8s^3 - 32s}{(s^2 + 4)^4}$, (viii) $\dfrac{s^3}{s^4 + 4\alpha^4}$, (ix) $\dfrac{e^{-s}}{s^2 + 1}$, (x) $\dfrac{1}{s}(1 - e^{-2s})$, (xi) $\dfrac{1 - e^{-3(s - 2)}}{s - 2}$,

(xii) $\dfrac{1}{s^2}\left(1 - e^{-s}\left\{\dfrac{2s + 1}{s + 1}\right\}\right)$. **2.** (i) $\dfrac{1}{\sqrt{3}} \sin \sqrt{(3)}\, t$, (ii) $2e^{-2t} - e^{-3t}$,

(iii) $e^{2t}(3 \cos 2t + 2 \sin 2t)$, (iv) $\frac{1}{8} e^{-3t/2}(6 - t)$, (v) $\frac{1}{2}(\cos t + 3 \sin t - e^{-t})$,
(vi) $14te^{2t} + e^{2t} + e^{-t}$, (vii) $e^t(2t^2 - 6t + 9) - 3t - 9$, (viii) $\frac{1}{3}e^{-t}(\sin t + \sin 2t)$,
(ix) $e^{\alpha t} + 2e^{-\alpha t/2} \cos \frac{\sqrt{3}}{2} \alpha t$, (x) $0, 0 < t < 2$; $e^{2-t} \sin 3(t - 2), t > 2$,
(xi) $t, 0 < t < 1; 1, t > 1$, (xii) $t, 0 < t < 1; 2 - t, 1 < t < 2; 0, t > 2$.

3. $\frac{1}{s^2} \left\{ \tan^{-1} \left(\frac{1}{s} \right) - 2 + 3s \right\}$. 4. $\frac{s - 5}{4(s + 3)^{5/2}} e^{-4/(s+3)}$. 6. (i) $y = t + 2 \cos t$,
(ii) $y = 2 \cos t + \sin t - 2e^{-t} \cos 2t$, (iii) $y = \frac{1}{12} t^4 e^{-2t}$, (iv) $y = t \cosh 3t + \sinh 3t$,
(v) $y = 2 \sinh t + \cosh t$. 8. (i) $y = t + \frac{1}{4}(1 - e^{4t}), z = \frac{1}{3} + e^{4t}$,
(ii) $y = t \cos t - 1, z = t \sin t + \cos t$, (iii) $y = e^t, z = e^t + t$,
(iv) $y = t - \sin 2t, z = \cos 2t$. 9. (i) $y = 2t + \cos 2t, 0 < t < \pi$;
$y = (1 + 2\pi) \cos 2t + \sin 2t, t > \pi$, (ii) $y = \frac{3}{2} \sin 2t - (\pi - 1) \cos 2t + \pi - t$,
$0 < t < 2\pi; y = \sin 2t + (1 - 2\pi) \cos 2t, t > 2\pi$, (iii) $y = 1 + \sin 2t, 0 < t < \pi$;
$y = 2 \cos 2t + \sin 2t - 1, \pi < t < 2\pi; y = \cos 2t + \sin 2t, t > 2\pi$,
(iv) $y = 2e^t - \cos 2t, 0 < t < \pi; y = 2e^{2\pi - t} + 2e^\pi \sin 2t - \cos 2t, t > \pi$.

Exercises, p. 410: 1. $y = \sin x \log (\sin x) - x \cos x$. 2. $y = \sin 3x \log \left(\tan \frac{3}{2} x \right)$.
3. $y = (e^x - e^{-2x}) \log (1 - e^{-x}) - xe^{-2x} - e^{-x} - \frac{1}{2}$.
4. $y = \frac{1}{4} \{e^{2x} \log (1 + e^{-2x}) - e^{-2x} \log (1 + e^{2x})\}$. 5. $y = xe^x \log x$.
7. $y = \alpha_0 (1 - x^2) + \alpha_1 \left(x - \frac{x^3}{1.3} - \frac{x^5}{3.5} - \frac{x^7}{5.7} - \cdots \right), |x| < 1$.
8. $y = \alpha_0 \left(1 - \frac{x^2}{1} + \frac{x^4}{1.3} - \frac{x^6}{1.3.5} + \cdots \right) + \alpha_1 \left(x - \frac{x^3}{2} + \frac{x^5}{2.4} - \frac{x^7}{2.4.6} + \cdots \right)$
9. $y = \alpha_0 \left(1 + 2x - 4x^2 + \frac{8}{3} x^3 - \frac{16}{3.5} x^4 + \frac{32}{3.5.7} x^5 - \cdots \right) + \alpha_1 x^{3/2} e^{-x}$.
10. $y = \frac{\alpha_0 + \alpha_1 \log x}{1 + x}$. 11. $y = e^{-x/2} \left(\alpha_0 + \alpha_1 \int x^{-3} e^{-x/2} \, dx \right)$.
12. $y = \frac{\alpha_0}{(1 - x)^2} + \frac{\alpha_1}{x^2}$. 13. $y = \frac{\alpha_0 x + \alpha_1 \overline{(x \log x + 1)}}{(1 - x)^2}$.
14. $y = \frac{\alpha_0 x^3}{1 - x} + \alpha_1 (1 + x + x^2)$. 15. $y = \alpha_0 \cos (\sqrt{x}) + \alpha_1 \sin (\sqrt{x})$.
16. $y = \alpha_0 \frac{1 + x}{x} + \alpha_1 \left\{ \frac{1 + x}{x} \log \left(\frac{x}{x + 1} \right) + \frac{1}{x} \right\}$. 17. $y = c_1 e^{-x} + c_2(x - 1)$.
18. $y = x^3 + \frac{1}{2}x$.

Exercises, p. 414: 1. $y = c_1 x^{1/2} + c_2 x^{-1/2} + x$. 2. $y = x^{-1/2}(c_1 + c_2 \log x)$.
3. $y = c_1 \cos (\log x) + c_2 \sin (\log x) + \log x$. 4. $y = x(c_1 + c_2 \log x + (\log x)^2)$.
5. $y = c_1 x^2 + c_2$. 6. $y = e^{-3x}(c_1 - x) + c_2$. 7. $y = c_1 e^{c_2 x}$.

8. $y = c_1 e^{c_2 x} - \dfrac{1}{c_2}$.   **9.** $(x - c_1)^2 + (y - c_2)^2 = 4$.   **10.** $y = -\log(1 - 2x)$.

11. $y = \sin x + 1$.   **12.** $y = 1 - x - 2\log(1 - x)$.   **13.** $y = (4x + 1)^{-1/2} - 2$.
14. $y = 2x + (1 - \log x)/x$.   **15.** $y = \sin^{-1} x$.   **16.** $y = \tan x$.

Exercises, p. 421: **1.** For $x = 0.2(0.2)1$, $y = 1.4241, 1.9133, 2.4954, 3.2017,$
4.0686.   **2.** $y = 0.2229, 0.5050, 0.8720, 1.3589, 2.0141$.   **3.** $y = 0.2015,$
$0.4131, 0.6497, 0.9335, 1.2999$.   **4.** $y = 0.2643, 0.5083, 0.7165, 0.8807,$
1.0000.   **5.** $y = 0.9557, 0.9417, 0.9495, 0.9713, 1.0000$.   **6.** $y(\frac{1}{4}) \simeq \frac{1}{21}$,
$y(\frac{1}{2}) \simeq \frac{1}{7}, y(\frac{3}{4}) \simeq \frac{8}{21}$.   **7.** $y(\frac{1}{4}) \simeq -\frac{2}{5}, y(\frac{1}{2}) \simeq -\frac{2}{5}, y(\frac{3}{4}) \simeq \frac{2}{5}$.

Miscellaneous Exercises, p. 425: **1.** $y = 3\sin x + x^2 - 2$.
2. $y = 2e^{-x}\cos 4x + 2xe^{-3x}$.   **3.** $y = (x^4 + x + 3)e^{-x}$.

4. $y = xe^x + \dfrac{2}{\sqrt{3}} e^{-x/2} \sin\dfrac{\sqrt{3}}{2}x$.   **5.** $y = \frac{1}{3} e^{-x}(\sin x + \sin 2x)$.

6. $y = 2(\cos 2x - \cos x)$.   **7.** $y = c_1(x - 1)e^x + c_2$.
8. $y = c_1\cos x + (c_2 + 2x)\sin x + \frac{1}{2}\cos 3x$.   **9.** $y^2 = c_1 x^2 + c_2 x + (4 + c_2^2)/4c_1$.

10. $y = c_1 x + c_2 x^{-1} + \left(\dfrac{x + 1}{x}\right)e^{-x}$.   **11.** $y = \cosh(x + c_1) + c_2$.

12. $y = c_1 x^{3/2} + x^{-2}(c_2 - \log x)$.   **13.** $y = c_1 x^{-1} + x(c_2 + c_3\log x)$.
14. $y = \log\sec(x + c_1) - \frac{1}{2} x^2 + c_2$.
15. $y = e^x\{c_1 - \frac{1}{4}\log(1 + e^{2x})\} + e^{3x}\{c_2 - \frac{1}{4}\log(1 + e^{-2x})\}$.
16. $y = e^{-t} - 3e^{4t}, z = e^{-t} + 2e^{4t}$.   **17.** $y = t + \frac{1}{2} e^t, z = \frac{1}{2} e^t - t$.

18. $y = \dfrac{2}{\sqrt{3}} \cosh\frac{1}{2} t \sin\dfrac{\sqrt{3}}{2}t - 2\sinh\frac{1}{2} t \cos\dfrac{\sqrt{3}}{2}t$,

$\qquad z = \cosh\frac{1}{2} t \cos\dfrac{\sqrt{3}}{2} t - \dfrac{1}{\sqrt{3}} \sinh\frac{1}{2} t \sin\dfrac{\sqrt{3}}{2} t + t - \cos t$.

19. $x = \frac{1}{3}(\alpha + \beta + \gamma)e^{2t} - \frac{1}{3}(\beta + \gamma - 2\alpha)e^{-t}$; y and z by cyclic permutation of
α, β, γ.   **20.** (i) $y = t - 2 + e^{-t}(t + 2), 0 < t < 1; y = e^{-t}(t + 2 - e), t > 1$.
(ii) $y = e^{-t}(t + 1) - \cos t, 0 < t < \pi; y = e^{-t}\{(t + 1)(1 + e^{\pi}) - \pi e^{\pi}\}, t > \pi$.
(iii) $y = 0, 0 < t < a; y = 1 - (t + 1 - a)e^{a-t}, a < t < b;$
$y = (t + 1 - b)e^{b-t} - (t + 1 - a)e^{a-t}, t > b$.

21. $y = \alpha_0 \left\{1 - \dfrac{2n}{2!} x^2 + \dfrac{2^2 n(n - 2)}{4!} x^4 - \cdots\right\}$

$\qquad + \alpha_1\left\{x - \dfrac{2(n - 1)}{3!}x^3 + \dfrac{2^2(n - 1)(n - 3)}{5!}x^5 - \cdots\right\}$.

22. $y = \alpha_0 \left\{1 - \dfrac{n^2}{2!}x^2 + \dfrac{n^2(n^2 - 2^2)}{4!} x^4 - \cdots\right\}$

$\qquad + \alpha_1\left\{x - \dfrac{(n^2 - 1^2)}{3!}x^3 + \dfrac{(n^2 - 1^2)(n^2 - 3^2)}{5!}x^5 - \cdots\right\}$;

closed form of solution is $y = c_1\cos(n\cos^{-1}x) + c_2\sin(n\cos^{-1}x)$.

23. $L_n(x) = 1 - \dfrac{n}{(1!)^2} x + \dfrac{n(n-1)}{(2!)^2} x^2 - \dfrac{n(n-1)(n-2)}{(3!)^2} x^3 + \cdots$.

26. $y = c_1 x + (x + c_2)/(x + 2) + x \log(x + 2)$.   **27.** $y = P(2ax^2 - \frac{10}{3} x^3)$,

$0 < x < \frac{1}{3}a$; $y = P(\frac{7}{6}x^3 - \frac{5}{2} ax^2 + \frac{3}{2}a^2 x - \frac{1}{6}a^3)$, $\frac{1}{3}a < x < a$.

28. For $x = 1.2(0.2)2.0$ the analytic solution values are, to 4 d.p., as follows: initial-value problem: $y = 0.5024, 0.8689, 1.1516, 1.3777, 1.5633$; boundary-value problem: $y = 0.3214, 0.5558, 0.7366, 0.8813, 1.0000$. Computed values do not differ by more than 0.0004.   **29.** $y = 0.0000, 0.0993, 0.1946, 0.2815, 0.3551, 0.4093$ (both formulations).   **30.** Intermediate values $y \simeq -0.4, 0.2, 0.8, 0.4$; exact solution $y = -0.7053 \sin \sqrt{(50)}x + \frac{1}{2} x$ gives the true values as $-0.597, -0.017, 0.929$ and 0.813 respectively, in reasonable qualitative agreement. Poor quantitative agreement is due to the coarse step length and the rapid variation of the solution over the range of integration.

CHAPTER 10

Exercises, p. 438:   **2.** $9°36'$ N of E, 4 hrs. 3.6 min.   **3.** $\sqrt{3}$ lb. wt. from mid pt. of BC to A, $\sqrt{57}$ lb. wt. at $6°32'$ to BA.   **4.** 10.05 ft.   **5.** (i) $\mathbf{0}, \hat{\imath}, -\hat{k}, \hat{\jmath}$, (ii) $\mathbf{0}, \hat{k}, \hat{\jmath} - \hat{\imath}$,   (iii) $\mathbf{0}, \hat{k}, \hat{\imath}, \hat{\jmath}$,   (iv) $\mathbf{0}, \mathbf{j}, -\hat{k}, -\hat{\imath}$.   **6.** $(3, 1, 4)$.   **7.** $\dfrac{1}{\alpha + \beta}$ $\beta \mathbf{a} + \alpha \mathbf{b}$.

9. $15\sqrt{5}$ lb. wt.   **10.** $\sqrt{3} (1 + \sqrt{2})$.

Exercises, p. 448:   **1.** $\dfrac{1}{\sqrt{35}} \{-3\hat{\imath} + \hat{\jmath} + 5\hat{k}\}$, $80°24'$.   **2.** $\frac{1}{2}\sqrt{30}, \dfrac{1}{\sqrt{30}} \{5\hat{\imath} - \hat{\jmath} + 2\hat{k}\}$.

3. $\mathbf{b} \times (\hat{c} \times \mathbf{a}) = 0$.   **4.** $\frac{1}{2} \{(x + y - z)\mathbf{a} + (y + z - x)\mathbf{b} + (x + z - y)\mathbf{c}\}$.   **6.** Hint: let $\mathbf{x} = \alpha \mathbf{u} + \beta \mathbf{v} + \gamma (\mathbf{u} \times \mathbf{v})$. Solution is:

$\mathbf{x} = \alpha \mathbf{u} - \dfrac{1}{|\mathbf{u}|^2} (\mathbf{u} \times \mathbf{v})$, $\mathbf{y} = (1 - \alpha)\mathbf{u} + \dfrac{1}{|\mathbf{u}|^2} (\mathbf{u} \times \mathbf{v})$.   **7.** $(v - \omega y)\hat{\imath} + \omega x \mathbf{j}$, $(0, v/\omega, z)$ for any z.   **8.** $\mathbf{M} = 3\hat{\jmath} - 3\hat{k}$.   **9.** P lies in the plane of A, B and C. $x + y - z - 2 = 0$.

Miscellaneous Exercises, p. 464:   **1.** Hint: differentiate $\omega \times \mathbf{r}$; $\dfrac{d}{dt} \omega \times \mathbf{r} - \omega^2 \mathbf{r}$.

2. $\mathbf{R} = -\hat{\imath} + 3\hat{\jmath} + p\hat{k}$, $\mathbf{G} = (p - 1)\hat{\imath} - (3 + p)\hat{\jmath} + \hat{k}$, $p = -\frac{8}{3}$.   **3.** $(\frac{6}{5}, \frac{3}{5}, 0)$.

4. $(\alpha, -\alpha - 2, 1)$ for any α.   **5.** $\mathbf{r} = \hat{\imath}$, $\mathbf{v} = w\hat{\jmath}$; path is a helix of radius 1.

6. $\begin{pmatrix} 16 & 1 & 0 \\ 1 & 24 & -7 \\ 0 & -7 & 20 \end{pmatrix}$, $17\hat{\imath} + 18\hat{\jmath} + 13\hat{k}$, 24 units.   **7.** Hint: show that velocity of point with position vector $\mathbf{r}$ is independent of $\mathbf{r}$.   **8.** Line of action passes through $(\frac{1}{4}, -\frac{1}{4}, -\frac{1}{4})$ and is parallel to $\hat{\imath} + \hat{\jmath}$.   **9.** $\dfrac{2v_3}{g}, \dfrac{2v_3}{g} \, (\sqrt{(v_1^2 + v_2^2)})$.

10. $\mathbf{r} = a \cos kt \, \hat{\imath} + \dfrac{v_0}{k} \sin kt \, \hat{\jmath}$; min $= v_0$, max. $= ka$.   **11.** $\mathbf{R}_1 = \mathbf{R}_2 = 3\hat{\imath} + \hat{\jmath} + 3\hat{k}$,
$\mathbf{G}_1 = -3\hat{\imath} + \hat{\jmath} - 3\hat{k}$, $\mathbf{G}_2 = -6\hat{\imath} - 5\hat{\jmath} + 2\hat{k}$.   **13.** Taking coordinate axes instantaneously parallel to the edges of the cube: (a) $8\hat{\imath} - 2\hat{\jmath} - 2\hat{k}$, 4, (b) $\dfrac{4}{\sqrt{3}}(\hat{\imath} + \hat{\jmath} + \hat{k})$, 2.

14. 4.   **17.** $\frac{4}{5}(\hat{\imath} + 2\hat{k})$, $-\frac{4}{5}\hat{\imath} - 4\hat{\jmath} + \frac{2}{5}\hat{k}$.

18. (a) $\displaystyle\int_0^1 \mathbf{F}_i(0, y, 0) \cdot \hat{\jmath} \, dy + \int_0^1 \mathbf{F}_i(x, 1, 0) \cdot \hat{\imath} \, dx$, for $i = 1, 2$.

(b) $\displaystyle\int_0^1 \mathbf{F}_i(x, 0, 0) \cdot \mathbf{i} \, dx + \int_0^1 \mathbf{F}_i(1, y, 0) \cdot \mathbf{j} \, dy$, for $i = 1, 2$.

(a) $1, \frac{5}{6}$, (b) $1, \frac{1}{3}$.   **19.** $5\sqrt{\frac{5}{2}}$ from a direction $\tan^{-1} \frac{1}{3}$ W of S.

20. Force $= 3\hat{\imath} + 2\hat{\jmath}$, couple $= \dfrac{5}{13}(3\hat{\imath} + 2\hat{\jmath})$; line of action through $\left(-\dfrac{10}{13}, \dfrac{15}{13}, \dfrac{38}{13}\right)$.

INDEX